Physics2000 *non calculus*

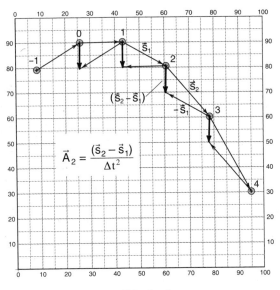

$$\vec{A}_2 = \frac{(\vec{S}_2 - \vec{S}_1)}{\Delta t^2}$$

Acceleration of Steel Ball Projectile.

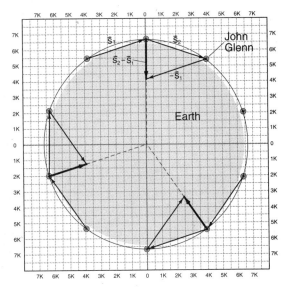

Acceleration of John Glenn in Orbit.

Elisha Huggins

Dartmouth College
Hanover, New Hampshire

Class testing and syllabus organization
Bryan Crump

Oakland Christian School
Auburn Hills, Michigan

www.physics2000.com

ISBN.0-9770828-290000 (*Physics 2000 non calculus* PART 1 + CD)
ISBN.0-9770828-390000 (*Physics 2000 non calculus* PART 2 + CD)
ISBN.0-9770828-490000 (*Physics 2000 non calculus* PART 1 + PART 2 + CD)
ISBN.0-9770828-590000 (*Physics 2000 non calculus* CD)

An adequate discussion of waves requires the discussion of the harmonics contained in a wave. How else do you explain to a student why two musical instruments playing the same note can sound different? To allow students to easily analyze the harmonic content of experimental data we developed the *free* program *MacScope II* which turns both Mac and Windows computers into capable audio oscilloscopes with Fourier analysis capability.

The MacScope program requires the student to select a section of an experimental curve that is assumed to repeat indefinitely. Pressing the Fourier analysis button displays the harmonic content of the selected curve, and displays a curve reconstructed from selected harmonics. You can also listen to the sound produced by the selected harmonics. MacScope's dual-beam triggered capability also allows experiments like measuring the speed of a sound pulse down a steel pipe, as seen in Figure (5).

With an understanding of Fourier analysis gained from the study of musical instruments, we are able, in the final chapter, to analyze the harmonic content of the photons contained in a very short (femtosecond) laser pulse. This analysis, combined with the probability interpretation, leads to a direct and straightforward derivation of the time-energy form of the uncertainty principle.

PHYSICS AND ART

In order to learn the computer language REALbasic that we used to write MacScope, we first wrote the program *Charges2000* to display electric field lines and contour maps of electric voltage. That the field line maps are accurate is illustrated in Figure (2) where, as predicted by Gauss' law, the lines are blown away from a uniform circle or sphere of charge.

We added the ability to choose any color you want for any of the components of these plots. The result is a flexible and intriguing art medium. This is illustrated by Figure (3) which our granddaughter constructed at age 10. There have been high school are competitions using the *completely free Charges2000* program.

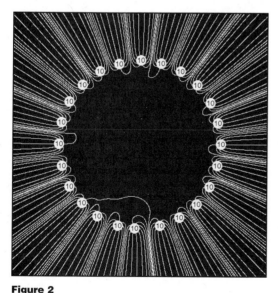

Figure 2
Electric field lines blown out of a circle of charge. Both these figures created by the Charges2000 program available on the CD and for a free download from www.physics2000.com.

Julia Anne Huggins

Figure 3
Potential plot by Julia Huggins done over a weekend when she visited at age 10. We have permission to use this graphic as part of the cover design.

Preface

ABOUT THE PHYSICS2000 TEXTS

How do you teach an introductory physics course that actually introduces physics as we understand it in the twentieth and twenty-first century? These textbooks are our answer to that question.

We begin in Chapter 1 with a basic law of physics that has become familiar to the current generation of jet traveling students. *You do not feel uniform motion.* We give it the more general statement that it is impossible to detect one's uniform motion relative to empty space, and call that statement the *principle of relativity*.

Next we see how the principle of relativity can be applied to other areas of physics, like the theory in which Maxwell derives a formula for the speed of light in empty space. A simple thought experiment demonstrates that this speed must be the same to all observers, as Einstein pointed out. Further thought experiments, like the light pulse clock illustrated below, show why moving clocks run slow, why the height of a moving mountain contracts, and why information cannot travel faster than the speed of light.

We discuss this in Chapter 1. In the remaining chapters we look at physics with a 20th century point of view in mind.

Another outstanding feature of twentieth century physics was the discovery of the particle-wave nature of matter, which is the subject of *quantum mechanics*. The organization of this text is to study the behavior of particles, then of waves, and then to see what happens when an object like an electron behaves both as a particle and as a wave.

We end with three chapters on quantum mechanics. The first is on the probability interpretation of the particle wave. The second is on the position-momentum form of the uncertainty principle. The final chapter is on the time-energy form of the uncertainty principle, which leads to a discussion of quantum fluctuations and the nature of the early universe.

MATHEMATICS IN THE COURSE

The only mathematics needed in our discussion of special relativity is algebra and the Pythagorean theorem. In the calculus version of Physics2000, we use the physics to teach calculus. In this non calculus version, we use strobe photographs to handle the calculus concepts of Newtonian mechanics.

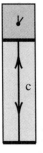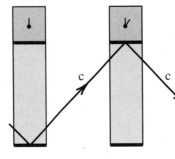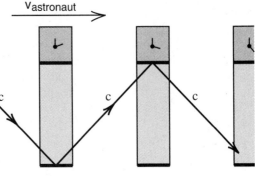

our clock

$V_{astronaut}$

astronaut's moving clock

Figure 1
Light pulse clocks. The light takes a longer path in the moving clock than in our clock at rest.

THE NON CALCULUS VERSION

When we finished creating the non calculus versions of the chapters in the *Physics2000* text, it was clear that the complete set of chapters would be too long for a one-year introductory physics course. The two reasons for this are first, calculus is an effective shorthand notation. A non calculus version needs a more detailed explanation. The second reason is that students in a non calculus course have less of a mathematics background than students who have taken a calculus course, and thus should have more time to digest the material.

To handle this, we have created a ***core text*** that makes a balanced treatment of classical and modern physics. We have balanced the particle (Newtonian) behavior of matter and the wave (Quantum) nature of matter. Our choice of material was heavily influenced by the syllabus of *Bryan Crump* who has been using the Physics2000 calculus based text in a non calculus introductory physics at the Oakland Christian High School. We also appreciate comments by Ron Revere who teaches at the Washington-Lee High School and used the non calculus version of the text.

The chapters left out of the core text are still available on the CD version of the text. We have, in a sense, demoted them to ***Satellite Chapters***, in much the same way that Pluto was demoted to a minor planet. As much as we may like some of the demoted chapters, for example, on Gyroscopes, Entropy, Faraday's Law, and Atoms and Chemistry, there is not time to do them all in a non calculus course. But the chapters are available for teachers who want to select some of them, and for students who may want to use them for project work.

We have included ***Essays*** which are overviews of the material in Satellite chapters. This has been particularly effective in describing Maxwell's contribution to the theory of Electricity and Magnetism, since we did not have to go through the details of the equations.

Figure 4
Student-built electron gun showing an electron beam moving through crossed electric and magnetic fields.

LABS AND HOMEWORK

Numerous labs and almost all homework exercises are included in the text material. We put the homework at precisely the point where we want the student to stop and think about the material. We avoid the approach of presenting scant text material and a flood of at the end of chapter exercises. Our goal is to introduce the concepts of physics and our exercises are carefully selected to do this.

Where possible, we have illustrated concepts with related experiments. We developed an electron gun that students could build and use to study the behavior of electron beams. Unfortunately, with the demise of vacuum tubes, parts for the electron gun are no longer available. Movies of some of the electron gun experiments are available on the accompanying CD.

However, with MacScope, for both Mac and Windows, we are able to supply a free and powerful audio oscilloscope. Not only does MacScope do Fourier analysis, it is a triggered dual beam scope that can do live signal averaging and store data. A good example of the dual beam capability is the experiment in Figure (5), directly measuring the time it takes a sound pulse to travel down a steel pipe. This experiment required the purchase of two external lapel mikes. Experiments recording the sound of musical instruments can be done using the computer's own sound input, at no additional expense.

MOVIES

The accompanying CD contains over 20 movies which can be run by clicking on a related diagram in the CD version of the text.

The main movies are the 38-minute muon lifetime movie which we use to introduce the Lorentz contraction, and the newsreel footage of the collapse of the Tacoma Narrows bridge. It took two years to negotiate for the rights to include the muon lifetime movie on our CD, and we got permission to include the Tacoma Narrows film from the son of the photographer.

ABOUT THE AUTHOR

Huggins taught physics at Dartmouth College beginning in 1961. He was an undergraduate at MIT and got his Ph.D. at Caltech. His Ph.D. thesis under Richard Feynman was on aspects of the quantum theory of gravity and the non uniqueness of energy momentum tensors. Since then much of his research was on superfluid dynamics and the development of new teaching tools like the student-built electron gun and MacScope™. He has written various textbooks, most of which are available at *www.physics2000.com*. The work of producing the texts is done by the author, and his wife, Anne Huggins. The text layout and design was by the author's daughter Cleo Huggins who designed eWorld™ for Apple Computer and the Sonata™ music font for Adobe Systems.

The author's eMail address is
   lish.huggins@dartmouth.edu
The author welcomes any comments.

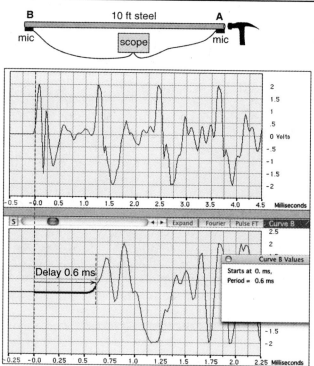

Figure 5
Using MacScope's dual beam triggering capability to measure the speed of a sound pulse in a steel pipe.

Table Of Contents
Physics2000 non calculus
Volume 1

CHAPTER 13   SPEED OF WAVE PULSES

CHAPTER 14   WAVE MOTION

CHAPTER 15   FOURIER ANALYSIS AND SOUND

Physics2000 non calculus
Volume 2

CHAPTER ON GEOMETRICAL OPTICS

SATELLITE CHAPTERS ARE ON THE CD

SATELLITE 1   BASIC PROGRAMMING

SATELLITE 2   KEPLER ORBITS

SATELLITE 14   ATOMS AND CHEMISTRY

SATELLITE 15   ELETRON SPIN AND MAGNETIC RESONANCE

Chapter 16 non calculus

Atoms, Molecules and Atomic Processes

To extract the basic laws of mechanics from the variety and confusion of the world around us required looking at matters on a large scale, looking out at the moon and planets whose motion is regular, periodic, and easier to understand. In this chapter we take a similarly large leap to the small scale of distance where simplicity and periodic behavior again allow us to gain insight into the working of nature. Here we find the world of atoms and their constituent particles, a world in which we observe the basic forces and particles ultimately responsible for the variety about us.

The jump down to the small scale of atoms is comparable to the jump out from the study of projectile motion in the lab, to the analysis of satellite orbits. Imagine, for example, that we could enlarge the golf balls used in our strobe labs to the size of the earth. The same enlargement of a hydrogen atom would give us an object about the size of a golf ball.

Only with the development of the new generation of microscopes in the late 1980s has it become possible to see and work with individual atoms. Figure (1) is the first atomic sized logo consisting of xenon atoms on a background of nickel, made by scientists at the IBM Research Laboratories in 1990. But despite great improvements in seeing and working with individual atoms, the images we now get are still fuzzy, and we are restricted to looking at atoms in solid structures where the atoms do not move around as much.

Our knowledge of atoms comes not from looking through microscopes, but instead from the study of chemical reactions, the measurement of the physical properties of substances, and the bombardment of materials with x-rays and other particles. This study essentially began with John Dalton's construction of the first periodic table in 1808. Other milestones were Thomson's discovery of the electron in 1895, Rutherford's discovery of the atomic nucleus in 1912, Neils Bohr's model of the hydrogen atom in 1913, and the discovery of the rules of quantum mechanics in the mid 1920s.

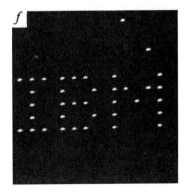

Figure 1
Thirty five xenon atoms were dragged across a nickel surface to form the letters IBM. (D. M. Eigler & E. K. Schweizer, Nature, 5 April 1990.)

In this chapter we start with an overview of atomic and molecular structures as simple as the hydrogen molecule and as complex as Kendrew's model of the myoglobin molecule.

We then look at some consequences of two atomic phenomena. One is the nature of molecular forces holding atoms together. In general, these forces are attractive when the atoms or molecules are close together, but strongly repulsive as you try to push them too close together. The other phenomenon is the fact that all atoms and molecules have a constant jiggling motion due to thermal kinetic energy.

Looking at the competition between molecular forces holding atoms together and thermal motion tending to break structures apart, provides an intuitive picture of phenomena such as why evaporation is a cooling process and why rubber bands are elastic. In an appendix we take a closer look at the structure of molecular forces in order to explain thermal expansion and why a steel pipe obeys Hooke's law.

There is hardly any limit to what one can say about atomic processes, even in a non calculus text. But there is a limit to the time available if we are to get to the most basic concepts involved in studying atoms, namely quantum mechanics. For this reason we put a discussion of the ideal gas law, and the important and interesting concept of entropy, in the Satellite Chapters 7 and 8.

MOLECULES

Atoms attract each other to form molecules, like the water molecule H_2O sketched in Figure (2). It was from x-ray studies of ice, the crystalline form of water, that we know the distance from the center of the oxygen atom to the center of a hydrogen atom is $.958 \times 10^{-8}$ cm and that the hydrogen atoms are spread out at an angle of 104.5 degrees as shown.

X-ray studies of large biological molecules began in the late 1950s. For example, myoglobin is a substance found in muscle tissue. The myoglobin molecule contains over 2500 atoms, mostly carbon, hydrogen, oxygen, nitrogen, and one iron atom. For determining the precise structure of the myoglobin molecule from x-rays of crystals of myoglobin, John Kendrew and Max Peritz received the 1963 Nobel Prize in chemistry. Their model of the molecule is shown in Figure (3).

Recent advances in computer modeling now provide detailed views of numerous kinds of molecules. An example is Figure (4) showing the cholera toxin B-subunit.

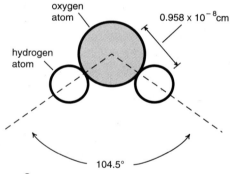

Figure 2
The water molecule H_2O. We know the precise location of the centers of the three atoms.

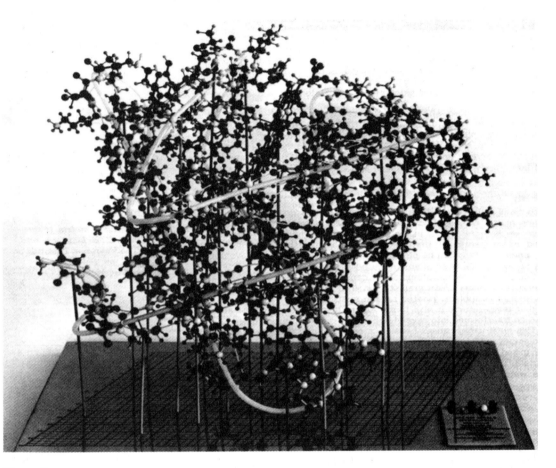

Figure 3
*Model of the myoglobin molecule. (Photograph
courtesy of J.C. Kendrew and H.C. Watson.) Kendrew
personally sent us this photograph.*

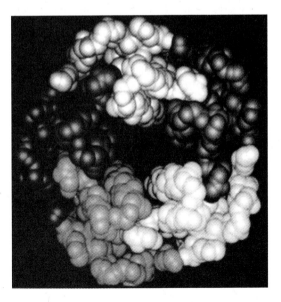

Figure 4
*Computer model of the cholera
toxin B-subunit. (Courtesy of
Argonne National Laboratory.)*

Temperature Scales

For the rest of this chapter, we will put aside any worries about zero point energy, and simply assume that the temperature of an object is proportional to the average thermal kinetic energy of the molecules in the object, and that absolute zero is where no thermal kinetic energy remains.

From this point of view, the simplest way to define a temperature scale is to equate the temperature with the average thermal kinetic energy, and measure temperature in energy units such as joules as shown in Figure (13). But you probably have not heard anyone describe temperature in joules, and for good reason. Telling your doctor that you are running a fever of 6.4423×10^{-21}, an increase of 23×10^{-25} over normal, could be a bit hard to explain when you are sick. It is much easier to say that you have a temperature of 100° F or about 38° C. Joules are too awkward a unit for most purposes.

Historically, thermometers were invented and temperature scales established long before the relation between temperature and the average kinetic energy of molecules became known. Throughout the world the most widely used temperature scale is the Centigrade scale, where the temperature of melting ice is arbitrarily set at 0° C (zero degrees Centigrade), and the boiling of water at 100° C. Commonly, changes in temperature are measured with a mercury thermometer. This device registers temperature changes when the mercury in a thin glass column expands or contacts. On the Centigrade scale, the distance between 0° C and 100° C is marked into 100 equally spaced smaller intervals which we call degrees.

A less arbitrary scale is the *Kelvin* or *absolute* scale, which measures temperature in Centigrade size degrees beginning at absolute zero. Using the absolute scale, we find that helium boils at 4 degrees Kelvin, ice melts at 273 degrees Kelvin and water boils at 373 degrees Kelvin. A comparison of various temperature scales (joules, degrees Kelvin, degrees Centigrade, and degrees Fahrenheit) is shown in Figure (13b).

Those who define standard nomenclature for physical quantities have decided, in their great wisdom, that the word "degrees" shall be omitted when talking about temperature in degrees Kelvin. Thus we should say that helium boils at 4 kelvins or 4K, ice melts at 273 kelvins or 273K, and the temperature difference between melting ice and boiling water is 100 kelvins or 100K. At least this nomenclature is easy to say and should not be confusing when you get used to it. We do not feel the same way about all recent changes in nomenclature.

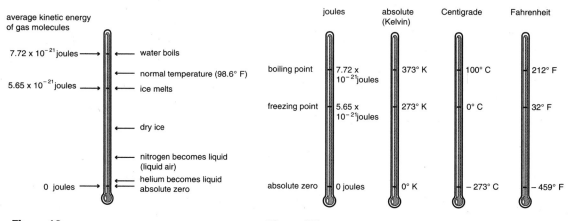

Figure 13a
Temperature scale in joules.

Figure 13b
Comparison of various temperature scales.

The conversion from one temperature scale to another is a relatively straightforward process. If you went to an American school, somewhere along the way you were taught how to convert from Fahrenheit to Centigrade degrees. You do not need to worry about that because we will not be using the obsolete Fahrenheit scale. But we will often want to convert from the absolute scale to the energy units joules. The conversion is written in the somewhat peculiar form

$$\left.\begin{array}{c}\text{average kinetic energy}\\\text{of gas molecules}\\\text{in joules}\end{array}\right\} = \frac{3}{2}\,kT \qquad (1)$$

where T is the temperature in kelvins, and the conversion factor k, known as ***Boltzman's constant*** has the numerical value

$$\left.\begin{array}{c}\text{Boltzman's}\\\text{constant k}\end{array}\right\} = 1.38 \times 10^{-23}\,\frac{\text{joules}}{\text{kelvin}} \qquad (2)$$

The important feature of Equation (1) is that the average kinetic energy of the molecules is proportional to the absolute temperature measured in kelvins. (We have written the proportionality constant as 3/2 k, putting in the numerical factor of 3/2 to get rid of a factor 2/3 that results from the ideal gas law.) Basically, think of Boltzman's constant as the conversion factor to go from temperature units to energy units or vice versa.

Exercise 2

Use Equation (1) to calculate the temperature of melting ice in joules. Compare your answer with the result in Figure (13).

Exercise 3

What would be the temperature in kelvins of a gas if the particles in the gas had an average kinetic energy of 1 joule?

Exercise 4

In Exercise 1 we said that the average speed of nitrogen molecules at room temperature was 518 meters/sec, and asked you to use that result to calculate the average speed of the other molecules and particles in the cigarette smoke. Now you are to calculate the speed of the nitrogen molecules using the fact that their average kinetic energy is 3/2 kT. (It is traditional to take room temperature as 300K = 27° C.)

Assume that a nitrogen molecule is 28 times as massive as a hydrogen atom, whose mass is essentially the same as a proton, or 1.67×10^{-27} kilograms. See if you get the answer of 518 meters/sec.

MOLECULAR FORCES

Much of the behavior of matter we see as we look around us is the result of a competition between molecular forces holding atoms together and thermal motion tending to pull them apart. Molecular forces can be subtle enough to form objects as complex as the myoglobin molecule. Yet knowing just some of the basic features of molecular forces is enough to provide an insight into processes like evaporation, osmotic pressure, elasticity of rubber, and the behavior of an ideal gas.

Figure (14), which describes the force between two nobel gas atoms like helium or argon, illustrates general features of molecular forces. In Figure (14a), where the atoms are about an atomic diameter apart, the attractive molecular force between the atoms is less than one percent of its maximum value. The point is that unless the atoms are very close together, within an atomic diameter of each other, molecular forces are negligible. This is why atoms in a gas often act as independent free particles. In the air we breath, the average spacing of atoms is about ten molecular diameters, so that molecular forces play no role except when molecules collide.

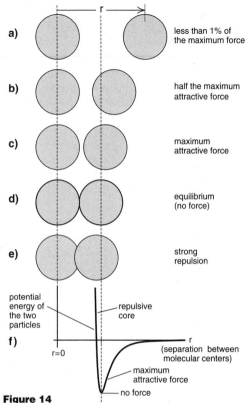

Figure 14
Interaction of two atoms via a Leonard Jones potential (f). When the atoms have an equilibrium separation (d), their potential energy of interaction is a minimum, and we can visualize one of the atoms as sitting at the bottom of the potential energy well. If the separation either increases or decreases, there is a force back toward equilibrium. The repulsion quickly builds up if you try to shove the atoms together, and the attraction dies rapidly after the atoms become separated by about one atomic diameter.

When atoms get closer than an atomic diameter, the attractive molecular force increases rapidly, reaching a maximum at a separation at about one tenth of an atomic diameter as shown in Figure (14c). Then the force rapidly drops to zero at the spacing shown in Figure (14d). When the force is zero, this is the equilibrium distance which determines the size of the atom in a chunk of matter. Effectively we can say that when the atoms are at their equilibrium separation, they are just touching, as we drew them in Figure (14d).

Try to shove the atoms closer together than the equilibrium position, and you encounter a repulsive force that builds very rapidly, much faster than the attractive force increases as you pull the atoms apart. This repulsion makes atoms behave as hard, nearly incompressible spherical objects. This repulsive force is often referred to as the repulsive core of the atom.

In Figure (14f) we have sketched the potential energy corresponding to the molecular force. As you can see the potential energy forms a well with the bottom at the equilibrium position. When two atoms form a molecule, like hydrogen (H_2), oxygen (O_2) or nitrogen (N_2), you can picture one of the atoms as sitting in the potential well created by the other, and vice versa. We only have to think about one of the atoms, for the same thing is happening to the other.

In the appendix to this chapter, we take a closer look at the energy diagram in Figure (14f). From that we explain effects such as thermal expansion, and why objects like a steel guitar string or a steel pipe obeys Hooke's law.

EVAPORATION

Simple features of molecular forces lead to a reasonable understanding of the transition from a liquid to a gaseous state, the process of evaporation. We start with a picture of a liquid as a collection of molecules that all attract each other, can move around past each other, but are nearly incompressible because the repulsive core in the molecular force prevents atoms from being squeezed into each other. The incompressibility of water can be seen from the fact that water in the deepest parts of the ocean, where the pressures are some 800 times atmospheric pressure, is only about 3% denser than the water at the surface.

A molecule in a liquid is free to move around because of its thermal kinetic energy and because there is essentially no net force on it. Although attracted to all of its neighbors, the neighbors surround the molecule as shown in Figure (15), and the net force is zero.

The situation is different for a molecule on the surface as shown in Figure (16). Such a molecule has neighbors only to the sides and below. If we try to lift such a molecule out of the surface, there will be a net force exerted by all of the molecules beneath it, pulling the molecule back in. To extract a molecule from the surface requires that you do work against these attractive forces. The amount of work required to extract a molecule from the surface depends upon the type of liquid and the temperature of the liquid, but some energy is required as long as the surface exists.

Example 2

To estimate the amount of energy required to extract a water molecule from the surface of water, we note that to boil 1 gram of water requires 2.25×10^3 joules of energy. Since there are 3.3×10^{22} molecules in 1 gram of water, this represents an energy of 6.8×10^{-20} joules per molecule. Some of the energy you supply goes into displacing the air above the water to make room for the steam, but most of it goes into supplying the energy each molecule needs to escape water at 100° C (373K).

Exercise 5

(a) What is the average kinetic energy of a molecule at a temperature of 373K?

(b) Is this enough energy for an average water molecule to escape through the surface of the water?

(c) At what temperature does the thermal kinetic energy equal to the 6.8×10^{-20} joules needed to escape?

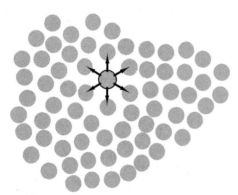

Figure 15
A molecule in the interior of a liquid is attracted by all its neighbors which surround it. As a result the net force is zero and the molecule is free to move about through the liquid.

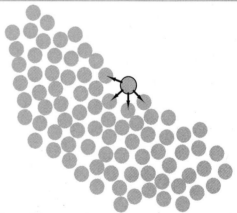

Figure 16
A molecule on the surface is attracted to its neighbors beneath it. To pull a molecule out of the surface, you have to overcome these forces. As a result it takes energy to remove a molecule from the liquid. This surface force is often referred to as **surface tension.**

If you worked Exercise 5, you realize that the average molecule, even in boiling water, has only about 10% of the thermal kinetic energy needed to escape through the surface. Yet even at room temperature water evaporates—even at these lower temperatures some molecules escape through the surface. The reason is that, while 3/2 kT is the average thermal kinetic energy of the molecules, some molecules have more kinetic energy than average, some less. Some have so much more kinetic energy than average that they can escape.

The rate of evaporation depends very much on the distribution of thermal kinetic energies. At a given temperature T what fraction of the molecules have a kinetic energy sufficiently far above average to be able to escape? It turns out that for a substance in thermal equilibrium, there is a precise formula for the distribution of thermal kinetic energies, a formula known as the *Boltzman distribution.* We will not go into that much detail. Instead, we will simply recognize that some molecules are hotter than average, some colder than average, and that it is the very hottest ones that have enough energy to escape.

If it is the hot molecules that escape during evaporation, then the cooler ones must be left behind and *evaporation must be a cooling process*. There must, however, be a net loss of molecules from the surface for cooling to occur. As we noted at the beginning of the chapter, the surface of water is a dynamic place where water molecules are continually leaving and returning. A returning water molecule, even if relatively cool when in the air above the water, gains as much kinetic energy when it reenters the water as the hot molecule lost when escaping. Thus reentering molecules become hot when they get back in the water, and thus the returning or condensation of water molecules is a warming process.

Whether you get evaporation or condensation depends upon the number of water molecules in the air above the water. If you cover a glass of water with a dish, soon the number of water molecules in the air in the glass builds up to the point that there is a balance between molecules leaving and molecules entering the liquid surface. When this balance is achieved, evaporation ceases and we say that the air above the water is at 100% relative humidity. In order to get cooling from evaporation, the relative humidity of the air must be less than 100%.

The human body uses evaporation for cooling which is effective on a hot, dry day but not on a humid one. When the relative humidity approaches 100% there is no net loss of water molecules and no cooling. Incidentally, you blow on soup to cool it, not necessarily because your breath is cooler than the soup, but because you are replacing the moist air over the soup with drier air so that more evaporation can take place.

THE IDEAL GAS LAW

When we have a dilute gas, that is, a gas where the average spacing between molecules is large compared to the size of the molecules, then we can neglect the forces between molecules and treat the molecules as tiny hard particles bouncing around. In this case there is a very simple law governing the behavior of the gas. The law is known as the ***ideal gas law***, and such a gas is referred to as an ***ideal gas***. The air in your living room is a good example of an ideal gas because the average spacing between molecules is about ten times the diameter of the air molecules.

In the Satellite Chapter 7, we use Newtonian mechanics and some rather far out assumptions about averaging molecular speeds to arrive at the ideal gas law. The surprise, perhaps, is that the simple arguments we use actually lead to the correct answer.

The ideal gas law itself is easy to state. If you have an ideal gas in a container of volume V at a temperature T, then the pressure P of the gas is given by the formula

$$P = \frac{NkT}{V} \qquad (10)$$

where N is the number of molecules inside the container and k is our familiar Boltzman's constant.

Equation (4) has an immediate and somewhat surprising consequence. If we rewrite the law, solving for the number N of particles in the container, we get

$$N = \frac{PV}{kT} \qquad (11)$$

What is surprising about Equation (11) is that it says nothing about the kind of gas that is in the container, it assumes only that it is an ideal gas.

Still another way to write the perfect gas law is in terms of the volume V.

$$V = \frac{NkT}{P} \qquad (12)$$

To put this result in more concrete terms, we first define a ***mole*** of molecules as 6.02×10^{23} molecules. This number, which is known as ***Avagadro's number***, is essentially the number of hydrogen atoms in one gram of hydrogen. Chemists also define standard temperature and pressure (***STP***) as a temperature of 300 kelvin (30°C) and atmospheric pressure.

If you use Equation (12), and have one mole of a gas at STP, the gas will occupy 22.4 liters of volume. This is true whether you have a mole of helium atoms, a mole of oxygen molecules, or a mole of complex hydrocarbon molecules. This result is known as ***Avagadro's law***, and the number 6.02×10^{23} for a mole is called ***Avagadro's constant***.

In Satellite Chapter 7, after deriving the ideal gas law, we show how to use it to construct an ideal gas thermometer, a device that does not depend on the thermal or mechanical properties of matter. Later in that chapter we also discuss specific heat, that is, the ability of materials to absorb thermal energy.

OSMOTIC PRESSURE

There are two other fairly familiar phenomena that can be understood qualitatively from a molecular point of view. One is the elasticity of rubber, and the other is the process of osmosis, which is essential for biological systems.

Osmosis is a rather peculiar but important effect that is easily explained with an atomic model. Ordinarily, when a liquid can flow between two vessels at the same height, the liquid will tend to seek the same level in both vessels. But this does not always happen. Suppose we have a tank separated by a membrane, as shown in Figure (20). On the right side (side 2) of the membrane we place pure water, indicated by the small molecules. On the left (side 1) we place a solution of water and some other substance consisting of large molecules. The membrane has a special characteristic: the small water molecules can pass through it easily, whereas the big molecules are prevented from passing through because the holes in the membrane are too small. Initially, the two compartments are filled to the same level on each side of the membrane.

Assume that some definite fraction, for instance 50%, of all water molecules that strike the membrane pass through it. Initially, more water molecules strike the membrane from side 2 than from side 1, simply because there are more water molecules on side 2. If more water molecules strike from side 2 than side 1, and if 50% of **all** the water molecules striking the membrane pass through it, there must be a net flow of water from side 2 to side 1.

As the flow continues, the level of the liquid on side 1 rises and the solution becomes diluted. As the solution becomes further diluted, the number of water molecules on side 1 facing each square centimeter of the membrane increases. Thus more flow back to side 2 so that the net flow into side 1 decreases. From this description alone, however, we would not expect the flow to stop, since we never get pure water on side 1.

The flow does stop eventually, because the level in side 1 rises to such an extent that the pressure at the bottom of side 1 becomes considerably greater than the pressure at the bottom of side 2 (a result of the increased weight of the column of water). This additional pressure, known as *osmotic pressure*, finally stops the flow of water from side 2 to side 1. The flow of the small molecules through the membrane is called *osmosis*; thus osmotic pressure is the pressure that finally stops osmosis.

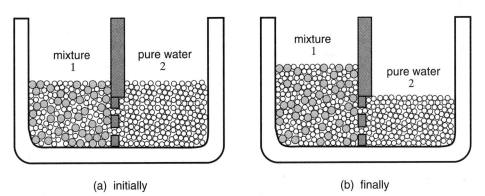

(a) initially   (b) finally

Figure 20
Osmosis. The two sides of the container are separated by a membrane that allows the water (small molecules) but not the large molecules to pass through. If the liquid levels are the same initially, as in (a), some of the pure water will flow through the membrane, raising the level on the side with the large molecules as shown in (b). This process is called osmosis.

Osmosis in Biology

Osmosis and osmotic pressure are crucial in biological processes. Osmosis is involved in the separation of nutrients and wastes in our own cells, the flow of fluids in our bodies, the flow of sap in plant life, and a number of other important processes.

The function and composition of blood is critically dependent on osmosis and osmotic pressure. Blood consists of red cells, white cells, and a fluid called *plasma*. The red cells are membrane sacs containing about 60% water and 40% hemoglobin molecules, molecules closely related to, but about four times as large as, the giant myoglobin molecule described in the beginning of this chapter. We may think of the red blood cell as representing side 1 in Figure (20) where the big molecules are the hemoglobin molecules. If red blood cells are removed from blood and placed in pure water, they absorb so much water by osmosis that they burst. The red hemoglobin flows away, leaving an empty, pale misshapen sac.

The function of the red blood cell and its hemoglobin is to carry oxygen to the other cells in the body. The plasma, which consists of 90% water, 9% protein molecules, and 1% salts, serves as a fluid in which to dissolve needed proteins and salts to be carried to the cells, and to make the blood fluid enough to flow through the minute capillaries.

The capillary walls through which blood flows are porous membranes that permit water and salts to pass freely through, but that restrict the passage of proteins. Pure water could not be pumped through the bloodstream because it would leak out through the capillary walls. You may wonder how blood plasma, which is 90% water, can be pumped through the porous capillaries. The reason is that the 9% of protein molecules in the plasma is sufficient to draw just enough water back into the capillary by osmosis to replace the water molecules that do leak out. Just as many water molecules are drawn back in as leak out, even though the pressure of the plasma inside the capillary is greater than the pressure of the fluids outside the leaky walls. Thus, side 1 in Figure (20) behaves in the same way as the capillary with the blood plasma inside it.

ELASTICITY OF RUBBER

A model for the elasticity of rubber was presented by Richard Feynman in a lecture to freshmen at Caltech in 1960. We select this model, not so much for its accuracy in describing the detailed behavior of molecules in rubber, but for developing an intuition for thermal processes. The mechanisms underlying the model and the behavior of rubber are fundamentally the same. The beauty of the model is that it is so outrageous that you are forced to think differently about thermal processes.

A Model of Rubber

Imagine that you enter a large room where there are a number of heavy chains loosely suspended from one end of the room to the other, as shown in Figure (21). These are massive chains, like the anchor chains used on old sailing ships, but they are hanging loosely, so that except for their weight, they are not exerting any force pulling the walls together.

On the floor are hundreds of cannonballs, lying there a couple of layers deep. This is our room at "absolute zero".

Now turn up the temperature in the room. The cannonballs start to jiggle and vibrate with an average thermal kinetic energy 3/2 kT. In this model, nothing melts. Instead, as we turn up the temperature the jiggling becomes stronger and stronger. When the average thermal kinetic energy 3/2 kT becomes as large as the gravitational potential energy mgh of a cannonball near the ceiling, then we will have cannonballs flying all around the room. We will have a gas of cannonballs.

As the cannonballs fly around, they strike the chains, kinking them up as indicated in Figure (22). The kinked-up chains are no longer hanging loose, instead they are taut and pulling the side walls of the room in.

If we raise the temperature of the gas of cannonballs, the cannonballs strike the chains harder and the chains pull harder on the walls.

Here is an experiment that stretches the imagination even more. Suppose we start with the room with a gas of cannonballs at a temperature T, and chains kinked by the colliding cannonballs, and suddenly pull the sides of the room apart so that the chains are straight and tight. When we suddenly straighten out the kinked chains, the chains will slap against the cannonballs transforming the work we do pulling the chains straight into increased thermal kinetic energy of the cannonballs. As a result by suddenly stretching the chains we raise the temperature of the cannonballs.

If we let the walls go back suddenly, the chains initially go slack, and it takes some of the thermal kinetic energy of the cannonballs to kink the chains up again. As a result of unstretching the chains, the temperature of the cannonballs drops.

Your lips are a good detector of small temperature changes. Place a loose rubber band between your lips and suddenly stretch it. You will notice that the rubber band becomes distinctly warmer. Now quickly release the rubber band by bringing your hands together. The rubber band becomes distinctly cool. Rubber consists of a long chain of molecules that are kinked up by thermal motion. When you stretch the rubber band, you increase the thermal kinetic energy of the molecules and raise their temperature. Releasing the band reduces the thermal motion and drops the temperature. The elastic restoring force you felt when you stretched the band is caused by thermal motions kinking the long chain molecules.

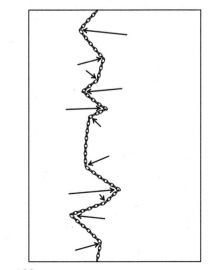

Figure 22
Top view of chains being struck by cannonballs.

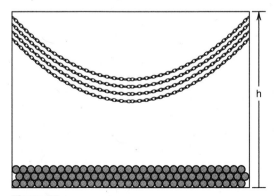

Figure 21
Room with suspended chains and cannonballs.

APPENDICES

I. MOLECULAR FORCES AND ENERGY

In this appendix we look at molecular forces from the point of view of potential energy. From this point of view, we get a fairly clear picture of the phenomenon of thermal expansion, and an explanation of why molecular forces in solids often behave as Hooke's law spring forces. This helps explain why we found that the speed of sound in steel is given by the Hooke's law formula $v = \sqrt{kL/\mu}$. We put this material in an appendix because it is closely related to what we have been studying, but not essential for the topics we are about to study.

In Figure (14) we described the force between two noble gas atoms like helium, neon and argon. While this is one of the simplest interactions, it has general features common to almost all atomic or molecular forces. When the atoms or molecules are one or two diameters apart, as in Figure (14a) there is a weak attractive force. The attractive force reaches a maximum when the particles are only a fraction of a diameter apart as in Figure (14c), but becomes very repulsive when the particles are too close together as in Figure (14e). When switching from an attractive to a repulsive force, there is a separation, shown in Figure (14d), where there is no net force between the particles. This separation is what we call the ***equilibrium separation***.

At the bottom of Figure (14), Figure (14f), is a diagram showing the potential energy of the two atoms. This diagram effectively summarizes all the information contained in Figures (14a) through (14e).

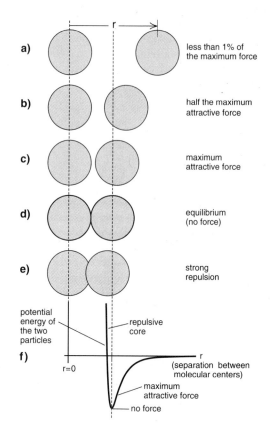

Figure 14 again
Interaction of two atoms via a Leonard Jones potential (f). When the atoms have an equilibrium separation (d), their potential energy of interaction is at a minimum, and we can visualize one of the atoms as sitting at the bottom of the potential energy well.

To relate the potential energy diagram to the forces involved, imagine that you are riding a bicycle in a hilly terrain. You come upon a valley shaped as in Figure (23), and decide to coast down the valley and up the far side.

As you start coasting, the gravitational force acting on you combines with the force of the road on the bicycle to give a net force that accelerates you and the bicycle forward down the hill. You pick up speed because this net force $\vec{F}$ attracts you toward the bottom of the valley. As the hill gets steeper, the force and your acceleration gets stronger, reaching a maximum value at the steepest part of the descent at point (c).

When you get down to the bottom of the valley, point (d), you have attained your maximum speed, but because the road is horizontal, there is no more force or acceleration.

As you go up the steep hill on the other side, you encounter a strong force opposing your motion, quickly bringing your bicycle to a halt.

This was an analysis of the motion of the coasting bicycle by visualizing the forces acting on the bicycle. An easier way to analyze the motion is to picture Figure (23) as a potential energy diagram for the bicyclist, and apply conservation of energy. As the bicycle goes down into the valley, the bicyclist loses gravitational potential energy mgh, but gains kinetic energy $1/2\ mv^2$.

At the bottom of the valley the bicycle's speed is the greatest because all the original potential energy is converted to kinetic energy (neglecting energy lost due to wind resistance, etc.). Going up the far side the kinetic energy is converted back into potential energy and the coasting bicycle comes to rest when it gets up to its original height h_0. Thus with energy arguments, you can predict the bicycle's motion without having to calculate the actual forces acting on the bicycle.

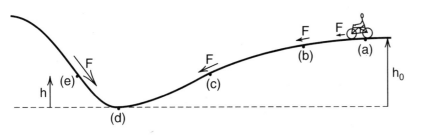

Speed determined by conservation of energy.

$$mgh + 1/2\ mv^2 = mgh_0$$

At the bottom of the valley where h = 0, the speed is

$$1/2\ mv^2 = mgh_0$$

Figure 23
There are two ways to analyze the motion of the bicycle. One is in terms of the net force acting on the bicycle and rider. A simpler way is to picture the valley as a potential energy diagram, and look at the transfer of potential energy into kinetic energy.

The result is that in many cases we can model molecular forces as spring forces as shown in Figure (28b). This is why a steel pipe obeys Hooke's law as far as a sound pulse is concerned. It is also why textbooks often draw atomic and molecular forces as springs. One of the best examples of this is the computer drawing of a three dimensional spring model of a solid shown in Figure (29).

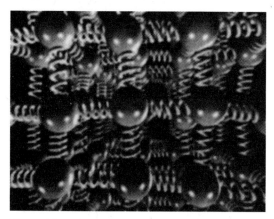

Figure 29
Ball spring model of a solid.

Computer model from the article "Bringing atoms into first-year physics" by Chabay and Sherwood. (**American Journal of Physics** *67 (12) December 1999.) The authors have constructed an introductory course that focuses on atomic structure. For an interesting article on their approach, go to* http://www4.ncsu.edu/~rwchabay/mi/ChabaySherwoodFundamentals.pdf

CHAPTER 16 REVIEW

A standard calculus based introductory physics text has about four chapters on the subjects related to heat and temperature. These are usually well written chapters that can be covered carefully in about four weeks. To cover the same material in a non calculus course would take longer because we do not have the same shortcuts available by the use of calculus. In addition, some of the students may have seen some or much of the material in a previous chemistry course.

In a comfortably paced course we have a choice. Do we spend those four weeks on developing a more complete picture of 19th century physics, or include quantum mechanics? Our choice is that in one core chapter, we cover basic concepts like thermal energy, molecular forces, and pressure—concepts that we will use later in the course. Other important topics like the Ideal Gas Law and Heat Capacity are covered in more detail in the Satellite Chapter 7 and the important topics of Entropy and the Second Law of Thermodynamics in Satellite Chapter 8. The concept of Entropy is sufficiently interesting and important, that we wrote Essay 4 on the subject.

In the overview, our focus will be on thermal energy, molecular forces, and pressure.

Temperature and Thermal Energy

One of the most universal and perhaps surprising aspects that atoms all have, whether they are in a solid, liquid or gas, is a thermal kinetic energy given by the formula

$$\text{thermal kinetic energy} = \frac{3}{2}kT \qquad (1)$$

The temperature is in kelvins and k is Boltzman's constant. The kelvin temperature scale starts at T = 0 (absolute zero), where there is no thermal kinetic energy, and goes up in centigrade sized degrees. The thermal kinetic energy became visible when we watched the jiggling of the smoke particles in the Brownian motion movie.

The only noticeable exception to Equation (1) is close to absolute zero, where quantum effects can be detected. According to quantum mechanics, any confined particle has unremovable kinetic energy called **zero point energy**. *The tighter the confinement the greater the zero point energy. For liquid helium, the zero point energy is great enough to keep the liquid from freezing even at absolute zero. In our discussion of quantum mechanics we will see where the zero point energy comes from.*

Molecular Forces

Although molecular forces can be fairly complex, and create very complex objects like the myoglobin molecule of Figure (3), molecular forces have some general features that are simple and universal. As shown in Figure (14) when two molecules are about two atomic diameters apart, there is only a weak attractive force. This attractive force becomes a maximum at a separation of about half an atomic radius. The force goes to zero when the two molecules are at an equilibrium separation. We can picture these molecules as just touching. Try to shove the molecules closer together and they encounter a strong, rapidly increasing repulsive force. It is this repulsive force that gives the molecules essentially a hard solid core.

We will later refer to this kind of molecular force as a **short range force**, *one that acts only at short ranges. This is in contrast to a force like gravity that can reach out great distances and hold together objects like solar systems and galaxies.*

Another way to view molecular force is in terms of the potential energy of the force. This approach is a simpler way of looking at the interaction, and can be used to explain why heated objects expand and why our steel guitar string and the steel pipe we hit with a hammer, all obey Hook's law. The three appendices on molecular force are worth reading if you have time, but are not as essential for the rest of the text as other topics in this chapter.

Pressure

The concept of pressure is almost as common a concept as temperature. The approach of a storm is usually heralded by a drop in atmospheric pressure. The skin of a blown up balloon is held in place by the pressure of the air inside the balloon.

A closer inspection shows that the air pressure on the skin of the balloon is caused by the constant bombardment of the air molecules hitting and bouncing off the rubber. We demonstrated the dependence of air pressure on thermal motion by cooling the balloon with liquid nitrogen. As the temperature of the balloon dropped, the pressure dropped, and the balloon shrank until only a puddle of liquid air was inside a wrinkled balloon.

We took the step of saying that the force caused by air molecules bouncing off the rubber was caused by the pressure P of the gas itself. We defined the pressure of the gas as the force the gas exerts on a unit area of the balloon surface. In the MKS system that would be the force in newtons that the gas exerts on a full square meter of surface area. This quantity, called a **pascal** *is generally a very inconvenient unit. Seldom do we deal with balloons with lots of square meters of surface area.*

For scuba divers, the best unit of pressure is atmospheric pressure at sea level. In Chapter 18 on Fluid Dynamics, we will see that the pressure of the water increases by an additional atmosphere every 10 meters or 33 feet. In scuba diving at a depth of 30 meters or 100 ft, you are breathing air at a pressure of 4 atmospheres.

In our discussion of the mercury barometer, we showed you how to measure pressure by the length h of the column of mercury that the air pressure supported. At sea level, at normal conditions, that column is 76 cm or 760 mm high. You may hear a weather forecaster say that with the approaching storm the pressure may go as low as 730 mm of mercury.

In science labs and engineering applications one often uses the name **torr** *for pressure of one millimeter of mercury. For modern vacuum systems, that is still too big a unit of pressure. Most commercial vacuum gauges are calibrated in microns, where one micron is the pressure that would support one millionth of a meter of mercury. The vacuums that are needed in the manufacture of computer chips are in the range of 10^{-7} microns.*

Chapter 17 non calculus

Electric Charge and Coulomb's Law

When he flew a kite in a thunderstorm, Ben Franklin both avoided killing himself and demonstrated that lightning was an electrical phenomenon. (The Russian scientist Georg-Wilheim Richman repeated Franklin's experiment and was killed in the process.) Franklin also introduced the concept of positive and negative charge to describe the two kinds of charge observed in electrostatic experiments.

In this chapter we will start with some simple electrostatic experiments that illustrate the fact that there are two kinds of electric charge. The experiments will also demonstrate why it is difficult to determine the electric force law from such eighteenth century apparatus.

In the nineteenth century, Charles Coulomb did careful experiments to verify that the electric force was a $1/r^2$ force law, and that the force between two charged objects is proportional to the product of the charges on the objects. Because of this work the electric force law is known as **Coulomb's law** and electric charge is measured in units called **coulombs**.

In the twentieth century we finally learned what carried electric charge. In the matter around us that we are familiar with, there are four kinds of basic particles. There are the protons and neutrons found in the atomic nucleus, the electrons that surround the nucleus to form complete atoms, and particles of light, called photons, that are the source of visible light. Of these particles, the photon and the neutron are electrically neutral, while the proton carries one kind of charge and the electron carries the other. Following Franklin's convention, the charge on the proton is positive and that on the electron is negative. And the fact that an electrically neutral atom contains equal numbers of protons and electrons tells us that the charge on the proton and electron are equal in magnitude, while opposite in sign.

After our discussion of the electrostatic experiments, we will compare Coulomb's $1/r^2$ electric force law with Newton's $1/r^2$ gravitational force law. While there are many similarities, there are some very important differences. We will then go on to a 20th century point of view of electric forces.

Two Kinds of Electric Charge

Some simple electrostatic experiments clearly demonstrate that there are two kinds of electric charge. For these experiments we use two small Styrofoam™ balls wrapped with aluminum foil and suspended by threads as shown in Figure (1a). We also need one glass rod, one rubber rod, a piece of silk cloth and a piece of cat fur. (We assume that these latter items were commonly available in eighteenth century physics labs.)

In the first experiment we rub the glass rod with the silk cloth and touch both balls with the glass rod. When things have settled down, we observe that the two balls are repelling each other as shown in Figure (1b).

Some peculiar things happen before we get the result shown in Figure (1b). As we bring the glass rod up to the first ball, the ball is attracted to the glass rod. After we touch the glass rod, the ball is repelled. Before we touch the second ball, we notice that it is attracted to the first ball. Only after we touch it with the glass rod do we see the balls repel each other as shown in Figure (1b).

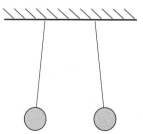

Figure 1a
Styrofoam balls wrapped in aluminum foil and suspended on threads.

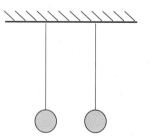

Figure 1b
After the two balls are touched by the same rod.

For the second experiment, we first touch both balls with our hand, and notice that afterward the balls hang straight down. Our hand has removed any electric charge placed on the balls by the glass rod. Then we rub the rubber rod with cat fur and touch both balls with the rubber rod. When things settle down, we see that the balls again repel each other as shown in Figure (1b).

The third experiment is the crucial one. Again we discharge both balls by touching them, so that they hang straight down as in Figure (1a). Then we touch one ball with the glass rod rubbed by silk, and the other ball with the rubber rod rubbed by cat fur. Instead of repelling each other as in Figure (1b), the two balls attract each other as shown in Figure (1c). This clearly demonstrates that there is something different about the charges deposited by the glass rod and the rubber rod. If the charges were the same kind on the two rods, the balls would still repel each other. Thus there are at least two kinds of electric charge.

A fourth experiment, which is a bit more complex than the first three, tells us more about the nature of electric charge. After you have charged the balls with different rods to get the attractive force shown in Figure (1c), move the threads together so that the balls touch each other. (Be careful that you do not touch the balls.) When you let go of the threads, one of two things happens. Either the balls then repel each other or hang straight down.

Most of the time the balls will repel somewhat. But if you get just the right amount of charge on each ball (by different amounts of rubbing of the rods), you can end up with the balls hanging straight down. When this happens, you can see that the charges on

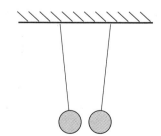

Figure 1c
After the two balls are touched by different rods.

the two balls cancelled each other. Such results led Franklin to name the two kinds of charge *positive* and *negative* charge. When you got equal amounts of positive and negative charge on the balls, then had them touch, the two charges cancelled each other leaving the balls uncharged.

Not knowing the origin of electric charge, Franklin simply chose to call the charge left on the glass rod positive charge, and that left on the rubber rod negative charge. Jumping to the 20th century, we know that the two kinds of charge are carried in ordinary matter by electrons and protons. Franklin's choice of the glass rod being positive leads to the proton being positive and the electron being negative.

The electrostatic experiments also demonstrate that electric charge is quite mobile. We could get charge on the rods by rubbing them, and we could transfer charge by touching the balls with the rods.

In the twentieth century we learned that this mobility of electric charge is caused by the fact that electrons can flow as a fluid through a conductor or be scraped off the surface of an insulator by rubbing.

When we rub the glass rod with a silk cloth, electrons are rubbed off the rod and stick to the cloth. The lack of electrons leaves more protons than electrons on the glass rod, and the glass rod ends up with a positive charge. When we touch the glass rod to the aluminum foil surrounding the ball, the positive glass rod sucks some electrons out of the aluminum foil leaving the ball positively charged.

On the other hand when we rub the rubber rod with cat fur, electrons are scraped off the cat fur and stick to the rubber rod. When the rubber rod touches the aluminum foil on the ball, electrons pass from the rod to the foil leaving the ball negatively charged.

That still leaves the question of why the neutral ball was attracted to a charged rod before the rod touched the ball. The answer is due to the mobility of the electrons in the aluminum foil. When we brought the positive rod up to the ball, the positive charge on the rod attracted electrons in the foil to the front side of the ball leaving a net positive charge on the back side as indicated in Figure (2a).

Since the negative charge is closer to the positive rod, the attractive force of the negative charge is stronger than the repulsive force of the positive charge, and there is a net force toward the rod. This is true even though there is no net charge on the ball.

We still get an attractive force as the negative rubber rod is brought up to the ball, because the minus charge on the ball pushes the electrons in the foil toward the back side of the ball, leaving a net positive charge on the front side, as indicated in Figure (2b). Since the plus charge on the ball is closer to the negative rod, it is more strongly attracted than the more distant negative charge is repelled.

Exercise 1

Explain why the ball jumps away from the rod after the rod touches the ball.

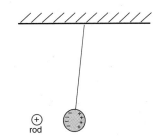

Figure 2a
The + rod attracts electrons to the front side.

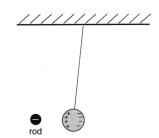
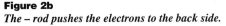

Figure 2b
The – rod pushes the electrons to the back side.

COULOMB'S ELECTRIC FORCE LAW

In the study of gravity, it is not difficult to demonstrate that the gravitational force between objects like stars and planets is accurately described by a $1/r^2$ force law. Newton knew this from his analysis of the Kepler orbits of the planets. We could determine this from our computer analysis of planetary orbits in Chapter 8. We saw that if we made even a small change in the exponent, from $1/r^2$ to $1/r^{1.9}$ we got the big change in the orbit shown in Figure (8-25) repeated here. When the exponent is not exactly $1/r^2$, the ellipse starts to precess. This precession is not present in a pure Kepler orbit.

In contrast, due to the mobility of electric charge, it is very difficult to show experimentally that the electric force law is a $1/r^2$ force. We just saw, for example, that the mobility electrons can even lead to an electric force between a charged rod and an electrically neutral ball. As we mentioned in the introduction, Charles Coulomb did some very careful experiments accurately verifying the $1/r^2$ nature of the electric force between point particles.

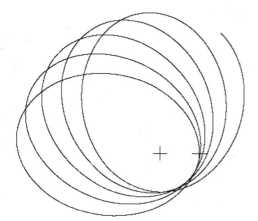

Figure 8-25 (repeated)
Planetary orbit when the gravitational force is modified to a $1/r^{1.9}$ force.

In many ways Coulomb's electric force law can be modeled on Newton's gravitational force law. For gravity the gravitational force F_g between two point masses m_1 and m_2 separated by a distance r is

$$F_g = \frac{Gm_1m_2}{r^2} \qquad \begin{array}{l}\textit{Newton's law}\\\textit{of gravity}\end{array} \qquad (9\text{-}3)$$

where G is the universal gravitational constant. Coulomb's law for electricity can be written in the form

$$F_e = \frac{KQ_1Q_2}{r^2} \qquad \begin{array}{l}\textit{Coulomb's electric}\\\textit{force law}\end{array} \qquad (1)$$

Where Q_1 and Q_2 are two point charges separated by a distance r, and K is the universal electric force constant.

In order to work with Newton's law of gravity, one must first have an experimental definition of mass. We still use, as the definition of a unit mass, the kilogram block of platinum kept in Paris, France. Copies of the unit mass are sent around the world so that various laboratories can calibrate their own sets of standard masses. Once you know what the masses m_1 and m_2 are in terms of the standard unit mass, you can then do a Cavendish experiment, measuring the force F_g when the masses are a distance r apart, and then solve for the gravitational constant

$$G = \frac{r^2F_g}{m_1m_2} \qquad (2)$$

The main point we just tried to make is that the value of the universal gravitational constant G depends on our choice of a unit mass. In the MKS system where mass is in kilograms and distance in meters, G has the value

$$G = 6.67 \times 10^{-11} \frac{\text{newton meter}^2}{\text{kilogram}^2}$$

In the CGS system, where mass is in grams, distance in centimeters and force measured in dynes (1 dyne $= 10^{-5}$ newtons) the universal gravitational constant is

$$G = 6.67 \times 10^{-8} \frac{\text{dyne cm}^2}{\text{gm}^2}$$

Imagine that we could use a similar procedure for Coulomb's electric force law. We create a unit charge and store it in a laboratory in Paris. We then send copies of the unit charge around the world so that each laboratory could calibrate their own set of standard charges. Then the laboratory responsible for physical standards (in the U.S. it is *The Institute of Standards and Technology*) would measure the electric force F_e between two known charges Q_1 and Q_2 separated by a distance r. They could then solve for the universal electric constant K, getting

$$K = \frac{r^2 F_e}{Q_1 Q_2} \tag{3}$$

The only problem with this approach is that you cannot easily store a unit charge. As we saw, if you put a charge on a glass or rubber rod and touch a piece of metal, the charge flows off the rod onto the metal. On a damp day the charge will flow off the rod into the moist atmosphere. In other words the approach used for the gravitational force law, first define the unit mass and use that to determine the universal force constant, does not work for electricity.

Instead, in electrical theory, one first defines the electric force constant K, and then one uses Coulomb's law to determine how big a unit charge is. For example, if you took two identical charges Q, separated them by a distance r, and measured the electric force F_e between them, you would get

$$F_e = \frac{KQ^2}{r^2} \; ; \quad Q = r\sqrt{\frac{F_e}{K}} \tag{4}$$

as the value of the charge Q.

MKS and CGS Units

As we saw in the case of gravity, the numerical value of the universal force constant G depends on the system of units used. The difference for electricity is that we first make an arbitrary choice for the universal force constant K, and later determine how big the unit charge is.

In the CGS system, a very simple choice is made, namely

$$K = 1 \qquad \begin{array}{l}\textit{electric force constant} \\ \textit{in the CGS system}\end{array} \tag{5}$$

with the result that Coulomb's law becomes

$$F_e = \frac{Q_1 Q_2}{r^2} \qquad \begin{array}{l}\textit{Coulomb's law} \\ \textit{in CGS units}\end{array} \tag{6}$$

The simplicity of this choice makes the CGS system of units sometimes useful in describing atomic phenomena.

On the other hand the CGS system is nearly a disaster when discussing practical electrical phenomena that we deal with every day. We are all familiar with volts (AA batteries are 1.5 volts), amps (household circuits usually now have 20 amp circuit breakers) and watts (you can buy 100 watt bulbs at the hardware store). The quantities volt, ampere, and watt are all MKS units.

The corresponding CGS quantities are **statvolts** (1 statvolt = 300 volts), **statamps** (1 statamp = 3 billion amps) and **ergs per second** (1 erg = 10^{-7} joules), all quantities you have never heard of and do not want to use. For this reason we use MKS units in this text.

The choice for the universal electric force constant in the MKS system of units, a choice made official in 1946, is

$$K(\text{MKS units}) \equiv 10^{-7}c^2 = 9.00 \times 10^9 \qquad (7)$$

where c is the speed of light $(3 \times 10^8 \text{m/s})$. While the choice $10^{-7}c^2$ appears rather arbitrary, it is the choice that gives us volts, amps and watts.

There is one more step in getting the standard form of Coulomb's law in MKS units. The universal electric constant K is written in the form

$$K \equiv \frac{1}{4\pi\varepsilon_0} \qquad (8)$$

so that Coulomb's law becomes

$$F_e = \frac{Q_1 Q_2}{4\pi\varepsilon_0 r^2} \qquad \text{*Coulomb's electric force law*} \qquad (9)$$

You would be quite justified in asking **why did they do that?** The answers are: the 4π was put into Coulomb's force law in order to get rid of a 4π that appears somewhere else (namely in our discussion of electric flux). And the constant ε_0 (epsilon naught) was put downstairs in order to make electrical theory in the 1800s look more like the theory of fluids.

We can use Equation (8) to solve for the numerical value of ε_0. We get

$$\varepsilon_0 \equiv \frac{1}{4\pi K} = \frac{1}{4\pi \times 10^{-7}c^2} = \frac{1}{4\pi \times 9 \times 10^9}$$

$$\varepsilon_0 = 8.85 \times 10^{-12} \qquad \text{*standard electric force constant*} \qquad (10)$$

THE COULOMB

With the choice of $K = 9.00 \times 10^9$ in the MKS system, the electric charge Q is measured in **coulombs**. Conceptually, we like to think of how big a coulomb of charge is by counting the number of electrons it takes to make up a coulomb of them. We discuss this in the next section.

CHARGE ON THE ELECTRON

The twentieth century has given us a fundamental definition of a unit charge, namely the charge (e) on an electron. The quantity (e) is actually the charge on the proton since the electron, by Franklin's definition, is negative. But we still call the positive number (e) the **charge on the electron**. In 1910, Robert Millikan, studying the motion of charged drops in a fine mist of oil, was able to measure the charge on an individual electron. The result is

$$e = 1.60 \times 10^{-19}\text{coulombs} \qquad \text{*charge on an electron*} \qquad (11)$$

From this we can immediately calculate how many electrons are in a coulomb of electrons. Using dimensions we have

$$e = 1.60 \times 10^{-19}\frac{\text{coulombs}}{\text{electron}}$$

$$\frac{1}{e} = 6.25 \times 10^{18}\frac{\text{electrons}}{\text{coulomb}} \qquad (12)$$

Thus in the MKS system the unit charge, one coulomb, turns out to be the amount of charge one would have in a bucket of 6.25×10^{18} electrons (again forgetting the minus sign).

Just as a liter of water is a large convenient collection of water molecules, 3.34×10^{25} of them, the coulomb can be thought of as a large collection of electron charges, 6.25×10^{18} of them.

THE HYDROGEN ATOM

The one place that Coulomb's law should apply, without the problem of dealing with a complex charge distribution, is in the case of the hydrogen atom. There we have a nucleus consisting of one proton of charge +e and one electron of charge –e. Since the proton is 1863 times as massive as the electron, the proton should sit at the center of the atom while the electron orbits around it. The force attracting the electron to the proton is $F_e = Ke^2/r^2$, and because of the analogy to a planet orbiting the sun, we might expect the electron to execute a Kepler orbit about the proton. This is suggested in Figure (3).

This does not happen, not because of a failure of the $1/r^2$ Coulomb's force law, but because of a failure of Newtonian mechanics. On an atomic scale the particle/wave nature of matter plays an increasingly important role, and must be taken into account in order to understand the behavior of the electron in hydrogen. Some classical ideas like conservation of energy and angular momentum still apply, but precise predictions of the electron behavior result only when we include the wave nature of the electron. We do this in detail in the quantum mechanics chapters.

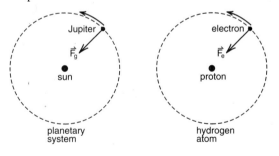

Figure 3
Classical picture of the hydrogen atom.

Molecular Forces

For now we will account for the wave nature of the electron by picturing the electron forming a negatively charged cloud surrounding the positive proton. For a neutral isolated hydrogen atom the cloud is spherical in shape, is most intense at the proton, and dies off in about 10^{-10} meters, which is called one angstrom, or $\overset{\circ}{A}$, as indicated in Figure (4).

In quantum mechanics, the density of the electron cloud at some point is interpreted as the probability of finding the electron there. For now we will picture the electron cloud as simply a cloud of negative charge. In a complete hydrogen atom, the cloud contains just as much negative charge as the proton has positive charge, so that the atom is electrically neutral.

If you look carefully at the atoms in a bottle of room temperature hydrogen gas, you would not find neutral hydrogen atoms. Instead the atoms will be found in pairs called hydrogen **molecules**, denoted by the chemists as H_2. The chemists would say that the hydrogen atoms are held together by a **covalent bond**, which is an example of the **molecular forces** that hold atoms together to form molecules, crystals, and most of the matter around us. What we can do now, with Coulomb's law and the picture of an electron cloud, is to see how the hydrogen covalent bond is formed.

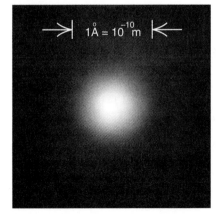

Figure 4
Cloud model of hydrogen atom.

HYDROGEN MOLECULE ION

To construct the hydrogen molecule, imagine that we start with a complete hydrogen atom and a single proton as indicated in Figure (5a). Here we are representing the electron cloud in the atom by an electron moving around to more or less fill a spherical region around its proton. In this case the external proton is attracted to the sphere of negative charge by a force that is just as strong as the repulsion from the hydrogen nucleus. As a result there is very little net force between the external proton and the neutral atom.

protron

electron

hydrogen atom

(a) A proton far from a complete hydrogen atom.

protron

(b) The external proton is brought closer
distorting the electron cloud

hydrogen atom

electron cloud formed
by one electron

(c) Electron orbits both protons

Hydrogen molecule ion

Figure 5a
Formation of a hydrogen molecule ion. To visualize how a hydrogen molecule ion can be formed, imagine that you bring a proton up to a neutral hydrogen atom.

Figure 5b
When the proton gets close, it distorts the hydrogen electron cloud. Since the distorted cloud is closer to the external proton, there is a net attractive force between the proton and the distorted hydrogen atom.

Figure 5c
If the protons get too close, they repel each other. As a result there must be some separation where there is neither attraction or repulsion. This equilibrium separation for the protons in a hydrogen molecule ion is 1.07 Angstroms. (1 Angstrom = 10^{-10} m.)

Now bring the external proton closer to the hydrogen atom. The electron cloud is now beginning to feel the attraction of external proton as well as its own proton. The result is that the cloud is distorted, sucked over a bit toward the external proton. The attractive force between the cloud and the external proton is now slightly greater than the repulsion between the protons. The external proton is now attracted to the neutral hydrogen atom for much the same reason that a charged rod attracted a neutral aluminium foil ball in our electrostatic experiment (shown in Figure (2a) reproduced here.

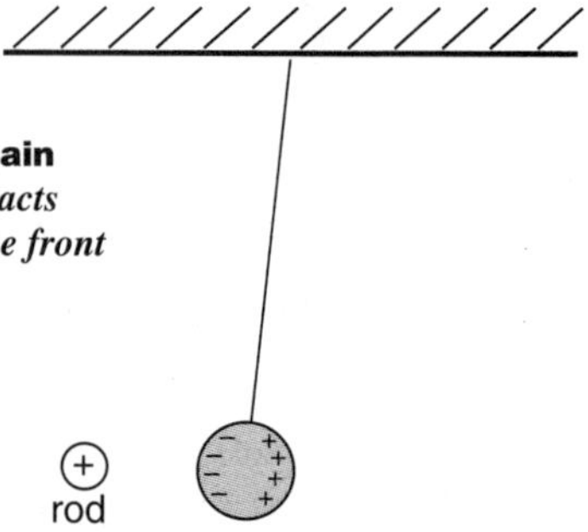

Figure 2a again
The + rod attracts electrons to the front side.

If we let go of the proton in Figure (5b), it will be sucked into the hydrogen atom. When it enters the electron cloud and gets close to the other proton, the repulsion between the protons can begin to exceed the attraction of the negative cloud. There is an intermediate position where the electron attraction and proton repulsion cancel and in Figure (5c) we have a stable object called a ***hydrogen molecule ion***. In the ion, the electron cannot tell the difference between the two protons, and thus forms a symmetric cloud about both. It is this shared electron cloud that forms the covalent bond between the two protons.

Hydrogen Molecule

Since the hydrogen molecule ion has two protons and only one electron, the total charge is +e and the ion can attract another electron into the cloud. Now we have a complete hydrogen molecule as indicated in Figure (6). This electron cloud with two electrons forms what is called a *double ionic bond*, which is even stronger than the *single bond* of the hydrogen molecule ion.

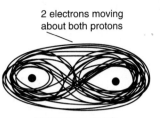

2 electrons moving
about both protons

Hydrogen molecule

Figure 6
The hydrogen molecule ion of Figure (5c) has a net positive charge +e, and therefore can attract and hold one more electron. In that case both electrons orbit both protons and we have a complete hydrogen molecule. The equilibrium separation expands to 1.48 Angstroms.

CONSERVATION OF ELECTRIC CHARGE

In the early 1930s, our view of the basic structure of matter was fairly simple. Matter was made up of atoms, and atoms consisted of nuclei made up of protons and neutrons. Electrons surrounded the nucleus, and a complete neutral atom contained equal numbers of protons and electrons.

Then in 1933 Carl Anderson at Caltech discovered a particle of the same mass as the electron but of the opposite sign. Dirac had already formulated a theory for this new particle. He had a relativistic wave equation for the electron, an equation that had two solutions. One solution was the familiar electron. The other solution, after some thought, turned out to be Anderson's particle which became known as the **positron**. It soon became clear that all relativistic wave equations for elementary particles would have two solutions, and the second solution became known as the **anti matter** solution.

A special feature of anti matter is that a particle and its anti particle can **annihilate** each other leaving behind only some form of energy. But in any such annihilation electric charge is conserved, meaning that the anti particle has the opposite charge of the particle. In the 1960s physicists were able to create the negative anti particle of the proton. (A matter-anti matter pair of particles can also be created from energy).

The elementary particle picture of matter gradually increased in complexity. In the early 1930s the **muon** was discovered. That is the particle we studied in the muon lifetime movie. After a positive anti particle muon stopped in the block of plastic, it sat around for a while and then decayed into a positron and a neutrino. The neutrino is electrically neutral and the positron has the same + charge as the original muon. Thus electric charge was conserved when the muon decayed.

By the 1950s, the number of known "elementary" particles had increased dramatically. In 1947 the family of π mesons was discovered, then K mesons and λ particles. The count of elementary particles had increased to the order of 100 or so by 1960. All but the familiar proton and electron are unstable and quickly decay after being created. Despite all the complexity of the creation and decay of all these particles, one result was simple. ***In every creation or decay, electric charge was conserved***. Just as much charge entered a reaction as came out of it.

In 1961, Murray Gell-Mann of Caltech devised a scheme that provided an orderly ranking of the myriad of elementary particles. His scheme, called the *eightfold way*, organized the elementary particles in much the same way that Mendeleev's periodic table organized the 100 or so different kinds of elements. I was privileged to be at Gell-Mann's first seminar introducing that scheme.

A few years later, Gell-Mann and George Zweig independently (both were from Caltech but Zweig was away on sabbatical) discovered the reason for the symmetry seen in Gell-Mann's plan. In their theory there were two families of particles. There were the light particles called **leptons** which consisted of the electron, muon and neutrino. All the rest of the particles, the proton, the neutron, the π mesons and the rest of the 100 or so particles were made up of **quarks** (a name Gell-Mann gave them).

The most common quarks are given the rather mundane names: the **up quark** and the **down quark**. The proton consists of two up quarks and one down quark, while the neutron consists of two down quarks and one up quark.

Charge on a Quark

The truly hard to believe feature of the quarks is their fractional electric charge. The up quark charge is (+2/3)e and the down quark charge is (–1/3)e. Thus the total charge on the proton is 2(2e/3) + (–e/3) = e as indicated in Figure (7). For the neutron, with two down quarks and one up quark, we have a charge 2(–e/3) + (2e/3) = 0. In neither case do we end up with a fractional charge.

There is a strict rule that ***quarks always form particles that have integer values of electric charge***. You have particles like the proton and neutron that are made up of three quarks, and the so called mesons that are made from quark-(anti quark) pairs. (An anti quark has the opposite charge from the corresponding quark.)

Why can't you violate this strict rule by simply pulling a single quark out of a proton? The answer lies in the nature of the force that hold the quarks together to form particles like the neutron and proton. This force, known as the ***strong nuclear force*** is quite unlike electricity or gravity. These latter two forces get weaker, as $1/r^2$, as we move two particles apart. In contrast the quark force gets stronger as we try to pull the quarks apart. (It's more like a spring force.)

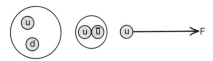

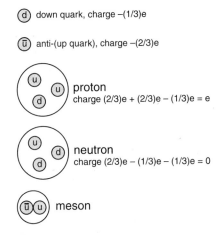

proton
charge (2/3)e + (2/3)e – (1/3)e = e

neutron
charge (2/3)e – (1/3)e – (1/3)e = 0

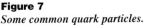
meson

Figure 7
Some common quark particles.

Imagine, for example, that you tried to pull a quark out of a proton as shown in Figure (8a). The farther out you get it, the harder you have to pull. The increasing work you do goes into increasing the potential energy of the system. (Think of stretching a spring.)

At some point the energy you have added is enough to create a quark-(anti quark) pair as shown in Figure (8b). The quark in this pair goes back into the proton, while the anti quark joins the quark you pulled out to create a meson. Instead of a free quark, you end up with the proton and a meson as shown in Figures (8c,d). This process explains why mesons are created in profusion in particle accelerator experiments

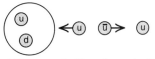

proton

a) Pulling an up quark out of a proton. The farther we pull it, the stronger the force required.

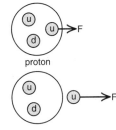

b) The potential energy we supplied creates a quark-(anti quark) pair.

c) The up quark of the pair goes back into the proton. The anti up quark joins the up quark we pulled out.

proton

meson

d) We end up with a proton and a neutral meson.

Figure 8
If we try to pull a single quark out of a proton or neutron, we get a meson instead. No one has ever seen a single quark.

APPENDIX

CLASSICAL MODEL OF HYDROGEN

(This material will be used when we get to the Bohr model of the hydrogen atom in Chapter 27.)

Despite the failure of Newton's second law at an atomic level, Neils Bohr found that a classical analysis of the hydrogen atom provided important clues as to the true nature of hydrogen. He considered a simple model in which the electron was moving in a circular orbit about the proton. Since the electron and proton both have a charge of magnitude e, the electric force $\vec{F}_e$ that the proton exerts on the electron is directed toward the proton and has a magnitude

$$F_e = \frac{Ke^2}{r^2} \tag{13}$$

The electron, traveling in a circle of radius r, has an acceleration $\vec{a}$, also directed toward the proton, with a magnitude

$$a = \frac{v^2}{r} \tag{14} \text{ also (5-8)}$$

Applying Newton's second law $\vec{F} = m\vec{a}$, and noting $\vec{F}$ and $\vec{a}$ are in the same directions, we get

$$F_e = ma; \qquad \frac{Ke^2}{r^2} = \frac{mv^2}{r} \tag{15}$$

One of the r's cancel and we immediately get the formula for the electron's kinetic energy

$$\frac{1}{2}mv^2 = \frac{Ke^2}{2r} \tag{16}$$

The electron also has electrical potential energy. We use the convention that *the potential energy is zero when the electron and proton are very far apart*. If we let the particles fall together they gain kinetic energy at the expense of electric potential energy. Since the potential energy started out at zero, it had to become *negative* as potential energy was lost. This is the same reason why the attractive gravitational force has negative potential energy.

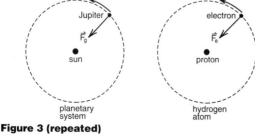

Figure 3 (repeated)
Classical picture of the hydrogen atom.

(We define gravitational potential energy as approaching zero when two masses are very far apart.)

The formula for the gravitational potential energy of particles of mass M_1 and M_2 separated by a distance r is

$$\left.\begin{array}{l}\text{Gravitational} \\ \text{potential} \\ \text{energy}\end{array}\right\} = -\frac{GM_1M_2}{r} \tag{10-43}$$

which we discussed on page (10-19). It looks like the formula for the magnitude of the gravitational force, except that the r is not squared.

We did not derive this formula, but did show that it led to conservation of energy when we calculated satellite orbits.

Since we can go back and forth between Newton's law of gravity and Coulomb's electrical force law by replacing GM_1M_2 by KQ_1Q_2, we should expect that the formula for the electric potential energy of a proton and an electron should also be obtained from Equation (10-43) by replacing GM_1M_2 by $KQ_1Q_2 = Ke^2$ to get

$$\left.\begin{array}{l}\text{Electrical} \\ \text{potential} \\ \text{energy}\end{array}\right\} = -\frac{Ke^2}{r} \tag{17}$$

Here is what may be a surprise. When an electron is in a circular orbit its negative electrical potential energy is twice as large as its positive kinetic energy of Equation (16). As a result the electron's total energy, kinetic plus potential energy is

$$\left.\begin{array}{l}\text{Total energy of} \\ \text{an electron in} \\ \text{a circular orbit}\end{array}\right\} = \frac{\text{kinetic}}{\text{energy}} + \frac{\text{potential}}{\text{energy}}$$

$$= \frac{Ke^2}{2r} - \frac{Ke^2}{r} \tag{18}$$

$$= -\frac{Ke^2}{2r}$$

We see that the electron's total energy is negative, and becomes more negative as the electron's orbital radius becomes smaller.

Another way of thinking of the electron's negative total energy is that the electron is in an energy well of depth $Ke^2/2r$. To get the electron out of that well, i.e., to pull the electron away from the proton, requires that we supply an amount of energy $Ke^2/2r$. One can call $Ke^2/2r$ the ***binding energy*** of the electron.

CHAPTER 17 REVIEW

*In this chapter our focus was on the concept of electric charge and Coulomb's force law. We began with a few electrostatic experiments that Ben Franklin could have used to demonstrate that there are two kinds of electric charge, which he called **positive** and **negative** charge. Due to Franklin's choice, that the charge on a glass rod that had been rubbed by silk was a positive charge, it turns out that the protons inside an atomic nucleus positive and the electrons surrounding the nucleus are negative.*

Conservation of Charge

The key feature of electric charge is that it is conserved. This conservation law shows up most clearly in elementary particle reactions where one kind of particle can turn into other kinds of particles, but there is no change in the total electric charge in the reaction.

As an example, we are reminded that all particles have an anti particle, and that it is sometimes easy to create or annihilate particle-anti particle pairs. But the anti particle always has the opposite charge of the particle, thus no electric charge is gained or lost in these pair creations and annihilations.

*Until the 1970s, it was thought that the fundamental unit of electric charge is what we call the **charge on the electron** and designated by the letter "e". That is a slight misnomer because electrons are negative and have a charge −e. It is the proton that has a charge +e.*

*Somewhat of a shock was the discovery in the 1970s, that protons, neutrons, and other similar particles are made up of more fundamental particles called **quarks**. The two most common quarks are the **up quark** that has a charge +2/3 e, and the **down quark** that has a charge −1/3 e. A proton consists of two up quarks and one down quark for a total charge 2/3e + 2/3e − 1/3e = +e. The neutron is made up of one up quark and two down quarks for a total charge 2/3e − 1/3e − 1/3e = 0.*

*A special feature of the so called **strong nuclear force** that holds quarks together, is that you cannot pull a single quark out of a proton or neutron. Quarks either come in groups of 3, or in quark-anti quark pairs in which the total charge is either +e, 0, or −e.*

Coulomb's Law

Both electricity and gravity are $1/r^2$ force laws, but the similarity essentially ends there. Both force laws can be written in the form

$$F_{gravity} = \frac{GM_1M_2}{r^2} \; ; \quad F_{electricity} = \frac{KQ_1Q_2}{r^2}$$

where r is the separation either between masses M_1 and M_2, or between charges Q_1 and Q_2.

The unit of mass is defined by the one kilogram platinum block kept in Paris, France. The result is that the universal gravitational constant can be determined by measuring the gravitational force between two masses and using the equation $G = F_{gravity}r^2/M_1M_2$.

This approach does not work for electric forces because it is not possible to create copies of a standard electrical charge that can be passed around for calibrating electrical measurements. We saw why in our few electrostatic measurements. Charge is very mobile and can leak off of charged rods onto foil balls and into moist air.

Rather than trying to first establish a unit charge, and then solving for the electric constant K, what was done was to first define the electric constant K and then find some other way to figure out how big a unit charge is. In the MKS system of units, the choice of K is

$$K \equiv 10^{-7} \times c^2 = 9.00 \times 10^9 \qquad MKS\,units$$

The choice K = $10^{-7}c^2$ for MKS units looks rather arbitrary, but it leads to the practical quantities of amperes, volts, and watts.

Essay 5 *Follows Chapter 17*

The Four Basic Forces and Nuclear Matter

In various parts of the text we have discussed the four basic forces in nature. Newton discovered the gravitational force law that explained the motion of planets and falling apples. Ben Franklin began the study of electricity with his introduction of the concept of positive and negative charge. The existence of a nuclear force became apparent with Rutherford's discovery of the atomic nucleus. (There had to be some kind of attractive force to hold all that positive charge together in a tiny nucleus.)

Enrico Fermi developed a theory of a force called the **weak interaction** *to explain the radioactive decays producing alpha(α) rays, beta(β) rays, gamma(γ) rays, and neutrinos.*

In this essay, our focus will be on the role each of the four forces plays in determining the structure and behavior of nuclear matter. To do this we will begin with a brief survey of what that structure and behavior is.

Neils Bohr and John Wheeler proposed that in nuclear fission, the nucleus was behaving much like a liquid drop. Here we see how a falling drop of water oscillates between a pancake and a dumbbell shape.

Satellite Chapter 9
Nuclear Matter

Related satellite chapter.

THE PERIODIC TABLE

When you walk into a classroom where chemistry is taught, on the wall there is likely to be a chart on the wall called the ***periodic table of the elements*** looking like Figure (1). The table shows all the elements discovered so far. The top nearly empty row has Hydrogen (^{1}H) on the left and Helium (^{2}He) on the right. On the chart the numbers (1) and (2) are directly above the symbols (H) and (He) representing the elements. These numbers are the number of protons in the nucleus, a number called the ***atomic number***.

On the next row we see the familiar elements Carbon (^{6}C), Nitrogen (^{7}N) and Oxygen (^{8}O), that play such an important role in our life. Down near the bottom are Uranium (^{92}U) and Plutonium (^{94}Pu), elements used in nuclear reactors and atomic bombs. We also want to take note of Iron (^{26}Fe) which plays an important role in the evolution of stars.

Periodic tables have rows and columns that have special meaning in chemistry class. The columns are determined by the structure of the electron clouds in the atom. That structure depends on the number of electrons in the atom, a number equal to the number of protons in a neutral atom. Thus adding a proton adds an electron and puts the atom in the next column or next row. This is why we identify the different elements by the different number of protons in the nucleus.

In this essay on nuclear matter, we will not be concerned with electron structures or chemical properties. As a result we will not worry about why there are various columns in the periodic table. For us, the interesting features in the periodic table of Figure (1) are the element symbols and corresponding proton numbers. In our table of nuclei, Table I on page 4, we list the elements both by name and symbol.

Group → / ↓ Period	1	2	3	4	5	6	7	8	9	10	11	12	13	14	15	16	17	18
1	1 H																	2 He
2	3 Li	4 Be											5 B	6 C	7 N	8 O	9 F	10 Ne
3	11 Na	12 Mg											13 Al	14 Si	15 P	16 S	17 Cl	18 Ar
4	19 K	20 Ca	21 Sc	22 Ti	23 V	24 Cr	25 Mn	26 Fe	27 Co	28 Ni	29 Cu	30 Zn	31 Ga	32 Ge	33 As	34 Se	35 Br	36 Kr
5	37 Rb	38 Sr	39 Y	40 Zr	41 Nb	42 Mo	43 Tc	44 Ru	45 Rh	46 Pd	47 Ag	48 Cd	49 In	50 Sn	51 Sb	52 Te	53 I	54 Xe
6	55 Cs	56 Ba	*	72 Hf	73 Ta	74 W	75 Re	76 Os	77 Ir	78 Pt	79 Au	80 Hg	81 Tl	82 Pb	83 Bi	84 Po	85 At	86 Rn
7	87 Fr	88 Ra	**	104 Rf	105 Db	106 Sg	107 Bh	108 Hs	109 Mt	110 Ds	111 Rg	112 Uub	113 Uut	114 Uuq	115 Uup	116 Uuh	117 Uus	118 Uuo

* Lanthanides	57 La	58 Ce	59 Pr	60 Nd	61 Pm	62 Sm	63 Eu	64 Gd	65 Tb	66 Dy	67 Ho	68 Er	69 Tm	70 Yb	71 Lu
** Actinides	89 Ac	90 Th	91 Pa	92 U	93 Np	94 Pu	95 Am	96 Cm	97 Bk	98 Cf	99 Es	100 Fm	101 Md	102 No	103 Lr

Figure 1
The Periodic Table, courtesy of Wikipedia, the free encyclopedia.

ISOTOPES

Atomic nuclei are made up of protons which carry a positive charge and neutrons which are electrically neutral. Protons and neutrons are about the same size, and have about the same mass which is nearly 1840 times as massive as an electron. Since there are the same number of electrons and protons in a neutral atom, this means that over 99.9% of an atom's mass is concentrated in the nucleus. But it is concentrated in a very small volume. If you pictured a hydrogen atom being enlarged so that its proton nucleus was the size of a grapefruit, the atom's electron would be moving around in a volume about 5 kilometers in diameter.

In Figure (2) we have sketched the composition of the five smallest nuclei found in nature. The three hydrogen nuclei, each with one proton, have different numbers of neutrons. These are called different *isotopes* of hydrogen. We could call them Hydrogen-1, Hydrogen-2, and Hydrogen-3, or H_1, H_2 and H_3 for short. The number, called the *mass number,* is the sum of the number of protons and neutrons. In the case of hydrogen, those isotopes have the special names, *Hydrogen* for H_1, *Deuterium* for H_2, and *Tritium* for H_3. The two helium nuclei are simply called *Helium Three* and *Helium Four* or He_3 and He_4.

The Stable or Most Stable Nuclei

Table I on the next page, lists all 118 elements observed so far. The list includes the element name, mass number, symbol, number of protons, and number of neutrons in the most common or most stable isotope of each element. When you look down this list, you will notice that for the light isotopes near the top of the list, there are essentially equal numbers of protons and neutrons in the common isotope. For example, there is Carbon-12 with 6 protons and 6 neutrons, Nitrogen-14 with 7 protons and 7 neutrons, and Oxygen-16 with 8 protons and 8 neutrons.

Down toward the bottom of the list, the big nuclei have a considerable excess of neutrons. For example the long lived isotope Uranium-238 has 92 protons and 146 neutrons. In our discussion of the role of the basic forces in nuclear structure, we will see that this increase in the relative number of neutrons is due to a competition between electric and nuclear forces acting in different ways on the particles in the nucleus.

To get a feeling for what a large nucleus looks like, we used red and white Styrofoam balls to construct a model of a Uranium-238 nucleus. The ball in Figure (3) contains 92 red balls representing protons and 146 white balls representing neutrons. If you measure the photograph, you will see that the ball representing the entire nucleus is about 6 Styrofoam ball diameters. In a real nucleus the protons and neutrons pack together a bit more closely than the Styrofoam ball. The diameter of a uranium nucleus is close to 5 proton diameters.

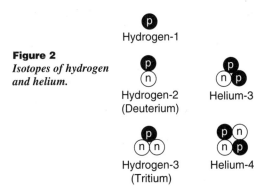

Figure 2
Isotopes of hydrogen and helium.

Hydrogen-1

Hydrogen-2
(Deuterium)

Helium-3

Hydrogen-3
(Tritium)

Helium-4

Figure 3
Model of the uranium nucleus constructed from Styrofoam balls. The red balls represent protons.

Element	Chemical symbol	No. of protons	No. of neutrons	Element	Chemical symbol	No. of protons	No. of neutrons
Hydrogen	H	1	0	Tellurium	Te	52	78
Helium	He	2	2	Iodine	I	53	74
Lithium	Li	3	4	Xenon	Xe	54	78
Beryllium	Be	4	5	Cesium	Cs	55	78
Boron	B	5	6	Barium	Ba	56	82
Carbon	C	6	6	Lanthanum	La	57	82
Nitrogen	N	7	7	Cerium	Ce	58	82
Oxygen	O	8	8	Praseodymium	Pr	59	82
Fluorine	F	9	10	Neodymium	Nd	60	82
Neon	Ne	10	10	Promethium	Pm	61	86
Sodium	Na	11	12	Samarium	Sm	62	90
Magnesium	Mg	12	12	Europium	Eu	63	90
Aluminum	Al	13	14	Gadolinium	Gd	64	94
Silicon	Si	14	14	Terbium	Tb	65	94
Phosphorus	P	15	16	Dysprosium	Dy	66	98
Sulfur	S	16	16	Holmium	Ho	67	98
Chlorine	Cl	17	18	Erbium	Er	68	98
Argon	A	18	22	Thulium	Tm	69	100
Potassium	K	19	20	Ytterbium	Yb	70	104
Calcium	Ca	20	20	Lutetium	Lu	71	104
Scandium	Sc	21	24	Hafnium	Hf	72	108
Titanium	Ti	22	26	Tantalum	Ta	73	108
Vanadium	V	23	28	Tungsten	W	74	110
Chromium	Cr	24	28	Rhenium	Re	75	112
Manganese	Mn	25	30	Osmium	Os	76	116
Iron	Fe	26	30	Iridium	Ir	77	116
Cobalt	Co	27	32	Platinum	Pt	78	117
Nickel	Ni	28	30	Gold	Au	79	122
Copper	Cu	29	34	Mercury	Hg	80	122
Zinc	Zn	30	34	Thallium	Tl	81	124
Gallium	Ga	31	38	Lead	Pb	82	126
Germanium	Ge	32	42	Bismuth	Bi	83	126
Arsenic	As	33	42	Polonium	Po	84	124 (3 yr)
Selenium	Se	34	46	Astatine	At	85	125 (8 hr)
Bromide	Br	35	44	Radon	Rn	86	136 (3 days)
Krypton	Kr	36	48	Francium	Fr	87	136 (21 min)
Rubidium	Rb	37	48	Radium	Ra	88	138 (1622 yr)
Strontium	Sr	38	50	Actinium	Ac	89	138 (22 hr)
Yttrium	Y	39	50	Thorium	Th	90	140 (80,000 yr)
Zirconium	Zr	40	50	Protactinium	Pa	91	140 (34,000 yr)
Niobium	Nb	41	52	Uranium	U	92	146 (4.5 billion yr)
Molybdenum	Mo	42	56	Neptunium	Np	93	144 (2.2 million yr)
Technetium	Tc	43	54 (> 100 yr)	Plutonium	Pu	94	145 (24,000 yr)
Ruthenium	Ru	44	58	Americium	Am	95	144 (490 yr)
Rhodium	Rh	45	58	Curium	Cm	96	146 (150 day)
Palladium	Pd	46	60	Berkelium	Bk	97	150 (1000 yr)
Silver	Ag	47	60	Californium	Cf	98	153 (800 yr)
Cadmium	Cd	48	66	Einsteinium	Es	99	155 (480 days)
Indium	In	49	66	Fermium	Fm	100	153 (23 hr)
Tin	Sn	50	70	Mendelevium	Md	101	155 (1.5 hr)
Antimony	Sb	51	70	Nobelium	No	102	152 (3 sec)
				Lawrencium	Lw	103	154 (8 sec)

Table 1

The most commonly found (most abundant in nature) isotope of each element is listed. In cases where an element has no stable isotopes, the isotope with the longest lifetime is listed.

RADIOACTIVITY

In our list of nuclei, you will see that all nuclei with more protons than lead and bismuth are unstable. Beside the neutron number we list the half lives of the most stable isotope of each of these elements. The longest lived is Uranium-238 with a half life of 4.5 billion years. This also happens to be the age of the earth. Thus half of the uranium that was present when the earth was formed is still here as U-238. This is where the uranium in uranium ore comes from.

When U-238 decays naturally, it first emits Rutherford's α particle which is a Helium-4 nucleus. Losing 2 protons, the uranium nucleus become a thorium nucleus with 90 protons. The thorium nucleus, which has a half life of 24 days, decays by emitting an electron. This turns a neutron into a proton and increases the nucleus's atomic number up to protactinium with 91 protons. After a number of emissions of either α particles or electrons, the uranium nucleus finally ends up as the stable isotope Lead-206 with 82 protons and 124 neutrons.

The reason for the radioactive decay of all elements with atomic numbers above lead and bismuth, is that the nucleus can find a path to a lower energy, lower mass isotope by emitting either an α particle or an electron. Natural radioactivity ceases when the emission of a helium nucleus or an electron requires energy rather than releasing it. In our discussion of the role of the basic forces, we will look into these energy requirements.

NUCLEAR FUSION AND FISSION

In addition to waiting for radioactive decay, there are two other ways to get energy out of atomic nuclei. You can either put together small nuclei in a process called *nuclear fusion* or break apart large nuclei in a process called *nuclear fission*. In each of these reactions some of the nuclear mass is converted to energy via Einstein's equation $E = mc^2$.

Our sun is powered by a fusion reaction. In a series of steps four hydrogen nuclei (protons) end up as a Helium-4 nucleus consisting of 2 protons and 2 neutrons. To conserve electric charge when two of the original protons became neutrons, two positive electron antiparticles are emitted, along with two neutrinos. These are the electron type neutrinos, some of which turned into muon type neutrinos on the trip to the earth. (See the discussion of neutrinos at the end of Chapter 11).

To see how much energy is released when hydrogen is fused into helium, start by adding together the rest mass of the original four protons. Then subtract the rest mass of a Helium-4 nucleus and the rest masses of the two electrons and neutrinos. The mass lost turns out to be 0.68% of the original mass of the protons. Multiply the mass lost by c^2 and you get the kinetic energy released.

Here on earth we have gotten energy from the fusion process in an uncontrolled way with the hydrogen bomb. We have tried for over 60 years to control the process, but have not succeeded yet. If we could convert hydrogen into helium here on earth we would have an unlimited supply of energy.

Energy is released in the fusion of nuclei smaller than Iron-56 with its 26 protons and 30 neutrons. It costs energy to make nuclei larger than Iron-56. That means that if you have a large nucleus like uranium, you get energy out of breaking the uranium nucleus into smaller nuclei. It turns out that the isotopes Uranium-235 and Plutonium-234 easily break apart when you hit them with a neutron. And when they break up they emit more neutrons that can break apart other nuclei, and so on, in what is called a *chain reaction*. If we do not control the process we have an atomic bomb. If we do control it, we have a nuclear reactor.

STELLAR EVOLUTION

Essentially all of the hydrogen, most of the helium, and some lithium were created in the big bang that created the universe. All the rest of the elements were either cooked inside of stars or slammed together in a supernova explosion. The dividing line is again Iron-56.

The cooking of hydrogen into helium takes place in the hot core of the sun. When the core of our sun runs out of hydrogen, it will have run out of fuel. The core will start to cool off, and then something surprising happens. As the core cools, it starts to shrink like the balloon we dunked in liquid nitrogen in the photographs of Figure (16-17). As the core shrinks this will release so much gravitational potential energy that the core will become hotter and brighter than before. The pressure of the light released will expand the surface of the sun out as far as the earth's orbit. At this point the sun will have become a *red giant* star. This will be the last big story for the sun. After a few million years the sun will shrink back down, becoming first a *white dwarf,* and finally a dark compact ember about the size of the Earth.

If the sun were more massive, the story would be different. In the Satellite Chapter 9 on Nuclear Matter, we describe the nuclear reactions in more detail, and then look at the life cycle of the star that ended up as the 1987 supernova explosion.

This star was 18 times as massive as the sun. As a result of this mass there is greater pressure and higher temperatures in the core. When the hydrogen in the core was used up, the star started burning helium to form elements like carbon and oxygen. This created a still hotter core that started fusing carbon and oxygen into heavier elements like silicon and sulfur.

Each new element was cooked up in a smaller, hotter core leaving shells of the previously cooked element. This process stops when the inner core becomes Iron-56, the dead ash of nuclear fusion. In the earlier stages the energy was liberated by radiating light. This process takes thousands of years before the energy can escape through the surface of the star. It is like a thermal blanket keeping the core warm.

By the time the Iron-56 core formed, the temperature was hot enough to create neutrinos. It takes only 10 minutes for neutrinos to escape out through the surface of the star. As a result the neutrinos represented a gigantic heat leak and the core started to quickly collapse. Because of the much greater mass of the star, the collapse was in the form of a powerful shock wave (like a sonic boom) headed toward the center of the star. When the shock wave hit the center, it rebounded as a powerful explosion that tore the star apart. This was the supernova explosion we saw in 1987.

So much energy is released in a supernova explosion that there is enough energy available to fuse medium sized nuclei together to create the heavy ones. All atoms in the universe with a mass greater than Iron-56 were created in a supernova explosion. The copper and zinc inside of you was created this way. Thus, part of you has been through a supernova explosion.

What is left over after a supernova explosion can be a white dwarf, a neutron star, or a black hole. We discuss these in more detail later and in Satellite Chapter 9.

Figure 16-17
Balloons collapsing in liquid nitrogen.

FORCES AND MATTER

As a preview of how the four basic forces control the structure and behavior of nuclear matter, let us first review how matter on the scale of atoms to galaxies is governed by two of these forces, gravity and electricity.

The basic properties of these two forces are

1) Both are long range forces, dropping off as $1/r^2$.
2) The electric forces between electrons and protons are more than 10^{36} times stronger than the gravitational force.
3) Electric forces can cancel, gravitational forces do not.

Deep down inside an atom, electrons can feel the full attractive electric force of the protons in the nucleus. Here gravity plays no role.

Outside the atom, cancellation of electric forces becomes important. There is very little force between two neutral atoms unless the atoms are close enough together so that they distort each other's electron cloud patterns. Then we get a relatively weak residual electric force called a *molecular force*. We had an example of a molecular force in our discussion of the covalent bond in Chapter 17.

Although molecular forces are weak and short range compared to the direct Coulomb forces, molecular forces are still strong enough to control the structure of DNA molecules, people, trees, and boulders as large as the rock of Gibraltar.

On a larger scale, from planets to galaxies, gravitational forces dominate because they always add up and never cancel themselves. The cancellation of electric forces is so complete that we do not need the gravitational attraction of an entire planet to notice gravity. We can even detect the gravitational force between two lead balls in the Cavendish experiment.

When we study nuclear matter, two more forces come into play. There is the nuclear force that holds atomic nuclei together, and the weak interaction which allows nuclei to decay. We will now look at how basic properties of these forces control the structure of nuclear matter.

THE NUCLEAR FORCE

With Rutherford's discovery of the atomic nucleus in 1911, it was almost immediately obvious that there had to be a strong attractive force that held all that positive charge together in a tiny ball at the center of the atom.

With the discovery of the neutron in 1932, it became clear that atomic nuclei consisted of a ball of protons and neutrons that attracted each other via this nuclear force. Experiments in the 1930s indicated that the nuclear force had the following properties

1) The nuclear force affects protons and neutrons equally. In a sense, it cannot tell the difference between them. To the nuclear force, protons and neutrons are simply what we call *nucleons*.
2) When nucleons are close together, the nuclear attraction is stronger than the electric repulsion between protons.
3) The nuclear force is short range. When two protons are more than about four proton diameters apart, the repulsive electric force becomes stronger than the attractive nuclear force.

When we compare the effects of the nuclear and electric forces, we can begin to understand several features of nuclear matter. Small nuclei with few nucleons can be stable because all the nucleons are close together, where the attractive nuclear force overcomes the electric repulsion.

The Iron-56 nucleus, with its 56 nucleons, is a ball about four proton diameters across. For protons on opposite sides of this nucleus, the attractive nuclear force has decreased to the point where the repulsive electric force is just as strong. There is no energy release to be gained by adding another proton.

A uranium nucleus with 235 or 238 nucleons is nearly six proton diameters across. Thus protons on opposite sides of this nucleus are actually repelling each other. The nucleus stays together because the *contact cement-like nuclear force* still holds neighboring nuclei together.

But if you hit a uranium nucleus with a neutron, the nucleus begins to oscillate, sometimes stretching out like a drop of water about to fall from a faucet. When the nucleus is stretched out in the dumbbell shape shown in Figure (4) the opposite sides are out of the attractive nuclear force range, and the electric force pushes the halves apart. Once the nucleus breaks apart, the fragment nuclei feel only the electric repulsion and go rushing apart releasing electric potential energy. It is this released electric potential energy that powers nuclear reactors and atomic bombs.

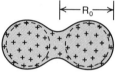

Figure 4a
Uranium nucleus in a dumbbell shape.
Think of R_0 as the range of the nuclear force.

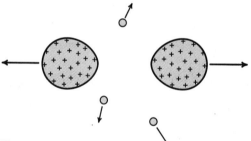

Figure 4b
When the nucleus flies apart, an enormous amount of electric potential energy is released.

Figure 4c
Styrofoam model of a Uranium nucleus in a dumbbell shape.

This competition between the strong but short range nuclear force, and the weaker but long range electric force, explains why it is hard to maintain a controlled nuclear fusion reaction.

If you can get two hydrogen nuclei (protons) close enough together so that they are within the range of the attractive nuclear force, they will bond together. Then one of the protons quickly turns into a neutron and you end up with a deuterium nucleus. In the sun, this process is the first step in the burning of hydrogen to form helium.

Until two protons are close enough to feel the nuclear force, they strongly repel each other due to the electric force. We can think of this as an electric barrier that the protons have to overcome to feel the nuclear attraction. In the sun, the core is so hot that the thermal kinetic energy is enough to allow some protons to cross over the electric barrier and fuse into deuterium nuclei.

On the earth we have succeeded creating a fusion reaction by surrounding an atomic bomb with hydrogen or other light nuclei. The atomic bomb, acting as a match, raises the temperature high enough so that the light nuclei can overcome the electric barrier and create a fusion reaction. The problem is that the process all happens suddenly with an enormous release of energy.

To control a fusion reaction you need some kind of a container that will confine nuclei at temperatures high enough to have some fusion, but not so high that the nuclei all fuse at once. We will see that the only container that does not melt or burn up at the required temperatures is a magnetic bottle. But magnetic confinement behaves in such peculiar ways that physicists have been working on the problem for over 60 years without great success.

The other approach is to hit small pellets of nuclear material with a laser, causing a lot of small fusion reactions. This approach has not succeeded that well either.

Later in this essay we will have more to say about the nuclear force. It turns out that the nuclear force we have been describing is not the basic one after all.

THE WEAK INTERACTION

We have mentioned that the weak interaction allows protons to turn into neutrons and vice versa. To understand how this ability affects the behavior of nuclei, we need one more fact. ***A neutron is slightly more massive than a proton***. In fact, its rest mass is slightly greater than the sum of the rest masses of a proton and an electron. As a result a neutron could turn into a proton and an electron in a process that conserves both electric charge and energy. It turns out that the weak interaction does cause a free individual neutron to decay this way with a half life of about 10 minutes. The weak interaction also requires that a neutrino also comes out in the process.

If an individual neutron is unstable and decays with a half life of 10 minutes, how can neutrons live forever inside a nucleus?

To answer this question, we invoke the rule that if the weak interaction can cause a nucleus to lower its energy, i.e., lose weight, it will. A free neutron can lose weight by turning into a proton.

Now consider a stable nucleus with a neutron. The simplest is the deuterium nucleus with one proton and one neutron. If the neutron in that nucleus turned into a proton, we would end up with a two proton nucleus, a very special isotope of helium.

The protons in a two proton nucleus have less rest mass than the proton-neutron nucleus, but we have forgotten something. If it were not for the nuclear force, it would take a lot of work against the repulsive electric force to shove two protons together until they touched. This work would show up as positive electric potential energy. We have to include this positive electric potential energy as part of the energy of the nucleus.

A straightforward calculation (which we do in Satellite Chapter 9) shows that the electric potential energy in a two proton nucleus is greater than the energy associated with the mass difference between a proton and a neutron. Thus a 2 proton nucleus can lose energy by turning one of the protons into a neutron. This is why the neutron in a deuterium nucleus is stable, it would cost energy rather than release energy to turn it into a proton.

We can now begin to see the reason for the structure of the chemists' periodic table. If it were not for the weak interaction the periodic table could possibly contain thousands of stable nuclear isotopes like a two proton helium nucleus, or something like a carbon isotope with 6 protons and 25 neutrons. This does not happen because the weak interaction allows nuclei to seek their lowest energy.

The lowest energy nucleus is the one with the best balance between the positive electric potential energy and the extra mass energy of the neutrons. If a nucleus has too many neutrons, it will get rid of some of the extra neutron mass energy by turning some neutrons into protons. If there are too many protons it can get rid of some of the electric potential energy by turning some protons into neutrons. The result is that each element has only one or a few stable or long lived isotopes.

In the process of figuring out which isotope is the lightest, you have to take into account the short range of the nuclear force. For the small nuclei, all the nucleons fit together within the range of the nuclear force. In this case it turns out that the best balance between electric potential energy and neutron mass energy is to have about equal numbers of protons and neutrons in the nucleus.

When we get up to nuclei as large as Iron-56, the diameter of the nucleus is becoming about as large as the range of the nuclear force. Adding protons to a big nucleus increases the electric potential energy, without the increased bonding of the nuclear force. To compensate for the increase in the effectiveness of the electric repulsion in the large nuclei, there is a gain in having more neutrons than protons. It is like adding more nuclear glue.

In Table 1 we see that we start to have an excess of neutrons a few elements above iron, and the gain becomes more pronounced as we get down to lead with 82 protons and 126 neutrons. Beyond lead and bismuth, the nucleus has become so big that there are no stable isotopes.

THE STRONG NUCLEAR FORCE

In the 1970s, our view of the nuclear force changed abruptly. To get a feeling for this change, imagine a world where scientists had carefully studied molecular forces and gravity, but had never looked inside an atom to see the direct electric force.

In this world, physics textbooks would discuss the two basic forces in nature. There would be the strong but short range molecular force and the weak but long range gravitational force. The textbooks would say that the reason gravity dominates matter on a large scale, from planets to galaxies, was because of gravity's long range.

Imagine that one day physicists were able to look inside atoms and discovered the even stronger electric force, which had the same long $1/r^2$ range as gravity. The molecular force would be demoted to being a residual force, and there would be a change in the explanation of why gravity dominates on a large scale. Instead of gravity winning because it is long range, the explanation would become that electricity loses because electric forces cancel.

With the discovery of quarks came the realization that *the real nuclear force is the force that holds quarks together to form protons and neutrons*. What we had been calling the nuclear force is just the residual affect of the real nuclear force.

Molecular forces, like Van der Waals' forces and covalent bonds are quite different than the underlying electric force. They are weak and short range rather than strong and long range. A similar thing happens with the nuclear force. The real or what has become called the *strong nuclear force*, actually gets stronger as you separate the quarks that are being held together. It gets so strong that quark-anti quark pairs are created from the potential energy you supply if you try to pull a quark out of a nucleon. As we saw in Chapter 17, this results in our getting a meson rather than a free quark.

As in the case of molecular forces, what is left over of the strong nuclear force between quarks, is the less strong, short range force that plays a role in the structure of atomic nuclei.

NEUTRON STARS

So far, gravity has not played any role in our discussion of nuclear matter. This is because we began with the chemist's version of the periodic table that left out one important nucleus. That is the *neutron star*.

Earlier we discussed the collapse of a balloon when we cooled the gas inside with liquid nitrogen. A similar collapse occurs in a star when the core runs out of nuclear fuel and begins to cool. But instead of a rubber balloon, it is the gravitational force of the matter in the star that is causing the collapse.

In a massive star, one with about eight or more solar masses, there is an iron core that cools rapidly due to a sudden energy leak caused by neutrinos. This leads to a rapid collapse where a shock wave (like a sonic boom) heads down to the core of the star compressing the material in the core.

The shock wave bounces off the core, blowing away the material outside the core. What is left of the core can either be 1) nothing—the core is torn apart, 2) a white dwarf consisting of very closely packed mixture of nuclei and electrons, 3) a neutron star, or 4) a black hole.

The neutron star is nuclear matter, a nucleus approximately 15 kilometers in diameter made up almost entirely of neutrons. It is gravity rather than the nuclear force that holds the neutron star together. In the black hole, gravity has overcome all other forces and crushed the star to something we are not able to explain with known laws of physics. Gravity overcomes all other forces because it has a long range and does not cancel.

We will take one final look at the neutron star. In this object, only two forces play a major role, gravity, which is holding the star together, and the nuclear force which keeps the neutrons from collapsing.

In our discussion of atomic nuclei, we focused on the attractive component of the nuclear force, when nucleons are less than about four proton radii apart. But if you try to shove two nucleons into each other, the nuclear force becomes strongly repulsive. That is why we can model the nucleus as a collection of nearly rigid spheres. It is this repulsive component of the nuclear force that keeps gravity from collapsing the neutron star.

The weak interaction played a role in the formation of the neutron star. As the core of a star collapses, enormous amounts of gravitational potential energy can be released by making the core smaller. One way to make the core smaller is to shove the atomic electrons into the nucleus, forcing the electrons and protons to combine via the weak interaction to become neutrons. Gravity supplies the mass energy needed to turn protons into neutrons.

The electric interaction does not play much of a role in the neutron star because the core started out with equal numbers of electrons and protons. When nearly all these are combined into neutrons, not much net electric charge remains.

BLACK HOLES

It is estimated that if a collapsing star has a mass greater than five or six times the mass of the sun, the gravitational force is strong enough to crush the repulsive component of the nuclear force and shove the neutrons together and cause further collapse.

What stops the further collapse? You can imagine that as the star gets smaller, some other force will come in and stop the collapse. But, according to the laws of physics, as we now understand them, no other force can do the job. There is nothing we know of that can stop further collapse.

Here is a rough explanation of why we think this is true. In our studies of the speed of sound, we saw that the more rigid an object is, the faster sound waves travel through it. In our stretched Slinky, which was the least rigid material we had available, compressional waves traveled about a meter per second. In a column of air, which is quite a bit more rigid, a compressional sound pulse travels about 300 meters per second. Still more rigid is a steel pipe where we saw that the speed of sound is 5,000 meters per second.

From our knowledge of the nuclear force, one can estimate the speed of sound in a neutron star. When nucleons are touching, the repulsive core of the nuclear force is so strong, making nuclear matter so rigid, that the speed of a compressional wave is close to the speed of light. Since sound waves cannot exceed the speed of light, the nuclear matter of a neutron star is as rigid as matter can become.

But there is no limit to how strong the gravitational attraction can become. Add more mass to the star and the gravitational force becomes stronger. Thus we have no idea what can possibly stop the collapse of a star headed to become a black hole.

Chapter 18 non calculus
Fluid Dynamics

Since the earth is covered by two fluids, air and water, much of our life is spent dealing with the dynamic behavior of fluids. This is particularly true of the atmosphere, where the weather patterns are governed by the interaction of large and small vortex systems that sometime strengthen into fierce systems like tornados and hurricanes. On a smaller scale our knowledge of some basic principles of fluid dynamics allows us to build airplanes that fly and sailboats that sail into the wind.

In this chapter we will discuss only a few of the basic concepts of fluid dynamics, the concept of the velocity field, of streamlines, Bernoulli's equation, and the basic structure of a well-formed vortex. While these topics are interesting in their own right, the subject is being discussed here to lay the foundation for many of the concepts that we will use in our discussion of electric and magnetic phenomena. This chapter is fairly easy reading, but it contains essential material for our later work. It is not optional.

The Current State of Fluid Dynamics

The ideas that we will discuss here were discovered well over a century ago. They are simple ideas that provide very good predictions in certain restricted circumstances. In general, fluid flows can become very complicated with the appearance of turbulent motion. Only in the twentieth century did we begin to gain confidence that we had the correct equations to explain fluid motion. Solving these equations is another matter and one of the most active research topics in modern science. Fluid theory has been the testbed of the capability of modern super computers as well as the focus of attention of many theorists. Only a few years ago, from the work of Lorenz, it was discovered that it was not possible, even in principle, to make accurate long-range forecasts of the behavior of fluid systems, that when you try to predict too far into the future, the chaotic behavior of the system destroys the accuracy of the prediction.

Relative to the current work on fluid behavior, we will just barely touch the edges of the theory. But even there we find important basic concepts such as a ***vector field***, ***streamlines***, and ***voltage***, that will be important throughout the remainder of the course. We are introducing these concepts in the context of fluid motion because it is much easier to visualize the behavior of a fluid than some of the more exotic fields we will discuss later.

THE VELOCITY FIELD

Imagine that you are standing on a bridge over a river looking down at the water flowing underneath you. If it is a shallow stream the flow may be around boulders and logs, and be marked by the motion of fallen leaves and specks of foam. In a deep, wide river, the flow could be quite smooth, marked only by the eddies that trail off from the bridge abutments or the whipping back and forth of small buoys.

Although the motion of the fluid is often hard to see directly, the moving leaves and eddies tell you that the motion is there, and you know that if you stepped into the river, you would be carried along with the water.

Our first step in constructing a theory of fluid motion is to describe the motion. At every point in the fluid, we can think of a small "particle" of fluid moving with a velocity $\vec{v}$. We have to be a bit careful here. If we picture too small a "particle of fluid", we begin to see individual atoms and the random motion between atoms. This is too small. On the other hand, if we think of too big a "particle", it may have small fluid eddies inside it and we can't decide which way this piece of fluid is moving. Here we introduce a not completely justified assumption, namely that there is a scale of distance, a size of our particle of fluid, where atomic motions are too small to be seen and any eddies in the fluid are big enough to carry the entire particle with it. With this idealization, we will say that the velocity $\vec{v}$ of the fluid at some point is equal to the velocity of the particle of fluid that is located at that point.

We have just introduced a new concept which we will call the *velocity field*. At every point in a fluid we define a vector $\vec{v}$ which is the velocity vector of the fluid particle at that point. To formalize the notation a bit, consider the point labeled by the coordinates (x, y, z). Then the velocity of the fluid at that point is given by the vector $\vec{v}(x, y, z)$, where $\vec{v}(x, y, z)$ changes as we go from one point to another, from one fluid particle to another.

As an example of what we will call a *velocity field*, consider the so-called bathtub vortex shown in Figure (1a). From the top view the water is going in a nearly circular motion around the vortex core as it spirals down the funnel. We have chosen Points A, B, C and D, and at each of the points drawn a velocity vector to represent the velocity of the fluid particle at that point. The velocity vectors are tangent to the circular path of the fluid and vary in size depending on the speed of the fluid. In a typical vortex the fluid near the core of the vortex moves faster than the fluid out near the edge. This is represented in Figure (1b) by the fact that the vector at Point D, in near the core, is much longer than the one at Point A, out near the edge.

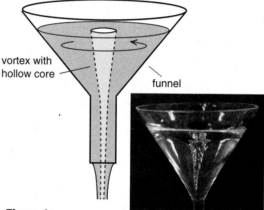

Figure 1a
The "bathtub" vortex is easily seen by filling a glass funnel with water, stirring the water, and letting the water flow out of the bottom.

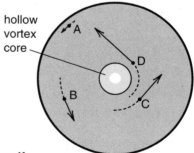

Figure 1b
Looking down from the top, we see the water moving around in a circular path, with the water near the core moving faster. The velocity vectors, drawn at four different points, get longer as we approach the core.

The Vector Field

The velocity field, illustrated in Figure (1), is our first example of a more general concept called a *vector field*. The idea of a vector field is simply that at every point in space there is a vector with an explicit direction and magnitude. In the case of the velocity field, the vector is the velocity vector of the fluid particle at that point. The vector $\vec{v}$ (x, y, z) points in the direction of motion of the fluid, and has a magnitude equal to the speed of the fluid.

It is not hard to construct other examples of vector fields. Suppose you took a 1 kg mass hung on the end of a spring, and carried it around to different parts of the earth. At every point on the surface where you stopped and measured the gravitational force $\vec{F} = m\vec{g} = \vec{g}$ (for m = 1) you would obtain a force vector that points nearly toward the center of the earth, and has a magnitude of about 9.8 m/sec² as illustrated in Figure (2). If you were ambitious and went down into tunnels, or up on very tall buildings, the vectors would still point toward the center of the earth, but the magnitude would vary a bit depending how far down or up you went. (Theoretically the magnitude of $\vec{g}$ would drop to zero at the center of the earth, and drop off as $1/r^2$ as we went out away from the earth). This quantity $\vec{g}$ has a magnitude and direction at every point, and therefore qualifies as a vector field. This particular vector field is called the ***gravitational field*** of the earth.

It is easy to describe how to construct the gravitational field $\vec{g}$ at every point. Just measure the magnitude and direction of the gravitational force on a non-accelerated 1 kg mass at every point. What is not so easy is to picture the result. One problem is drawing all these vectors. In Figure (2) we drew only five $\vec{g}$ vectors. What would we do if we had several million measurements?

The gravitational field is a fairly abstract concept—the result of a series of specific measurements. You have never seen a gravitational field, and at this point you have very little intuition about how gravitational fields behave (do they "behave"? do they do things?). Later we will see that they do.

In contrast you have seen fluid motion all your life, and you have already acquired an extensive intuition about the behavior of the velocity field of a fluid. We wish to build on this intuition and develop some of the mathematical tools that are effective in describing fluid motion. Once you see how these mathematical tools apply to an easily visualized vector field like the velocity field of a fluid, we will apply these tools to more abstract concepts like the gravitational field we just mentioned, or more importantly to the electric field, which is the subject of the next six chapters.

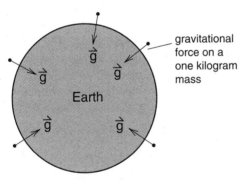

Figure 2
We can begin to draw a picture of the earth's gravitational field by carrying a one kilogram mass around to various points on the surface of the earth and drawing the vector $\vec{g}$ representing the force on that unit mass (m = 1) object.

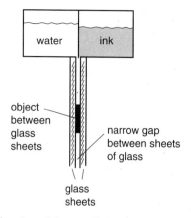

(a) Edge-view of the so-called Hele-Shaw cell.

object
between
glass
sheets

narrow gap
between sheets
of glass

glass
sheets

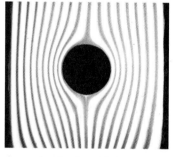

(b) Flow around a circular object.

(c) Flow around airplane wing shapes.

Figure 3
In a Hele-Shaw cell, bands of water and ink flow down through a narrow gap between sheets of glass. With this you can observe the flow around different shaped objects placed in the gap. The alternate black and clear bands of water and ink mark the streamlines of the flow.

STREAMLINES

We have already mentioned one problem with vector fields—how do you draw or represent so many vectors? A partial answer is through the concept of *streamlines* illustrated in Figure (3). In that figure we have two plates of glass separated by a narrow gap with water flowing down through the gap. In order to see the path taken by the flowing water, there are two fluid reservoirs at the top, one containing ink and the other clear water. The ink and water are fed into the gap in alternate bands producing the streaks that we see. Inside the gap are plastic cut-outs, first with a cylinder and and then the cross section of an airplane wing. This allows you to visualize how the fluid flows past these obstacles.

The lines drawn by the alternate bands of clear and dark water are called streamlines. Each band forms a separate stream, the clear water staying in clear streams and the inky water in dark streams. What these streams or streamlines tell us is the direction of motion of the fluid. Because the streams do not cross and because the dark fluid does not mix with the light fluid, we know that the fluid is moving along the streamlines, not perpendicular to them.

In Figure (4) we have sketched a pair of streamlines and drawn the velocity vectors $\vec{v}_1$, $\vec{v}_2$, $\vec{v}_3$ and $\vec{v}_4$ at four points along one of the streams. What is obvious is that the velocity vector at some point must be parallel to the streamline at that point, for that is the way the fluid is flowing. The streamlines give us a map of the directions of the fluid flow at the various points in the fluid.

Figure 4
Velocity vectors in a streamline. Since the fluid is flowing along the stream, the velocity vectors are parallel to the streamlines. Where the streamlines are close together and the stream becomes narrow, the fluid must flow faster and the velocity vectors are longer.

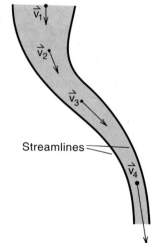

Streamlines

CONTINUITY EQUATION

When we have a set of streamlines such as that in Figure (4), we have a good idea of the directions of flow. We can draw the direction of the velocity vector at any point by constructing a vector parallel to the streamline passing through that point. If the streamline we have drawn or photographed does not pass exactly through that point, then we can do a fairly good job of estimating the direction from the neighboring streamlines.

But what about the speed of the fluid? Every vector has both a magnitude and a direction. So far, the streamlines have told us only the directions of the velocity vectors. Can we determine or estimate the fluid speed at each point so that we can complete our description of the velocity field?

When there is construction on an interstate highway and the road is narrowed from two lanes to one, the traffic tends to go slowly through the construction. This makes sense for traffic safety, but it is just the wrong way to handle an efficient fluid flow. The traffic should go faster through the construction to make up for the reduced width of the road. (Can you imagine the person with an orange vest holding a sign that says "Fast"?) Water, when it flows down a tube with a constriction, travels faster through the constriction than in the wide sections. This way, the same volume of water per second gets past the constriction, as passes per second past a wide section of the channel. Applying this idea to Figure (4), we see why the velocity vectors in the narrow sections of the streamline channels are longer, the fluid speed higher, than in the wide sections.

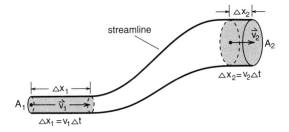

Figure 5
During the time Δt, water entering the small section of pipe travels a distance $v_1 \Delta t$, while water leaving the large section goes a distance $v_2 \Delta t$. Since the same amount of water must enter as leave, the entrance volume $A_1 \Delta x_1$ must equal the exit volume $A_2 \Delta x_2$.

It is not too hard to go from the qualitative idea that fluid must flow faster in the narrow sections of a channel, to a quantitative result that allows us to calculate how much faster. In Figure (5), we are considering a section of streamline or flow tube which has an entrance area A_1, and exit area A_2 as shown. In a short time Δt, the fluid at the entrance travels a distance $\Delta x_1 = v_1 \Delta t$, while at the exit the fluid goes a distance $\Delta x_2 = v_2 \Delta t$.

The volume of water that entered the stream during the time Δt is the shaded volume at the left side of the diagram, and is equal to the area A_1 times the distance Δx_1 that the fluid has moved

$$\left. \begin{array}{c} \text{volume of water} \\ \text{entering in } \Delta t \end{array} \right\} = A_1 \Delta x_1 = A_1 v_1 \Delta t \quad (1)$$

The volume of water leaving the same amount of time is

$$\left. \begin{array}{c} \text{volume of water} \\ \text{leaving during } \Delta t \end{array} \right\} = A_2 \Delta x_2 = A_2 v_2 \Delta t \quad (2)$$

If the water does not get squeezed up or compressed inside the stream between A_1 and A_2, if we have an **incompressible fluid**, which is quite true for water and in many cases even true for air, then the volume of fluid entering and the volume of the fluid leaving during the time Δt must be equal. Equating Equations (1) and (2) and cancelling the Δt gives

$$\boxed{A_1 v_1 = A_2 v_2} \quad \text{continuity equation} \quad (3)$$

Equation (3) is known as the **continuity equation** for incompressible fluids. It is a statement that we do not squeeze up or lose any fluid in the stream. It also tells us that the velocity of the fluid is inversely proportional to the cross sectional area of the stream at that point. If the cross sectional area in a constriction has been cut in half, then the speed of the water must double in order to get the fluid through the constriction.

If we have a map of the streamlines, and know the entrance speed v_1 of the fluid, then we can determine the magnitude and direction of the fluid velocity $\vec{v}_2$ at any point downstream. The direction of $\vec{v}_2$ is parallel to the streamline at Point (2), and the magnitude is given by $v_2 = v_1 (A_1/A_2)$. Thus a careful map of the fluid streamlines, combined with the continuity equation, give us almost a complete picture of the fluid motion.

FLUX

Sometimes simply changing the name of a quantity leads us to new ways of thinking about it. In this case we are going to use the word *flux* to describe the *amount of water flowing per second* out of some volume. From the examples we have considered, the flux of water out through volumes V_1 and V_2 are given by the formulas

$$\left.\begin{array}{c}\text{flux of}\\\text{water}\\\text{out of }V_1\end{array}\right\} \equiv \left\{\begin{array}{c}\text{volume of}\\\text{water flowing}\\\text{per second}\\\text{out of }V_1\end{array}\right\} = v_1 A_1$$

$$\left.\begin{array}{c}\text{flux of}\\\text{water}\\\text{out of }V_2\end{array}\right\} = v_2 A_2$$

The continuity equation can be restated by saying that the flux of water out of V_1 must equal the flux out of V_2 if the water does not get lost or compressed as it flows from the inner to the outer surface.

So far we have chosen simple surfaces, a sphere and a cylinder, and for these surfaces the flux of water is simply the fluid speed v times the area out through which it is flowing. Note that for our cylindrical surface shown in Figure (8), no water is flowing out through the ends of the cylinder, thus only the outside area $(2\pi r L)$ counted in our calculation of flux. A more general way of stating how we calculate flux is to say that it is the fluid speed v times the *perpendicular area* $A_\perp$ through which the fluid is flowing. For the cylinder, the perpendicular area $A_\perp$ is the outside area $(2\pi r L)$; the ends of the cylinder are parallel to the flow and therefore do not count.

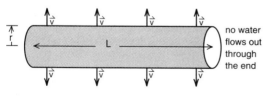

Figure 8
With a line source, all the water flows through the cylindrical surface surrounding the source and none through the ends. Thus $A_\perp$, the perpendicular area through which the water flows is $(2\pi r) \times L$.

BERNOULLI'S EQUATION

Our discussion of flux was fairly lengthy, not so much for the results we got, but to establish concepts that we will use extensively later on in our discussion of electric fields. Another topic, Bernoulli's law, has a much more direct application to the understanding of fluid flows. It also has some rather surprising consequences which help explain why airplanes can fly and how a sailboat can sail into the wind.

Bernoulli's law involves an energy relationship between the pressure, the height, and the velocity of a fluid. The theorem assumes that we have a constant density fluid moving with a steady flow, and that viscous effects are negligible, as they often are for fluids such as air and water.

Consider a small tube of flow bounded by streamlines as shown in Figure (9). In a short time Δt a small volume of fluid enters on the left and an equal volume exits on the right. If the exiting volume has more energy than the entering volume, the extra energy had to come from the work done by pressure forces acting on the fluid in the flow tube. Equating the work done by the pressure forces to the increase in energy gives us Bernoulli's equation.

To help visualize the situation, imagine that the streamline boundaries of the flow tube are replaced by frictionless, rigid walls. This would have no effect on the flow of the fluid, but focuses our attention on the ends of the tube where the fluid is flowing in on the left, at what we will call Point (1), and out on the right at Point (2).

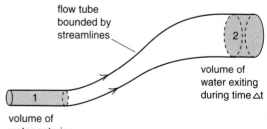

Figure 9
In order to derive Bernoulli's equation, we start with a flow tube where water is entering at Point (1) and exiting at Point (2).

In Figure (10) we show the pressure forces acting on the fluid inside our streamline. The force $\vec{F}_1$ is the pressure force exerted by the outside fluid at the entrance to the streamline tube, and $\vec{F}_2$ the pressure force exerted by the outside fluid at the exit. To help visualize a pressure force, imagine that a small frictionless piston is temporarily inserted into the entrance of the tube as shown. Then you can picture the pressure force $\vec{F}_1$ as pushing on the piston in a distance $\Delta \vec{x}_1$. We can picture this pressure force acting while the fluid moves a distance $\Delta \vec{x}_1$ into the streamline.

Work Done by the Pressure Forces

In our discussion of work on page 10-12, we defined the work done by a force $\vec{F}$ as the energy supplied by the force acting on a moving object. The result was that the work W done by a force is equal to the magnitude F of the force times the distance x that the object moves in the direction of the force.

Our example was slowly lifting an object up a distance h. Our lifting force was of magnitude $F = mg$, and the distance up was $x = h$. Thus we did an amount of work $W = Fx = (mg)h$, and our work all went into increasing the object's gravitational potential energy by an amount mgh.

In Figure (10) the pressure force $\vec{F}_1$ pushes the hypothetical piston a distance $\Delta \vec{x}_1$, which means the pressure force did an amount of work W_1 given by

$$W_1 = F_1 \Delta x_1 \tag{6a}$$

At the exit, the fluid moves a distance Δx_2 opposite to the direction of the external pressure force F_2. The external force F_2 is taking energy from the internal fluid. It is doing negative work W_2 of magnitude

$$W_2 = -F_2 \Delta x_2 \tag{6b}$$

The net amount of work that the pressure forces do on the internal fluid is

$$\left. \begin{array}{l} \text{net work done by} \\ \text{two pressure forces} \end{array} \right\} = W_1 + W_2$$

$$= F_1 \Delta x_1 - F_2 \Delta x_2 \tag{6c}$$

Next we use the fact that pressure is a force per unit area. Thus a pressure p_1 acting on an area A_1 exerts a perpendicular force of magnitude $F_1 = P_1 A_1$. Likewise, the magnitude of the pressure force at the exit is $F_2 = P_2 A_2$. Using these results in Equation (6c) gives

$$\left. \begin{array}{l} \text{net work done} \\ \text{by two pressure} \\ \text{forces} \end{array} \right\} = (P_1 A_1) \Delta x_1 - (P_2 A_2) \Delta x_2$$

$$\tag{7}$$

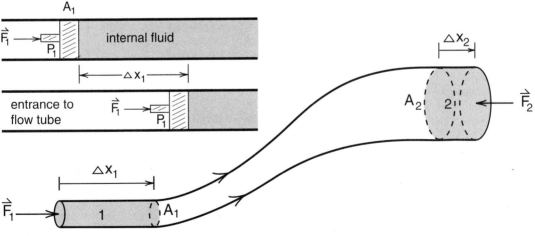

Figure 10
In order to derive Bernoulli's equation, we start with a flow tube where water is entering at Point (1) and exiting at Point (2).

APPLICATIONS OF BERNOULLI'S EQUATION

Bernoulli's equation is a rather remarkable result that some quantity $\left(P + \rho gh + 1/2\rho v^2 \right)$ has a value that doesn't change as you go along a streamline. The terms inside, except for the P term, look like the energy of a unit volume of fluid. The P term came from the work part of the energy conservation theorem, and cannot strictly be interpreted as some kind of pressure energy. As tempting as it is to try to give an interpretation to the terms in Bernoulli's equation, we will put that off for a while until we have worked out some practical applications of the formula. Once you see how much the equation can do, you will have a greater incentive to develop an interpretation.

Hydrostatics

Let us start with the simplest application of Bernoulli's equation, namely the case where the fluid is at rest. In a sense, all the fluid is on the same streamline, and we have

$$P + \rho gh = \begin{cases} \text{constant} \\ \text{throughout} \\ \text{the fluid} \end{cases} \qquad (16)$$

Suppose we have a tank of water shown in Figure (12). Let the pressure be atmospheric pressure at the surface, and set $h = 0$ at the surface. Therefore at the surface

$$P_{at} + \rho gh = P_{at} + \rho g \times 0$$
$$= P_{at} = \text{constant}$$

and thus the constant is P_{at}.

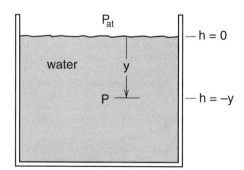

Figure 12
Hydrostatic pressure at a depth y is atmospheric pressure plus ρgy.

For any depth $y = -h$, we have

$$P - \rho gy = \text{constant} = P_{at}$$

$$\boxed{P = P_{at} + \rho gy} \qquad (17)$$

We see that the increase in pressure at a depth y is ρgy, a well-known result from hydrostatics.

Exercise 1

The density of water is $\rho = 10^3 \text{Kg/m}^3$ and atmospheric pressure is $P_{at} = 1.0 \times 10^5 \text{N/m}^2$. At what depth does a scuba diver breath air at a pressure of 2 atmospheres? (At what depth does $\rho gy = P_{at}$?) (Your answer should be 10.2m or 33 ft.)

Exercise 2

What is the pressure, in atmospheres, at the deepest part of the ocean? (At a depth of 8 kilometers.)

Leaky Tank

For a slightly more challenging example, suppose we have a tank filled with water as shown in Figure (13). A distance h below the surface of the tank we drill a hole and the water runs out of the hole at a speed v. Use Bernoulli's equation to determine the speed v of the exiting water.

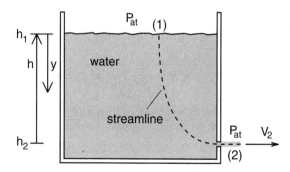

Figure 13
Water squirting out through a hole in a leaky tank. A streamline connects the leak at Point (2) with some Point (1) on the surface. Bernoulli's equation tells us that the water squirts out at the same speed it would have if it had fallen a height h.

Solution: Somewhere there will be a streamline connecting the free surface of the water at Point (1) to a Point (2) in the exiting stream. Applying Bernoulli's equation to Points (1) and (2) gives

$$P_1 + \rho g h_1 + \frac{1}{2}\rho v_1^2 = P_2 + \rho g h_2 + \frac{1}{2}\rho v_2^2$$

Now $P_1 = P_2 = P_{at}$, so the P's cancel. The water level in the tank is dropping very slowly, so that we can set $v_1 = 0$. Finally $h_1 - h_2 = h$, and we get

$$\frac{1}{2}\rho v_2^2 = \rho g(h_1 - h_2) = \rho g h \qquad (18)$$

The result is that the water coming out of the hole is moving just as fast as it would if it had fallen freely from the top surface to the hole we drilled.

Airplane Wing

In the example of a leaky tank, Bernoulli's equation gives a reasonable, not too exciting result. You might have guessed the answer by saying energy should be conserved. Now we will consider some examples that are more surprising than intuitive. The first explains how an airplane can stay up in the air.

Figure (14) shows the cross section of a typical airplane wing and some streamlines for a typical flow of fluid around the wing. We copied the streamlines from our demonstration in Figure (3).

The wing is purposely designed so that the fluid has to flow farther to get over the top of the wing than it does to flow across the bottom. To travel this greater distance, the fluid has to move faster on the top of the wing (at Point 1), than at the bottom (at Point 2).

Arguing that the fluid at Point (1) on the top and Point (2) on the bottom started out on essentially the same streamline (Point 0), we can apply Bernoulli's equation to Points (1) and (2) with the result

$$P_1 + \frac{1}{2}\rho v_1^2 + \cancel{\rho g h_1} = P_2 + \frac{1}{2}\rho v_2^2 + \cancel{\rho g h_2}$$

We have crossed out the $\rho g h$ terms because the difference in hydrostatic pressure $\rho g h$ across the wing is negligible for a light fluid like air.

Here is the important observation. Since the fluid speed v_1 at the top of the wing is higher than the speed v_2 at the bottom, *the pressure P_2 at the bottom must be greater than P_1 at the top* in order that the sum of the two terms $(P + 1/2\rho v^2)$ be the same. The extra pressure on the bottom of the wing is what provides the lift that keeps the airplane up in the air.

There are two obvious criticisms of the above explanation of how airplanes get lift. What about stunt pilots who fly upside down? And how do balsa wood gliders with flat wings fly? The answer lies in the fact that the shape of the wing cross-section is only one of several important factors determining the flow pattern around a wing.

Figure (15) is a sketch of the flow pattern around a flat wing flying with a small angle of attack θ. By having an angle of attack, the wing creates a flow pattern where the streamlines around the top of the wing are longer than those under the bottom. The result is that the fluid flows faster over the top, therefore the pressure must be lower at the top (higher at the bottom) and we still get lift. The stunt pilot flying upside down must fly with a great enough angle of attack to overcome any downward lift designed into the wing.

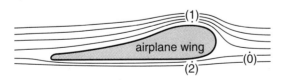

Figure 14
Streamline flow around an airplane wing. The wing is shaped so that the fluid flows faster over the top of the wing, Point (1), than underneath, Point (2). As a result the pressure is higher beneath Point (2) than above Point (1).

Figure 15
A balsa wood model plane gets lift by having the wing move forward with an upward tilt, or angle of attack. The flow pattern around the tilted wing gives rise to a faster flow and therefore reduced pressure over the top.

Sailboats

Sail boats rely on Bernoulli's principle not only to supply the "lift" force that allows the boat to sail into the wind, but also to create the "wing" itself. Figure (16) is a sketch of a sailboat heading at an angle θ off from the wind. If the sail has the shape shown, it looks like the airplane wing of Figure (14), the air will be moving faster over the outside curve of the sail (Position 1) than the inside (Position 2), and we get a higher pressure on the inside of the sail. This higher pressure on the inside both pushes the sail cloth out to give the sail an airplane wing shape, and creates the lift force shown in the diagram. This lift force has two components. One pulls the boat forward. The other component , however, tends to drag the boat sideways. To prevent the boat from slipping sideways, sailboats are equipped with a centerboard or a keel.

The operation of a sailboat is easily demonstrated using an air cart, glider and fan. Mount a small sail on top of the air cart glider (the light plastic shopping bags make excellent sail material) and elevate one end of the cart as shown in Figure (17) so that the cart rests at the low end. Then mount a fan so that the wind blows down and across as shown. With a little adjustment of the angle of the fan and the tilt of the air cart, you can observe the cart sail up the track, into the wind.

If you get the opportunity to sail a boat, remember that it is the Bernoulli effect that both shapes the sail and propels the boat. Try to adjust the sail so that it has a good airplane wing shape, and remember that the higher speed wind on the outside of the sail creates a low pressure that sucks the sailboat forward. You'll go faster if you keep these principles in mind.

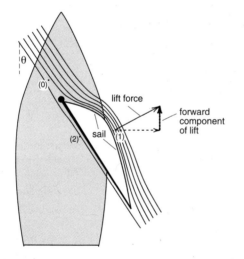

Figure 16
A properly designed sail takes on the shape of an airplane wing with the wind traveling faster, creating a lower pressure on the outside of the sail (Point 1). This low pressure on the outside both sucks the canvas out to maintain the shape of the sail and provides the lift force. The forward component of the lift force moves the boat forward and the sideways component is offset by the water acting on the keel.

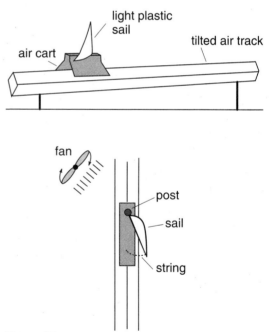

Figure 17
Sailboat demonstration. It is easy to rig a mast on an air cart, and use a small piece of a light plastic bag for a sail. Place the cart on a tilted air track so that the cart will naturally fall backward. Then turn on a fan as shown, and the cart sails up the track into the wind.

The Venturi Meter

Another example, often advertised as a simple application of Bernoulli's equation, is the Venturi meter shown in Figure (18). We have a tube with a constriction, so that its cross-sectional area A_1 at the entrance and the exit, is reduced to A_2 at the constriction. By the continuity Equation (3), we have

$$v_1 A_1 = v_2 A_2; \quad v_2 = \frac{v_1 A_1}{A_2}$$

As expected, the fluid travels faster through the constriction since $A_1 > A_2$.

Now apply Bernoulli's equation to Points (1) and (2). Since these points are at the same height, the $\rho g h$ terms cancel and Bernoulli's equation becomes

$$P_1 + \frac{1}{2}\rho v_1^2 = P_2 + \frac{1}{2}\rho v_2^2$$

Since $v_2 > v_1$, the pressure P_2 in the constriction must be less than the pressure P_1 in the main part of the tube. Using $v_2 = v_1 A_1/A_2$, we get

$$\left. \begin{array}{l} \text{pressure} \\ \text{drop in} \\ \text{constriction} \end{array} \right\} = (P_1 - P_2)$$

$$= \frac{1}{2}\rho(v_2^2 - v_1^2)$$

$$= \frac{1}{2}\rho(v_1^2 A_1^2 / A_2^2 - v_1^2) \quad (19)$$

$$= \frac{1}{2}\rho v_1^2 (A_1^2 / A_2^2 - 1)$$

To observe the pressure drop, we can mount small tubes (A) and (B) as shown in Figure (18), to act as barometers. The lower pressure in the constriction will cause the fluid level in barometer (B) to be lower than in the barometer over the slowly moving, high pressure stream. The height difference h means that there is a pressure difference

$$\left. \begin{array}{l} \text{pressure} \\ \text{difference} \end{array} \right\} = (P_1 - P_2) = \rho g h \quad (20)$$

If we combine Equations (19) and (20), ρ cancels and we can solve for the speed v_1 of the fluid in the tube in terms of the quantities g, h, A_1 and A_2. The result is

$$v_1 = \sqrt{\frac{2gh}{\left(A_1^2/A_2^2 - 1\right)}} \quad (21)$$

Because we can determine the speed v_1 of the main flow by measuring the height difference h of the two columns of fluid, the setup in Figure (18) forms the basis of an often used meter to measure fluid flows. A meter based on this principle is called a *Venturi* meter.

Exercise 3

Show that all the terms in Bernoulli's equation have the same dimensions. (Use MKS units.)

Exercise 4

In a classroom demonstration of a Venturi meter shown in Figure (18a), the inlet and outlet pipes had diameters of 2 cm and the constriction a diameter of 1 cm. For a certain flow, we noted that the height difference h in the barometer tubes was 7 cm. How fast, in meters/sec, was the fluid flowing in the inlet pipe?

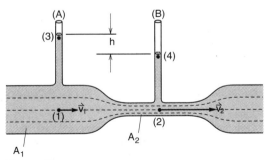

Figure 18
Venturi meter. Since the water flows faster through the constriction, the pressure is lower there. By using vertical tubes to measure the pressure drop, and using Bernoulli's equation and the continuity equation, you can determine the flow speeds v_1 and v_2.

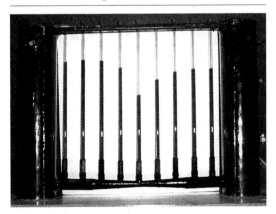

Figure 18a
Venturi demonstration. We see about a 7cm drop in the height of the barometer tubes at the constriction.

We obviously did not invent the word voltage; the name is commonly used in discussing electrical devices like high voltage wires and low voltage batteries. It turns out that there is a precise analogy between the concept of voltage used in electricity theory, and the Bernoulli term we have been discussing. To emphasize the analogy, we are naming the Bernoulli term hydrodynamic voltage. The word "hydrodynamic" is included to remind us that we are missing some of the electrical terms in a more general definition of voltage. We are discussing hydrodynamic voltage before electrical voltage because hydrodynamic voltage involves fluid concepts that are more familiar, easier to visualize and study, than the corresponding electrical concepts.

Town Water Supply

One of the familiar sights in towns where there are no nearby hills is the water tank somewhat crudely illustrated in Figure (23). Water is pumped from the reservoir into the tank to fill the tank up to a height h, as shown.

For now, let us assume that all the pipes attached to the tanks are relatively large and frictionless so that we can neglect viscous effects and apply Bernoulli's equation to the water at the various points along the water system. At Point (1), the pressure is simply atmospheric pressure P_{at}, the water is essentially not flowing, and the hydrodynamic voltage consists mainly of P_{at} plus the gravitational term gh_1

$$\left.\begin{array}{l}\text{hydrodynamic}\\\text{voltage}\end{array}\right\}_1 = P_{at} + gh_1$$

By placing the tank high up in the air, the gh_1 term can be made quite large. We can say that the tank gives us "high voltage" water.

Bernoulli's equation tells us that the hydrodynamic voltage of the water is the same at all the points along the water system. The purpose of the water tank is to ensure that we have high voltage water throughout the town. For example, at Point (2) at one of the closed faucets in the second house, there is no height left ($h_2 = 0$) and the water is not flowing. Thus all the voltage shows up as high pressure at the faucet.

$$\left.\begin{array}{l}\text{hydrodynamic}\\\text{voltage}\end{array}\right\}_2 = P_2$$

At Point (3) we have a break in the pipe and water is squirting up. Just above the break the pressure has dropped to atmospheric pressure and there is still no height. At this point the voltage appears mainly in the form of kinetic energy.

$$\left.\begin{array}{l}\text{hydrodynamic}\\\text{voltage}\end{array}\right\}_3 = P_{at} + \frac{1}{2}\rho v^2$$

Finally at Point (4) the water from the break reaches its maximum height and comes to rest before falling down again. Here it has no kinetic energy, the pressure is still atmospheric, and the hydrodynamic voltage is back in the form of gravitational potential energy. If no voltage has been lost, if Bernoulli's equation still holds, then the water at Point (4) must rise to the same height as the water at the surface in the town water tank.

In some sense, the town water tank serves as a huge "battery" to supply the hydrodynamic voltage for the town water system.

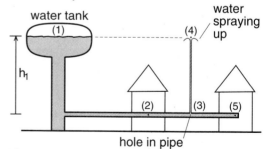

Figure 23
The pressure in the town water supply may be maintained by pumping water into a water tank as shown. If the pipes are big enough we can neglect the viscous effect and apply Bernoulli's equation throughout the system, including the break in the water pipe at Point (3), and the top of the fountain, Point (4).

VISCOUS EFFECTS

We said that the hydrodynamic analogy of voltage involves familiar concepts. Sometimes the concepts are too familiar. Has your shower suddenly turned cold when someone in the kitchen drew hot water for washing dishes; or turned hot when the toilet was flushed? Or been reduced to a trickle when the laundry was being washed? In all of these cases there was a pressure drop at the shower head of either the hot water, the cold water, or both. A pressure drop means that you are getting lower voltage water at the shower head than was supplied by the town water tank (or by your home pressure tank).

Figure 18a (repeated)
In our Venturi demonstration of Figure (18a), the heights are lower on the exit side than the entrance side due to viscosity acting in the constriction.

The hydrodynamic voltage drop results from the fact that you are trying to draw too much water through small pipes, viscous forces become important, and Bernoulli's equation no longer applies. Viscous forces always cause a drop in the hydrodynamic voltage. This voltage drop can be seen in a classroom demonstration, Figure (24), where we have inserted a series of small barometer tubes in a relatively small flow tube. If we run a relatively high speed stream of water through the flow tube, viscous effects become observable and the pressure drops as the water flows down the tube. The pressure drop is made clear by the decreasing heights of the water in the barometer tubes as we go downstream.

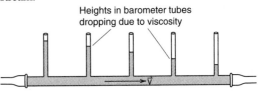

Figure 24
If we have a fairly fast flow in a fairly small tube, viscosity causes a pressure drop, or as we are calling it, a "hydrodynamic voltage" drop down the tube. This voltage drop is seen in the decreasing heights of the water in the barometer tubes.
(In our Venturi demonstration of Figure (18a), the heights are lower on the exit side than the entrance side due to viscosity acting in the constriction.)

VORTICES

The flows we have been considering, water in a pipe, air past a sailboat sail, are tame compared to a striking phenomena seen naturally in the form of hurricanes and tornados. These are examples of a fluid motion called a *vortex*. They are an extension, to an atmospheric scale, of the common bathtub vortex like the one we created in the funnel seen in Figure (25).

Vortices have a fairly well-defined structure which is seen most dramatically in the case of the tornado (see Figures (29) and (30). At the center of the vortex is the core. The core of a bathtub vortex is the hollow tube of air that goes down the drain. In a tornado or water spout, the core is the rapidly rotating air. For a hurricane it is the eye, seen in Figures (27) and (28), which can be amazingly calm and serene considering the vicious winds and rain just outside the eye.

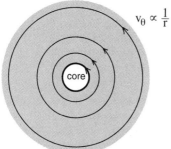

Figure 25
Bathtub vortex in a funnel. We stirred the water before letting it drain out.

$$v_\theta \propto \frac{1}{r}$$

core

Figure 26
Vortices tend to have a circular velocity field about the core, a velocity field v_θ whose strength tends to drop off as 1/r as you go out from the core.

Outside the core, the fluid goes around in a circular pattern, the speed decreasing as the distance from the center increases. It turns out that viscous effects are minimized if the fluid speed drops off as 1/r where r is the radial distance from the center of the core as shown in Figure (26). At some distance from the center, the speed drops to below the speed of other local disturbances and we no longer see the organized motion.

The tendency of a fluid to try to maintain a 1/r velocity field explains why vortices have to have a core. You cannot maintain a 1/r velocity field down to r = 0, for then you would have infinite velocities at the center. To avoid this problem, the vortex either throws the fluid out of the core, as in the case of the hollow bathtub vortex, or has the fluid in the core move as a solid rotating object ($v_\theta = r\,\omega$) in the case of a tornado, or has a calm fluid when the core is large (i.e., viscous effects of the land are important) as in the case of a hurricane.

While the tornado is a very well organized example of a vortex, it has been difficult to do precise measurements of the wind speeds in a tornado. One of the best measurements verifying the 1/r velocity field was when a tornado hit a lumber yard, and a television station using a helicopter recorded the motion of sheets of 4' by 8' plywood that were scattered by the tornado. (Using Doppler radar, a wind speed of 318 miles per hour was recorded in a tornado that struck Oklahoma city on May 3, 1999—a world wind speed record!)

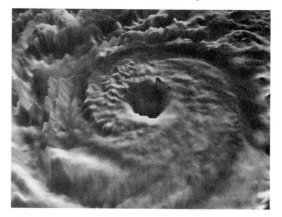

Figure 27
*Eye of hurricane Allen viewed from a satellite.
(Photograph courtesy of A. F. Haasler.)*

Figure 29
Tornado in Kansas.

Figure 30
A tornado over water is called a water spout.

Figure 28
Hurricane approaching the east coast of the U.S.

Quantized Vortices in Superfluids

For precision, nothing beats the "quantized" vortex in superfluid helium. We have already mentioned that superfluid helium flows up and down the little barometer tubes in a Venturi meter, giving no height difference and nullifying the effectiveness of the device as a velocity meter. This happened because superfluid helium has **NO** viscosity (absolutely none as far as we can tell) and can therefore flow into tiny places where other fluids cannot move.

More surprising yet is the structure of a vortex in superfluid helium. The vortex has a core that is about one atomic diameter across (you can't get much smaller than that), and a precise 1/r velocity field outside the core. Even more peculiar is the fact that the velocity field outside the core is given by the formula

$$v_\theta = \frac{\kappa}{2\pi r} \; ; \quad \kappa = \frac{h}{m_{He}} \tag{24}$$

where κ, called the "circulation of the vortex", has the precisely known value h/m_{He}, where m_{He} is the mass of a helium atom, and h is an atomic constant known as *Planck's constant*. The remarkable point is that the strength of a helium vortex has a precise value determined by atomic scale constants. (This is why we say

that vortices in superfluid helium are quantized.) When we get to the study of atoms, and particularly the Bohr theory of hydrogen, we can begin to explain why helium vortices have precisely the strength $\kappa = h/m_{He}$. For now, we are mentioning vortices in superfluid helium as examples of an ideal vortex with a well-defined core and a precise 1/r velocity field outside.

Quantized vortices of a more complicated structure also occur in superconductors and play an important role in the practical behavior of a superconducting material. The superconductors that carry the greatest currents, and are the most useful in practical applications, have quantized vortices that are pinned down and cannot move around. One of the problems in developing practical applications for the new high temperature superconductors is that the quantized vortices tend to move and cause energy losses. Pinning these vortices down is one of the main goals of current engineering research.

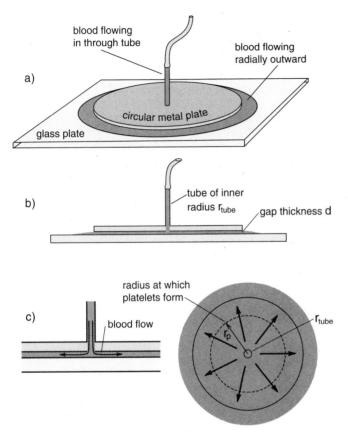

a)

blood flowing
in through tube

blood flowing
radially outward

circular metal plate

glass plate

b)

tube of inner
radius r_{tube}

gap thickness d

c)

radius at which
platelets form

blood flow

r_p

r_{tube}

Figure 31 a,b,c
Experiment to measure the blood flow velocity at which platelets stick to a glass plate. This is an application of the continuity equation.

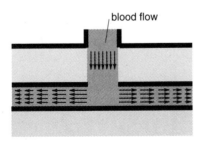

blood flow

Figure 31d
Neglect fluid friction at walls, and assume that the flow is uniform across the radius of the inlet pipe and across the gap.

Exercise 5

This was an experiment, performed in the 1970s to study how platelets form plaque in arteries. The idea was that platelets deposit out of the blood if the flow of blood is too slow. The purpose of the experiment was to design a flow where one could easily see where the plaque began to form and also know what the velocity of the flow was at that point.

The apparatus is shown in Figure (31). Blood flows down through a small tube and then through a hole in a circular plate that is suspended a small distance d above a glass plate. When the blood gets to the glass it flows radially outward as indicated in Figure (31c). As the blood flowed radially outward, its velocity decreases. At a certain radius, call it r_p, platelets began to deposit on the glass. The flow was photographed by a video camera looking up through the glass.

For this problem, assume that the tube radius was $r_t = .4mm$, and that the separation d between the circular plate and the glass was $d = .5mm$. If blood were flowing down the inlet tube at a rate of half a cubic centimeter per second, what is the average speed of the blood

a) inside the inlet tube?

b) at a radius $r_p = 2cm$ out from the hole in the circular plate?

(By average speed, we mean neglect fluid friction at walls, and assume that the flow is uniform across the radius of the inlet pipe and across the gap as indicated in Figure (31d).

Exercise 6

A good review of both the continuity equation and Bernoulli's equation, is to derive on your own, without looking back at the text, the formula

$$v_1 = \sqrt{\frac{2gh}{A_1^2/A_2^2 - 1}} \qquad (21)$$

for the flow speed in a Venturi meter. The various quantities v_1, h, A_1 and A_2 are defined in Figure (18) reproduced below. (If you have trouble with the derivation, review it in the text, and then a day or so later, try the derivation again on your own.

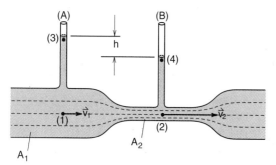

Figure 18
Venturi meter. Since the water flows faster through the constriction, the pressure is lower there. By using vertical tubes to measure the pressure drop, and using Bernoulli's equation and the continuity equation, you can determine the flow speeds v_1 *and* v_2.

CHAPTER 18 REVIEW

The concepts and equations introduced in this chapter are the following:

1. Vector Field

Mathematicians define a vector field as a vector at every point in space. Since that is a bit hard to picture, we chose as our fist example of a vector field the velocity field of an incompressible fluid like water. Now the velocity field is just the velocity vectors of the fluid particles. Since you have observed the flow of water all your life, you already have experience with the velocity field of water.

2. Streamline

The second new concept we introduced was the idea of a **streamline** *which is beautifully illustrated by the streams of flow in a Hele-Shaw cell shown in Figure (3) and reproduced here. The streamlines immediately show you the direction of flow. Note that streamlines never cross each other. If they did, that would mean that some fluid particles would be flowing in two directions at once.*

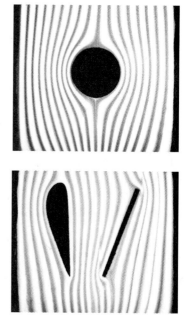

Figure 3
In a Hele-Shaw cell, the alternate black and clear bands of water and ink mark the streamlines of the flow.

3. Continuity Equation

We began to visualize the streamlines as small flow tubes. If the flow is steady, we could replace the edges of streamlines by solid frictionless walls without affecting the flow. We then noted that if the fluid is incompressible, then the volume of fluid entering one end of a flow tube each second must equal the volume of fluid leaving the other end of the flow tube each second. If a flow tube has a cross sectional area A_1 at the front and A_2 at the back, and velocity v_1, and leaves a velocity v_2, then the condition that there is no pileup of fluid in the tube is

$$v_1 A_1 = v_2 A_2 \qquad \text{continuity equation} \qquad (3)$$

*which we called the **continuity equation**.*

Those who have navigated a river in a boat are familiar with aspects of the continuity equation. Where the river is wide or deep, where its cross sectional area is big, the river runs slowly. Where the river is narrow or shallow and its area is small, the water runs fast. The product of the river velocity v and cross sectional area A has, to remain constant, if there are no tributaries adding or removing water.

4. Flux

*Mainly for use in later chapters, we introduced the word **flux** to describe the volume of fluid flowing per second through an area. The continuity equation $v_1 A_1 = v_2 A_2$ can be restated as saying that the flux of fluid $v_1 A_1$ entering a flow tube equals the flux $v_2 A_2$ out, if the fluid is incompressible.*

5. Velocity Field of Point and Line Sources

An incompressible fluid flowing out of a point source has to flow through increasingly large concentric spheres. Since the area A of a sphere is $4\pi r^2$, which increases as r^2, the velocity v has to decrease as $1/r^2$ to keep the flux vA constant.

From a line source, the fluid flows out through the sides of increasingly large concentric cylinders. Since the area A of a cylinder of height h and radius r is $2\pi rh$, increases as r, the fluid velocity v must drop off as $1/r$ to keep the flux vA constant.

6. Bernoulli's Equation

Almost all aspects of fluid flow covered in introductory physics courses are handled by Bernoulli's equation

$$\boxed{P + \rho g h + \frac{1}{2}\rho v^2 = \begin{array}{l}\text{constant along}\\ \text{a streamline}\end{array}} \qquad (15)$$

Since the derivation is somewhat lengthy, this is an equation worth memorizing.

We used this equation to develop formulas for hydrostatic pressure, flow out of a leaky tank, explain how a Venturi meter and aspirator works, explain how airplanes fly and sailboats sail, and the reason for a water tank in a town water supply. That makes it a fairly versatile equation.

Vortices

Another aspect of fluid motion is the vortex. In the absence of viscosity and obstructions, a vortex would have a circular velocity field that increased as 1/r as we went into the center of the vortex. Since this type of velocity cannot keep increasing down to r = 0, vortices form a core at which the 1/r vortex velocity field ceases. In a bathtub vortex, the water is thrown out of the core and the core becomes hollow. In a hurricane the core is the calm eye of the storm at the center. In superfluid helium, where there is truly NO viscosity, the velocity field of the quantized vortex increases as 1/r down to a radius of about one atomic diameter.

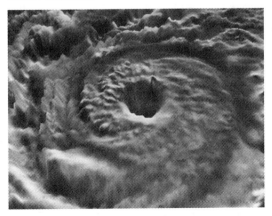

Figure 27
Eye of hurricane Allen.

CHAPTER EXERCISES

Exercise 1 On page 12

At what depth does a scuba diver breath air at a pressure of 2 atmospheres?

Exercise 2 On page 12

What is the pressure, in atmospheres, at the deepest part of the ocean? (At a depth of 8 kilometers.)

Exercise 3 On page 15

Show that all the terms in Bernoulli's equation have the same dimensions. (Use MKS units.)

Exercise 4 On page 15

In a classroom demonstration of a Venturi meter how fast was the fluid flowing in the inlet pipe?

Exercise 5 On page 23

Analyze a blood flow experiment.

Exercise 6 On page 24

Derive, on your own, the formula for the flow speed of a fluid in a Venturi meter.

REVIEW EXERCISES & QUESTIONS

Exercise 7

As you move away from a light source, the intensity or brightness decreases. How does it decrease as you go away from:

a) an ordinary light bulb?

b) a very long fluorescent light bulb? (So long you don't notice the ends.)

c) in each case, if the intensity is I_0 at a distance of 10 centimeters from the bulb, what is the intensity I at one meter from the bulb?

[The intensity of light is defined as the amount of energy striking a unit area every second. As the light spreads out, energy is not lost unless the light strikes something and is absorbed.]

Exercise 8

In Chapter 16 we introduced the mercury barometer which is shown in Figure (16-18) [Page 16-18]. The top of the lift and of the mercury column, point 1, has a vacuum above it. The top of the right end has air above at atmospheric pressure P_{at}. The difference in height h is about 76 cm on a typical day.

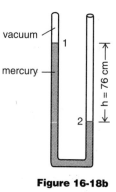

Figure 16-18b

a) Use Bernoulli's equation to find a formula for the atmospheric pressure P_{at} in terms of the density ρ of mercury, the gravitational acceleration g and the height difference h.

b) The density of mercury is 13.6 grams/cm^3 while the density of water is 1 gram/cm^3. If we made a barometer using water instead of mercury, what would the height h be on a day that the mercury column is 76 cm high?

c) In the MKS system, pressure is measured in **pascals**. (One pascal is a pressure of one newton per square meter.) Use the results of part (a) to calculate atmospheric pressure in pascals when h for the mercury column is 76 cm. (The density of mercury is 13.6 grams/cm^3. You have to convert this to the rather unimaginable density in kilograms/meter^3.)

Exercise 9

A popular science radio show *Science Friday* on Public Broadcasting, Ira Flatow said that Bernoulli's equation couldn't explain how a plane could fly upside down, or explain the lift on a flat wing glider. What did he miss that allows Bernoulli's equation to work in these two cases? (I usually agree with Ira, and like his show.)

Exercise 10

Why can't you use a Venturi meter to measure the speed of flow of superfluid helium?

Exercise 11

In a quantized vortex in superfluid helium, the speed of the helium one millimeter (.1cm) out from the core is $v = 1.57 = 10^{-3}$cm/sec . What is the speed just outside the core, at a radius $r = 10^{-8}$cm, about one atomic diameter out from the axis? Give your answer in cm/second, meters/second, and kilometers/hour.

Chapter 19 non calculus

Electric Fields and Gauss' Law

In Chapter 17 we saw that Coulomb's electric force law was similar to Newton's law of gravity in that both are $1/r^2$ force laws. That is, the force between two point particles drops off as the inverse of the square of their separation. That is where the similarity ends.

In applications of Newton's law of gravity, typically involving stars, planets, and satellites, the objects being studied can usually be treated as point particles. It is a straightforward process to write down all the forces involved and write a computer program to predict motion. We did this for the Kepler orbits of the planets in Satellite Chapter 2.

In electric force problems, you typically have to figure out where the charges are before you can begin to solve for electric forces. We saw, for example, that when we brought a + charged rod up to a neutral aluminum foil ball, the rod sucked electrons in the foil to the front side of the ball, creating a net attractive force between the charged rod and neutral ball.

As a result, in order to study electric forces, we need to develop new conceptual and mathematical tools to help us solve electric force problems. The most powerful concept, developed and used effectively by Michael Faraday, is the idea of an electric field.

To a mathematician, the electric field is an example of a **vector field**, which they define as a **vector at every point in space**. An electric field is an electric force vector at every point in space, a concept that can be abstract and daunting when you first encounter it.

To make the idea of a vector field more visualizable and familiar, we chose in Chapter 18 to introduce the velocity field of a fluid, like water, as our first example of a vector field. For the velocity field of water, the velocity vectors of the individual water molecules are close enough to the mathematicians' concept of a vector at each point in space.

We have all seen the flow of water in sinks, bathtubs, and rivers. The fact that water is an incompressible fluid (or nearly so) leads immediately to some important mathematical properties of the velocity field, like the continuity equation for the flow along a streamline, and the fact that the velocity field of a point source drops off as $1/r^2$.

Coulomb's law tells us that the electric force created by a point charge also drops off as $1/r^2$. Thus when we construct an electric field from electric force vectors, we find that the electric field has the same mathematical properties as the velocity field of an incompressible fluid. This allows us to map the electric field using streamlines that obey a continuity equation, and solve problems like calculating the electric field of a line of charge.

COULOMB'S LAW REVIEW

As we have noted, both Newton's law of gravity and Coulomb's electric force law are both $1/r^2$ force laws that can be written as follows

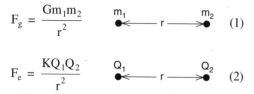

$$F_g = \frac{Gm_1m_2}{r^2} \qquad (1)$$

$$F_e = \frac{KQ_1Q_2}{r^2} \qquad (2)$$

where G is Newton's universal gravitational constant and K is a universal electric force constant.

While the fundamental laws are similar, when we get to applying the laws, the similarity goes away. The first difference is in the way we define the constants G and K.

Even in Newton's time there were simple ways of measuring masses like m_1 and m_2, but it was a century before Cavendish could determine the constant G by directly measuring the gravitational force between two lead balls. Thus G was determined from the formula

$$G = \frac{F_g r^2}{m_1 m_2} \qquad \begin{array}{l}\textit{determining G from the}\\ \textit{Cavendish experiment}\end{array} \qquad (3)$$

We could repeat Cavendish's measurement of G by getting a replica of the standard kilogram from Paris, recoiling the replica from our lead balls to determine m_1 and m_2, and measuring the force F_g when the balls are a distance r apart.

A similar procedure will not work for the electric force constant K. As we discussed in Chapter 17, there is no way that standard unit charges like standard unit masses, can be sent out from Paris. If you tried to repeat the Cavendish experiment for electrical forces, you run into problems like there being an electric attractive force between a charged rod and a neutral $(Q_2 = 0)$ ball.

What physicists have done instead is give the constant K an arbitrary definition, and then using that definition, did experiments to find out how big a unit charge was. In the MKS system of units, which we will use in this and the next five chapters, the constant K is defined as

$$\boxed{K \equiv 10^{-7}c^2 = 9 \times 10^9} \qquad (17\text{-}7)$$

where $c = 3 \times 10^8$ is the speed of light.

With this definition of K we can solve for the size of a unit charge, which is called one **coulomb**. To get a feeling for how big a coulomb is, imagine that we take two unit charges $(Q_1 = Q_2 = 1)$ and place them one meter apart $(r = 1)$. The force between them would have a magnitude

$$F_e = \frac{KQ_1Q_2}{r^2} = \frac{K \times 1 \times 1}{1}$$
$$= K = 9 \times 10^9 \text{newtons} \qquad (4)$$

Thus two unit + charges, one meter apart, would repel each other by a force of nine billion newtons! No wonder Paris does not send out replicas of the unit charge.

Historical precedent becomes tangled into the definition of the electrical force constant. Instead of calling it simply K, in the MKS system of units, K is written in the form

$$K \equiv \frac{1}{4\pi\varepsilon_0} \qquad (17\text{-}8)$$

where the new constant ε_0 (called **epsilon naught**) has the value

$$\varepsilon_0 = \frac{1}{4\pi K} = \frac{1}{4\pi \times 9 \times 10^9}$$
$$= 8.85 \times 10^{-12} \qquad (17\text{-}10)$$

and Coulomb's law is written as

$$\boxed{F_e = \frac{Q_1Q_2}{4\pi\varepsilon_0 r^2}} \qquad \begin{array}{l}\textit{Coulomb's law}\\ \textit{in MKS units}\end{array} \qquad (17\text{-}9)$$

The 4π here will cancel a 4π that appears later in Gauss' law, and the ε_0 was put downstairs to make the theory look like a 19th century fluid theory.

THE ELECTRIC FIELD

In our first example of an electrical phenomena, we brought a charged rod up to a neutral aluminum foil ball and discovered that there was an attractive force between them. When we realized that a positively charged rod would suck electrons to the front side of the ball, leaving positive charge behind as shown in Figure (1), we could see that we were dealing with the force between two *charge distributions*. On the rod the charge is spread along the rod. On the ball, the minus charge is closer to the rod than the plus charge, giving rise to a net force. The point is that electricity problems, on a scale larger than an atom, involve the interaction of distributions of charge.

To solve electricity problems we will begin with a simpler setup than the one shown in Figure (1). We will replace the foil ball with two point charges Q_A and Q_B of equal, but opposite charges, as shown in Figure (2). Think of these charges as being nailed down so that they do not move when another charge is brought near them. We will call these two charges our *fixed charge distribution*.

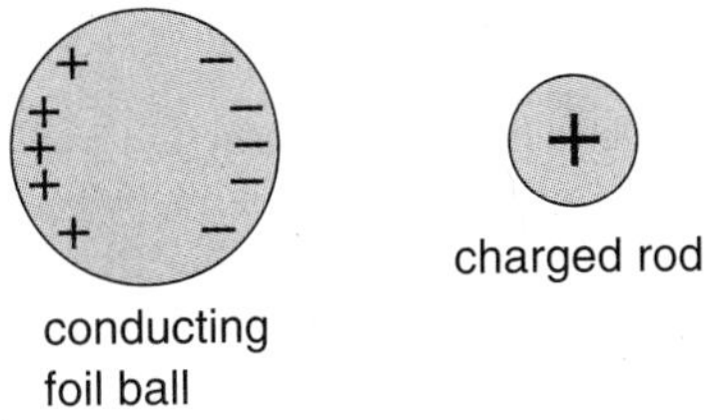

We will replace the charged rod with a point positive charge Q_T which we will call a *test charge*. The idea is that we will move our test charge Q_T around in the neighborhood of the charge distribution $(Q_A \& Q_B)$ to test the nature of the electric force $\vec{F}_T$ in that region.

When our test particle is located as shown in Figure (2), our positive test charge Q_T is repelled by the positive charge Q_A and attracted to the negative charge Q_B. The repulsive and attractive forces are $\vec{F}_A$ and $\vec{F}_B$ as shown in Figure (2), and the net force on our test particle is the vector sum

$$\vec{F}_T = \vec{F}_A + \vec{F}_B \quad \begin{matrix} \textit{net force on} \\ \textit{test particle} \end{matrix} \quad (5)$$

In order to calculate this vector sum, we first have to use Coulomb's law to calculate the magnitudes of $\vec{F}_A$ and $\vec{F}_B$

$$\left| \vec{F}_A \right| = \frac{KQ_TQ_A}{r^2_A} \; ; \qquad \left| \vec{F}_B \right| = \frac{KQ_TQ_B}{r^2_B} \quad (6)$$

where for now we will use K for the electric force constant. Once we have these magnitudes, we have to do the vector addition to get the total force $\vec{F}_T$.

conducting
foil ball

charged rod

Figure 1
When we bring a positively charged rod up to a neutral conducting ball, the positive charge sucks electrons in the ball toward the rod. This leads to a net force between the rod and ball.

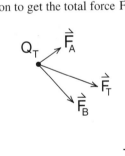

Q_A

Q_B

Figure 2
Forces exerted by two fixed charges Q_A and Q_B on the test particle Q_T.

Before we move Q_T around to map the electric force, we want to do another calculation. We want to first see what happens to the force $\vec{F}_T$ if we change the size of the charge Q_T on our test particle.

Suppose, for example, we double Q_T to $2Q_T$. Then the forces $\vec{F}_A$ and $\vec{F}_B$ become $\vec{F}_A'$ and $\vec{F}_B'$ with new magnitudes

$$\left|\vec{F}_A'\right| = \frac{K(2Q_T)Q_A}{r^2_A} = 2\left|\vec{F}_A\right| \tag{7a}$$

$$\left|\vec{F}_B'\right| = \frac{K(2Q_T)Q_B}{r^2_B} = 2\left|\vec{F}_B\right| \tag{7b}$$

The vectors $\vec{F}_A'$ and $\vec{F}_B'$ are now twice as long as $\vec{F}_A$ and $\vec{F}_B$, but, as shown in Figure (3), point in the same directions as before. When we add new vectors $\vec{F}_A'$ and $\vec{F}_B'$ we get a new vector $\vec{F}_T'$ that points in the same direction as $\vec{F}_T$ but is twice as long. Thus, changing the size of our test charge Q_T only changes the size of the force $\vec{F}_T$ acting on it, not the direction (as long as we keep Q_T positive).

We will now introduce the convention that we always set $Q_T = +1$ coulomb. Of course this is ridiculous. We saw that if you had two 1 coulomb charges one meter apart, the force between them would be 9 billion newtons. If you moved a real 1 coulomb charge around any real charge distribution, your test particle would tear the charge distribution apart.

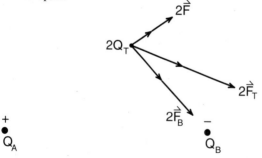

Figure 3
If we double our test charge Q_T, we double all the forces acting on it.

In electricity theory, physicists allow themselves to live in a rather imaginary world. They think of the test particle Q_T as being a ***very small coulomb***, one so small that the force between it and the charge distribution has no effect on the distribution. As far as the charge distribution is concerned, the test particle is a quiet, unseen visitor.

Our next step is to give the force $\vec{F}_T$ a name when we make the choice $Q_T = 1$ coulomb. That name is the ***electric field***. In addition we use the letter $\vec{E}$ rather than $\vec{F}_T$ for this force.

$$\boxed{\begin{array}{l} \text{electric} \\ \text{field } \vec{E} \end{array} \equiv \begin{array}{l} \text{force on a} \\ \text{unit test} \\ \text{particle} \end{array}} \quad \begin{array}{l} \textit{definition of} \\ \textit{electric field} \end{array} \tag{8}$$

You get the magnitudes of the electric fields $\vec{E}_A$ and $\vec{E}_B$ produced by charges Q_A and Q_B alone by setting $Q_T = 1$ in Equations (7) giving

$$\left|\vec{E}_A\right| = \frac{KQ_A}{r^2_A} \qquad \begin{array}{l} \textit{electric field magnitudes} \\ \textit{of } Q_A \textit{ and } Q_B \textit{ separately} \end{array} \tag{9}$$

$$\left|\vec{E}_B\right| = \frac{KQ_B}{r^2_B}$$

We then get the total electric field (the total force $\vec{E}$ on our unit test particle) by taking the vector sum of the individual forces $\vec{E}_A$ and $\vec{E}_B$.

$$\boxed{\vec{E} = \vec{E}_A + \vec{E}_B} \tag{10}$$

We see that the electric field at a given point is the vector sum of the fields produced by the individual particles.

FIELD OF A POINT CHARGE

Since we will be using MKS units, we will need formulas for the electric field expressed in terms of the electric constant ε_0 rather than K. If we have an isolated point charge +Q, then the electric field $\vec{E}$ a distance r away, points radially outward and has a magnitude E(r) given by

$$E(r) = \frac{KQ}{r^2} = \frac{Q}{4\pi\varepsilon_0 r^2} \quad \begin{array}{l} \textit{field of a} \\ \textit{point charge} \end{array} \quad (11)$$

where we used $K \equiv 1/4\pi\varepsilon_0$.

What Can You Do with $\vec{E}$?

Let us assume that you have moved the unit test charge around the charge distribution of Q_A and Q_B in Figures (2) and (3), and have measured the force $\vec{E}$ acting on it at every point. What can you do with the result?

Suppose a friend of yours came by with a particle of charge $Q_2 = 2$ coulombs . Could she use the results of your many calculations of the field $\vec{E}$? As we saw, using twice as large a test particle produces twice as large a force acting on it. Thus the force on her 2 coulomb particle will be twice the force on your 1 coulomb test charge, or $2\vec{E}$. If her friend used a 7 coulomb test particle, the force would be $7\vec{E}$. Soon it becomes obvious that anyone coming along with a particle of magnitude Q will experience a force $\vec{F}$ equal to $Q\vec{E}$. Thus the general formula for the force of an electric field $\vec{E}$ on a charge Q is

$$\boxed{\vec{F} = Q\vec{E}} \quad \begin{array}{l} \textit{formula for the force} \\ \vec{F} \textit{ acting on a charge} \\ Q \textit{ in a field } \vec{E} \end{array} \quad (12)$$

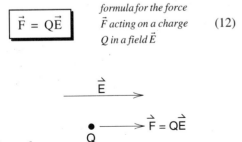

Figure 4
Once we know the electric field $\vec{E}$ at some point, we find the force $\vec{F}$ acting on a charge $\mathbf{Q}$ at that point by the simple formula $\vec{F} = Q\vec{E}$.

Equation (12) shown graphically in Figure (4), turns out to be a crucial component of this chapter. We are going to learn various techniques for calculating or estimating the electric field of a given charge distribution. Once you know the electric field $\vec{E}$, you can use the formula $\vec{F} = Q\vec{E}$ in determining the force $\vec{F}$ acting on a charge $\mathbf{Q}$ located anywhere in the field.

MAPPING THE ELECTRIC FIELD

In Figure (5), we started with a simple charge distribution +Q and –Q as shown, placed our unit test particle at various points in the region surrounding the fixed charges, and drew the resulting force vectors $\vec{E}$ at each point. If we do the diagram carefully, as in Figure (5), a picture of the electric field begins to emerge. Once we have a complete picture of the electric field $\vec{E}$, once we know $\vec{E}$ at every point in space, then we can find the force on any charge Q by using $\vec{F} = Q\vec{E}$. The problem we wish to solve, therefore, is how to construct a complete map or picture of the electric field $\vec{E}$.

Exercise 1

In Figure (5), we have labeled 3 points (1), (2), and (3). Sketch the force vectors $\vec{F}_Q$ on :

(a) a charge Q = 1 coulomb at Point (1)

(b) a charge Q = –1 coulomb at Point (2)

(c) a charge Q = 2 coulombs at Point (3)

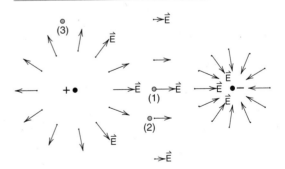

Figure 5
If we draw the electric field vectors $\vec{E}$ at various points around our charge distribution, a picture or map of the electric field begins to emerge.

In part (c) of Exercise (1), we asked you to sketch the force on a charge $Q = 2$ coulombs located at Point (3). The answer is $\vec{F}_3 = Q\vec{E}_3 = 2\vec{E}_3$, but the problem is that we have not yet calculated the electric field $\vec{E}_3$ at Point (3). On the other hand we have calculated $\vec{E}$ at some nearby locations. From the shape of the map that is emerging from the $\vec{E}$ vectors we have drawn, we can make a fairly accurate guess as to the magnitude and direction of $\vec{E}$ at Point (3) without doing the calculation. With a map we can build intuition and make reasonably accurate estimates without calculating $\vec{E}$ at every point.

In Figure (5) we were quite careful about choosing where to draw the vectors in order to construct the picture. We placed the points one after another to see the flow of the field from the positive to the negative charge. In Figure (6), we have constructed a similar picture for the electric field surrounding a single positive charge.

The difficulty in drawing maps or pictures of the electric field is that we have to show both the magnitude and direction at every point. To do this by drawing a large number of separate vectors quickly becomes cumbersome and time consuming. We need a better way to draw these maps, and in so doing will adopt many of the conventions developed by map makers.

Field Lines

As a first step in simplifying the mapping process, let us concentrate on showing the direction of the electric force in the space surrounding our charge distribution. This can be done by connecting the arrows in Figures (5) and (6) to produce the line drawings of Figures (7a) and (7b) respectively. The lines in these drawings are called *field lines*.

There is another way of picturing how we constructed the field lines shown in Figures (7). Take Figure (7a), for example, and imagine that it is a map of the territory in the region of the two charges $+Q$ and $-Q$. To construct this map, imagine that you start at the point labeled (1) and carry a special kind of compass. This compass points, not in the direction of the magnetic field like a real compass, but in the direction of the force $\vec{E}$ on the unit test particle inside the compass. Your job, starting from point (1) is to always walk in the direction pointed to by your new compass. Your path, the track you leave behind, is the electric field line we show in Figure (7a). The vectors we drew in Figure (5) suggest that by following the direction of the electric field, you will get to the point labeled (2), heading into the $-Q$ charge.

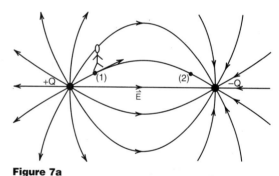

Figure 7a
We connected the arrows of Figure (5) to create a set of field lines for 2 point charges.

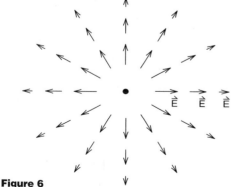

Figure 6
Electric field of a point charge.

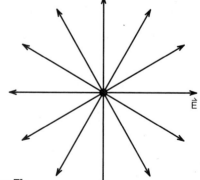

Figure 7b
Here we connected the arrows in Figure (6) to draw the field lines for a point charge.

Toward the end of the chapter we will introduce a computer program that draws field lines by following paths pointed to by the electric field vector $\vec{E}$. This program can handle fairly complex charge distributions and can lead to new insights as to the structure of electric fields. But before we get to the computer program, we are going to show you how to draw fairly accurate maps freehand. You do not need a computer to learn the basics of drawing field maps.

Continuity Equation for Electric Fields

Figure (8) is our old diagram (18-6) for the velocity field of a point source of fluid (a small sphere that created water molecules). We applied the continuity equation to the flow outside the source and saw that the velocity field of a point source of fluid drops off as $1/r^2$.

Figure (9) is more or less a repeat of Figure (7b) for the electric field of a point charge. By Coulomb's law, the strength of the electric field drops off as $1/r^2$ as we go out from the point charge. We have the same field structure for a point source of an incom-

pressible fluid and the electric field of a point charge. Is this pure coincidence, or is there something we can learn from the similarity of these two fields?

The crucial feature of the velocity field that gave us a $1/r^2$ flow was the continuity equation. Basically the idea is that all of the water that is created in the small sphere must eventually flow out through any larger sphere surrounding the source. Since the area of a sphere, $4\pi r^2$, increases as r^2, the speed of the water has to decrease as $1/r^2$ so that the same volume of water per second flows through a big sphere as through a small one.

If we think of the electric field as some kind of an incompressible fluid, and think of a point charge as a source of this fluid, then the continuity equation applied to this electric field gives us the correct $1/r^2$ dependence of the field. In a sense *we can replace Coulomb's law by a continuity equation*. Explicitly, we will use streamlines or field lines to map the direction of the field, and use the continuity equation to calculate the magnitude of the field. This is our general plan for constructing electric field maps; we now have to fill in the details.

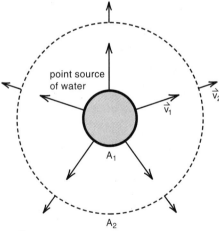

Figure 8
This is our old Figure (18-6) for the velocity field of a point source of water. The continuity equation $v_1A_1 = v_2A_2$, requires that the velocity field $\vec{v}$ drops off as $1/r^2$ because the area through which the water flows increases as $4\pi r^2$.

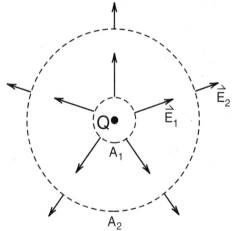

Figure 9
From Coulomb's law, $|\vec{E}| = KQ/r^2$, we see that the electric field of a point source drops off in exactly the same way as the velocity field of a point source. Thus the electric field must obey the same continuity equation $E_1A_1 = E_2A_2$ as does the velocity field.

Flux

To see how the continuity equation can be applied to electric fields, let us review the calculation of the $1/r^2$ velocity field of a point source of fluid, and follow the same steps to calculate the electric field of a point charge.

In Figure (10) we have a small sphere of area A_1 in which the water is created. The volume of water created each second, which we called the *flux* of the water, and which we will now designate by the Greek letter Φ, is given by

$$\left.\begin{array}{l}\text{volume of water}\\\text{created per second}\\\text{in the small sphere}\end{array}\right\} \equiv \Phi_1 = v_1 A_1 \qquad (13)$$

The flux of water out through a larger sphere of area A_2 is

$$\left.\begin{array}{l}\text{volume of water}\\\text{flowing per second}\\\text{out through a}\\\text{larger sphere}\end{array}\right\} \equiv \Phi_2 = v_2 A_2 \qquad (14)$$

The continuity equation $v_1 A_1 = v_2 A_2$ requires these fluxes be equal

$$\Phi_1 = \Phi_2 \equiv \Phi \qquad \begin{array}{l}\textit{continuity}\\\textit{equation}\end{array} \qquad (15)$$

Using Equations (14) and (15), we can express the velocity field v_2 out at the larger sphere in terms of the flux of water Φ created inside the small sphere

$$\boxed{v_2 = \frac{\Phi}{A_2} = \frac{\Phi}{4\pi r_2^2}} \qquad (16)$$

Let us now follow precisely the same steps for the electric field of a point charge. Construct a small sphere of area A_1 and a large sphere A_2 concentrically surrounding the point charge as shown in Figure (11). At the small sphere the electric field has a strength E_1, which has dropped to a strength E_2 out at A_2.

Let us define $E_1 A_1$ as the flux of our electric fluid flowing out of the smaller sphere, and $E_2 A_2$ as the flux flowing out through the larger sphere

$$\Phi_1 = E_1 A_1 \qquad (17)$$

$$\Phi_2 = E_2 A_2 \qquad (18)$$

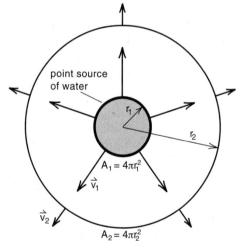

Figure 10
The flux Φ_1 of water out of the small sphere is $\Phi_1 = v_1 A_1$ and the flux through the larger sphere is $\Phi_2 = v_2 A_2$. Noting that no water is lost as it flows from the inner to outer sphere, i.e., equating Φ_1 and Φ_2, gives us the result that the velocity field drops off as $1/r^2$ because the area increases as r^2.

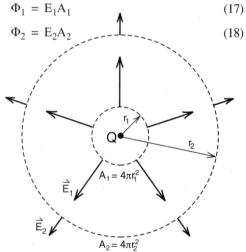

Figure 11
The flux Φ_1 of the electric field out of the small sphere is $\Phi_1 = v_1 A_1$ and the flux through the larger sphere is $\Phi_2 = v_2 A_2$. Noting that no flux is lost as it flows from the inner to outer sphere, i.e., equating Φ_1 and Φ_2, gives us the result that the electric field drops off as $1/r^2$ because the area increases as r^2.

Applying the continuity equation $E_1A_1 = E_2A_2$ to this electric fluid, we get

$$\Phi_1 = \Phi_2 = \Phi \tag{19}$$

Again we can express the field at A_2 in terms of the flux

$$E_2 = \frac{\Phi}{A_2} = \frac{\Phi}{4\pi r_2^2} \tag{20}$$

Since A_2 can be any sphere outside, but centered on the point charge, we can drop the subscript 2 and write

$$\boxed{E(r) = \frac{\Phi}{4\pi r^2}} \quad \text{\textit{continuity equation}} \tag{21}$$

In Equation (21), we got the correct $1/r^2$ dependence for the electric field, but what is the appropriate value for Φ? How much electric flux Φ flows out of a point charge?

To find out, start with a fixed charge Q as shown in Figure (12), place our unit test charge a distance r away, and use Coulomb's law to calculate the electric force $\vec{E}$ on our unit test charge. The result is

$$\boxed{\left|\vec{E}\right| = \frac{Q}{4\pi\varepsilon_0 r^2}} \quad \text{\textit{Coulomb's Law}} \tag{22}$$

where now we are explicitly putting in $1/4\pi\varepsilon_0$ for the proportionality constant K.

Comparing Equations (21) and (22), we see that if we choose

$$\boxed{\Phi = \frac{Q}{\varepsilon_0}} \quad \text{\textit{flux emerging from a charge Q}} \tag{23}$$

then the continuity equation (21) and Coulomb's law (22) give the same answer. Equation (23) is the key that allows us to apply the continuity equation to the electric field. If we say that a point charge Q creates an electric flux $\Phi = Q/\varepsilon_0$, then apply the continuity equation, we get the same results as Coulomb's law. (You can now see that by putting the 4π into Coulomb's law, there is no 4π in our formula (23) for flux.)

Negative Charge

If we have a negative charge –Q, then our unit test particle Q_T will be attracted to it as shown in Figure (13). From a hydrodynamic point of view, the electric fluid is flowing **into** the charge –Q and being destroyed there. Therefore a generalization of our rule about electric flux is that a positive charge creates a positive, outward flux of magnitude Q/ε_0, while a negative charge destroys the electric flux, it has a negative flux $-Q/\varepsilon_0$ that flows into the charge and disappears.

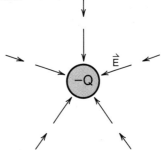

Figure 13
The electric field of a negative charge flows into the charge. Just as positive charge creates flux, negative charge destroys it.

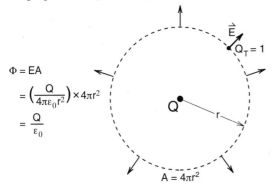

$$\Phi = EA$$
$$= \left(\frac{Q}{4\pi\varepsilon_0 r^2}\right)\times 4\pi r^2$$
$$= \frac{Q}{\varepsilon_0}$$

$A = 4\pi r^2$

Figure 12
Using Coulomb's law for the electric field of a point charge Q, we calculate that the total flux out through any centered sphere surrounding the point charge is $\Phi = Q/\varepsilon_0$.

FLUX TUBES

In our first pictures of fluid flows like Figure (18-5) reproduced here, we saw that the streamlines were little tubes of flow. The continuity equation, applied to a streamline was $\Phi = v_1 A_1 = v_2 A_2$. This is simply the statement that the flux of a fluid along a streamline is constant. We can think of the streamlines as small tubes of flux. By analogy *we will think of our electric field lines as small tubes of electric flux*.

Conserved Field Lines

When we think of the field line as a small flux tube, the continuity equation gives us a very powerful result, namely the *flux tubes must be continuous*, must maintain their strength in any region where the fluid is neither being created nor destroyed. For the electric fluid, the flux tubes or field lines are created by, or start at, positive charge. And they are destroyed by, or stop at, negative charge. But in between, the electric fluid is conserved, and the field lines are continuous. We will see that this continuity of the electric field lines is a very powerful tool for mapping electric fields.

A Mapping Convention

If an electric field line represents a small flux tube, the question remains as to how much flux is in the tube? Just as we standardized on a unit test charge $Q_T = 1$ coulomb for the definition of the electric field $\vec{E}$, we will standardize on a unit flux tube as the amount of flux represented by one electric field line. With this convention, we should therefore draw $\Phi = Q/\varepsilon_0$ field lines or unit flux tubes coming out of a positive charge $+Q$, or stopping on a negative charge $-Q$. Let us try a few examples to see what a powerful mapping convention this is.

In Figure (14) we have a positive charge $Q/\varepsilon_0 = +5$, and a negative charge $Q/\varepsilon_0 = -3$, located as shown. By our new mapping convention we should draw 5 unit flux tubes or field lines out of the positive charge, and we should show 3 of them stopping on the negative charge. Close to the positive charge, the negative charge is too far away to have any effect, and the field lines must go radially out as shown. Close to the negative charge, the lines must go radially in because the positive charge is too far away.

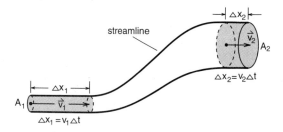

Figure 18-5
Flux tube in the flow of water.

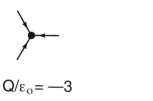

$Q/\varepsilon_0 = -3$

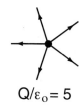

$Q/\varepsilon_0 = 5$

Figure 14
We begin a sketch of the electric field by drawing the field lines in close to the charges, where the lines go either straight in or straight out. Here we have drawn 3 lines into the charge $-3\varepsilon_0$ and 5 lines out of the charge $+5\varepsilon_0$. To make a symmetric looking picture, we oriented the lines so that one will go straight across from the positive to the negative charge.

Now we get to the interesting part; what happens to the field lines out from the charges? The basic rule is that *the lines can start on positive charge, stop on negative charge, but must be continuous in between*. A good guess is that 3 of the lines starting on the positive charge go over to the negative charge in roughly the way we have drawn in Figure (15). There is no more room on the minus charge for the other two lines, so that all these two lines can do is to continue on out to infinity.

Let us take Figure (15), but step far back, so that the + and the – charge look close together as shown in Figure (16). Between the charges we still have the same heart-shaped pattern, but we now get a better view of the two lines that had nowhere to go in Figure (15). To get a better understanding for Figure (16), we draw a sphere around the charges as shown. The net charge inside this sphere is

$$\left[\frac{Q_{net}}{\varepsilon_o}\right]_{inside\,sphere} = +5 - 3 = 2$$

Thus by our mapping convention, two field lines should emerge from this sphere, and they do. Far away where we cannot see the space between the point charges, it looks like we have a single positive charge of magnitude $Q/\varepsilon_0 = 2$.

Summary

With a little experience, most students get quite good at sketching field patterns. The basic constraints are that Q/ε_o lines start on positive charges, or stop on negative charges. Between charges the lines are unbroken and should be smooth, and any lines left over must either go to, or come from, infinity as they did in Figure (16).

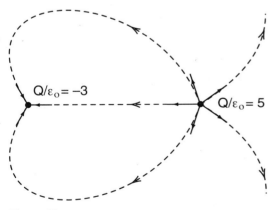

Figure 15
Once the in close field lines have been drawn, we can sketch in the connecting part of the lines as shown. Three of the lines starting from the positive charge must end on the negative one. The other must go out to infinity. Using symmetry and a bit of artistic skill, you will become quite good at drawing these sketches.

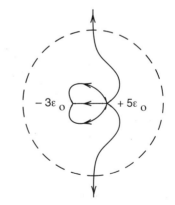

Figure 16
Distant view of our charge distribution. If we step way back from the charge distribution of Figure (15), we see a small object whose net charge is $-3\varepsilon_0 + 5\varepsilon_0 = +2\varepsilon_0$. Thus 2 lines must finally emerge from this distribution as shown.

A Computer Plot

Figure (17) is a computer plot of the electric field lines for the +5, -3 charge distribution of Figures (15) and (16). The first thing we note is that the computer drew a lot more lines than we did. Did it violate our mapping convention that the lines represent unit flux tubes, with Q/ε_0 lines starting or stopping on a charge Q? Yes. The computer drew a whole bunch of lines so that we could get a better feeling for the shape of the electric field. Notice, however, that the ratio of the number of lines starting from the positive charge to the number ending on the negative charge is still 5/3. One of the standard tricks in map making is to change your scale to make the map look as good as possible. Here the computer drew 10 lines per unit flux tube rather than 1. We will see that the only time we really have to be careful with the number of lines we draw, is when we are using a count of the number of lines to estimate the strength of the electric field.

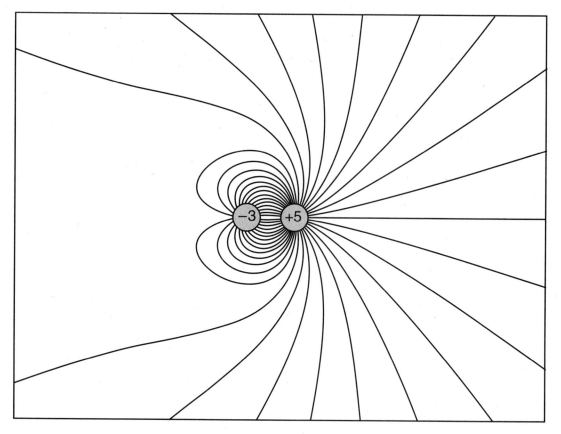

Figure 17

Computer plot of the field lines of a –3 and +5 charge distribution. Rather than drawing Q/ε_0 out of a positive charge or into a negative charge, the computer is programmed to draw enough lines to make the shape of the electric field as clear as possible.

GAUSS' LAW

The idea of using the continuity equation to map field lines was invented by Frederick Gauss and is known as ***Gauss' law***. A basic statement of the law is as follows. Conceptually construct a closed surface (often called a ***Gaussian surface***) around a group of sources or sinks, as shown in Figure (18). In that figure we have drawn the Gaussian surface around three sources and one sink. Then calculate the total flux Φ_{tot} coming from these sources. For Figure (18), we have

$$\Phi_{tot} = \Phi_1 + \Phi_2 + \Phi_3 + \Phi_4 \qquad (24)$$

where Φ_2 happens to be negative. Then if the fluid is incompressible, or we have an electric field, the total flux flowing out through the Gaussian surface must be equal to the amount of flux Φ_{tot} being created inside.

Gauss' law applies to any closed surface surrounding our sources and sinks. But the law is useful for calculations when the Gaussian surface is simple enough that we can easily write the formula for the flux flowing through the surface. To illustrate the way we use Gauss' law, let us, one more time, calculate the electric field of a point charge.

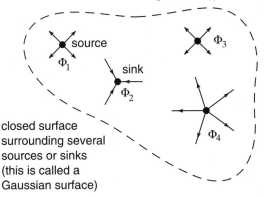

closed surface surrounding several sources or sinks (this is called a Gaussian surface)

Figure 18
If these were sources and sinks in a fluid, it would be obvious that the total flux of fluid out through the closed surface is equal to the net amount of fluid created inside. The same concept applies to electric flux. The net flux Φ_{tot} out through the Gaussian surface is the sum of the fluxes $\Phi_1 + \Phi_2 + \Phi_3 + \Phi_4$ created inside.

In Figure (19), we have a point charge Q, and have drawn a spherical Gaussian surface around the charge. The flux produced by the point charge is

$$\Phi_{tot} = \frac{Q}{\varepsilon_o} \qquad \begin{array}{l}\textit{flux produced}\\ \textit{by the point}\\ \textit{charge}\end{array} \qquad (25)$$

At the Gaussian surface there is an electric field $\vec{E}$ (which we wish to calculate), and the surface has an area $A = 4\pi r^2$. Therefore the electric flux flowing out through the sphere is

$$\begin{aligned}\Phi_{out} &= EA\\ &= E \times 4\pi r^2 \end{aligned} \qquad \begin{array}{l}\textit{flux flowing}\\ \textit{out through}\\ \textit{the sphere}\end{array} \qquad (26)$$

Equating the flux created inside Equation (25) to the flux flowing out Equation (26) gives

$$E \times 4\pi r^2 = \frac{Q}{\varepsilon_o} \qquad (27)$$

$$\boxed{E = \frac{Q}{4\pi\varepsilon_o r^2}} \qquad \begin{array}{l}\textit{old result}\\ \textit{obtained}\\ \textit{new way}\end{array}$$

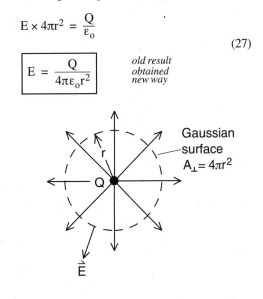

Figure 19
Calculating the electric field of a point charge by equating the flux Q/ε_0 created by the point charge to the flux $\Phi = EA_\perp$ flowing through the Gaussian surface. This gives

$$Q/\varepsilon_0 = E \times 4\pi r^2$$

$$E = Q/4\pi\varepsilon_0 r^2$$

as we expect.

ELECTRIC FIELD OF A LINE CHARGE

Back in Chapter 18 we used the continuity equation to calculate the velocity field of a line source. As an example of a line source, we pictured a sprinkler hose used to water gardens. These hoses have a series of holes that let the water flow radially outward.

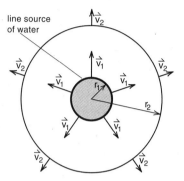

a) End view of line source

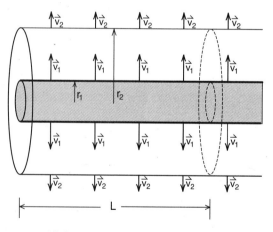

b) Side view of line source

Figure 18-7
Line source of water. In a line source, the water flows radially outward through a cylindrical area whose length we chose as L and whose circumference is $2\pi r$.

We imagined such a hose running down the center of an immense swimming pool. In Figure (18-7) reproduced here we are looking at a section of the hose and the radial velocity field it produces. In this case the water flows radially out through a cylindrical surface rather than the spherical surface we had for a point charge.

We will first calculate the magnitude of this cylindrical velocity field using the continuity equation and the concept of flux, and then we will do a similar calculation to determine the electric field of a line of electric charge.

The flux of water out of a section of length L of the hose is given by the formula [see Equation (18-5a)]

$$\Phi_1 = v_1 A_1 \qquad \begin{array}{l}\textit{flux of water}\\\textit{coming out of } A_1\end{array} \qquad (28)$$

where A_1 is the surface area of this section of hose. That area is a cylinder of circumference $2\pi r$ and length L. If we cut the cylinder open and spread it out, we get a rectangle with sides of length $2\pi r$ and L, thus the area is $A_1 = 2\pi r_1 L$.

By the continuity equation the same amount of flux (volume of water per second) has to flow out through the larger radius cylinder of area $A_2 = 2\pi r_2 L$ surrounding the hose. Equating the fluxes gives

$$\Phi_1 = \Phi_2 = v_2 A_2 \qquad (29)$$

Solving for v_2 in terms of the flux Φ_1 created by the hose gives

$$v_2 = \frac{\Phi_1}{A_2} = \frac{\Phi_1}{2\pi r_2 L} = \frac{1}{r_2} \times \left[\frac{\Phi_1}{2\pi L}\right] \qquad (30)$$

Thus we see that the velocity field of a line source of water drops off as $1/r$ rather than $1/r^2$ as we had for a point source.

Almost exactly the same steps can be applied to the calculation of the electric field of a line of charge. It is traditional to describe a line charge by giving the charge density λ which is the number of coulombs on one meter of the line

$$\lambda \frac{coulombs}{meter} \qquad charge\ density \qquad (31)$$

Thus a section of line with a charge density λ and a length L would have a total charge Q given by

$$Q_L\,coulombs = \lambda \frac{coulombs}{meter} \times L\ meters \qquad (32)$$

We know that a charge Q creates an electric flux Φ given by

$$\Phi = \frac{Q}{\varepsilon_0} \qquad electric\ flux \qquad (18\ repeated)$$

Thus the total flux created by our length L of line charge is

$$\Phi_L = \frac{Q_L}{\varepsilon_0} = \frac{\lambda L}{\varepsilon_0} \qquad \begin{matrix} flux\ created \\ inside\ L \end{matrix} \qquad (33)$$

If we draw a cylinder of length L and arbitrary radius r around our line charge as shown in Figure (20), the electric flux $\Phi = EA$ through it is

$$\Phi_L = E(r) \times 2\pi rL \qquad \begin{matrix} flux\ flowing\ out \\ through\ cylinder \end{matrix} \qquad (34)$$

Equating the flux created [Equation (33)] to the flux out through the big cylinder [Equation (34)] gives

$$E(r) \times 2\pi rL = \frac{\lambda L}{\varepsilon_0} \qquad (35)$$

The lengths L cancel and we are left with

$$\boxed{E(r) = \frac{\lambda}{2\pi\varepsilon_0 r}} \qquad \begin{matrix} electric\ field\ of \\ a\ line\ charge \end{matrix} \qquad (36)$$

as the formula for the radial electric field E (r) that flows out from a line charge of charge density λ. We put a box around this result because this formula is going to play an important role in our introduction to the magnetic fields in Chapter 23.

Exercise 2

In Chapter 23 on Magnetism, we will consider the case where a long straight wire carrying an electric current (i) has a positive charge density λ given by the formula

$$\lambda = \frac{iv}{c^2} \qquad (23\text{-}10)$$

where v is the speed of the electrons in the wire, and c is the speed of light. (We get this formula from special relativity.)

(a) What is the formula for the magnitude of the electric field a distance r from the wire?

(b) If a negative charge –q is placed a distance r from the wire, what is the direction and magnitude of the electric force on –q ?

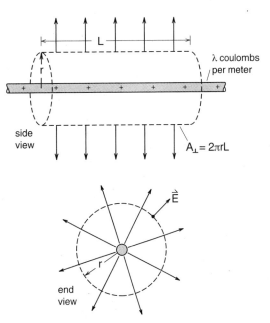

Figure 20
Using Gauss' law to calculate the electric field of a line charge. Draw the Gaussian surface around a section of the rod. The flux all flows out through the cylindrical surface.

FIELD LINES AND GEOMETRY

Figures (21) are photographs of models we made to show the connection between the structure of the electric field and the geometry of the charge distribution. In Figure (21a) we stuck wires into holes spaced around half of a billiard ball. You see that the wires spread out through spherical surfaces whose area increases as $4\pi r^2$. Thus the density of wires piercing any concentric sphere drops off as $1/r^2$.

In Figure (21b) the wires come cylindrically out from half of a small log. You can see that the wires do not spread out as much as they did for the point source. Since the area of a cylinder increases as r, the density of wires decreases as $1/r$ as we go out from the log.

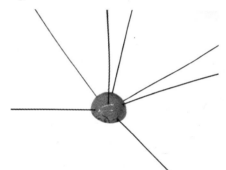

Figure 21a
Wires fanning out in 3 dimensions.
The density of wires drops off as $1/r^2$.

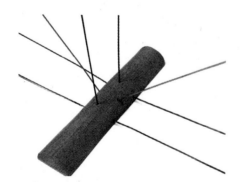

Figure 21b
Wires fanning out in 2 dimensions.
The density of wires drops off as $1/r$.

In Figure (21c) we stuck the wires in holes in a flat board. You can see that in order to maintain the symmetry of the flat board, the wires cannot spread out at all. The density of wires does not decrease as we go out from the board. This tells us that the strength of the electric field E out from a plane of charge does not decrease at all as you move away from the plane.

The intensity or flux of light obeys the same rules that we have just seen for the electric field. If you have an ordinary light bulb, which is essentially a point source of light, the light travels radially out through ever increasing spheres, thus the light intensity has to drop off as $1/r^2$ (if there is no fog).

If you are close to a fluorescent bulb, the long cylindrical ones, the intensity drops off only as $1/r$. However, if you get far away from the fluorescent bulb, so far that the bulb looks like a point source, then the light intensity drops off as $1/r^2$. In between close and far, the intensity changes from $1/r$ to a $1/r^2$ dependence.

In some offices you will find flat panel lighting over the entire ceiling of the room. The result is that the intensity of the light does not decrease as you move away from the flat panels. This lighting gives a more or less uniform illumination throughout the room.

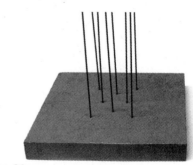

Figure 21c
When the wires emerge from a plane,
the density of wires is constant.

A Spherical Shell and Coulomb's Law

Another example of Gauss' law is the calculation of the electric field of a spherical shell of electric charge. This example illustrates not only a basic application of Gauss' law, but is also the setup Coulomb used to demonstrate that the electric force law was a $1/r^2$ force law.

The typical way one thinks of solving physics problems is to get an equation and plug in numbers to get an answer. That is not the way to use Gauss' law effectively. Instead, for many problems, one uses the idea of symmetry combined with the continuity equation. What this tells us is that the electric field lines we draw have to have the same symmetry as the charge distribution, and the continuity equation simply requires that the lines we draw never start or stop in empty space. This is all we need to solve the charged shell problem.

Figure (22) is our sketch of the charge distribution and electric field lines produced by a uniform thin shell of positive charge. In drawing the field lines, we knew that the lines had to start on the + charges on the shell, and because there is no negative charge around, the field lines have to end up going out to infinity. Because the charge is uniformly spread out on a sphere, the field lines must have the same spherical symmetry. The lines we drew do just that.

Why, you might ask, did we not draw any electric field lines inside the sphere. Our reply is—*try to do it*. You might try by having the field lines cross each other at the center. But you are not allowed to do that. If you have two field lines cross, at the point where they cross, the electric field $\vec{E}$ would point in two different directions. But $\vec{E}$, being the force vector acting on a unit test charge, can point in only one direction. When you think about it, you simply cannot draw any field lines which go inside the shell and preserve the spherical symmetry of the charge distribution.

If the electric force law were a $1/r^3$ force law, we would not have a continuity equation and electric field lines would end in empty space. In such a case, electric field lines could enter the region inside the shell and stop in empty space as shown in Figure (23).

The continuity equation, which prevented field lines from entering inside the shell in Figure (22) is a unique consequence of the fact that the electric force law is a $1/r^2$ force law. This is how Coulomb demonstrated that the electric force was a $1/r^2$ force, by demonstrating that there was no electric field inside a uniform spherical shell of charge.

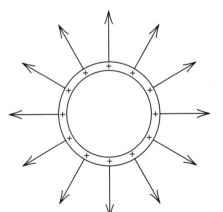

Figure 22
Electric field of a shell of charge.

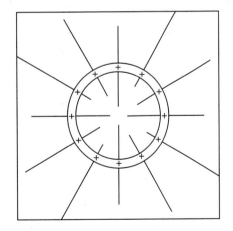

Figure 23
Field lines for $1/r^3$ force can stop in empty space.

CHARGES2000 PROGRAM

As we pointed out earlier, even though the gravitational and electrical force laws are similar, there is a great difference in the way we use these laws to make physical predictions. In the case of gravity most of the objects we deal with can be treated as point particles and we solve problems by directly calculating the gravitational force and then using Newton's second law.

For electricity problems, we deal with more complex distributions of electric charge. The approach introduced in this chapter is to first calculate or estimate the electric field $\vec{E}$ produced by the charge distribution, and then determine the force $\vec{F}$ on a charge Q using the relationship $\vec{F} = Q\vec{E}$.

In this chapter we have shown you how to use concepts such as the continuity equation and Gauss' law to predict the structure of an electric field $\vec{E}$, when we have relatively simple or symmetric charge distributions. But a computer can be very useful in checking predictions we make using symmetry arguments, or refining the sketches we make. For example, the computer plot in Figure (17) with charges +5 and –3 gives added confidence that our earlier sketches were essentially correct.

What we will do in this section is discuss the computer program *Charges2000* which we wrote to make it easy to plot electric field structures produced by distribution of point charges. The program is on the *Physics2000 CD* and can be used for free by anyone anywhere (you can download the program from *www.physics2000.com*).

To introduce *Charges2000*, our first example will be the electric field of a single point particle. The result will be seen in Figure (24). Then we see how the program handles the electric field of a plus and a minus charge which we discussed back in Figure (7a). We plot the field lines for two point particles producing $1/r^2$ 3D fields, and for two line charges producing $1/r$ 2D fields.

One of the successes of the use of Gauss' law was to argue that there is no electric field inside a uniform sphere of electric charge. We argued this by saying that if you tried to draw electric field lines, heading inside the sphere, the lines would either have to cross or stop in empty space, two things that electric field lines cannot do. But one might ask, what happens to the lines that start by heading toward the inside of the sphere?

In Figure (27) we will show you how to use the *Charges2000* program to simulate a uniform sphere of charge. Then in Figure (28) we see what happens to the lines that tried to enter the sphere.

The best use of *Charges2000* is to develop your own intuition for the structure of the electric field lines produced by various charge distributions. You can make up your own charge distribution, predict what the field lines will do, and then use the computer to check your prediction.

Field of a Point Charge

When you open *Charges2000*, you get a plotting board where you can place charges. Click on the plotting board and a charge is placed at that point. The value of the charge is determined by a slider in the control panel. You can choose an integer value from +80 to -80. The number you choose determines the number of lines that either start or stop on that charge. (According to Gauss' law the number of lines is really Q/ε_0 rather than Q, but you can think of *Charges2000* as using a value $\varepsilon_0 = 1$.)

In Figure (24) we clicked once to get one charge, selected Q = 10, chose **Choose 2D field** and got 10 lines coming symmetrically out of the charge. You get the same picture if you select **Choose 3D field**. If you draw 3D lines, the program assumes that your charges are point particles and has the field drop off as $1/r^2$. If you select 2D lines, the program assumes that you are looking at the ends of line charges and has the field drop off as $1/r$ as you go away from the lines. In all cases, however, a continuity equation is assumed. Lines only start on positive charge and end on negative charge or go to infinity (i.e., way off the plotting board).

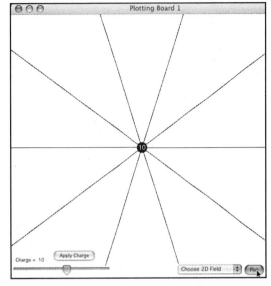

Figure 24
Plotting board of the **Charges2000** *program. We clicked once on the plotting board and used the control panel slider to select charge = 10.*

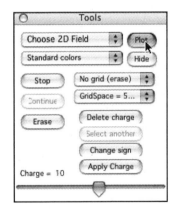

Figure 24a
Control panel for **Charges2000***. To plot the field lines, we selected "Choose 2D Field" and then pressed the "Plot" button.*

Two Charges

Our first example of a charge distribution was having equal and opposite charges +Q and –Q as shown in Figure (7a) reproduced here. Noting that Figure (7a) has 12 lines starting from +Q and ending on –Q, we placed charges +12 and –12 on our plotting board as shown in Figure (25).

In Figure (25a) we selected a 1/r 2D plot, and in (25b), a 1/r² 3D plot. Now you can begin to see a slight difference in the two patterns. In the 3D plot the lines go radially outward for a greater distance before they bend over to head to the other charge.

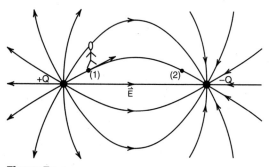

Figure 7a
We connected the arrows of Figure (10) to create a set of field lines for 2 point charges.

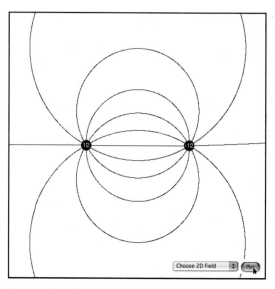

Figure 25a 2D Plot
We placed +12 and –12 charges on the plotting board, choose 2D field and pressed Plot. The result is a drawing of 12 lines of a 2 dimensional field. (I.e., we are looking at the ends of line charges.)

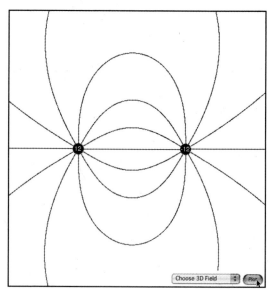

Figure 25b 3D Plot
Three dimensional lines produced by point charges. (These lines are in a plane that passes through the two charges.)

Old and New Computer Plots

In Figure (17), we had a computer plot from an older computer program showing field lines for a charge distribution of (−3) and (+5). The program did not actually do that good a job, we had to clean it up a bit, make it symmetric top and bottom using the *Adobe Illustrator™* program. In Figure (26) we used *Charges2000*, we got essentially the cleaned up plot of Figure (17) using charges +49 and −30.

That is as close to the ratio of −3 to +5 as we could go and get a good looking plot. When we used −30, +50 lines, one line did not fit in very well. With *Charges2000* you may have to add or remove a line to get the plot you want.

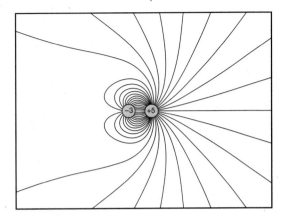

Figure 17
Older computer plot of the field lines of a −3 and +5 charge distribution.

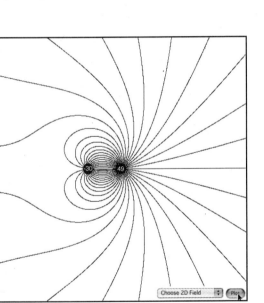

Figure 26a
We got nearly the same result from **Charges2000** *using (−30) and (+49) line charges in a 2D plot.*

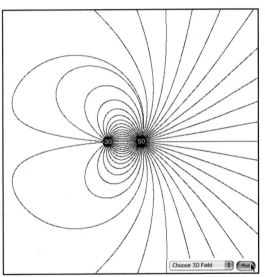

Figure 26b
You can now see a bigger difference between 2D and 3D plots.

Sphere of Charge

Now let us look at the problem of a spherical shell of charge. We are going to approximate the shell with a circle of equally spaced, equal sized, + charges. So that you can accurately place charges on the plotting board, *Charges2000* provides both rectangular and circular grids. In Figure (27) we used the circular grid to place 24 charges around in a circle. We chose Q = 10 for each charge so that 10 lines would emerge from each.

In Figure (28) we selected a 2D field plot and now begin to see why there is no electric field inside a uniform shell of charge. Even the lines that started toward the inside of the shell are blown outside.

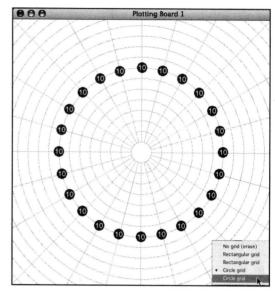

Figure 27
Laying out a circle of charges.

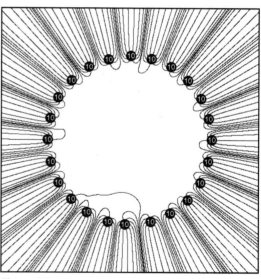

Figure 28
The inside field is blown out.

Changing Colors

The *Charges2000* program was designed so that you can change the color of any line or area in the plot. We did this because there is a great deal of symmetry contained in Coulomb's and Gauss' laws, a symmetry that can lead to surprisingly artistic results.

The *Color palette* lets you change the color of individual parts of the plot. We also have sets of standard color schemes that you can choose from the regular *Tools palette* as shown in Figure (29a). In Figure (29b) we have repeated Figure (26a) using Reversed grayscale colors. In Figure (29c) we have a Reversed grayscale plot of the field lines of 9 charges in a circle.

Figure 29b
This is our 49, –30 plot in Reversed grayscale.

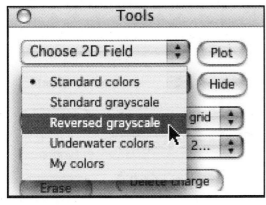

Figure 29a
Selecting a color scheme from the Color menu in the Tools palette.

Figure 29c
Nine charges in a circle.

Exercises

The main exercise for this chapter is for the student to become familiar with the *Charges2000* program, and then use it to check her or his own sketches of field lines for various charge distributions. We are suggesting only two more exercises, the first to test the student's appreciation of Gauss' law, and the second to construct a field pattern that we will encounter later in the course.

Exercise 3

You have a spherical shell with a charge +Q spread evenly around it, and a point charge –Q located at the center. Sketch the field lines for this setup. After that, use the Charges2000 program to check your sketch.

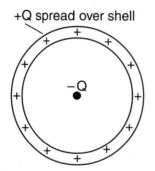

+Q spread over shell

Figure 30
A charge –Q is inside a shell with a charge +Q spread around the surface.

Exercise 4

In our introduction to the theory of magnetism, we will encounter a situation where we have a rod with an excess of positive charge along the rod but negative charge on the ends. Overall, the rod is neutral, the amount of positive charge along the rod being equal in size to the total negative charge on the ends. We want to use *Charges2000* to see what the field pattern of this charge distribution looks like. In Figure (31) we used the rectangular grid to set up a line of eight (+2) charges ended by two (–8) charges, spaced 1 1/2 grid lines apart. Try this, or a pattern of your own choice, and see what the field lines look like.

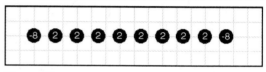

Figure 31
Sketch what you think the field lines look like.

APPENDIX
DESIGN OF THE
CHARGES2000 PROGRAM

In our discussion of the Figure (7a) we mentioned that one way to map field lines would be to carry a special compass where the needle always pointed in the direction of the electric field $\vec{E}$. If you walked always in the direction pointed to by this compass, your track would be an electric field line.

To write a program that draws electric field lines, we first created a plotting board where you could place charges wherever you wanted and assign a number to each charge.

We then imagined that the electric field lines would be traced by cannon balls that had no inertia, that always moved in the direction of $\vec{E}$. If you requested a charge of +24, we would place 24 cannons around the charge as shown in Figure (32) in order to fire 24 cannon balls. All charges, both positive and negative, got the number of cannons equal to the magnitude of the assigned charge.

One thing we knew from Gauss' law was that the cannon balls from a positive charge would either hit a negative charge or go out to infinity, and a cannon ball from a negative charge would hit a positive charge or go to infinity.

The program picks one of the charges and starts firing the cannons. If the cannon ball from a positive charge strikes a negative charge, it destroys the nearest cannon. If we have the charge distribution +5 and –3, and if the +5 charge fires first, three of the cannon balls will destroy the 3 cannons (the charge) on the –3 charge, and the other two balls have to go out to infinity. If the –3 charge fired first, its 3 cannon balls will destroy three of the +5 cannons on the +5 charge. Then the +5 charge fires its remaining two cannons and those two balls have to go out to infinity. This scheme works quite well in drawing fairly good looking maps that are in close agreement with Gauss' law.

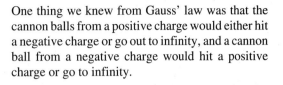

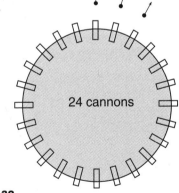

Figure 32
A charge Q is given Q cannons to fire.

CHAPTER 19 REVIEW

In the previous chapter, we studied the velocity field of an incompressible fluid like water, introducing streamlines, deriving a continuity equation, and showing that a point source of water would have a radial velocity field that dropped off as $1/r^2$. The continuity equation guaranteed that the streamlines could not end in the middle of the flow but had to go continuously from the start to the end of the stream.

In this chapter we defined the electric field $\vec{E}$ as the electric force felt by a hypothetical test particle that had a tiny unit charge. If at any point in space the test particle measured a force $\vec{E}$, a real charge q placed at that point would feel a force

$$\vec{F} = q\vec{E} \qquad \begin{array}{l}\text{force on charge}\\ \text{in field } \vec{E}\end{array} \qquad (12)$$

By Coulomb's law the force between a charge Q and our test charge $q_{test} = 1$ *coulomb is*

$$\left|\vec{E}\right| = \frac{Q\, q_{test}}{4\pi\varepsilon_0 r^2} = \frac{Q}{4\pi\varepsilon_0 r^2}$$

which gives us the formula for the magnitude of the electric field of a point charge Q.

The most important point of the chapter was the observation that both the velocity field of a point source of an incompressible fluid, and the electric field of a point charge had radially directed fields that dropped off as $1/r^2$. For the velocity field we used the incompressibility to derive the $1/r^2$ field of a point source. For the electric field we went the other way. We used the $1/r^2$ field of a point charge to argue that the electric field should behave in the same way as an incompressible fluid. This allowed us to introduce the concept of streamlines of the electric field, streamlines that we renamed "electric field lines".

An essential property of a streamline is that it cannot stop in midstream. This implies that electric field lines cannot stop, or start in empty space. We saw that electric field lines start on positive charge, stop on negative charge, or go out to or come from infinity.

For the velocity field, the continuity equation was

$$vA = constant \qquad \text{\textit{along a streamline}}$$

*where v is the magnitude of the velocity and A the cross sectional area of any point along a streamline. We called the quantity vA the **flux** of water flowing along the streamline. (In MKS units, it would be the number of cubic meters of water per second flowing, for instance, under a bridge.)*

For the electric field, the continuity equation is

$$EA = constant \qquad \text{\textit{along a field line}}$$

For a point charge Q, the electric field is $E = Q/4\pi\varepsilon_0 r^2$ and the area of a sphere surrounding it is $A = 4\pi r^2$, thus the total flux out of a point charge Q is

$$\begin{array}{l}\text{total flux out}\\ \text{of charge Q}\end{array} = EA_{total}$$

$$= \frac{Q}{4\pi\varepsilon_0 r^2} \times 4\pi r^2$$

$$= \frac{Q}{\varepsilon_0}$$

A convenient mapping convention is to draw Q/ε_0 flux lines or field lines emerging from a positive charge $+Q$ or stopping on a negative charge $-Q$.

An important test of our mapping techniques for describing electric fields, was to draw the electric field of a spherical shell of positive charge. The result was shown in Figure (22) reproduced here.

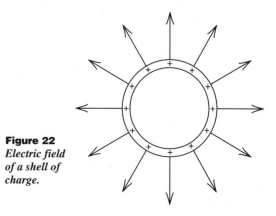

Figure 22
Electric field of a shell of charge.

The rules that Q/ε_0 field lines had to start from each positive charge, not end in empty space, and maintain spherical symmetry, meant that we could not draw any lines that went inside the sphere. This result, that there is no field inside a uniform sphere of charge, is what Charles Coulomb used to prove that the electric field was a $1/r^2$ field.

Another important result of the field mapping technique was that we were able to calculate the electric field of a line of charge. The field goes radially out from the line charge as shown in our model in Figure (21b) reproduced here. A line charge density of λ coulombs/meter produced an electric field of strength

$$E_{line\ charge} = \frac{\lambda}{2\pi\varepsilon_0 r} \qquad (36)$$

This is a result that you should be able to derive on your own without looking back at the text. We will use this result in our introduction to the theory of magnetism.

---

*Beyond these basics, **the main thing we want you to get out of this chapter is experience constructing field lines from various charge distributions using the Charges2000 computer program.***

In that program we draw Q lines rather than Q/ε_0 lines coming out of every positive charge $+Q$ or going into every negative charge $-Q$. As a test of the program, we plotted the field of a circle of 24 charges each with a charge $Q = +10$. The plot shown in Figure (28) shows how the field lines that were initially headed inside the circle get blown out by the other charges.

CHAPTER EXERCISES

Exercise 1 0n page 5
Sketch force vectors on a charge in an electric field.

Exercise 2 0n page 15
Calculations involving the electric field of a line charge.

Exercise 3 0n page 24
Use the program Charges2000 to find the field of a circle of charges.

Exercise 4 0n page 24
Use the program Charges2000 to find the field of a special line charge distribution. (The charge distribution comes from a special relativity thought experiment that we will discuss shortly.)

Figure 21b
Wires fanning out in 2 dimensions. The density of wires drops off as 1/r.

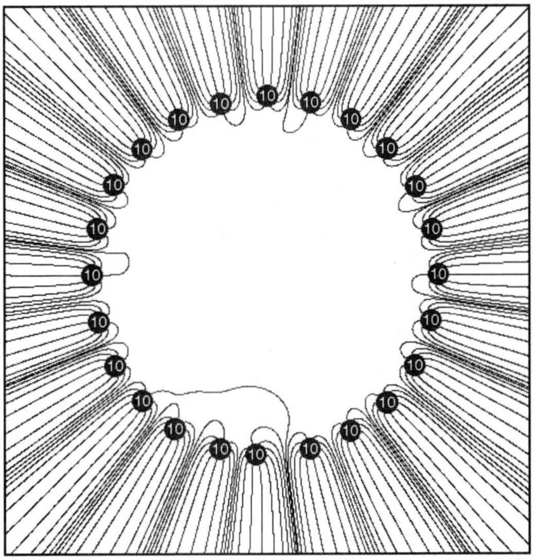

Figure 28
The inside field is blown out.

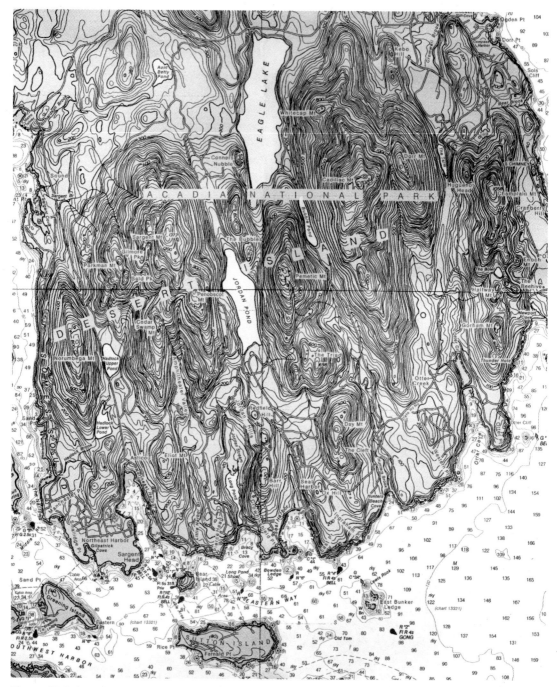

Figure 20-0
Mt. Desert Island on the coast of Maine.
Courtesy of National Oceanic and Atmospheric Administration
Coast Survey

Chapter 20 non calculus

Electric Potential Maps and Voltage

On the facing page is a contour map of part of Mt. Desert Island on the coast of Maine. This island has the highest mountains of any island or shoreline on the east coast of the United States. Looking at the map you can immediately see that the island is mountainous. Each contour line represents a change in altitude of 100 feet (30 meters). The tallest mountain, Mt. Cadillac, at 3,186 feet high, requires 31 contour lines above the zero contour line at the shore's edge.

In the last chapter, we said that we were going to use the tools developed by map makers to help visualize the structure of the electric field produced by charge distributions. We drew maps of electric field lines, but the field lines are not contour lines. In this chapter we will introduce contour lines for the electric field, as **lines of constant electric potential energy**.

We will see that these constant potential energy lines, commonly called **equipotential lines** or **lines of constant voltage**, are equally effective in mapping the electric field and mountain ranges. We complete our map making kit by discussing the intimate relationship between field lines and contour lines. The **Charges2000** program can plot both.

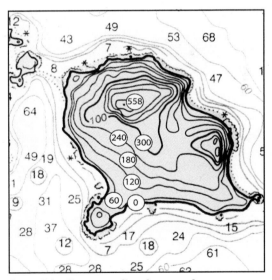

Butter Island's contour lines have now become equipotential lines. The value (gh) of each line is given in the white circles.

THE CONTOUR MAP

We will begin our discussion of contour maps with a simpler example than the complex mountain ranges on Mt. Desert Island. Figure (1a) is a map of a small group of islands just north of Vinelhaven Island on Penobscott Bay in Maine. We are going to focus our attention on the small Island in the upper right hand side, Butter Island.

Figure (1b) is the contour map for Butter Island. Here the contour lines represent equal height gains of 20 feet (6 meters). From the shape of the lines we see that there are two hills on the island, one 186 feet high on the north side (9 contour lines) and the other with two bumps over 140 feet high on the east side. If we were looking for a beach on this island, we would look on the gently sloping south side where the contour lines are far apart. Rock climbers looking for a steep slope would head for the east side of the east hill where the contour lines are very close together.

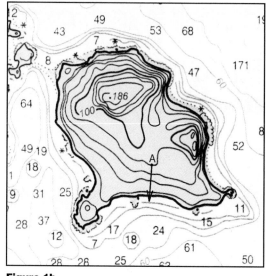

Figure 1b
Contour map of Butter Island.

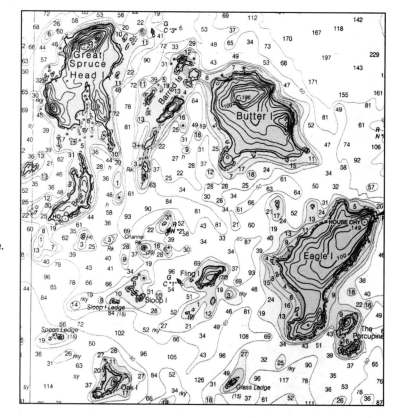

Figure 1a
Group of islands north of Vinelhaven in Penobscot Bay, Maine. We are going to look closely at Butter Island in the upper right side of the map. Courtesy of National Oceanic and Atmospheric Administration.

Although we would rather picture this island as being in the south seas, our island is in the North Atlantic, and we will imagine that a storm has just covered it with a sheet of ice. You are standing at the point labeled A in Figure (1), and start to slip. If the surface is smooth, which way would you start to slip?

A contour line runs through Point A which we have shown in an enlargement in Figure (2). You would not start to slide along the contour line because all the points along the contour line are at the same height. Instead, you would start to slide in the steepest downhill direction, which is *perpendicular* to the contour line as shown by the arrow.

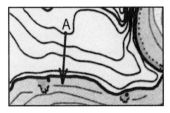

Figure 2
The direction you would start to slip, the direction of steepest descent, is perpendicular to the contour lines.

If you do not believe that the direction of steepest descent is perpendicular to the contour line, choose any smooth surface like the top of a rock, mark a horizontal line (an equal height line) for a contour line, and carefully look for the directions that are most steeply sloped down. You will see that all along the contour line the steepest slope is, in fact, perpendicular to the contour line.

Skiers are familiar with this concept. When you want to stop and rest and the slope is icy, you plant your skis along a contour line so that they will not slide either forward or backward. The direction of steepest descent is now perpendicular to your skis, in a direction that ski instructors call the *fall line*. The fall line is the direction you will start to slide if the edges of your skis fail to hold.

In Figure (3), we have redrawn our contour map of the island, but have added a set of perpendicular lines to show the directions of steepest descent, the direction of the net force on you if you were sitting on a slippery surface. These lines of steepest descent, are also called **lines of force**. They can be sketched by hand, using the rule that the lines of force must always be perpendicular to the contour lines.

In Figure (4) we have the same island, but except for the zero height contour outlining the island, and the top contours, we show only the lines of force. The exercise here, which you should do now, is sketch in the contour lines. Just use the rule that the contour lines must be drawn perpendicular to the lines of force. The point is that you can go either way. Given the contour lines you can sketch the lines of force, or given the lines of force you can sketch the contour lines. This turns out to be a powerful technique in the mapping of any complex physical or mathematical terrain.

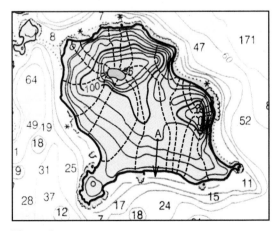

Figure 3
We have added a set of perpendicular lines to show the directions of steepest descent. These are called the lines of force.

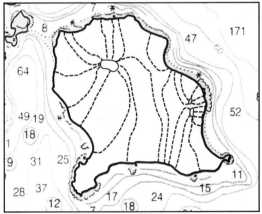

Figure 4
Map of the lines of force.

GRAVITATIONAL POTENTIAL

The lines in a contour map give us the lines of constant height in the terrain. If you walk along a contour line you neither gain or lose height h or gravitational potential energy mgh (where m is your mass). As a result, another name for these contour lines could be "lines of constant gravitational potential energy".

If we are to draw maps of potential energy rather than height, we do not want the m in the formula mgh because m is your mass, and a different person would want to use a different mass. We can solve this problem by drawing maps of constant potential energy of a unit mass (m = 1 kg), and call the result (gh) the *gravitational potential*. In Figure (5) we have redrawn the contour map of Butter Island, but labeled the contour lines with their values of gravitational potential (gh) in MKS units rather than h in feet. The difference in gravitational potential between lines, instead of being 20 feet, is now

$$gh = 9.8 \frac{\text{meter}}{\text{sec}^2} \times 20 \text{ ft} \times .3048 \frac{\text{meter}}{\text{ft}}$$

$$gh = 60 \frac{\text{meters}^2}{\text{sec}^2} \quad \begin{array}{l} \textit{difference in} \\ \textit{gravitational} \\ \textit{potential between} \\ \textit{contour lines} \end{array} \quad (1)$$

You can see that with gh having the dimensions of $\text{meters}^2/\text{sec}^2$, that mgh has the dimensions $\text{kg meters}^2/\text{sec}^2$ which is the same as kinetic energy $1/2\,mv^2$. That set of dimensions is called a joule.

If a 50 kg person climbed from one contour line to the next (from one equipotential line to the next) the amount of gravitational potential energy she would gain would be

$$\begin{array}{l} \text{energy} \\ \text{gained} \end{array} = mgh$$

$$= 50 \text{ kg} \times 60 \frac{\text{m}^2}{\text{sec}^2} \quad (2)$$

$$= 300 \text{ joules}$$

Since we get the gravitational potential energy in joules by multiplying the gravitational potential (gh) by the mass m of the person climbing, we can see that that the gravitational potential has the dimensions of joules/kilogram.

$$\boxed{\begin{array}{l} \text{gravitational} \\ \text{potential} \end{array} = gh \frac{\text{joules}}{\text{kg}}} \quad (3)$$

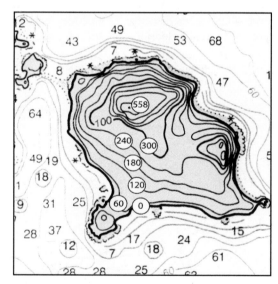

Figure 5
Butter Island's contour lines have now become equipotential lines. The value (gh) of each line is given in the white circles.

ELECTRIC POTENTIAL

Drawing contour maps for the electric field involves steps similar to what we just did for the contour map of gravitational potential.

First we need to find a relationship between the electric field $\vec{E}$ and potential energy. For this we will start with the electric field of a plane of positive charge. As we saw in Figure (19-21c) of the last chapter, a plane of charge produces a uniform electric field. Consider the plane of charge and uniform field $\vec{E}$ shown in Figure (6). If we have a point charge +Q in that field, the charge feels a downward force $Q\vec{E}$. When we lift the charge Q from a height h_1, up to a height h_2, a distance h as shown, the work we do and the electrical potential energy gained is

$$\begin{matrix} \text{potential} \\ \text{energy} \\ \text{gained} \end{matrix} = \frac{\text{force} \times}{\text{distance}} = (QE) \times h \; joules \quad (4)$$

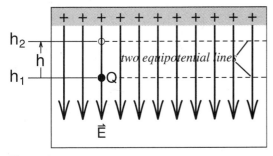

$$\vec{E}$$

Figure 6
When you lift a charge Q a distance h up against a downward force of magnitude QE, the amount of work you do is your force QE times the distance h, or QEh. The work you do is stored as electrical potential energy.

The lines of constant potential energy are for this diagram horizontal lines like the lines at heights h_1 and h_2.

In the case of gravity where we had lines of constant potential energy mgh, we got rid of the m by considering the potential energy of a unit mass (m = 1). For electricity we will do an analogous thing and draw lines of constant potential energy of a unit charge (Q = 1) and call the result *electric equipotential lines*.

$$\begin{matrix} \text{electric} \\ \text{potential} \end{matrix} = E \times h \; \frac{joules}{coulomb} \quad (5)$$

The dimensions come out as joules/coulomb so that when we multiply E×h in joules/coulomb by Q coulombs, you get (QE)×h joules.

In our discussion of potential energy, we saw that the zero of potential energy was arbitrary and could be chosen for convenience. For the contour map of an island, the standard zero of potential energy, or zero height, is the average sea level at low tide. Anything below that is negative height, above that, is positive. Similarly, we can choose any electric equipotential line as the zero of electrical potential energy.

Figure 19-21c
When the wires emerge from a plane, the density of wires is constant.

ELECTRIC POTENTIAL
OF A POINT CHARGE

At the end of the last chapter we discussed the electric fields of a point charge, a line charge and a plane of charge. If we want to draw contour maps for these three fields, the answers are quite obvious. For a point charge the equipotential surfaces are concentric spheres centered on the charge as indicated in Figure (7). For a line charge, the equipotential surfaces are concentric cylinders centered on the line.

For a plane of charge where the field lines are straight out from the plane, the equipotential surfaces are planes parallel to the plane of charge, as indicated back in Figure (6).

To calculate the potential difference between two surfaces for the point and line charges requires the calculation of the amount of work we do in moving a charge from one surface to another. This calculation is relatively easy using calculus, but difficult without. We faced this problem back in Chapter 10 when we tried to calculate the change in gravitational potential energy when an object was carried far from the surface of the earth. We will briefly review the results of our gravitational discussion and apply the results to determine potential energies for point charges.

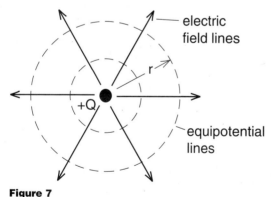

Figure 7
The <u>electric potential</u> is the potential energy of a positive unit test charge $q_{test} = +1$ *coulomb.*

Gravitational Potential Energy
of a Point Mass

When we discussed the potential energy of objects acting as point masses, like the earth and sun, or the earth and a satellite, it was not convenient to choose the surface of the earth as the zero of potential energy. Instead we said that two masses m_1 and m_2 have zero potential energy when they are so far apart that we can almost neglect the gravitational force between them.

If the two masses were the only masses in the universe, and we left them at rest very far apart, there would still be a tiny attractive gravitational force. If we came back later, we would see the masses starting to move toward each other. As we watched, their speed would gradually increase, until finally they would crash into each other at relatively high speeds. Just before they hit, they would have quite a bit of kinetic energy. Where did this kinetic energy come from?

Obviously the kinetic energy came from gravitational potential energy, just as when we drop a ball on the floor. But we said that the two masses, when very far apart, had no gravitational potential energy. Starting from zero potential energy how could they convert potential energy into kinetic energy? Just the same way you can write checks on a bank account that started with a zero balance. Both your balance and the ball's potential energy become negative.

In talking about electric potential energy of point charges, we use the same convention. We say that if the charges are very far apart, their electrical potential energy is zero. If we have a positive and a negative charge that attract each other like our two masses, the electrical potential energy becomes negative as the charges approach each other.

If, however, we have two charges of the same sign that repel each other, we have to push them together to get them near each other. The work we do pushing them together is stored as positive electrical potential energy. Once we have them together, and let go, the charges will fly apart, converting the potential energy we supplied into kinetic energy.

Thus if we use the convention that potential energy is zero when particles are far apart, then ***attractive forces have negative potential energy, while repulsive forces have positive potential energy***.

Potential Energy Formula

In Chapter 10, Equation (43), we wrote down the formula for the gravitational potential energy of two masses m_1 and m_2 a distance r apart. It was

$$\begin{matrix}\text{gravitational}\\ \text{potential}\\ \text{energy}\end{matrix} = -\frac{Gm_1m_2}{r} \qquad (10\text{-}43)$$

This was derived from the gravitational force

$$\left|\vec{F}_g\right| = \frac{Gm_1m_2}{r^2}$$

What may seem surprising is that the gravitational potential energy formula looks like the force formula, except that $1/r^2$ is replaced by $1/r$.

If you think about dimensions, something like this has to happen. Remember that energy has the dimensions of force times distance. If we start with the formula Gm_1m_2/r^2 for force, and want to multiply by a distance, the only distance available is r. Multiplying by r gives Gm_1m_2/r, which except for a minus sign, is the potential energy formula.

Precisely the same thing happens for the potential energy formula for point charges. Starting with Coulomb's law for force

$$\left|\vec{F}_e\right| = \frac{KQ_1Q_2}{r^2} \qquad (17\text{-}1)$$

the potential energy formula becomes

$$\boxed{\begin{matrix}\text{electrical}\\ \text{potential}\\ \text{energy}\end{matrix} = \frac{KQ_1Q_2}{r}\ joules} \qquad (6)$$

There is an interesting coincidence in Equation (6) for electric potential energy. If the charges have opposite signs, then the product Q_1Q_2 is negative. But if they have opposite signs, the force is attractive and the potential energy is negative. In contrast if Q_1 and Q_2 have the same sign, then the product Q_1Q_2 is positive, and if they have the same sign then the potential energy is positive. Thus Equation (6) gives the correct sign for the potential energy for any two charges.

Our final step is writing the formula for the electrical potential energy of a point charge is to use MKS units where $K = 1/4\pi\varepsilon_0$. The result is

$$\boxed{\begin{matrix}\text{electrical potential}\\ \text{energy between}\\ Q_1\ \text{and}\ Q_2\end{matrix} = \frac{Q_1Q_2}{4\pi\varepsilon_0 r}\ joules} \qquad (7)$$

Electric Potential of a Point Charge

In our discussion of gravitational potential energy and contour maps, we found it convenient to define the *gravitational potential* as the potential energy of a unit mass $(m = 1)$. We will now define the electric potential of a charge Q as the electric potential energy between our charge Q and a unit charge $(Q_2 = 1)$. The result is

$$\begin{aligned}\begin{matrix}\text{electrical potential}\\ \text{of a charge Q}\end{matrix} &= \frac{Q \times 1}{4\pi\varepsilon_0 r}\\[2mm] &= \frac{Q}{4\pi\varepsilon_0 r}\ \frac{joules}{coulomb}\end{aligned} \qquad (8)$$

Again we mention that the dimensions of the electric potential are joules/coulomb, so that when we multiply by a charge Q_2 we get back to a potential energy in joules.

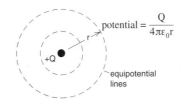

Figure 7a
The electric potential of a point charge.

ELECTRIC VOLTAGE

In our discussion of Bernoulli's equation, we gave the collection of terms $(P + \rho g h + 1/2\rho v^2)$ the name *hydrodynamic voltage*. The content of Bernoulli's equation is that this hydrodynamic voltage is constant along a stream line when the fluid is incompressible and viscous forces can be neglected. Two of the three terms, $\rho g h$ and $1/2\rho v^2$ represent the energy of a unit volume of the fluid, thus we see that our hydrodynamic voltage has the dimensions of energy per unit volume.

Electric voltage is a quantity with the dimensions of *energy per unit charge* that in different situations is represented by a series of terms like the terms in Bernoulli's hydrodynamic voltage. There is the potential energy of an electric field, the chemical energy supplied by a battery, even a kinetic energy term, seen in careful studies of superconductors, that is strictly analogous to the $1/2\rho v^2$ term in Bernoulli's equation. In other words, electric voltage is a complex concept, but it has one simplifying feature. Electric voltages are measured by a common experimental device called a *voltmeter*. In fact we will take as the definition of electric voltage, that quantity which we measure using a voltmeter.

This sounds like a nebulous definition. Without telling you how a voltmeter works, how are you to know what the meter is measuring? To overcome this objection, we will build up our understanding of what a voltmeter measures by considering the various possible sources of voltage one at a time. Bernoulli's equation gave us all the hydrodynamic voltage terms at once. For electric voltage we will have to dig them out as we find them.

Our first example of an electric voltage term is the *electric potential energy of a unit test charge*. This has the dimensions of energy per unit charge which in the MKS system is joules/coulomb and called volts.

$$1\,\frac{\text{joule}}{\text{coulomb}} \equiv 1\text{ volt} \qquad (9)$$

Figure (8) shows the electric field lines and equipotential lines for a point charge Q. We see from Equation (8) that a unit test particle at Point (1) has a potential energy, or voltage V_1 given by

$$V_1 = \frac{Q}{4\pi\varepsilon_0 r_1} \qquad \begin{array}{l}\textit{electric potential or}\\ \textit{voltage at Point}(1)\end{array}$$

At Point (2), the electric potential or voltage V_2 is given by

$$V_2 = \frac{Q}{4\pi\varepsilon_0 r_2} \qquad \begin{array}{l}\textit{electric potential or}\\ \textit{voltage at Point}(2)\end{array}$$

Voltmeters have the property that they only measure the ***difference in voltage*** between two points. Thus if we put one lead of a voltmeter at Point (1), and the other at Point (2), as shown, then we get a voltage reading V given by

$$\begin{array}{l}\text{voltmeter}\\ \text{reading}\end{array} \quad V \equiv V_2 - V_1 = \frac{Q}{4\pi\varepsilon_0}\left(\frac{1}{r_2} - \frac{1}{r_1}\right) \quad (10)$$

If we put the two voltmeter leads at points equal distances from Q, i.e., if $r_1 = r_2$, then the voltmeter would read zero. Since the voltage difference between any two points on an equipotential line is zero, the voltmeter reading must also be zero when the leads are attached to any two points on an equipotential line.

This observation suggests an experimental way to map equipotential lines or surfaces. Attach one lead of the voltmeter to some particular point, call it Point (A). Then move the other lead around. Whenever you get a zero reading on the voltmeter, the second

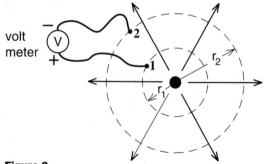

Figure 8
A voltmeter measures the difference in electrical voltage between two points.

lead must be at another point of the same equipotential line as Point (A). By marking all the points where the meter reads zero, you get a picture of the equipotential line.

The discussion we have just given for finding the equipotential lines surrounding a point charge Q is not practical. This involves electrostatic measurements that are extremely difficult to carry out. Just the damp air from your breath would affect the voltages surrounding a point charge, and typical voltmeters found in the lab cannot make electrostatic measurements. Sophisticated meters in carefully controlled environments are required for this work.

But the idea of potential plotting can be illustrated nicely by the simple laboratory apparatus illustrated in Figure (9). In that apparatus we have a tray of water (slightly salty or dirty, so that it is somewhat conductive), and two metal cylinders attached by wire leads to a battery as shown. There are also two probes consisting of a bent, stiff wire attached to a block of wood and adjusted so that the tips of the wires stick down in the water. The other end of the probes are attached to a voltmeter so we can read the voltage difference between the two points (A) and (B), where the probes touch the water.

If we keep Probe (A) fixed and move Probe (B) around, whenever the voltmeter reads zero, Probe (B) will be on the equipotential line that goes through

Point (A). Without too much effort, one can get a complete plot of the equipotential line. Each time we move Probe (A) we can plot a new equipotential line. A plot of a series of equipotential lines is shown in Figure (10).

Once we have the equipotential lines shown in Figure (10), we can sketch the lines of force by drawing a set of lines perpendicular to the equipotential as we did in Figure (11). With a little practice you can sketch fairly accurate plots, and the beauty of the process is that you did not have to do any calculations!

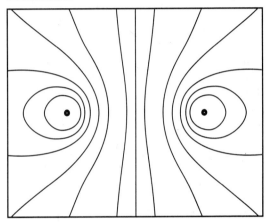

Figure 10
Plot of the equipotential lines from a student project by B. J Grattan. Instead of a tray of water, Grattan used a sheet of conductive paper, painting two circles with aluminum paint to replace the brass cylinders.

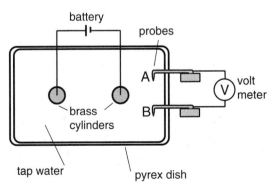

Figure 9
Simple setup for plotting fields. You plot equipotentials by placing one probe (A) at a given position and moving the other (B) around. Whenever the voltage V on the voltmeter reads zero, the probes are at points of equipotential.

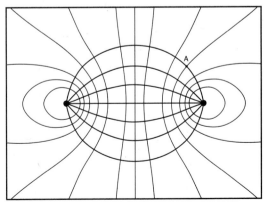

Figure 11
To draw field lines, draw smooth lines, always perpendicular to the equipotential lines, and maintain any symmetry that should be there.

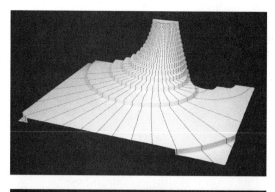

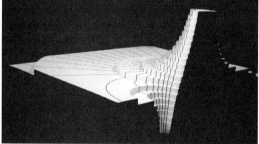

Figure 12
Model of the electric field in the region of two point charges $Q_+ = +3$, $Q_- = -1$. Using the analogy to a topographical map, we cut out plywood slabs in the shape of the equipotentials from the computer plot of Figure (13), and stacked the slabs to form a three dimensional surface. The field lines, which are marked with narrow black tape on the model, always lead in the direction of steepest descent on the surface.

Figure 14
Potential plot along the line of the two charges +3, –1. The positive charge creates an upward spike, while the negative charge makes a hole.

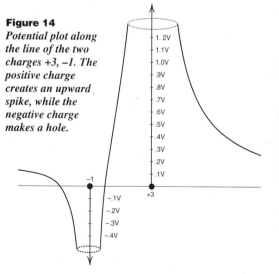

A Field Plot Model

The analogy between a field plot and a map maker's contour plot can be made even more obvious by constructing a plywood model like that shown in Figure (12).

To construct the model, we made a computer plot of the electric field of charge distribution consisting of a charge +3 and –1, seen on the next page in Figure (13). We enlarged the computer plot and then cut out pieces of plywood that had the shapes of the contour lines. The pieces of plywood were stacked on top of each other and glued together to produce the three dimensional view of the field structure.

In this model, each additional thickness of plywood represents one more equal step in the electric potential or voltage. The voltage of the positive charge Q = +3 is represented by the fat positive spike that goes up toward $+\infty$ and the negative charge q = –1 is represented by the smaller hole that heads down to $-\infty$. These spikes can be seen in the back view in Figure (12), and the potential plot in Figure (14).

In addition to seeing the contour lines in the slabs of plywood, we have also marked the lines of steepest descent with narrow strips of black tape. These lines of steepest descent are always perpendicular to the contour lines, and are in fact, the electric field lines, when viewed from the top as in the photograph of Figure (13).

Figure (15) is a plywood model of the electric potential for two positive charges, Q = +5, Q = +2. Here we get two hills, somewhat like Butter Island.

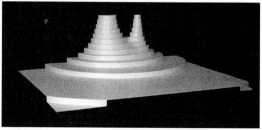

Figure 15
Model of the electric potential in the region of two point charges Q = +5 and Q = +2.

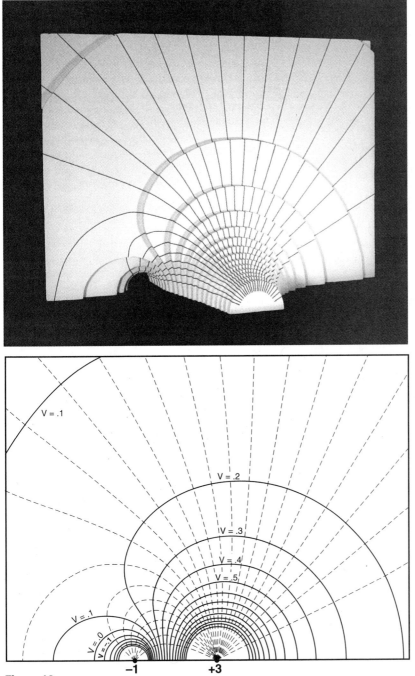

Figure 13
Computer plot of the field lines and equipotentials for a charge distribution consisting of a positive charge + 3 and a negative charge – 1. These lines were then used to construct the plywood model. (We are assuming that the thickness of the plywood represents a step of .1 volts.)

COMPUTER PLOTS

In order to construct the plywood models we just saw, we used computer plots of the equipotential lines surrounding the charges. These lines become the contour lines of the voltage landscape produced by the charges.

At the end of the previous chapter we described the fairly complex way we drew the fields lines of a charge distribution. The calculation of the equipotential lines is much easier to describe. What we do is use the voltage formulas like Equation (10) to calculate the voltage at each pixel in the plotting board. Then we change the pixel color at specified voltage intervals.

For example, suppose the voltage ranges from –4 volts up to 12 volts and we want equipotential lines at 1 volt intervals. We plot all the pixels in the range –4 volts to –3 volts in the minus voltage color, which is blue for the standard colors. Then we leave as white all the pixels in the –3 volt to –2 volt range. Those in the –2 volt to –1 volt range are blue again. We use the same scheme for the positive voltages, except we use pink for the standard positive voltage color.

To show how to obtain voltage plots, we start in Figure (16) with the field line plot of two point charges placed to match our experimental plot of Figure (11) reproduced here. We then go to the tools palette and use the pull down menu to select "Choose both 2D" which means to plot both the field lines and voltage colors for a two dimensional plot. Pressing "Plot" we got the result shown in Figure (18).

You should notice that the lines separating colors in Figure (18) are fairly close to the experimental equipotential lines of the student project in Figure (11).

Our reasoning for choosing pink, white and blue for the standard colors came from using red for positive charges and voltages and blue for negative ones. We let the field lines remain black. The color scheme is clear but hardly inspiring. Back in Figure (19a) in the last chapter, we showed how to chose a different color scheme for more interesting plots. Figure (18) looks a lot better if you plot using "Underwater Colors". We leave it up to the reader to find out what the result is.

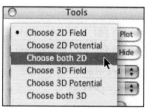

Figure 11
Equipotential lines from a student project. We sketched in the field lines.

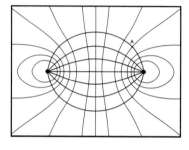

Figure 17
Selecting to plot both field and equipotential lines.

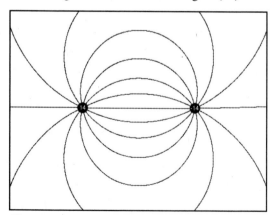

Figure 16
Field lines for two point charges.

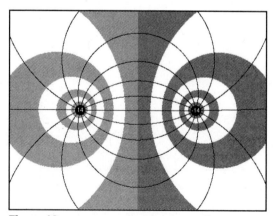

Figure 18
Field and equipotential lines for two point charges.

The Color Palette

If you want some really interesting results, you can use the Color Palette shown in Figure (19). That control panel allows you to change the color of any area or line in the plot. For example, if you want to change the pink color of positive voltages, you click on the pink area in the palette. A cross appears where you clicked and the three color sliders show the value of the color in the clicked area. Instead of having you choose the amount of red, green, and blue, the standard for TV screen

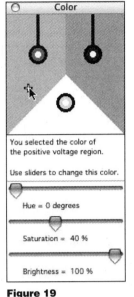

Figure 19
Color Palette.

colors, we give you the choice of **Hue**, **Saturation** and **Brightness**. Play with these sliders and you will quickly see what these terms mean, and why they are much more convenient than trying to express a color in terms of how much red, green and blue are in the mixture. Figures (20) and (21) are examples of what you can accomplish using the Color Palette.

Suggested Laboratory Work

Because the computer program is available, we suggest that you do something more creative in the lab than simply plotting the equipotential lines of two charges. We leave the choice up to the student and instructor, but would very much like to see any interesting results.

As an Art Form

The field line and potential plots you can get from *Charges2000* have an underlying symmetry because they are based on Coulomb's law and represent allowed flow patterns of an incompressible fluid. If you put in some symmetry of your own, you can get some very interesting artistic patterns, like Figure (20) which our granddaughter created at age 10. She had not learned about Coulomb's law, but she had that pattern in her mind when she arrived at our house.

We encourage the use of Charges2000 as an art medium, and enjoy seeing results emailed to us at: lish.huggins@dartmouth.edu. We have already seen some very interesting ones.

Figure 20
Design by Julia Huggins, at age 10.

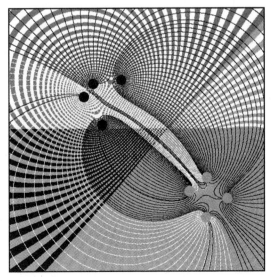

Figure 21
A pair of four charges.

CHAPTER 20 REVIEW

The aim of this chapter is to apply mapmaker's techniques to describe and visualize the electric field $\vec{E}$.

We began with a contour map of a small island, a map showing contour lines of equal height h. In Figure (5) we relabeled the contour lines as lines of **gravitational potential** *gh. The name gravitational potential came from the fact that gh is the gravitational potential energy mgh of a unit mass m = 1 kilogram.*

Earlier, in Figure (3) we drew another set of lines that are everywhere perpendicular to the contour lines. These are the lines along which you would start to slide if the island were covered with a sheet of ice in an ice storm. They are called **lines of force** *and are directed in the most downhill direction, which is always perpendicular to the horizontal contour lines.*

In the last chapter we introduced the electric field lines $\vec{E}$ which show the direction of the force on a unit test charge $q_{test} = 1$ coulomb. These are also called **lines of force**. *In this chapter, instead of going from contour lines to lines of force as we did for the gravitational potential, we went the other way. We started with the lines of force and drew a set of perpendicular lines which represented lines of con-* *stant electric potential. These lines of constant electric potential are the lines along which our unit test charge q_{test} has constant electric potential energy.*

Another name for the electric potential energy of a unit charge is **voltage**. *The set of lines perpendicular to the electric field lines are lines of* **constant voltage**.

For working with electric phenomena, we have a convenient way to measure voltage, at least differences in voltage between two points. That device is called a **voltmeter**.

To become familiar with how a voltmeter can be used to study electric fields, we have a very important laboratory exercise. By placing a couple of brass cylinders in a tray of tap water, and attaching a battery of voltage V_b across the cylinders, we set up a voltage difference in the water between the cylinders. We then attached two probes to the voltmeter. We set one probe at some location in the water and move the other probe around in the water until the voltmeter reads zero volts. That means that the two probes are located on the same constant voltage line. You have thus located two points on a voltage contour line. Moving the second probe around you can locate a number of points on this contour line and then sketch the line.

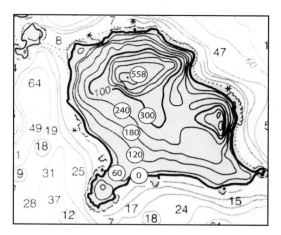

Figure 5
Butter Island's contour lines have now become equipotential lines. The value (gh) of each line is given in the white circles.

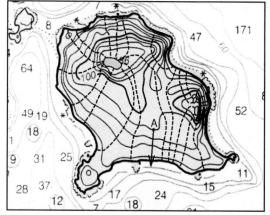

Figure 3
We have added a set of perpendicular lines to show the directions of steepest descent. These are called the lines of force.

Once we have drawn the voltage contour lines, we can, as in Figure (3), then draw the perpendicular set of electric field lines. We did this in going from Figure (10) to Figure (11), starting with a student's experimental constant voltage lines.

In Figure (12) we showed how to construct a three dimensional model of the electric voltage contour lines and electric field lines for a charge $Q - = -1$ coulomb near a charge $Q + = +3$ coulombs. With this model you can see that there is a complete analogy between electric field and voltage maps, and the mapmaker's contour maps.

*In the previous chapter we introduced the computer program **Charges2000** for drawing the electric field lines produced by various distributions of charge. Another feature of the program is that at each point on the plotting board, it calculates the*

electric voltage produced by the charge distribution. By using the same color to plot all points in a certain voltage range, say, from 1 volt to 2 volts, then a different color for all points in the next range, say, from 2 volts to 3 volts, the voltage contour lines lie along the borders where the color changes.

Comparing Figures (11) and (18) on page 20-12, we see that the computer plot and the student's lab work are close.

CHAPTER EXERCISES

The important lessons from this chapter are:

(1) Develop an intuitive feeling for the perpendicular sets of lines, one marking lines of constant voltage, the other, lines for force.

(2) Become familiar with using a voltmeter to measure lines of constant voltage.

(3) Become familiar with the use of **Charges2000** to plot both field lines and voltage contours.

Working numerical problems is not the aim of this chapter.

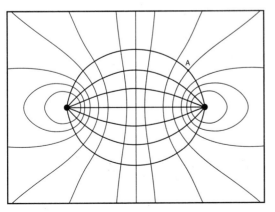

Figure 9
Experimental setup.

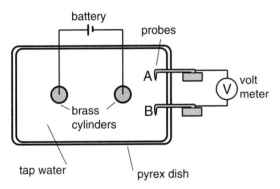

Figure 11
Equipotential and field lines from student project.

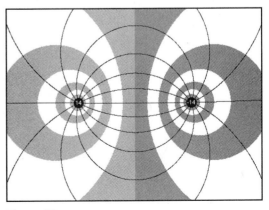

Figure 18
Field and equipotential lines for two point charges.

Chapter 21 non calculus
Electric Fields and Conductors

In this chapter we will first discuss the behavior of electric fields in the presence of conductors, and then apply the results to three practical devices, the Van de Graaff generator, the electron gun, and the parallel plate capacitor. Each of these examples provides not only an explanation of a practical device, but also helps build an intuitive picture of the concept of electric voltage.

Another important result is the introduction of the **electron volt** *as a unit of energy.*

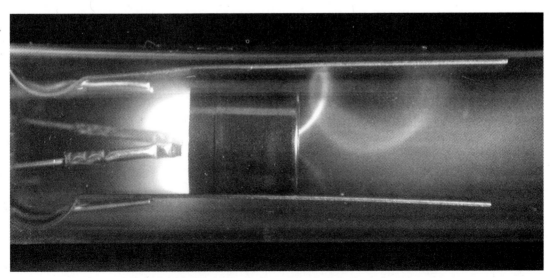

Electron beam emerging from a student built electron gun.

ELECTRIC FIELD INSIDE A CONDUCTOR

If we have a piece of metal a few centimeters across as illustrated in Figure (1), and suddenly turn on an electric field, what happens? Initially the field goes right through the metal. But within a few pico seconds (1 pico second = 10^{-12} seconds) the electrons in the metal redistribute themselves inside the metal creating their own field that soon cancels the external applied electric field, as indicated in Figure (2).

The very concept of an electrical conductor requires that, in the steady state, there be no electric field inside. To see why, imagine that there is a field inside. Since it is a conductor, the electrons in the conductor are free to move. If there is a field inside, the field will exert a force on the electrons and the electrons will move. They will continue to move until there is no force on them, i.e., until there is no field remaining inside. *The electrons must continue to move until the field they create just cancels the external field you applied.*

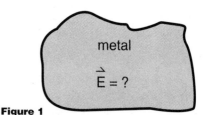
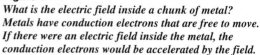

Figure 1
What is the electric field inside a chunk of metal? Metals have conduction electrons that are free to move. If there were an electric field inside the metal, the conduction electrons would be accelerated by the field.

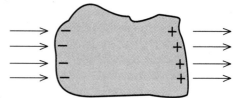
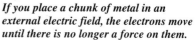

Figure 2
If you place a chunk of metal in an external electric field, the electrons move until there is no longer a force on them.

Surface Charges

Where does the redistributed charge have to go in order to create an electric field that precisely cancels the applied electric field? Gauss' law provides a remarkably simple answer to this question. The redistributed charge must reside on the *surface of the conductor.* This is because Gauss' law requires that there be no net charge inside the volume of a conductor.

To see why, let us assume that a charge Q is inside a conductor as shown in Figure (3). Draw a small Gaussian surface around Q. Then by Gauss' law the flux $\Phi = \vec{E} \cdot \vec{A}$ coming out through the Gaussian surface must be equal to Q_{in}/ε_0 where Q_{in} is the net charge inside the Gaussian surface. But if $\vec{E} = 0$, there is no field inside the conductor, the flux $\vec{E} \cdot \vec{A}$ out through the Gaussian surface must be zero, and therefore the charge Q_{in} must be zero.

If there is no charge inside the conductor, then the only place any charge can exist is in the surface. If there is a redistribution of charge, the redistributed charge must lie on the surface of the conductor.

Figure (4) is a qualitative sketch of how surface charge can create a field that cancels the applied field. In Figure (4a) we see the electric field just after it has been turned on. Since the electrons in the metal are negatively charged (q = –e), the force on the electrons $\vec{F} = (-e)\vec{E}$ is opposite to $\vec{E}$ and directed to the left.

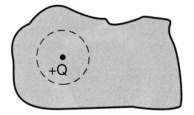

Figure 3
Is there any electric charge inside a conductor? To find out, draw a Gaussian surface around the suspected charge. Since there is no electric field inside the conductor, there is no flux out through the surface, and therefore no charge inside.

In Figure (4b), electrons have been sucked over to the left surface of the metal, leaving positive charge on the right surface. The negative charge on the left surface combined with the positive charge on the right produced the left directed field $\vec{E}'$ shown by the dotted lines. The oppositely directed fields $\vec{E}$ and $\vec{E}'$ cancel in Figure (4c) giving no net field inside the metal.

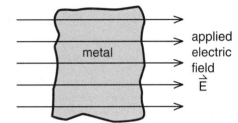

Figure 4a
An external field is applied to a block of metal.

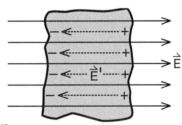

Figure 4b
In response to the electric field, the electrons move to the left surface of the metal, leaving behind positive charge on the right surface. These two surface charges have their own field $\vec{E}'$ that is oppositely directed to $\vec{E}$.

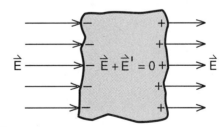

Figure 4c
Inside the block of metal the fields cancel. The result is that the external field on the left stops on the negative surface charge. The field on the right starts again on the positive surface charge.

Example: Field
in a Hollow Metal Sphere

Suppose we have the hollow metal sphere shown in Figure (5). A total charge Q is placed on the sphere. What are the electric fields outside and inside the sphere?

One key to solving this problem is to realize that since the sphere is symmetric, the fields it produces must also be symmetric. We are not interested in fields that do one thing on the left side and something else on the right, for we do not have any physical cause for such an asymmetry.

In Figure (6) we have drawn a Gaussian surface surrounding the metal sphere as shown. Since there is a net charge +Q on the sphere, and therefore inside the Gaussian surface, there must be a net flux Q/ε_0 out through the surface. Since the Gaussian surface has an area $4\pi r^2$, Gauss' law gives

$$\Phi = E_{out}A_\perp = E_{out} \times 4\pi r^2 = \frac{Q}{\varepsilon_0}$$

$$E_{out} = \frac{Q}{4\pi\varepsilon_0 r^2} \tag{1}$$

which happens to be the field of a point charge.

In Figure (7) we have drawn a Gaussian surface inside the metal at a radius r_i. Since there is no field inside the metal, $EA_\perp = 0$ and there is no flux flowing out through the Gaussian surface. Thus by Gauss' law there can be **no net charge inside the Gaussian surface**. Explicitly this means that there is no surface charge on the inside of the conductor. The charge Q we spread on the conducting sphere **all went to the outside surface**!

Finally in Figure (8) we have drawn a Gaussian surface inside the hollow part of the hollow sphere. Since there is no charge—only empty space inside this Gaussian surface, there can be no flux out through the surface, and the **field $\vec{E}$ inside the hollow part of the sphere is exactly zero**. This is a rather remarkable result considering how little effort was required to obtain it.

Figure 5
We place a charge Q on a hollow metal sphere. Where do the charge and the field lines go?

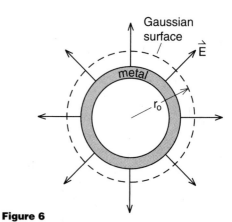

Figure 6
If we place a Gaussian surface around and outside the sphere, we know that the charge Q must be inside the Gaussian surface, and therefore Q/ε_o flux lines must come out through the surface.

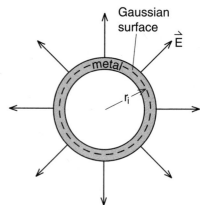

Figure 7
If we place our Gaussian surface inside the metal where $\vec{E} = 0$, no lines come out through the Gaussian surface and therefore there must be no net charge Q inside the Gaussian surface. The fact that there is no charge within that surface means all the charge we placed on the sphere spreads to the outside surface.

Exercise 1

A positive charge +Q is surrounded concentrically by a conducting sphere with an inner radius r_a and outer radius r_b as shown in Figure (9). The conducting sphere has no net charge. Using Gauss' law, find the electric field inside the hollow section ($r < r_a$), inside the conducting sphere ($r_a < r < r_b$) and outside the sphere ($r > r_b$).

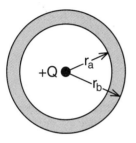

Figure 9
Start with an uncharged hollow metal sphere and place a charge +Q inside. Use Gauss' law to determine the electric field and the surface charges throughout the region.

Exercise 2

A chunk of metal has an irregularly shaped cavity inside as shown in Figure (10). There are no holes and the cavity is completely surrounded by metal.

The metal chunk is struck by lightning which produces huge electric fields and deposits an unknown amount of charge on the metal, but does not burn a hole into the cavity. Show that the lightning does not create an electric field inside the cavity. *(For a time on the order of pico seconds, an electric field will penetrate into the metal, but if the metal is a good conductor like silver or copper, the distance will be very short.)*

(What does this problem have to do with the advice to stay in a car during a thunderstorm?)

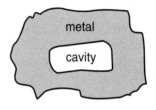

Figure 10
A chunk of metal with a completely enclosed hollow cavity inside is struck by lightning.

Exercise 3

Repeat Exercise 1 assuming that the conducting sphere has a net charge of –Q. Does the charge on the conducting sphere have any effect on the field inside the sphere? Why is there no field outside the sphere?

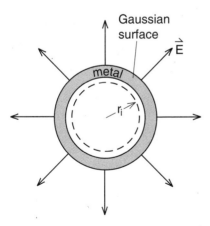

Figure 8
If the Gaussian surface is drawn inside the hollow cavity as shown, then there is no charge inside the Gaussian surface. Thus no field lines emerge through the Gaussian surface, and $\vec{E}$ must be zero inside the cavity.

VAN DE GRAAFF GENERATOR

The Van de Graaff generator is a conceptually straight-forward device designed to produce high voltages. A sketch of the apparatus is shown in Figure (11), where we have a hollow metal sphere with a hole in the bottom, and a conveyer belt whose purpose is to bring charge up into the sphere. The belt is driven by a motor at the bottom.

The first step is to get electric charge onto the belt. This is done electrostatically by having an appropriate material rub against the belt. For example, if you rub a rubber rod with cat fur, you leave a negative charge on the rubber rod. If you rub a glass rod with silk, a positive charge will be left on the glass rod. I do not know what sign of charge is left on a comb when you run it through your hair on a dry day, but enough charge can be left on the comb to pick up small pieces of paper. For our discussion, it is sufficient to visualize that some kind of rubbing of the belt at the bottom near the motor deposits charge on the belt.

Acting like a conveyor belt, the motorized belt carries the charge up and into the inside of the hollow metal sphere. If there is already charge on the sphere, then, as we have seen in Example (1), there will be an electric field outside the sphere as shown in Figure (12). (For this example we are assuming that the belt is carrying positive charge.) But inside the sphere there will be no field. (The hole in the bottom of the sphere lets a small amount of electric field leak inside, but not enough to worry about.)

As the charge is being carried up by the belt, the electric field outside the sphere pushes back on the charge, and the belt has to do work to get the charge up to the sphere. The more charge that has built up on the sphere, the stronger the electric field $\vec{E}$, and the more work the belt has to do. In a typical Van de Graaff generator used in lecture demonstration, you can hear the motor working harder when a large charge has built up on the sphere.

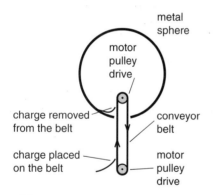

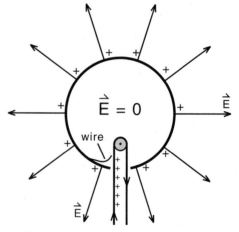

Figure 11
The Van de Graaff generator. Electric charge is carried up the belt and dumped inside the hollow metal sphere. Since there are no electric fields inside the sphere, the electric charge freely flows off the belt to the sphere, where it then spreads evenly to the <u>outside</u> surface of the sphere.

Figure 12
It takes work to carry the charge up to the sphere against the electric field that is pushing down on the charge. But once inside the sphere where there is almost no field, the charge freely moves off the belt, onto the wire, charging up the sphere. The more charge on the sphere, the stronger the electric field $\vec{E}$ outside the sphere, and the more work required to bring new charge up into the sphere. (In the demonstration model, you can hear the motor slow down as the sphere becomes charged up.)

When the charge gets to the sphere how do we get it off the belt onto the sphere? When the sphere already has a lot of positive charge on it, why would the positive charge on the belt want to flow over to the sphere? Shouldn't the positive charge on the belt be repelled by the positive sphere?

Here is where our knowledge of electric fields comes in. As illustrated in Figure (12), there may be very strong electric fields outside the sphere, but inside there are none. Once the conveyor belt gets the charge inside the sphere, the charge is completely free to run off to the sphere. All we need is a small wire that is attached to the inside of the sphere that rubs against the belt. In fact, the neighboring + charge on the belt helps push the charge off the belt onto the wire.

Once the charge is on the wire and flows to the inside of the sphere, it must immediately flow to the outside of the sphere where it helps produce a stronger field $\vec{E}$ shown in Figure (12).

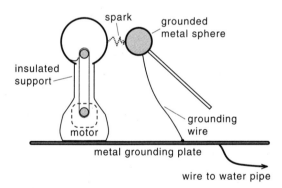

Figure 13
We can discharge the Van de Graaff generator by bringing up a grounded sphere as shown. Since about 100,000 volts are required to make a spark 2.5 cm (one inch) long, we can use the maximum length of sparks to estimate the voltage produced by the Van de Graaff generator.

Electric Discharge

When a large amount of charge has accumulated on the metal sphere of the Van de Graaff generator, we can produce some very strong fields and high voltages. We can estimate the voltage by bringing a grounded sphere up to the Van de Graaff generator as shown in Figure (13). A voltage of about 100,000 volts is required to make a spark jump about an inch (2.5 cm) through air. Thus if we get a spark about 2 inches long between the Van de Graaff generator and the grounded sphere, we have brought enough charge onto the generator sphere to create a voltage of about 200,000 volts. (The length of the sparks acts as a crude voltmeter!)

As an exercise, let us estimate how many coulombs of charge must be on the Van de Graaff generator sphere to bring it up to a voltage of 200,000 volts.

Outside the Van de Graaff generator sphere, the electric field is roughly equal to the electric field of a point charge. Thus the voltage or electric potential of the sphere should be given by Equation (20-8) as

$$V = \frac{Q}{4\pi\varepsilon_0 r} \qquad (20\text{-}8)$$

where r is the radius of the Van de Graaff generator sphere. *(Remember that r is not squared in the formula for potential energy or voltage.)*

Let us assume that r = 10 cm or .1 m, and that the voltage V is up to 200,000 volts. Then Equation (20-8) gives

$$Q = 4\pi\varepsilon_0 r V$$
$$= 4\pi \times 8.85 \times 10^{-12} \times .1 \times 200{,}000$$
$$Q \approx 2 \times 10^{-6} \text{ coulombs}$$

A couple millionths of a coulomb of charge is enough to create 200,000 volt sparks. As we said earlier, a whole coulomb is a huge amount of charge!

Grounding

The grounded sphere in Figure (13) that we used to produce the sparks, provides a good example of the way we use conductors and wires.

Beneath the Van de Graaff generator apparatus we have placed a large sheet of aluminum called a grounding plane that is attached to the metal pipes and the electrical ground in the room. (Whenever we have neglected to use this grounding plane during a demonstration we have regretted it.) We have attached a copper wire from the grounding plane to the "grounded" sphere as shown.

Thus in Figure (13), the grounding plane, the room's metal pipes and electrical ground wires, and the grounded sphere are all attached to each other via a conductor. Since there can be no electric field inside a conductor, all these objects are at the same electric potential or voltage. (If you have a voltage difference between two points, there must be an electric field between these two points to produce the voltage difference.) It is common practice in working with electricity to define the voltage of the water pipes (or a metal rod stuck deeply into the earth) as zero volts or **ground**. (The ground wires in most home wiring are attached to the water pipes.) Any object that is connected by a wire to the water pipes or electrical ground wire is said to be **grounded**. The use of the earth as the definition of the zero of electric voltage is much like using the floor of a room as the definition of the zero of the gravitational potential energy of an object.

In Figure (13), when the grounded sphere is brought up to the Van de Graaff generator and we get a 2 inch long spark, the spark tells us that the Van de Graaff sphere had been raised to a potential of at least 200,000 volts above ground.

Van de Graaff generators are found primarily in two applications. One is in science museums and lecture demonstration to impress visitors and students. The other is in physics research. Compared to modern accelerators, the 200,000 volts or up to 100 million volts that Van de Graaff generators produce, is small. But the voltages are very stable and can be precisely controlled. As a result the Van de Graaff's make excellent tools for studying the fine details of the structure of atomic nuclei.

THE ELECTRON GUN

In Figure (14) we have a rough sketch of a television tube which has an electron gun at one end to create a beam of electrons, deflection plates to move the electron beam, and a phosphor screen at the other end to produce a bright spot where the electrons strike the end of the tube.

Figure (15) illustrates how a picture is drawn on a television screen. The electron beam is swept horizontally across the face of the tube, then the beam is moved down one line and swept horizontally again. An American television picture (the old analog TV) has about 500 horizontal lines in one picture.

As the beam is swept across, the brightness of the spot can be adjusted by changing the intensity of the electron beam. In Figure (15), line 3, the beam starts out bright, is dimmed when it gets to the left side of the letter A, shut off completely when it gets to the black line, then turned on to full brightness to complete the line. In these television sets, one sweep across the tube takes about 60 microseconds. To draw fine details a television set requires that the intensity of the beam can be turned up and down in little more than a tenth of a microsecond.

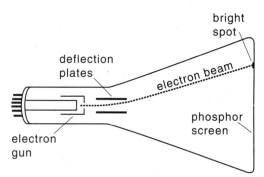

Figure 14
Cathode ray tubes, like the one shown above, were commonly used in television sets, oscilloscopes, and computer monitors. The electron beam (otherwise known as a "cathode ray") is created in the electron gun, is aimed by the deflection plates, and produces a bright spot where it strikes the phosphor screen.

The heart of this system is the electron gun which creates the electron beam. The actual electron gun in a television tube is a complex looking device with indirect heaters and focusing rings all mounted on the basic gun. What we will describe instead is a student-built gun which does not produce the fine beam of a commercial gun, but which was easy to build and easy to understand. (Due to advances in solid state technology, few electronic vacuum tubes are sold, and the parts we used in the student built electron gun are no longer available. But we do have movies of the use of this simple gun.)

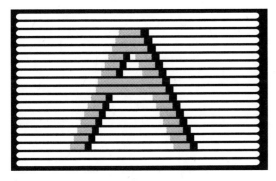

Figure 15
The letter A on a TV screen. To construct an image the electron beam is swept horizontally, and turned up where the picture should be bright and turned down when dark. The entire image consists of a series of these horizontal lines, evenly spaced, one below the other.

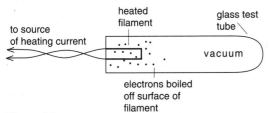

Figure 16
Source of the electrons. The tungsten filament is heated by an electric current. When it becomes red-hot, electrons boil out through the surface. The white coating on the filament makes it easier for the electrons to escape.

The Filament

As shown in Figure (16), the source of the electrons in an electron gun is the **filament**, a piece of wire that has been heated red-hot by the passage of an electric current. At these temperatures, some of the electrons in the filament gain enough thermal kinetic energy to evaporate out through the surface of the wire. The white coating you may see on a filament reduces the amount of energy an electron needs to escape out through the metal surface, and therefore helps produce a more intense beam of electrons.

At standard temperature and pressure, air molecules are about 10 molecular diameters apart as indicated in Figure (17). Therefore if the filament is in air, an electron that has evaporated from the filament can travel, at most, a few hundred molecular diameters before striking an air molecule. This is why the red-hot burner on an electric stove does not emit a beam of electrons. The only way we can get electrons to travel far from the filament is to place the filament in a vacuum as we did in Figure (16). The better the vacuum, the farther the electrons can travel.

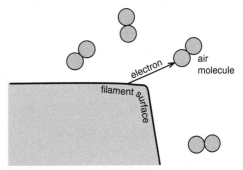

Figure 17
Whenever we heat a metal to a high enough temperature, electrons boil out of the surface. But if the metal is in air at standard pressure, the electrons do not get very far before striking an air molecule.

Accelerating Field

Once the electrons are out of the filament we use an electric field to accelerate them. This is done by placing a metal cap with a hole over the end of the filament as shown in Figure (18). The filament and cap are attached to a battery as shown in Figure (19) so that the cap is positively charged relative to the filament.

Intuitively the gun works as follows. The electrons are repelled by the negatively charged filament and are attracted to the positively charged cap. Most of the electrons rush over, strike, and are absorbed by the cap as shown in Figure (20). But an electron headed for the hole in the cap discovers too late that it has missed the cap and goes on out to form the electron beam.

A picture of the resulting electron beam is seen in Figure (21). The beam is visible because some air remains inside the tube, and the air molecules glow when they are struck by an electron.

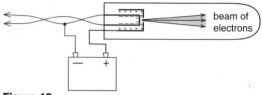

Figure 19
We then attach a battery to the metal cap so that the cap has a positive voltage relative to the filament.

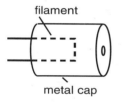

Figure 18
To create a beam of electrons, we start by placing a metal cap with a hole in it, over the filament.

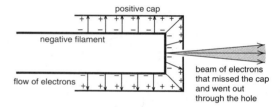

Figure 20
Electrons flow from the negative filament to the positive cap. The beam of electrons is formed by the electrons that miss the cap and go out through the hole.

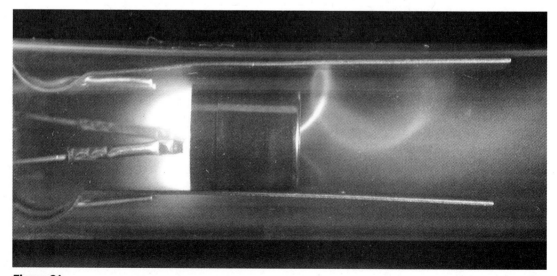

Figure 21
Student built electron gun. Here the blue electron beam is moving through crossed electric and magnetic fields.

A Field Plot

A field plot of the electric field lines inside the electron gun cap gives a more precise picture of what is happening. Figure (22) is a computer plot of the field lines for a cylindrical filament inside a metal cap. We chose a cylindrical filament rather than a bent wire filament because it has the cylindrical symmetry of the cap and is therefore much easier to calculate and draw. But the fields for a wire filament are not too different.

First notice that the field lines are perpendicular to both metal surfaces. There is a good reason for this. If the field had a component parallel to the surface, the field would try to drag electrons along the surface. Since electrons can move in the metal, they would move until their own field cancelled the parallel component. In contrast, the perpendicular component is trying to pull electrons *out* of the metal, which does not happen unless the metal is hot, or the fields are very strong.

The second thing to note is that due to the unfortunate fact that the charge on the electron is negative, the electric field points oppositely to the direction of the force on the electrons. The force is in the direction of $-\vec{E}$.

Equipotential Plot

Once we know the field lines, we can plot the equipotential lines as shown in Figure (22). The lines are labeled assuming that the filament is grounded (0 volts) and that the cap is at 100 volts. The shape of the equipotentials, shown by dashed lines, does not change when we use different accelerating voltages, only the numerical value of the equipotentials changes.

The reason that the equipotential lines are of such interest in Figure (23) is that they can also be viewed as a map of the electron's kinetic energy.

Remember that the voltage V is the potential energy of a unit positive test charge. A charge q has a potential energy qV, and an electron, with a charge $-e$, has an electric potential energy $-eV$.

In our electron gun, the electrons evaporate from the filament with very little kinetic energy, call it zero. By the time the electrons get to the 10 volt equipotential, their electric potential energy has dropped to $(-e \times 10)$ joules, and by conservation of energy, their kinetic energy has gone up to $(+e \times 10)$ joules. At the 50 volt equipotential the electron's kinetic energy has risen to $(e \times 50)$ joules, and when the electrons reach the 100 volt cap, their energy is up to $(e \times 100)$ joules. Thus the equipotential lines in Figure (24) provide a map of the kinetic energy of the electrons.

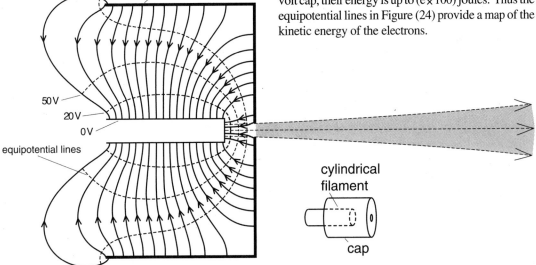

Figure 22
Plot of the electric field in the region between the filament and the cap. Here we assume that we have a cylindrical filament heated by a wire inside.
We see that by the time the electrons have reached the hole in the cap, they have crossed the same equipotential lines and therefore have gained as much kinetic energy as the electrons that strike the cap. (Plot from a student project by Daniel Leslie and Elad Levy.)

ELECTRON VOLT AS A UNIT OF ENERGY

What is perhaps most remarkable about the electron gun is that every electron that leaves the filament and strikes the cap gains precisely the same kinetic energy. If we use a battery that produces 100 volt accelerating voltage, then every electron gains precisely $(e \times 100)$ joules of kinetic energy. This is also true of the electrons that miss the cap and go out and form the electron beam.

The amount of energy gained by an electron that falls through a 1 volt potential is $(e \times 1 \text{ volt}) = 1.6 \times 10^{-19}$ joules. This amount of energy is called an *electron volt* and designated by the symbol *eV*.

$$1eV = \begin{array}{l} \text{energy gained by an electron} \\ \text{falling through a 1 volt potential} \end{array}$$

$$= (e \text{ coulombs}) \times (1 \text{ volt})$$

$$= 1.6 \times 10^{-19} \text{ joules} \qquad (2)$$

The dimensions in Equation (2) make a bit more sense when we realize that the volt has the dimensions of joule/coulomb, so that

$$1eV = (e \text{ coulombs}) \times (1 \frac{\text{joule}}{\text{coulomb}})$$

$$= (e) \text{ joules} \qquad (3)$$

The electron volt is an extremely convenient unit for describing the energy of electrons produced by an electron gun. If we use a 100 volt battery to accelerate the electrons, we get 100 eV electrons. Two hundred volt batteries produce 200 eV electrons, etc.

To solve problems like calculating the speed of a 100 eV electron, you need to convert from eV to joules. The conversion factor is

$$\boxed{1.6 \times 10^{-19} \frac{\text{joules}}{\text{eV}}} \qquad \begin{array}{l}\textit{conversion} \\ \textit{factor}\end{array} \qquad (4)$$

For example, if we have a 100 eV electron, its kinetic energy $1/2 \, mv^2$ is given by

$$KE = 1/2 \, mv^2$$

$$= 100 \text{ eV} \times 1.6 \times 10^{-19} \frac{\text{joules}}{\text{eV}} \qquad (5)$$

Using the value $m = 9.11 \times 10^{-31} \text{ kg}$ for the electron mass in Equation (5) and solving for v gives

$$v = \sqrt{\frac{2 \times 100 \times 1.6 \times 10^{-19}}{9.11 \times 10^{-31}}}$$

$$= 6 \times 10^6 \frac{\text{meters}}{\text{sec}}$$

which is 2% the speed of light.

In studies involving atomic particles such as electrons and protons, the electron volt is both a convenient and very commonly used unit. If the electron volt is too small, we can measure the particle energy in MeV (millions of electron volts) or GeV (billions of electron volts or *Gigavolts*).

$$1 \text{ MeV} \equiv 10^6 \text{ eV}$$

$$1 \text{ GeV} \equiv 10^9 \text{ eV} \qquad (6)$$

For example, if you work the following exercises, you will see that the rest energies m_0c^2 of an electron and a proton have the values

$$\boxed{\begin{array}{l} \text{electron rest energy} = .51 \text{ MeV} \\ \text{proton rest energy} = .93 \text{ GeV} \end{array}} \qquad (7)$$

The reason that it is worth remembering that an electron's rest energy is about .5 MeV and a proton's about 1 GeV, is that when a particle's kinetic energy gets up toward its rest energy, the particle's speed approaches the speed of light, and nonrelativistic formulas like $1/2 \, mv^2$ for kinetic energy no longer apply.

Example: Electron Rest Energy

$$E = \frac{m_0c^2 \text{ joules}}{1.6 \times 10^{-19} \frac{\text{joules}}{\text{eV}}}$$

$$= \frac{9.11 \times 10^{-31} \times \left(3 \times 10^8\right)^2}{1.6 \times 10^{-19}} \text{ eV}$$

$$= .51 \times 10^6 \text{ eV}$$

Exercise 4

Calculate the rest energy of a proton in eV and GeV.

Exercise 5

What accelerating voltage must be used in an electron gun to produce electrons whose kinetic energy equals their rest energy?

THE PARALLEL PLATE CAPACITOR

Our final example in this chapter of fields and conductors is the parallel plate capacitor. Here we will work with a much simpler field structure than for the electron gun, and will therefore be able to calculate field strengths and voltages. The parallel plate capacitor serves as the prototype example of a capacitor, a device used throughout physics and electrical engineering for storing electric fields and electric energy.

Suppose we take two circular metal plates of area A, separate them by a distance d, and attach a battery as shown in Figure (23). This setup is called a parallel plate capacitor, and the field lines and equipotential for this setup are shown in the computer plot of Figure (24).

Except at the edges of the plates, the field lines go straight down from the positive to the negative plate, and the equipotentials are equally spaced horizontal lines parallel to the plates. If the plate separation d is small compared to the diameter D of the plates, then we can neglect the fringing of the field at the edge of the plates. The result is what we will call an ideal parallel plate capacitor whose field structure is shown in Figure (25). The advantage of working with this ideal capacitor is that we can easily derive the relationship between the charging voltage V, and the charge Q.

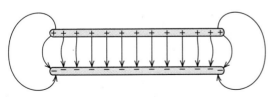

Figure 23
The parallel plate capacitor. The capacitor is charged up by connecting a battery across the plates as shown.

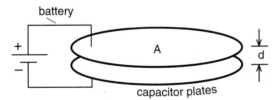

Figure 24
The electric field between and around the edge of the capacitor plates.

Let us take a close look at what we have in Figure (25). The electric field lines $\vec{E}$ leave the positively charged top plate and go straight down to the negatively charged bottom plate. Since all the lines starting at the top plate stop at the bottom one, there must be an equal and opposite charge +Q and −Q on the two plates. There is no net charge on the capacitor, only a separation of charge. And because the field lines go straight down, nowhere do they get closer together or farther apart, the field must have a uniform strength E between the plates. [See Figure (19-21) on page 19-16.]

We can use Gauss' law to quickly calculate the field strength E. The top plate has a charge Q, therefore the total flux out of the top plate must be $\Phi = Q/\varepsilon_0$. But we also have a field of strength E flowing out of a plate of area A. Thus flux of E flowing between the plates is $\Phi = EA$. Equating these two formulas for flux gives

$$\Phi = EA = \frac{Q}{\varepsilon_0}.$$

$$\boxed{E = \frac{Q}{\varepsilon_0 A}} \tag{8}$$

We can relate the voltage V and the field strength E by remembering that *E* is the *force on a unit test charge* and *V* is the *potential energy of a unit test charge*. If I lift a unit positive test charge from the bottom plate a distance d up to the top one, I have to exert an upward force of strength *E* for a distance *d* and therefore do an amount of work *E×d*. This work is stored as the electric potential energy of the unit test charge, and is therefore the voltage *V*

$$\boxed{V = E\,d} \tag{9}$$

plate of area A

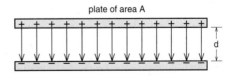

Figure 25
In our idealized parallel plate capacitor the field lines go straight from the positive to the negative plate, and the field is uniform between the plates.

It may seem surprising, but V is also the voltage of the battery (see Figure 23) used to charge up the capacitor.

There is also a simple relationship between the charge Q on the capacitor plates and the voltage difference V between them. Substituting the value of $E = Q/\varepsilon_0 A$ from Equation (8) into Equation (9), $V = Ed$, gives

$$V = \frac{d}{\varepsilon_0 A} Q \qquad (10)$$

Equation (10) makes an interesting prediction. If we have a fixed charge Q on the capacitor (say we charged up the capacitor and removed the battery), then if we increase the separation d between the plates, the voltage V will increase.

One problem with trying to measure this increase in voltage is that if we attach a common voltmeter between the plates to measure V, the capacitor will quickly discharge through the voltmeter. In order to see this effect we must use a special voltmeter called an ***electrometer*** that will not allow the capacitor to discharge. The classic electrometer, used in the 1800s, is the gold leaf electrometer shown in Figures (26) and (27). When the top plate of the electrometer is charged, some of the charge flows to the gold leaves, forcing the leaves apart. The greater the voltage, the greater the charge and the greater the force separating the leaves. Thus the separation of the leaves is a rough measure of the voltage.

In Figure (26), we see a gold leaf electrometer attached to two metal capacitor plates. When the plates are charged, the gold leaves separate, indicating that there is a voltage difference between the plates.

In Figures (27a,b), we are looking through the electrometer at the edge of the capacitor plates. In going from (27a) to (27b), we moved the plates apart without changing the charge on the plates. We see that when the plates are farther apart, the gold leaves are more separated, indicating a greater voltage as predicted by Equation (10).

Figure 26
Gold leaf electrometer attached to a parallel plate capacitor.

Figure 27a
Looking through the electrometer at the edge of the charged capacitor plates.

Figure 27b
Without changing the charge, the plates are moved farther apart. The increased separation of the gold leaves shows that the voltage difference between the capacitor plates has increased.

Exercise 6

Two circular metal plates of radius 10 cm are separated by microscope slide covers of thickness d = .12 mm. A voltage difference of 5 volts is set up between the plates using a battery as shown in Figure (23). What is the charge Q on the plates?

Exercise 7

In what is called the Millikan oil drop experiment, shown in Figure (28), a vapor of oil is sprayed between two capacitor plates and the oil drops are electrically charged by radioactive particles.

Consider a particular oil drop of mass m that has lost one electron and therefore has an electric charge q = + e. (The mass m of the drop was determined by measuring its terminal velocity in free fall in the air. We will not worry about that part of the experiment, and simply assume that the drop's mass m is known.) To measure the charge q on the oil drop, and thus determine the electron charge e, an upward electric field $\vec{E}$ is applied to the oil drop. The strength of the field E is adjusted until the upward electric force just balances the downward gravitational force. When the forces are balanced, the drop, seen through a microscope, will be observed to come to rest due to air resistance.

The electric field $\vec{E}$ that supports the oil drop is produced by a parallel plate capacitor and power supply that can be adjusted to the desired voltage V. The separation between the plates is d.

a)   Reproduce the sketch of Figure (28), Then put a + sign beside the positive battery terminal and a – sign beside the negative one.

b)   Find the formula for the voltage V required to precisely support the oil drop against the gravitational force. Express your answer in terms of the geometry of the capacitor (plate separation d, area A, etc.) the drop's mass m, the acceleration due to gravity g, and the electron charge e.

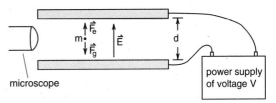

Figure 28
Millikan oil drop apparatus.

CHAPTER 21 REVIEW

This is the chapter where we begin to reap the benefits of the work we have done introducing Gauss' law and developing the electric field mapping techniques. When we come to describe the behavior of electric fields in the presence of conductors, just the name "conductor" tells us what will happen.

In a conductor like a metal, some of the electrons are free to move, to flow like a fluid. If there is an electric field inside a conductor, that means that there is a force on these electrons, and they will move until there is no longer a force. The electrons will redistribute themselves, creating an electric field that cancels the one that was applied. This happens rapidly in the order of nanoseconds, with the simple result that there are no electric fields inside a conductor.

Now Gauss' law comes in. One question is, is there any net charge inside a conductor? The answer is NO! To see why imagine that in some region inside a conductor there is a net charge Q. By Gauss' law, Q/ε_0 lines of electric flux must flow out of this region. But electric flux is represented by streamlines of the electric field $\vec{E}$. If there is no electric field $\vec{E}$ inside the conductor, there is no electric flux, and therefore $Q/\varepsilon_0 = 0$.

That raises the question, suppose you have a conductor and you charge it, say by touching it with a glass rod rubbed by silk. The conductor gains a net charge Q. Where does that charge go? Since no net charge can remain inside the conductor, all the charge you apply must go to the conductor's surface.

*These ideas allow us to explain the operation of three important electrical devices, the Van de Graaff generator, the electron gun, and the parallel plate capacitor. The electron gun allows us to introduce an important and convenient unit of energy called the **electron volt**.*

The Van de Graaff Generator

We start by asking what happens if we add charge to a hollow metal sphere, as shown in Figure (7) reproduced here. First of all, we know that the charge must go to a surface, either as inner or the outer surface or both. Put a Gaussian spherical surface inside the metal where the electric field $\vec{E} = 0$, and we see that no flux comes out through that surface. Thus there can be no charge inside the Gaussian surface and therefore none of the charge we added went to the sphere's inside surface. All the charge must have gone to the outside surface as shown. The important consequence is that there can be no charge or electric fields inside a hollow conducting metal sphere no matter how much charge Q we place on the outside.

The Van de Graaff generator takes advantage of this effect. Charge is brought up on a conveyer belt through a small hole cut in the bottom of a hollow conducting sphere. Once inside the sphere, where there are only negligible fields leaking in through the holes, the charge is free to flow off and add to the charge Q on the outside. This can continue until the charge Q becomes so large, the voltage becomes so high, that the air, acting as an insulator, breaks down and we get a spark discharging the sphere.

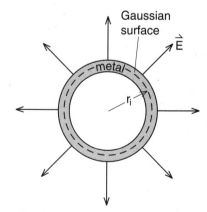

Figure 7
If we place our Gaussian surface inside the metal where $\vec{E} = 0$, no lines come out through the Gaussian surface and therefore there must be no net charge Q inside the Gaussian surface. The fact that there is no charge within that surface means all the charge we placed on the sphere spreads to the outside surface.

The Electron Gun

The electron gun gets us into the subject of 20th century electronics. (The student-built electron gun, which was a lot of fun to operate, was built from vacuum tube technology parts that are no longer available. Those labs are a victim of the transistor and late 20th century technology.)

The main advantage of discussing the electron gun is that we can easily get at electrons, create beams of them, and control these beams with electric and magnetic fields. Not everything is just theory and Gauss' law.

The electron gun begins with a filament heated red hot so that it will boil off electrons. The red-hot burner on an electric stove also boils off electrons in a similar way. The reason we do not see beams of electrons coming from the strobe is that the stove's electrons quickly hit air molecules while the electron gun filament is in an evacuated tube. You have to get the air pressure in the tube down to the region of 1 to 10 microns before you can see good beams.

To accelerate the electrons that boil off the filament, we place a metal cap over the filament, and charge the cap up to about 100 volts relative to the filament.

(We use an electronic battery called a power supply.) The negative electrons leave the filament and are attracted to the positively charged cap.

Figure (22) is a student generated sketch of the electric field inside the metal cap. The field lines start at the positive charge inside the cap and end on the negatively charged filament. Because of Ben Franklin's convention, the field lines point in a direction opposite to the force on the negative electrons.

As we saw in the previous chapter, once you have a plot of electric field lines, you can immediately draw a perpendicular set of lines representing constant electric potential or constant voltage. These are the lines you mapped in the experiment with two brass cylinders and a tray of water. In Figure (22), the dotted lines represent our sketch of the constant voltage lines perpendicular to the electric field lines.

[Project Suggestion: In the tray of water place conductors that have the shape of the filament and cap. Then use a voltmeter to map the equipotential, constant voltage lines. Finally draw a perpendicular set of electric field lines and see how close you come to Figure (22).]

In Figure (22) we have assumed that the filament is at 0 volts, and using a power supply made the cap at a voltage of +100 volts. The filament and the cap represent two of the constant voltage lines. The others are at 20 volts, 50 volts and 80 volts. We now want to ask, what happens to the electrons as they cross these constant voltage lines?

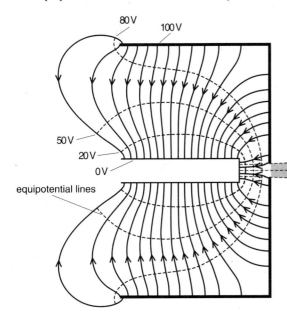

Figure 22
Plot of the electric field in the region between the filament and the cap. We see that by the time the electrons have reached the hole in the cap, they have crossed the same equipotential lines and therefore have gained as much kinetic energy as the electrons that strike the cap.

The Electron Volt

Remember that voltage is the electric potential energy of a unit, one coulomb, charge. If we moved one coulomb of charge from a voltage of zero volts up to a voltage of 100 volts, the charge would gain 100 joules of potential energy. If the coulomb of charge were negative, it would loose 100 joules of potential energy. If the negative charge were allowed to fall freely, the electric potential energy lost would become kinetic energy.

The electrons in the gun are negative, thus they lose electric potential energy, but gain kinetic energy, as they approach the cap. Since an electron's charge is only 1.60×10^{-19} coulombs, one electron gains only 1.60×10^{-19} as much kinetic energy as a whole coulomb would gain.

We define an electron volt (eV) as the kinetic energy gained by an electron as it falls through a voltage of 1 volt. Since a coulomb falling through a volt gains a joule of energy, an electron gains only 1.60×10^{-19} joules. Thus the electron volt is

$$1 \; electron \; volt \; (eV) \; = \; 1.60 \times 10^{-19} joules$$

and the conversion factor from joules to eV is

$$\boxed{1.60 \times 10^{-19} \frac{joules}{eV}} \qquad (4)$$

The electrons in Figure (22), which fall across a 100 volt gap, gain 100 eV of kinetic energy. See how convenient a unit of energy an electron volt is! Apply 100 volts to the electron gun, and the electrons have 100 eV of kinetic energy when they reach the cap.

What is interesting is that from our plot of the constant voltage lines in the electron gun, we can tell how the electrons are gaining kinetic energy as they move from the filament to the cap. When an electron crosses the 20 volt line, it has gained 20 eV of kinetic energy. At the 50 volt line, it has 50 eV of kinetic energy, etc.

If all the electrons hit the cap, we would not get much of an electron beam. But the electrons headed for the hole in the cap find out, too late, that there is no cap there and go rushing out—forming the electron beam. Because there are no more constant voltage lines outside the cap, all the electrons emerging from the cap keep their 100 eV of kinetic energy. If we use a 100 volt accelerating voltage, we get a beam of 100 eV electrons.

The important exercises for this chapter are to get used to the electron volt as a unit of energy. We would like to know how fast a 100 eV electron is moving. If the eV is a unit of energy, we can ask what the electron's rest mass energy $m_e c^2$ is expressed in eV, and so on. These exercises are important because in atomic physics the electron volt is the most common and convenient unit of energy.

The Parallel Plate Capacitor

*A capacitor is an electronic device often used to store electric charge. The **parallel plate capacitor** is conceptually the simplest design for a capacitor.*

In Chapter 17, page 17-12 we worked an exercise in which we calculated the repulsive force between two, one coulomb, charges one meter apart. The force was 10^{10} newtons, not an easy force to control. Earlier we pointed out another problem with storing charge. As we saw when we touch a foil ball with a charged rod, charge can easily move around, or leak off the rod. However, electric charge is easily stored in a capacitor.

In a capacitor we do not have a net charge, just a separation of charge. In the parallel plate capacitor one plate has a positive charge while the other plate has the opposite amount of negative charge. All the electric field lines run from the positive plate down to the negative plate. No lines go wandering off to infinity.

In the ideal parallel plate capacitor we assume that all the electric field lines go straight down from the positive upper plate to the negative lower plate. This neglects the curvature of the lines at the edge of the plate, a reasonable approximation if the separation d between the plates is small.

The simplest geometry of the parallel plate capacitor allows us to relate the voltage V we apply to the capacitor and the amount of charge Q we store in the capacitor.

By Gauss' law, the upper plate with a charge Q creates an amount of electric flux Q/ε_0. The electric flux flowing down from the upper plate is equal to the strength E of the electric field times the area A of the plate. Equating this flux EA to that created by the upper plate gives

$$flux = EA = Q/\varepsilon_0 \qquad (8)$$

which gives $E = Q/\varepsilon_0 A$

Then we noted that the voltage between the plates was

$$V = E\,d$$

Remember that voltage is the potential energy of a unit charge, and E is the force on a unit charge. Thus a force E times a distance d is potential energy V, all for a unit charge.

Combining Equations (8) and (9), we got

$$V = \frac{d}{\varepsilon_0 A}Q \qquad (10)$$

We then did some experiments to show that if you kept the charge Q constant and increased the separation d between the plates, the voltage V actually increased.

The best review of this discussion of parallel plate capacitors is to start with an empty desk and a clean sheet of paper and derive Equation (10).

plate of area A

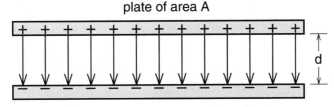

Figure 25
In our idealized parallel plate capacitor the field lines go straight from the positive to the negative plate, and the field is uniform between the plates.

CHAPTER EXERCISES

Exercise 1 On page 5
Calculate the electric field of a positive charge surrounded by an uncharged metal sphere.

Exercise 2 On page 5
Lightning strikes a metal object surrounding a cavity. Show that no electric field is created inside the cavity.

Exercise 3 On page 5
Calculate the electric field of a positive charge surrounded by a metal sphere with the opposite charge.

Exercise 4 On page 12
Calculate the rest energy of a proton in eV and GeV.

Exercise 5 On page 12
What accelerating voltage must be used in an electron gun to produce electrons whose kinetic energy equals their rest energy?

Exercise 6 On page 15
Calculate the charge on a parallel plate capacitor.

Exercise 7 On page 15
Analysis of the Milikan oil drop experiment.

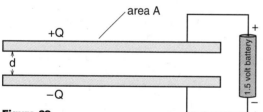

Figure 29
A parallel plate capacitor charged by a 1.5 volt battery. (Figure for Exercise 11.)

REVIEW EXERCISES

Exercise 8
What is your rest mass in electron volts?

Exercise 9
An electron gun produces electrons that are traveling at 1/10th the speed of light. What accelerating voltage was used? (Non relativistic formulas are OK at this speed.)

Exercise 10
See if you can derive, without looking back, the formula

$$V = \frac{d}{e_0 A} Q \tag{10}$$

for the voltage V on a parallel plate capacitor whose plates have an area A and separation d when the plates have charges +Q and -Q. Start with a sketch showing the field lines, then calculate the flux out of the positive plate, and then the voltage produced by the resulting electric field.

Exercise 11
From Equation (10), you can see that as you increase the charge Q on the capacitor, you get a proportional increase in the voltage V. Suppose that you want to build a parallel plate capacitor that stores one coulomb of charge Q for every volt V applied to the capacitor. (For example, attaching a 1.5 volt battery as shown in Figure (29), your capacitor would store 1.5 coulombs of positive charge on the positive plate and - 1.5 coulombs on the negative plate.

(a) If the separation of the plates were d = 1 millimeter, what would the area A of the plates have to be?

(b) If the separation were 10^{-7} meters, which is the value for some capacitors, what would the plate area A have to be?

Exercise 12
Two circular metal plates of radius 10 cm are separated by microscope slide covers of thickness d = . 12 mm. A voltage difference of 5 volts is set up between the plates using a battery as shown in Figure (25). What is the charge Q on the plates?

Chapter 22 non calculus

Current and Electric Circuits

*In the modern age (post 1870) we have been sur-
rounded by electric circuits. House wiring is our most
familiar example, but we have become increasingly
familiar with electric circuits in radio and television
sets, and even the digital watch you may be wearing. In
this chapter we will discuss the basic electric circuits in
order to introduce the concepts of electric current,
resistance, and voltage drops around the circuit. We
will restrict ourselves to devices like batteries, resistors, light bulbs, and capacitors. The main purpose is
to develop the background needed to work with electric
circuits and electronic measuring equipment in the
laboratory.*

ELECTRIC CURRENT

An electric current in a wire is conceptually somewhat like the current of water in a river. We can define the current in a river as the amount of water per second flowing under a bridge. The amount of water could be defined as the number of water molecules, but a more convenient unit would be gallons, liters, or cubic meters.

An electric current in a wire is usually associated with the flow of electrons and is measured as the amount of charge per second flowing past some point or through some cross-sectional area of the wire, as illustrated in Figure (1). We could measure the amount of charge by counting the number of electrons crossing the area, but it is more convenient to use our standard unit of charge, the coulomb, and define an electric current as the number of coulombs per second passing the cross-sectional area. The unit of current defined this way is called an ***ampere***.

$$1 \text{ ampere } = \begin{array}{l} 1 \text{ coulomb per} \\ \text{second passing} \\ \text{a cross–sectional} \\ \text{area of wire} \end{array} \qquad (1)$$

From your experience with household wiring you should already be familiar with the ampere (amp) as a unit of current. A typical light bulb draws between 1/2 and 1 ampere of current, and so does the typical motor in an electric appliance (drill, eggbeater, etc.). A microwave oven and a toaster may draw up to 6 amps, and hair dryers and electric heaters up to 12 amps. Household wiring is limited in its capability of carrying electric current. If you try to carry too much current in a wire, the wire gets hot and poses a fire hazard.

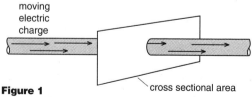

moving
electric
charge

cross sectional area

Figure 1
An electric current is defined as the amount of __charge per second__ flowing past a cross-sectional area.

Household wiring is protected by fuses or circuit breakers that shut off the current if it exceeds 15 or 20 amps. (You can see why you do not want to run a hair dryer and an electric heater on the same circuit.)

There is a common misconception that the electrons in a wire travel very fast when a current is flowing in the wire. After all when you turn on a wall light switch the light on the other side of the room appears to turn on instantly. How did the electrons get there so fast?

The answer can be seen by an analogy to a garden hose. When you first attach an empty hose to a spigot and turn on the water, it takes a while before the hose fills up with water and water comes out of the other end. But when the hose is already full and you turn on the spigot, water almost instantly comes out of the other end. Not the water that just went in, but the water that was already in the hose.

A copper wire is analogous to the hose that is already full of water; the electrons are already there. When you turn on the light switch, the light comes on almost instantly because all the "electric fluid" in the wire starts moving almost at once.

To help build an intuition, let us estimate how fast the electrons must move in a copper wire with a 1 millimeter cross-sectional area carrying an electric current of one ampere. This is not an unreasonable situation for household wiring.

A copper atom has a nucleus containing 29 protons surrounded by a cloud of 29 electrons. Of the 29 electrons, 27 are tightly bound to the nucleus and 2 are in an outer shell, loosely bound. (All metal atoms have one, two, and sometimes 3 loosely bound outer electrons.) When copper atoms are collected together to form a copper crystal, the 27 tightly bound electrons remain with their respective nuclei, but the two loosely bound electrons are free to wander throughout the crystal. In a metal crystal or wire, it is the loosely bound electrons (called ***conduction electrons***) that form the electric fluid that makes the wire a conductor.

Copper has an atomic weight of 63.5, thus there are 63.5 grams of copper in a mole. And the density of copper is 9 gm /cm³, thus a mole of copper has a volume

$$\begin{matrix} \text{volume of one} \\ \text{mole of copper} \end{matrix} \Bigg\} = \frac{63.5 \text{gm} / \text{mole}}{9 \text{gm} / \text{cm}^3} = 7 \frac{\text{cm}^3}{\text{mole}}$$

Since a mole of a substance contains an Avogadro's number 6×10^{23} of particles of that substance, and since there are 2 conduction electrons per copper atom, 7 cm³ of copper contain 12×10^{23} conduction electrons. Dividing by 7, we see that there are 1.7×10^{23} conduction electrons in every cubic centimeter of copper and 1.7×10^{20} in a cubic millimeter. Converting this to coulombs, we get

$$\begin{matrix} \text{number of} \\ \text{coulombs of} \\ \text{conduction} \\ \text{electrons} \\ \text{in 1 mm}^3 \\ \text{of copper} \end{matrix} \Bigg\} = \frac{1.7 \times 10^{20} \text{electrons/mm}^3}{6.25 \times 10^{18} \text{electrons/coulomb}}$$

$$= 27 \text{coulombs/mm}^3$$

In our 1 millimeter cross-sectional area wire, if the electrons flowed at a speed of 1 millimeter per second, 27 coulombs of charge would flow past any point in the wire per second, and we would have a current of 27 amperes. To have a current of 1 ampere, the electrons would have to move only 1/27 as fast, *or 1/27 of a millimeter per second!* This slow speed results from the huge density of conduction electrons.

Positive and Negative Currents

If you are using a hose to fill a bucket with water, there is not much question about which way the current of water is flowing—from the hose to the bucket. But with electric current, because there are two kinds of electric charge, the situation is not that simple. As shown in Figure (2), there are two ways to give an object a positive charge; add positive charge or remove negative charge. If a wire connected to the object is doing the charging, it may be difficult to tell whether there is a current of positive charge into the object or a current of negative charge out of the object. Both have essentially the same effect.

You may argue that at least for copper wires a current of positive charge doesn't make sense because the electric current is being carried by the negative conduction electrons. But a simple model of an electric current will clearly demonstrate that a positive current flowing one way is essentially equivalent to a negative current flowing the other way.

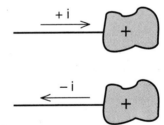

Figure 2
A current of positive charge into an object, or a current of negative charge out, leaves the object positively charged.

In Figure (3) we have tried to sketch a picture of a copper wire in which the conduction electrons are moving to the left producing a left directed negative current. The problem with Figure (3) is that it is hard to show the conduction electrons flowing through the lattice of stationary positive copper nuclei. The picture is difficult to draw, and Figure (3) is not particularly informative.

To more clearly show that the positive charge is at rest and that it is the negative charge that is moving, we have in Figure (4) constructed a model of a copper wire in which we have two separate rods, one moving and one at rest. The stationary rod has the positive copper nuclei and the moving rod has the negative conduction electrons. This model is not a very good representation of what is going on inside the copper wire, but it does remind us clearly that the positive charge is at rest, and that the current is being carried by the moving negative charge.

When you see this model, which we will use again in later discussions, think of the two rods as merged together. Picture the minus charge as flowing through the lattice of positive charge. Remember that the only reason that we drew them as separate rods was to clearly show which charge was carrying the electric current.

Using the results of the previous section, we can make our model of Figure (4) more specific by assuming it represents a copper wire with a 1 millimeter cross section carrying a current of one ampere. In that example the average speed of the conduction electrons was 1/27 of a millimeter per second, which we will take as the speed v of the moving negative rod in Figure (4).

Figure (5a) is the same as Figure (4), except we have drawn a stick figure representing a person walking to the left at a speed v. The person and the negatively charged rod are both moving to the left at the same speed.

Figure (5b) is the same situation from the point of view of the stick figure person. From her point of view, the negative rod is at rest and it is the positive rod that is moving to the right. *Our left directed negative current in Figure (5a) is seen by the moving observer to be a right directed positive current Figure (5b).* Whether we have a left directed negative current or a right directed positive current just depends upon the point of view of the observer.

But how fast was our moving observer walking? If Figure (5) is a model of a 1 mm^2 copper wire carrying a current of 1 ampere, *the speed v in Figure (5) is 1/27 of a millimeter per second.* This is about 2 millimeters per minute! Although faster than the continental drift, this motion should certainly have little effect on what we see. If the wire is leading to a toaster, the toast will come out the same whether or not we walk by at a speed of 2 mm per minute. For most purposes, we can take a left directed negative current and a right directed positive current as being equivalent. Relatively sophisticated experiments, such as those using the Hall effect (to be discussed later) are required to tell the difference.

positive copper   moving conduction
ions at rest   electrons

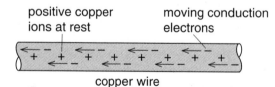

copper wire

Figure 3
A copper wire at rest with the conduction electrons moving to the left. This gives us a left-directed negative current.

positively charged
rod at rest

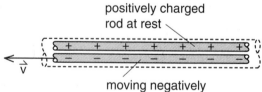

moving negatively
charged rod

Figure 4
Model of a copper wire carrying an electric current. We are representing the positive copper ions by a positively charged rod at rest, and the conduction electrons by a moving, negatively charged rod.

A Convention

It was Ben Franklin who made the assignment of positive and negative charge. The charge left on a glass rod rubbed by silk was defined as positive, and that left on a rubber rod rubbed by cat fur as negative. This has often been considered a tragic mistake, for it leaves the electron, the common carrier of electric current, with a negative charge. It also leads to the unfortunate intuitive picture that an atom that has lost some electrons ends up with a positive charge.

Some physics textbooks written in the 1930s redefined the electron as being positive, but this was a disaster. We cannot undo over two centuries of convention that leads to the electron as being negative.

The worst problem with Franklin's convention comes when we try to handle the minus signs in problems involving the flow of electrons in a wire. But we have just seen that the flow of electrons in one direction is almost completely equivalent to the flow of positive charge in the other. If we do our calculations for positive currents, then we know that the electrons are simply moving in the opposite direction.

In order to maintain sanity and not get tangled up with minus signs, in this text we will, whenever possible, talk about the flow of positive currents, and talk about the force on positive test charges. If the problem we are working on involves electrons, we will work everything assuming positive charges and positive currents, and only at the end of the problem we will take into account the negative sign of the electron. With some practice, you will find this an easy convention to use.

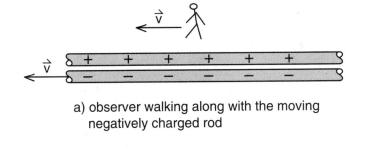

a) observer walking along with the moving
   negatively charged rod

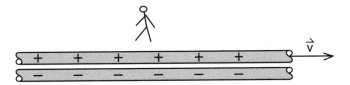

b) from the observer's point of view the negative
   rod is at rest and the positive charge is moving
   to the right

Figure 5 a, b
In (a) we have a left directed negative current, while in (b) we have a right directed positive current. The only difference is the perspective of the observer. (You can turn a negative current into an oppositely flowing positive one simply by moving your head.)

CURRENT AND VOLTAGE

Students first studying electricity can have difficulty conceptually distinguishing between the concepts of current and voltage. This problem can be handled by referring back to our hydrodynamic analogy of Chapter 18.

In Chapter 18 we were discussing Bernoulli's equation which stated that the quantity $(P + \rho gh + 1/2\, \rho v^2)$ was constant along a streamline if we could neglect viscous effects in the fluid. Because of the special nature of this collection of terms, we gave them the name *hydrodynamic voltage*.

$$\left.\begin{array}{c}\text{hydrodynamic}\\\text{voltage}\end{array}\right\} = P + \rho gh + \frac{1}{2}\rho v^2 \quad (18\text{-}23)$$

(The second and third terms in the hydrodynamic voltage are the potential energy of a unit volume of fluid and the kinetic energy. The pressure term, while not a potential energy, is related to the work required to move fluid into a higher pressure region.)

Many features of hydrodynamic voltage should already be familiar. If you live in a house with good water pressure, when you turn on the faucet the water comes out rapidly. But if someone is running the washing machine in the basement or watering the garden, the water pressure may be low, and the water just dribbles out of the faucet. We will think of the high pressure water as *high voltage* water, and the low pressure water as *low voltage* water.

Let us look more carefully at high voltage water in a faucet. When the faucet is shut off, the water is at rest but the pressure is high, and the main contribution to the hydrodynamic voltage is the P term. When the faucet is on, the water that has just left the faucet has dropped back to atmospheric pressure but it is moving rapidly. Now it is the $1/2\, \rho v^2$ that contributes most to the hydrodynamic voltage. If the water originally comes from a town water tank, when the water was at the top of the tank it was at atmospheric pressure and not moving, but was at a great height h. In the town water tank the hydrodynamic voltage comes mainly from the ρgh term.

Let us focus our attention on the high pressure in a faucet that is shut off. In this case we have high voltage water but no current. We can get a big current if we turn the faucet on, but the voltage is there whether or not we have a current.

In household wiring, the electrical outlets may be thought of as faucets for the electrical fluid in the wires. The high voltage in these wires is like the high pressure in the water pipes. You can have a high voltage at the outlet without drawing any current, or you can connect an appliance and draw a current of this high pressure electrical fluid.

Resistors

In an electric heater the electrical energy supplied by the power station is converted into heat energy by having electric current flow through a dissipative or resistive material. The actual process by which electrical energy is turned into heat energy is fairly complex but not unlike the conversion of mechanical energy to heat through friction. One can think of resistance as an internal friction encountered by the electric current.

In our discussion of Bernoulli's equation we saw that the hydrodynamic voltage $P + \rho gh + 1/2\, \rho v^2$ was constant along a streamline if there were no viscous effects. But we also saw in Figure (18-24) that when there were viscous effects this hydrodynamic voltage dropped as we went along a streamline.

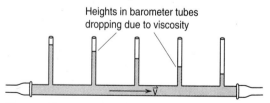

Heights in barometer tubes dropping due to viscosity

Figure 18-24
Hydrodynamic voltage drop due to viscous effects.

In fluid flows, we get the most dissipation where the fluid is moving rapidly through a narrow constriction. This is seen in our Venturi demonstration of Figure (18-18), reproduced here in Figure (6). Here we have a large tube with a constriction. The glass barometer tubes show us that the pressure remains relatively constant before the constriction, but does not return to its original value afterward. There is a net pressure drop of ρgh, where h is the height drop indicated in the figure.

Consider the points in the fluid at the dots labeled (2) and (9), in the center of the stream below tubes 2 and 9. These points are at the same heights ($h_2 = h_9$), and the fluid velocities are the same ($v_2 = v_9$) because the flow tube has returned to its original size. Because of the pressure drop ($P_9 < P_2$), the hydrodynamic voltage ($P_9 + \rho gh_9 + 1/2\ \rho v_9^2$) at point (9) is less than that at point (2) by an amount equal to $P_2 - P_9 = \rho gh$. The barometer tubes 2 and 9 are acting as *hydrodynamic voltmeters* showing us where the voltage drop occurs.

Just as in fluid flows, dissipation in electric currents are associated with voltage drops, in this case electrical voltage drops. In general, the amount of the voltage drop depends on the amount of current, the geometry of the flow path, on the material through which the current is flowing, and on the temperature of the material. But in a special device called a *resistor*, the voltage drop ΔV depends primarily on the current i through the resistor

and is proportional to that current. *When the voltage drop ΔV is proportional to the current i, the resistor is said to obey Ohm's law.* This can be written as the equation

$$\boxed{\Delta V = iR} \qquad \textit{Ohm's law} \qquad (2)$$

The proportionality constant R is called the *resistance R* of the resistor. From Equation (2) you can see that R has the dimensions volt/amp. This unit is called an *ohm*, a name which is convenient in practice but which further complicates the problem of following dimensions in electrical calculations.

$$R = \frac{\Delta V}{i} \frac{\text{volts}}{\text{amps}} = \frac{\Delta V}{i} \text{ohms}$$

Resistors are the most common element in electronic circuits. They usually consist of a small cylinder with wire pigtails sticking out each end as shown in Figure (7). The material inside the cylinder which creates the voltage drop, which turns electrical energy into heat energy, is usually carbon.

The resistors you find in an electronics shop come in a huge selection of values, with resistances ranging from about 0.1 ohm up to around 10^9 ohms in a standard series of steps. The physical size of the resistor depends not on the value of the resistance but on the amount of electrical energy the resistor is capable of dissipating without burning up. The value of the resistance is usually indicated by colored stripes painted on the resistor, there being a standard color code so that you can read the value from the stripes.

(A light bulb is a good example of an electrical device that dissipates energy, in this case mostly in the form of heat and some light. The only problem with a light bulb is that as the filament gets hot, its resistance increases. If we wish to use Ohm's law, we have to add the qualification that the bulb's resistance R increases with temperature.)

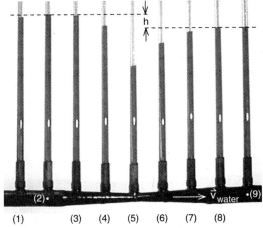

Figure 6
The hydrodynamic voltage, as measured by the barometer tubes, drops by an amount ρgh in going across the constriction from Point (2) to Point (9).

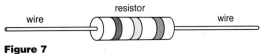

Figure 7
The resistor, which is found in most electronic circuits. The purpose of the resistor is to cause an electric voltage drop analogous to the hydrodynamic voltage drop we saw in Figure (6) across the restriction in the flow tube.

A Simple Circuit

To get some intuition for how resistors are used, consider the circuit shown in Figure (8) containing a battery and a resistor connected by wires. In drawing circuits, it is convention to use a line _____ for a wire, the symbol —WWW— for a resistor, and —+|⊢— for a battery. In the symbol for a battery, the short perpendicular line represents the negative terminal of the battery and the long side the positive terminal. When we have a current i flowing through the wire we draw an arrow indicating the direction of flow of positive charge —i—> and label the current with a letter such as i, i_1, etc.

In Figure (9), we have labeled the voltages V_1, V_2, V_3 and V_4 at four points around the circuit. By definition we will take the negative side of the battery as being zero volts, or what we call **_ground_**

$$V_4 = 0 \text{ volts} \qquad \textit{by definition}$$

On the positive side of the battery, the voltage is up to the battery voltage V_b which is 1.5 volts for a common flashlight battery and up to 9 volts for many transistor radio batteries

$$V_1 = V_b \qquad \textit{the battery voltage} \qquad (3)$$

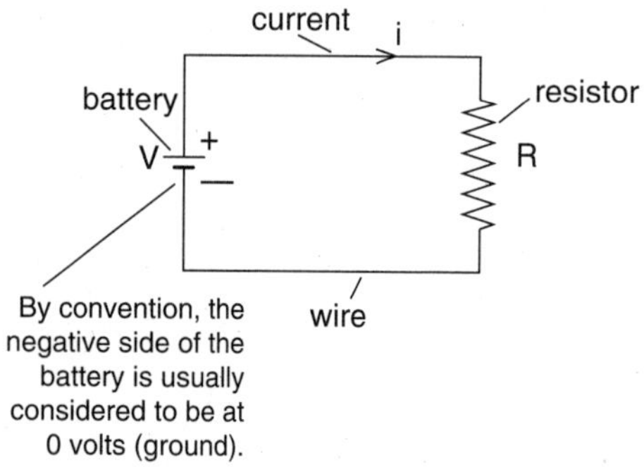

Point (2) at the upper end of the resistor, is connected to the positive terminal of the battery, Point (1), by a wire. In our circuit diagrams we always assume that our wires are good conductors, having no electric fields inside them and therefore no voltage drops along them. Thus

$$V_2 = V_1 \ (= V_b) \qquad \begin{array}{l}\textit{no voltage drop} \\ \textit{along a wire}\end{array} \qquad (4)$$

The bottom of the resistor is connected to the negative terminal of the battery by a wire, therefore

$$V_3 = V_4 \ (= 0) \qquad \begin{array}{l}\textit{no voltage drop} \\ \textit{along a wire}\end{array} \qquad (5)$$

Equations (4) and (5) determine the voltage drop ΔV that must be occurring at the resistor

$$\Delta V = V_2 - V_3 = V_b \qquad (6)$$

And by Ohm's law, Equation (1), this voltage drop is related to the current i through the resistor by

$$\Delta V = iR = V_b \qquad \textit{Ohm's law} \qquad (7)$$

Solving for the current i in the circuit gives

$$\boxed{i = \frac{V_b}{R}} \qquad (8)$$

In future discussions of circuits we will not write out all the steps as we have in Equations (3) through (8), but the first time through a circuit we wanted to show all the details.

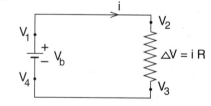

Figure 9
Voltages around the circuit.

current i

battery
V +
–

resistor
R

By convention, the
negative side of the
battery is usually
considered to be at
0 volts (ground).

wire

Figure 8
About the simplest electrical circuit consists of a battery connected to a resistor. If the resistor were a light bulb, you would have a flashlight.

Equation (8) is the one that really shows us how resistors are used in a circuit. We can see from Equation (8) that if we use a small resistor, we get a big current, and if we use a large resistor we get a small current. *In most applications resistors are used to control the flow of current.*

In modern electronics such as radios and computers, typical battery voltages are around 2 volts and typical currents a milliampere (10^{-3} amps). What size resistor R do we have to use in Equation (8) so that we get a one milliampere current from a 2 volt battery? The answer is

$$R = \frac{V_b}{i} = \frac{2 \text{ volts}}{10^{-3} \text{ amps}} \qquad (9)$$
$$= 2000 \text{ ohms} \equiv 2000 \; \Omega$$

where we used the standard symbol Ω for ohms. Many of the resistors in electronics circuits have values like this in the 1,000 Ω to 10,000 Ω range.

The Short Circuit

Equation (8) raises an interesting problem. What if R = 0 ? The equation predicts an infinite current! We could try to make R = 0 by attaching a wire rather than a resistor from Points (2) to (3) in Figure (9). What would happen is that a very large current would start to flow and either melt the wire, start a fire, drain the battery, or destroy the power supply. (A power supply is an electronic battery.) When this happens, you have created what is called a *short circuit*. The common lingo is that you have *shorted* out the battery or power supply and this is not a good thing to do.

Power

As one of the roles of a resistor is electrical power dissipation, let us determine the power that is being dissipated when a current is flowing through a resistor. Recall that power is the amount of energy transferred or dissipated per unit time. In the MKS system, power has the dimensions of joules per second which is called a *watt*

$$\text{Power} = \frac{\text{joules}}{\text{second}} = \text{watt} \qquad (10)$$

Now suppose we have a current flowing through a resistor R as shown in Figure (10). The voltage drop across the resistor is V, from a voltage of V volts at the top to 0 volts at the bottom as shown.

Because V is the electric potential energy of a unit charge (the coulomb), every coulomb of charge flowing through the resistor loses V joules of electric potential energy which is changed to heat.

If we have a current i, then i coulombs flow through the resistor every second. Thus the energy lost per second is the number of coulombs (i) times the energy lost per coulomb (V) or (iV):

$$\text{Power} = i\frac{\text{coul}}{\text{sec}} \times V\frac{\text{joules}}{\text{coul}}$$
$$= iV\frac{\text{joules}}{\text{sec}} = iV \text{ watts} \qquad (11)$$

Ohm's law, Equation (1), can be used to express the power in terms of R and either i or V

$$\text{Power} = iV = i^2R = \frac{V^2}{R} \qquad (11a)$$

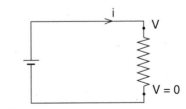

Figure 10
The voltage drops from V to 0 as the current i flows through the resistor. The power dissipated is the current i coulombs/second times the voltage drop V joules/coulomb, which is iV joules/second, or watts.

Exercise 1

These are some simple exercises to have you become familiar with the concepts of volts and amps.

a) Design a circuit consisting of a 9 volt battery and a resistor, where the current through the resistor is 25 milliamperes (25×10^{-3} amps).

b) A flashlight consists of a 1.5 volt battery and a 1 watt light bulb. How much current flows through the bulb when the flashlight is on?

c) When you plug a 1000 watt heater into a 120 volt power line, how much current goes through the heater? What is the resistance R of the heater when the filament is hot?

d) In most households, each circuit has a voltage of 120 volts and is fused for 20 amps. (The circuit breaker opens up if the current exceeds 20 amps). What is the maximum power you can draw from one circuit in your house?

e) An electric dryer requires 3000 watts of power, yet it has to be plugged into wires that can handle only 20 amps. What is the least voltage you can have on the circuit?

f) In many parts of the world, the standard voltage is 240 volts. The wires to appliances are much thinner. Explain why.

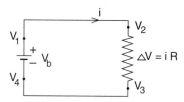

Figure 9 (redrawn)
Voltages around the circuit.

KIRCHOFF'S LAW

Imagine that you are going for an afternoon hike on a nearby mountain. You drive up to the base lodge, park your car, and start up the trail. The trail goes up over a ridge, down into a ravine, up to the peak of the mountain, down the other side and then around the mountain back to the base lodge. When you get back to your car, how much gravitational potential energy have you gained from the trip? The answer is clearly zero—you are right back where you started.

If you defined **gh**, which is the potential energy of a unit mass, as your gravitational voltage, then as you went up the ridge, there was a voltage rise as h increased. Going down into the ravine there was a voltage drop, or what we could call a negative voltage rise. The big voltage rise is up to the top of the mountain, and the big negative voltage rise is down the back side of the mountain. When you add up all the voltage rises for the complete trip, counting voltage drops as negative rises, the sum is zero.

Consider our Figure (9) redrawn here. If we start at Point (4) where the voltage is zero, and "walk" around the circuit in the direction of the positive current i, we first encounter a voltage rise up to $V = V_b$ due to the battery, then a voltage drop back to zero at the resistor. When we get back to the starting point, the sum of the voltage rises is zero just as in our trip through the mountains. Even in more complicated circuits with many branches and different circuit elements, it is usually true that the sum of the voltage rises around any complete path, back to your starting point, is zero. It turns out that this is a powerful tool for analyzing electric circuits, and is known as **Kirchoff's law**. (Kirchoff's law can be violated, we can get a net voltage rise in a complete circuit, if changing magnetic fields are present. We treat this phenomenon in the Satellite Chapter (11) on Faraday's law. Here we will discuss the usual situation where Kirchoff's law applies.)

Application of Kirchoff's Law

There are some relatively standard, cookbook like procedures that make it easy to apply Kirchoff's law to the analysis of circuits. The steps in the recipe are as follows:

(1) Sketch the circuit and use arrows to show the direction of the positive current in each loop as we did in Figure (11). Do not be too concerned about getting the correct direction for the current i. If you have the

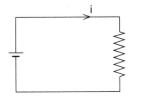

Figure 11
Labeling the direction of the current.

arrow pointing the wrong way, then when you finish solving the problem, i will turn out to be negative.

(2) Label all the ***voltage rises*** in the circuit. Use arrows to indicate the direction of the voltage rise as we did in Figure (12). Note that if we go through the resistor in the direction of the current, we get a voltage drop. Therefore the arrow showing the voltage rise in a resistor must point back, opposite to the direction of the

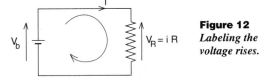

Figure 12
Labeling the voltage rises.

current i in the resistor. (The analogy is to a rock strewn waterfall where the water loses hydrodynamic voltage as it flows down through the rocks. The direction of the voltage rise is back up the waterfall, in a direction opposite to that of the current.)

(3) The final step is to "***walk***" around the loop in the direction of i (or any direction you choose), and set the sum of the voltage rises you encounter equal to zero. If you encounter an arrow that points in the direction you are walking, it counts as a positive voltage rise (like V_b in Figure 12). If the arrow points against you (like V_R), then it is a negative rise. Applying this rule to Figure (12) gives

$$\left.\begin{array}{l}\text{sum of the voltage rises} \\ \text{going clockwise around} \\ \text{the circuit of Figure (12)}\end{array}\right\} \begin{array}{l}= V_b + V_R \\ \\ = V_b + (-iR) \\ \\ = 0\end{array} \quad (12)$$

Equation (12) gives

$$i = \frac{V_b}{R} \qquad (13)$$

which is the result we had back in Equation (8).

Series Resistors

By now we have beaten to death our simple battery resistor circuit. Let us try something a little more challenging—let us put in two resistors as shown in Figure (13). In that figure we have drawn the circuit and labeled the direction of the current (Step 1), and drawn in the arrows representing the voltage rises (Step 2). Setting the sum of the voltage rises equal to zero (Step 3) gives

$$V_b + (-iR_1) + (-iR_2) = 0 \qquad (14)$$

$$i = \frac{V_b}{(R_1 + R_2)} \qquad (15)$$

The two resistors in Figure (13) are said to be connected in series. Comparing Equation (13) for a single resistor and Equation (15) for the series resistors, we see that if

$$R_1 + R_2 = R \quad \text{(series resistors)} \qquad (16)$$

then we get the same current i in both cases (if we use the same battery). We say that if $R_1 + R_2 = R$ then the series resistors are equivalent to the single resistor R.

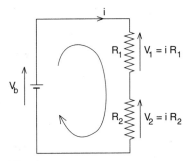

Figure 13
Two resistors in series.

Exercise 2 The Voltage Divider

We wish to measure the voltage V_b produced by a high voltage power supply, but our voltmeter has the limited range of +2 to -2 volts. To make the measurement we use the voltage divider circuit shown below, containing a big resistor R_1 and a small resistor R_2. If, for example, R_2 is 1000 times smaller than R_1, then the voltage across R_2 is 1000 times smaller than that across R_1. By measuring the small voltage across the small resistor we can use this result to determine the big voltage V_b.

a) What current i flows through the circuit? Express your answer in terms of V_b.

b) Find the formula for V_b in terms of V_2, the voltage measured *across* the small resistor.

c) Find a formula for V_b in terms of V_2, R_1 and R_2, assuming $R_1 >> R_2$, so that you can replace $(R_1 + R_2)$ by R_1 in the equation for i.

d) Our voltmeter reads $V_2 = .24$ volts. What was V_b?

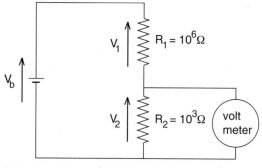

Voltage divider circuit

Parallel Resistors

This section on parallel resistors and the derivation of Equation (22) may be treated as an optional section intended mainly for laboratory work.

A bit more challenging is the circuit of Figure (14) where the resistors are wired in "parallel". In Step (1), we drew the circuit and labeled the currents. But here we have something new. When the current gets to the point labeled (A), it is like a fork in the stream and the current divides. We have labeled the two branch currents i_1 and i_2, and have the obvious subsidiary condition (conservation of current, if you like).

$$i_1 + i_2 = i \qquad (17)$$

There is no problem with Step (2), the voltage rises are V_b, i_1R_1 and i_2R_2 as shown. But we get something new when we try to write down Kirchoff's law for the sum of the voltage rises around a complete circuit. Now we have three different ways we can go around a complete circuit, as shown in Figures (15 a, b, c).

Applying Kirchoff's law to the path shown in Figure (15a) we get

$$V_b + (-i_1R_1) = 0 \qquad (18)$$

For Figure (15b) we get

$$(-i_2R_2) + (i_1R_1) = 0 \qquad (19)$$

and for Figure (15c) we get

$$V_b + (-i_2R_2) = 0 \qquad (20)$$

The main problem with using Kirchoff's laws for complex circuits is that we can get more equations than we need or want. For our current example, if you solve Equation (18) for $V_b = i_1R_1$, then put that result in Equation (20), you get $i_1R_1 - i_2R_2 = 0$ which is Equation (19). In other words Equation (19) does not tell us anything that we did not already know from Equations (18) and (20). The mathematicians would say that Equations (18), (19), and (20) are not *linearly independent*.

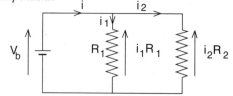

Figure 14
Two resistors in parallel.

Let us look at the situation from a slightly different point of view. To completely solve the circuit of Figure (15), we have to determine the currents i, i_1 and i_2. We have three unknowns, but four equations, Equations (17), (18), (19) and (20). It is well known that you need as many equations as unknowns to solve a system of equations, and therefore we have one too many equations.

We cannot arbitrarily throw out one of the equations, because the remaining three must be *linearly indepen-dent*. For example, if we threw out Equation (17), and tried to solve Equations (18), (19), and (20) for i_1, i_2, and i, we couldn't get an answer because we would not have three independent equations. [You can derive Equation (19) from Equations (18) and (20).]

When you are working with a system of linear equa-tions, the hardest problem is to decide which is a set of independent equations. To do this you can use a standard set of procedures that mathematicians have developed for solving linear equations. These proce-dures involve *determinants and matrices*, which are easily handled on a computer, but are tedious to work by hand.

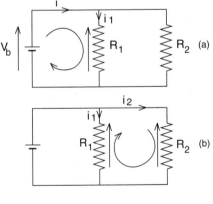

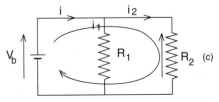

Figure 15
Three possible loops for analyzing the parallel resistance circuit. They give more equations than needed.

In our treatment of circuit theory we will limit our discussion to simple circuits where we can use grade school methods for solving the equations. Problems of linear independence, determinants and matrices will be left to other treatments of the topic.

To solve our parallel resistor circuit of Figure (14), we have from Equation (18)

$$i_1 = \frac{V_b}{R_1}$$

and from Equation (20)

$$i_2 = \frac{V_b}{R_2}$$

Substituting these values into Equation (17) gives

$$i = i_1 + i_2 = \frac{V_b}{R_1} + \frac{V_b}{R_2}$$
$$= V_b \left(\frac{1}{R_1} + \frac{1}{R_2} \right) \tag{21}$$

Comparing Equation (21) for parallel resistors, and Equation (13) for a single resistor

$$i = V_b \left(\frac{1}{R} \right) \tag{13}$$

We see that two parallel resistors R_1 and R_2 are equiva-lent to a single resistor R if they obey the relationship

$$\boxed{\frac{1}{R} = \frac{1}{R_1} + \frac{1}{R_2}} \quad \begin{array}{l} \textit{equivalent} \\ \textit{parallel} \\ \textit{resistors} \end{array} \tag{22}$$

Exercise 3

You are given a device, sealed in a box, with electrical leads on each end. (Such a device is often referred to as a "black box", the word black referring to our lack of knowledge of the contents, rather than the actual color of the device.) You use an instrument called an **ohmmeter** to measure the electrical resistance be-tween the two terminals and find that its resistance R is 470 ohms (470 Ω).

R = 470 Ω

a) Sketch a circuit, containing the black box and one resistor, where the total resistance of the circuit is 500 Ω.

b) Sketch a circuit, containing the black box and one resistor, where the total resistance of the circuit is 400 Ω.

CAPACITANCE AND CAPACITORS

In addition to the resistor, another common circuit element is the capacitor. A resistor dissipates energy, causes a voltage drop given by Ohm's law $V = iR$, and is often used to limit the amount of current flowing in a section of a circuit. A capacitor is a device for storing electrical charge and maintains a voltage proportional to the charge stored. We have already seen one explicit example of a capacitor, the parallel plate capacitor studied in the last chapter. Here we will abstract the general features of capacitors, and see how they are used as circuit elements.

Hydrodynamic Analogy

Before focusing on the electrical capacitor, it is instructive to consider an accurate hydrodynamic analogy—the cylindrical water tank shown in Figure (16). If the tank is filled to a height h, then all the water in the tank has a hydrodynamic voltage

$$V_h = P + \rho gh + \frac{1}{2}\rho v^2 = \rho gh \qquad (23)$$

For water at the top of the tank, y = h, the voltage is all in the form of gravitational potential energy ρgh. (We will ignore atmospheric pressure.) At the bottom of the tank where y = 0, the voltage is all in the pressure term $P = \rho gh$. The dynamic voltage term $1/2\,\rho v^2$ does not play a significant role.

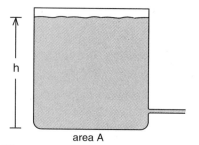

Figure 16
Analogy between a cylindrical tank of water and an electrical capacitor. In the tank, all the water in the tank is at a hydrodynamic voltage $V_h = \rho gh$, and the quantity Q of water in the tank, given by Q = Ah = $(A/\rho g)\rho gh = (A/\rho g)V_h$ is proportional to V_h.

Let us denote by the letter Q the quantity or volume of water stored in the tank. If we talk only about cylindrical tanks (of cross-sectional area A), then this volume is proportional to the height h and therefore the hydrodynamic voltage V_h

$$\begin{array}{l}\text{volume of water} \\ \text{in cylindrical tank}\end{array} \equiv Q = Ah = \left[\frac{A}{\rho g}\right]\rho gh$$

$$Q = \left[\frac{A}{\rho g}\right]V_h \qquad (24)$$

If we define the proportionality constant $A/\rho g$ in Equation (24) as the **capacitance C** of the tank

$$C = \frac{A}{\rho g} \equiv \begin{array}{l}\text{capacitance of} \\ \text{a cylindrical tank} \\ \text{with a cross} - \\ \text{sectional area A}\end{array} \qquad (25)$$

then we get

$$\boxed{Q = CV_h} \qquad (26)$$

as the relation between the hydrodynamic voltage and volume Q of water in the tank.

Cylindrical Tank as a Constant Voltage Source

One of the main uses of a water storage tank is to maintain a water supply at constant hydrodynamic voltage.

Figure (17) is a schematic diagram of a typical town water supply. Water is pumped from the reservoir up into the water tank where a constant height h and therefore constant voltage ρgh is maintained. The houses in the town all draw constant voltage water from this tank.

Let us see what would happen if the water tank were too small. As soon as several houses started using water, the level h in the tank would drop and the pump at the reservoir would have to come on. The pump would raise the level back to h and shut off. Then the level would drop again and the pump would come on again. The result would be that the hydrodynamic voltage or water pressure supplied to the town would vary and customers might complain.

On the other hand if the town water tank has a large cross-sectional area and therefore large capacitance C, a few houses drawing water would have very little effect on the level h and therefore voltage ρgh of the water. The town would have a constant voltage water supply and the water company could pump water from the reservoir at night when electricity rates were low.

We will see that one of the important uses of electrical capacitors in electric circuits is to maintain constant or nearly constant electric voltages. There is an accurate analogy to the way the town water tank maintains constant voltage water. If we use too small a capacitor, the electrical voltage will also fluctuate when current is drawn.

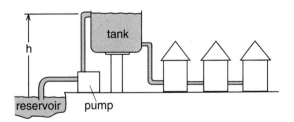

Figure 17
Town water supply. By maintaining a constant height h of water in the storage tank, all the water supplied to the town has a constant hydrodynamic voltage $V_h \rho gh$.

Electrical Capacitance

Figure (18) is a repeat of the sketch of the ideal parallel plate capacitor we discussed in Chapter 21. We have two metal plates of area A separated by a distance d. The electric field $\vec{E}$ created by the charge +Q on the top plate all goes down and ends on the –Q charge on the bottom plate, creating a downward flux Φ given by

$$\Phi = EA \tag{27}$$

By Gauss' law, the charge +Q creates a flux Φ equal to Q/ε_0. Equating these two values of flux gives

$$\Phi = \frac{Q}{\varepsilon_0} = EA; \qquad E = \frac{Q}{\varepsilon_0 A} \tag{28}$$

which is our old Equation (21-8).

Recall that one form of electric voltage is the electric potential energy of a unit test charge. To lift a positive unit test charge from the bottom plate to the top one requires an amount of work equal to the force E on a unit charge times the distance d the charge was lifted. This work $E*d$ is equal to the increase of the potential energy of the unit charge, and therefore to the increase in voltage in going from the bottom to the top plate. If we say that the bottom plate is at a voltage V = 0, then the voltage at the top plate is

$$V = Ed \tag{29}$$

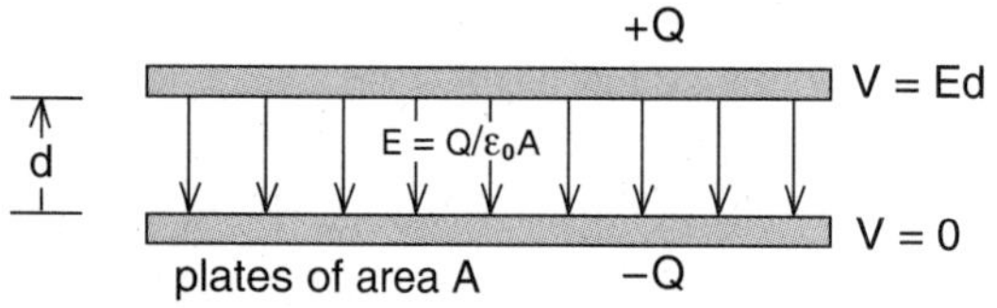

$$E = Q/\varepsilon_0 A$$

Figure 18
The parallel plate capacitor. If we place charges + Q and – Q on plates of area A, the charge density on the plates will be $\sigma = Q/A$, the electric field will be $E = \sigma/\varepsilon_0$ and the voltage between the plates V = Ed.

Using Equation (28) for E gives

$$V = Ed = \frac{Q}{\varepsilon_0 A} d$$

or

$$Q = \left(\frac{\varepsilon_0 A}{d}\right) V \tag{30}$$

As in our hydrodynamic analogy, we see that the quantity of charge Q stored in the capacitor is proportional to the voltage V on the capacitor. Again we call the proportionality constant the capacitance C

$$Q = CV \qquad \begin{array}{l}\textit{definition of}\\ \textit{electrical}\\ \textit{capacitance}\end{array} \tag{31}$$

Comparing Equations (30) and (31) we see that the formula for the capacitance C of a parallel plate capacitor is

$$C = \frac{\varepsilon_0 A}{d} \qquad \begin{array}{l}\textit{capacitance of a}\\ \textit{parallel plate}\\ \textit{capacitor of area A,}\\ \textit{plate separation d}\end{array} \tag{32}$$

For both the parallel plate capacitor and the cylindrical water tank, the capacitance is proportional to the cross-sectional area A. The new feature for the electrical capacitor is that the capacitance increases as we make the plate separation d smaller and smaller.

Our parallel plate capacitor is but one example of many kinds of capacitors used in electronic circuits. In some, the geometry of the metal conductors is different, and in others the space between the conductors is filled with a material called a dielectric which increases the effective capacitance. But in all common capacitors the amount of charge Q is proportional to voltage V across the capacitor, i.e., Q = CV, where C is constant independent of the voltage V and in most cases independent of the temperature.

The dimensions of capacitance C are coulombs per volt, which is given the name **farad** in honor of Michael

Faraday who pioneered the concept of an electric field. Although such an honor may be deserved, this is one more example of the excessive use of names in the MKS system that make it hard to follow the dimensions in a calculation.

To get a feeling for the size of a farad, suppose that we have two metal plates with an area $A = 0.1$ meter^2 and make a separation $d = 1$ millimeter $= 10^{-3}$ meters. These plates will have a capacitance C given by

$$C = \frac{\varepsilon_0 A}{d} = \frac{9 \times 10^{-12} \times .1}{10^{-3}}$$

$$= 9 \times 10^{-10} \text{ farads}$$

which is about one billionth of a farad. If you keep the separation at 1 millimeter you would need plates with an area of 100 million square meters (an area 10 kilometers on a side) to have a capacitance of 1 farad.

Commercial capacitors used in electronic circuits come in various shapes like those shown in Figure (19), and in an enormous range of values from a few farads down to 10^{-14} farads.

Our calculation of the capacitance of a parallel plate capacitor demonstrates that it is not an easy trick to produce capacitors with a capacitance of 10^{-6} farads or larger. One technique is to take two long strips of metal foil separated by an insulator, and roll them up into a small cylinder. This gives us a large plate area with a reasonably small separation, stuffed into a relatively small volume.

In a special kind of a capacitor called an electrolytic capacitor, the effective plate separation d is reduced to almost atomic dimensions. Only this way are we able to create the physically small 4 farad capacitor shown in Figure (19). The problem with electrolytic capacitors is that one side has to be positive and the other negative, as marked on the capacitor. If you reverse the voltage on an electrolytic capacitor, it will not work and may explode.

Exercise 4 - Electrolytic Capacitor

In an *electrolytic capacitor*, one of the plates is a thin aluminum sheet and the other is a conducting dielectric liquid surrounding the aluminum. A nonconducting oxide layer forms on the surface of the aluminum and plays the same role as the air gap in the parallel plate capacitors we have been discussing. The fact that the oxide layer is very thin means that you can construct a capacitor with a very large capacitance in a small container.

dielectric liquid

aluminum

oxide layer

For this problem, assume that you have a dielectric capacitor whose total capacitance is 1 farad, and that the oxide layer acts like an air gap 10^{-7} meters thick in a parallel plate capacitor. From this, estimate the area of the aluminum surface in the capacitor.

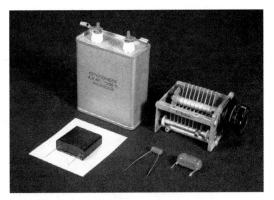

Figure 19
Examples of capacitors used in electronic circuits. The one on the right is a variable capacitor whose plate area is changed by turning the knob. The square black capacitor is a 4 farad electrolytic. Its capacitance is one million times greater than the tall regular capacitor behind it.

ENERGY STORAGE IN CAPACITORS

In physics, one of the important uses of capacitors is energy storage. The advantage of using capacitors is that large quantities of energy can be released in a very short time. For example, Figure (20) is a photograph of the Nova laser at the Lawrence Livermore National Laboratory. This laser produces short, but very high energy pulses of light for fusion research. The laser is powered by a bank of capacitors which, for the short length of time needed, can supply power at a rate about 200 times the power generating capacity of the United States.

To calculate the energy stored in a capacitor we will calculate the amount of work required to charge up the capacitor. Imagine that I start with two uncharged plates and take little pieces of positive charge out of the bottom plate and lift them up to the top plate. I keep doing this until the top plate gets the full charge $+Q$, and the bottom plate has a charge deficit $-Q$.

How much work did it take to do this? When I lifted the first piece of charge, there was no field between the plates and I had to do essentially no work. For the last piece of charge, the full field $E = Q/\varepsilon_0 A$ was almost in place and I had to do a lot of work. The average field $E_{average}$ that I lifted against was half way between zero and E, or

$$E_{average} = \frac{Q}{2\varepsilon_0 A} \qquad (33)$$

Figure 20
The Nova laser, powered by a bank of capacitors. While the laser is being fired, the capacitors supply 200 times as much power as the generating capacity of the United States.

I can say that I lifted the entire charge $+Q$ against this average field $E_{average}$. The force $F_{average}$ that $E_{average}$ would exert on Q is

$$F_{average} = QE_{average} = \frac{Q^2}{2\varepsilon_0 A} \qquad (34)$$

The work I do lifting Q a distance d against the force $F_{average}$ is

$$work = F_{average} \times d = \frac{Q^2 d}{2\varepsilon_0 A} \qquad (35)$$

Since the work I do is the energy stored in the capacitor, Equation (35) is the formula for the energy stored in an ideal parallel plate capacitor charged up to a charge Q.

There are several different ways to express this formula for the energy stored in a capacitor. First, remembering that the formula for the capacitance C of the parallel plate capacitor was $C = \varepsilon_0 A/d$, we see that the $d/\varepsilon_0 A$ in Equation (35) is simply $1/C$ giving

$$\begin{array}{c}\text{energy stored} \\ \text{in capacitor}\end{array} = \frac{Q^2}{2C} \qquad (35a)$$

Next we note that it is much easier to measure the voltage V on a capacitor than the charge Q stored inside. Using the relationship $Q = CV$ we get

$$\begin{array}{c}\text{energy stored} \\ \text{in capacitor}\end{array} = \frac{C^2 V^2}{2C} = \frac{CV^2}{2} \qquad (35b)$$

Equation (35b) tells us that as we charge up the capacitor, the energy stored goes up as the square of the voltage applied.

In our derivation of Equations (35), all our calculations were based on an idealized parallel plate capacitor. But we ended up with formulas like (35a) and (35b) that depended on the capacitance $C = Q/V$ and not on details of the construction of the capacitor. What may seem surprising is that the formulas (35a) and (35b) apply to all the capacitors we have discussed, no matter how they were constructed.

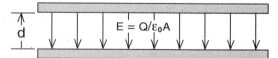

Figure 21
The volume occupied by the electric field E is d×A.

ENERGY DENSITY IN AN ELECTRIC FIELD

There is another result that we can get from Equations (35) and that has more far reaching consequences than giving formulas for energy storage. To see what we mean, start with Equation (35) and express Q in terms of the final electric field E in the capacitor

$$E = \frac{Q}{\varepsilon_0 A} \; ; \quad Q = \varepsilon_0 A E \qquad \text{(28) repeated}$$

we get from Equation (35a)

$$\begin{aligned}\frac{\text{energy stored}}{\text{in capacitor}} &= \frac{Q^2 d}{2\varepsilon_0 A} = \frac{(\varepsilon_0^2 A^2 E^2) d}{2\varepsilon_0 A} \\ &= \frac{\varepsilon_0}{2} E^2 (A \times d)\end{aligned}$$

As illustrated in Figure (21), the quantity (A×d) is the volume occupied by the electric field $\vec{E}$. Thus

$$\frac{\text{energy stored}}{\text{in capacitor}} = \frac{\varepsilon_0}{2} E^2 \times \begin{bmatrix} \text{volume occupied} \\ \text{by electric field} \end{bmatrix} \quad \textit{(36a)}$$

Equation (36) is telling us that the energy stored in the capacitor is proportional to the volume of electric field. If for a given value of $\vec{E}$, we doubled the volume, we would have twice as much energy. One way to interpret this equation is to say that the energy is actually stored in the electric field itself.

By way of analogy, suppose you have a cup full of water. The mass of water in the cup is the **density of water** times the volume of the cup. We now have a capacitor filled with an electric field E. The energy stored in the capacitor is the **density of energy** in the electric field times the volume of the capacitor. As an equation, this is

$$\frac{\text{energy stored}}{\text{in capacitor}} = \begin{bmatrix} \text{energy} \\ \text{density} \end{bmatrix} \times \begin{bmatrix} \text{volume occupied} \\ \text{by electric field} \end{bmatrix}$$

$$\text{(36b)}$$

Comparing Equations (36a) and (36b), we see that the formula for the energy density of the electric field is the factor $\varepsilon_0 E^2 / 2$ in Equation (36b). Thus

$$\boxed{\begin{array}{l} \text{energy density in} \\ \text{an electric field E} \end{array} = \frac{\varepsilon_0}{2} E^2}$$

$$\text{(37)}$$

While Equation (37) was derived for the special case of an ideal parallel plate capacitor, the result is far more general and far reaching. For example, Maxwell's theory of light treats light as a wave of electric and magnetic fields. From just feeling the warmth of light from the sun, you know that light waves carry energy. It turns out that Equation (37) is the formula for the energy density in the electric field of a light wave.

This interpretation of Equation (37) *represents a turning point in our theory of electricity*. We began with the electric field as simply being a mapping convention—the force on an imaginary unit test particle. But with Equation (37) the concept of an electric field is beginning to take on substance; it is something that has energy. In addition, from Einstein's $E = mc^2$ Equation for energy, we will find that mass also has to be associated with the electric field. There is much more to come!

Exercise 5

A parallel plate capacitor consists of two circular aluminum plates with a radius of 11 cm separated by a distance of 1 millimeter. The capacitor is charged to a voltage of 5 volts.

a) What is the capacitance, in farads, of the capacitor?

b) Using Equation (35), calculate the energy stored in the capacitor.

c) What is the magnitude of the electric field E between the plates?

d) Using Equation (36), calculate the energy density in the electric field.

e) What is the volume of space, in cubic meters, between the plates?

f) From your answers to parts d) and e), calculate the total energy in the electric field between the plates. Compare your answer with your answer to part b).

g) Using Einstein's formula $E = mc^2$, calculate the mass, in kilograms, of the electric field between the plates.

h) The mass of the electric field is equal to the mass of how many electrons?

APPENDIX I
CAPACITORS AS
CIRCUIT ELEMENTS

The material in this appendix is intended mostly for laboratory work. It is not essential for the theory we will be discussing.

Figure (22) is a simple circuit consisting of a battery of voltage V_b and a capacitor of capacitance C. The standard circuit symbol for a capacitor is ⎯|⎯ , which is a sketch of a parallel plate capacitor.

When the battery is attached to the capacitor, the upper plate becomes positively charged and the lower one negatively charged as shown. The upper plate could actually become positively charged either by positive charge flowing into it or negative charge flowing out—it does not matter. We have followed our convention of always showing the direction of positive currents, thus we show i flowing into the positive plate and out of the negative one.

We have also followed our convention of labeling the voltage rises with an arrow pointing in the direction of the higher voltage. The voltage V_c on the capacitor is related to the charge Q stored by the definition of capacitance, $V_c = Q/C$.

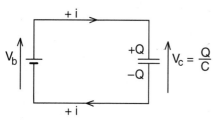

Figure 22
A battery and a capacitor in a circuit. We have drawn the diagram showing positive current flowing into the top plate and out of the bottom plate. (The upper plate could have become positively charged by having a negative current flowing out of it.) The arrow designating the voltage on the capacitor points in the direction of the voltage rise.

Applying Kirchoff's law to Figure (22), i.e., setting the sum of the voltage rises around the circuit equal to zero, we get

$$V_b + (-V_c) = V_b - Q/C = 0$$

$$Q = CV_b \tag{38}$$

Thus we get a relatively straightforward result for the amount of charge stored by the battery.

For something a little more challenging, we have connected two capacitors in parallel to a battery as shown in Figure (23). Because single wires go all the way across the top and across the bottom, the three voltages V_b, V_1 and V_2 must all be equal, and we get

$$Q_1 = C_1 V_b \qquad\qquad Q_2 = C_2 V_b$$

The total charge Q stored on the two capacitors in parallel is therefore

$$Q = Q_1 + Q_2 = (C_1 + C_2) V_b$$

Comparing this with Equation (38), we see that two capacitors in parallel store the same charge as a single capacitor C given by

$$\boxed{C = C_1 + C_2} \quad \begin{array}{l}\textit{capacitors}\\\textit{attached in}\\\textit{parallel}\end{array} \tag{39}$$

Comparing this result with Equation (16), we find that for capacitors in parallel or resistors in series, the effective capacitance or resistance is just the sum of the values of the individual components.

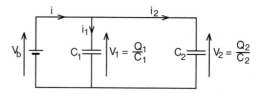

Figure 23
Capacitors connected in parallel. The three voltages V_b, V_1 and V_2 must all be level because the wires go all the way across the three elements.

In Figure (24) we have two capacitors in series. The trick here is to note that all the charge that flowed out of the bottom plate of C_1 flowed into the top plate of C_2, as indicated in the diagram. But if there is a charge $-Q$ on the bottom plate of C_1, there must be an equal and opposite charge $+Q$ on the top and we have $Q_1 = Q$. Similarly we must have $Q_2 = Q$.

To apply Kirchoff's law, we set the sum of the voltage rises to zero to get

$$V_b + \frac{-Q_1}{C_1} + \frac{-Q_2}{C_2} = 0$$

Setting $Q_1 = Q_2 = Q$ gives

$$V_b = Q\left(\frac{1}{C_1} + \frac{1}{C_2}\right) \tag{40}$$

Comparing Equation (40) with Equation (38) in the form $V_b = Q/C$ we see that

$$\boxed{\frac{1}{C} = \frac{1}{C_1} + \frac{1}{C_2}} \quad \begin{array}{l}\textit{capacitors}\\\textit{attached in}\\\textit{series}\end{array} \tag{41}$$

is the formula for the effective capacitance of capacitors connected in series. This is analogous to the formula for parallel resistors.

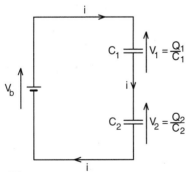

Figure 24
Capacitors in series. In this case the sum of V_1 and V_2 must be equal to the battery voltage V_b.

It is interesting to note that for storing charge, parallel capacitors are more efficient because the charge can flow into both capacitors as seen in Figure (23). When the capacitors are in series, charge flowing out of the bottom of one capacitor flows into the top of the next, and we get no enhancement in charge storage capability. What we do get from series capacitors is higher voltages, the total voltage rise across the pair is the sum of the voltage rise on each.

Exercise 6

You have a 5 microfarad (abbreviated 5µf) capacitor and a 10 µf capacitor. What are all the values of capacitor you can make from these two?

APPENDIX II
THE RC CIRCUIT

The capacitor circuits we have discussed so far are not too exciting. When you are working with an electronic circuit you do not hitch capacitors together in series or parallel, you simply go to the parts drawer and select a capacitor of the desired value.

If we add a resistor to the circuit as shown in Figure (25), we begin to get some interesting results. The circuit is designed so that if the mercury switch is closed, the capacitor is charged up to a voltage V_b by the battery. Then, at a time we will call $t = 0$, the switch is opened, so that the capacitor will discharge through the resistor. During the discharge, the battery is disconnected and the only part of the circuit that is active is that shown in Figure (26). (The reason for using a mercury switch was to get a clean break in the current. Mechanical switches do not work well.)

Figure (27) shows the capacitor voltage just before and for a while after the switch was opened. We are looking at the experimental results of discharging a $C = 10^{-6}$ farad (one microfarad) capacitor through an $R = 10^4$ ohm resistor. We see that a good fraction of the capacitor voltage has decayed in about 10 milliseconds (10^{-2} seconds).

In the calculus version of the text we apply Kirchoff's law to the circuit of Figure (26), and end up with what is called a ***differential equation*** for the charge Q on the capacitor. Differential equations, which involve the calculus derivative, are unlike the familiar algebra equations whose solution is a number, as in $x^2 = 4$ gives $x = \pm 2$. Instead, the solution of a differential equation is a curve rather than a number.

When Kirchoff's law is solved for the charge Q or the voltage V in discharging the capacitor, the result is the so called ***exponential decay*** curve seen in Figure (27). An exponential decay leads to the concept of a half life. If you look at Figure (27), you see that the curve starts at $V = 4$ volts, and by the end of about 7 milliseconds (7×10^{-3} sec), the curve has dropped to 2 volts. At the end of another 7 milliseconds (at $t = 14$ ms), the voltage is down to 1 volt. Another 7 ms later ($t = 21$ ms), the voltage is down to 1/2 volt. Every 7 milliseconds the voltage drops by another factor of 1/2.

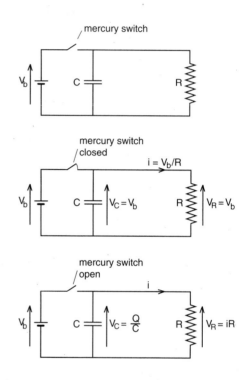

Figure 25
An RC circuit. When the mercury switch is closed, the capacitor quickly charges up to a voltage $V_C = V_b$. When the switch is opened, the capacitor discharges through the resistor.

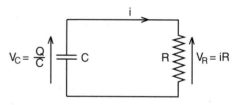

Figure 26
Capacitor discharge. When the switch is open, the only part of the circuit we have to look at is the capacitor discharging through the resistor.

The differential equation from Kirchoff's law also predicts that the half life of this *RC decay curve* is given by the formula

$$\text{half life} = .7 \times RC \qquad (42)$$

where the factor of .7, or more precisely .693, is the so called *natural logarithm of 2*. (On your calculator, press 2, then press the *ln* button and you get .693147...

For a calculus based course the solution of Kirchoff's law for the capacitance decay curve provides an excellent example of the use of calculus in physics. For a non calculus text, we will omit that derivation and just check the prediction that the half life is .7 RC. For this experiment R was $10^4 \Omega$ and C was 10^{-6} farads, giving a predicted half life of

$$.7RC = .7 \times 10^4 \times 10^{-6} = .007 \text{ seconds}$$
$$= 7 \text{ milliseconds}$$

Thus the half life formula works.

This is not the first time in the course we have witnessed an exponential decay and half life. In the muon lifetime experiment, the muons which stopped in the plastic, undergo an exponential decay. To estimate the muon half life, we can use the results that they recorded 568 muons in an hour, and 28 of them lived over 6 microseconds (see Figure (1-19a). To see how many half lives that represents, start with 568 and keep multiplying by 1/2 until we get close to 28. We have

$$568/2 = 284$$
$$284/2 = 142$$
$$142/2 = 71$$
$$71/2 = 35.5$$

Thus in six microseconds, the muons underwent about four half lives, giving a time of about 6/4 = 1.5 microseconds, for the muon half life.

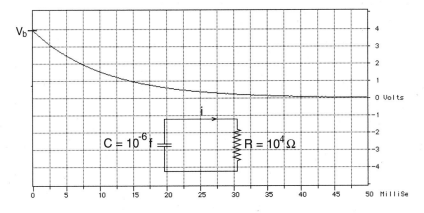

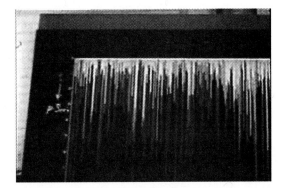

Figure 27
Experimental results from discharging the one microfarad ($10^{-6}f$) capacitor through a 10 k ohm ($10^4 \Omega$) resistor. The switch, shown in Figure (26), is thrown at time t = 0.

Figure (1-19a) -- Muon Lifetime Movie
The lifetimes of 568 muons, traveling at a speed of .994c, were plotted as vertical lines. If the muon's clocks did not run slow, these lines would show how far the muons could travel before decaying. A total of 28 muons survived for 6 microseconds.

Exercise 7

Figure (28a) shows the circuit used to observe the discharge of a capacitor. The capacitor is made from the two circular aluminum plates shown in Figure (28b). The plates have a diameter of 22 cm and are separated a distance (d) by small pieces of glass. In Figure (28c), we are observing the discharge of the capacitor through a 10kΩ ($10^4\Omega$) resistor. For this discharge, what is the separation (d) of the plates?

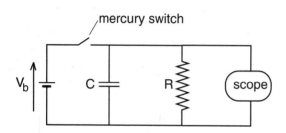

Figure 28a
Circuit for observing the discharge of a capacitor.

Figure 28b
The capacitor plates.

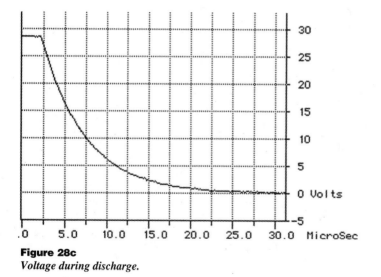

Figure 28c
Voltage during discharge.

CHAPTER 22 REVIEW

A Gravitational analogy

When you start working with electric circuits, it is easy to confuse terms such as voltage and current, and not be sure whether a circuit should be wired in series or parallel. A gravitational analogy to ski lifts should help keep these concepts straight.

*In a ski area, the purpose of the ski lift is to get skiers to the top of the hill. An obvious definition of the current of skiers is the **number of skiers per hour** that the lift carries to the top of the hill. In an electric circuit with a battery, the current (i) through the battery is the **number of coulombs per second** that the battery lifts to the higher voltage.*

*In electrical theory, the voltage V is defined as the **electrical potential energy of a unit charge** (one coulomb). By analogy, we define the gravitational voltage as the **gravitational potential energy of a unit mass** (one kilogram). The gravitational potential energy of a skier of mass m, up at a height h, is mgh. Thus for a unit mass, $m = 1$, the gravitational voltage is simply $V_g = gh$. We can think of a ski lift as a device that increases the gravitational voltage gh of the skiers.*

Series and Parallel

When you replace the batteries in a camera or radio, there are definite markings showing how the batteries are to be inserted. Inside the device, the batteries are wired together either in series or parallel. To see why, consider the ski lift analogy shown in Figures (29) and (30).

In Figure (29), the ski area attaches several short lifts, one after another, in series, in order to get the skiers to the top of the hill. When the lifts are connected in series, the gravitational voltages of the lifts add. A skier riding all three lifts gains a gravitational voltage $V_g = gh_1 + gh_2 + gh_3 = gh$.

We have a portable VHF ratio that uses six, 1.5 volt, double A batteries to supply the 9 volts needed by the radio. The batteries are wired in series so that the six batteries will give a 9 volt voltage rise.

Figure (30) shows a ski area where the lifts are long enough to go all the way from the base of the hill to the top. But on weekends, the area is so crowded, that a single lift provides an inadequate current of skiers. To solve this problem, the area installed three similar lifts in parallel. With three lifts instead of one, there is no increase in gravitational voltage, it is still gh, but they get three times the current of skiers.

In our digital camera where only 1.5 volts are needed, there are slots for four AA, 1.5 volt batteries. These batteries are wired in parallel so that more coulombs of charge can be raised to 1.5 volts before the batteries wear out.

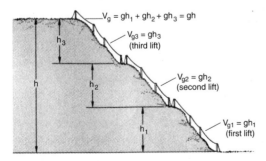

Figure 29
Ski lifts mounted in series.

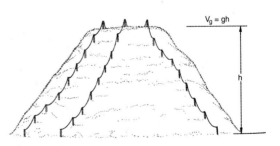

Figure 29
Ski lifts mounted in parallel.

A simple Electric Circuit

We began this chapter discussing the simple electrical circuit shown in Figure (8), where a battery of voltage V pushes a current (i) around the circuit through a resistor R.

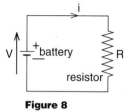

Figure 8

In this review we will think of the resistance R as any device that dissipates the energy being supplied by the battery. It could be a light bulb, the electronics in a camera, or it could be a calibrated resistor that obeys Ohm's law V = iR. In essence, it is a device that dissipates energy.

Series and Parallel Circuits

Our examples of series and parallel circuits are shown in Figures (13) and (14). In the series connection of Figure (13) all the current (i) flows down through both resistors. In the parallel connection of Figure (14), the current (i) divides, part flowing through one resistor, the rest through the other.

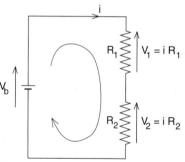

Figure 13
Series circuit.

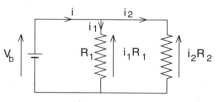

Figure 14
Parallel circuit.

The classic example of series and parallel wiring involves strings of Christmas tree lights. In that case the battery is the household voltage V, which in the U.S. is 110 volts. If you have 10 identical bulbs hooked up in series as in Figure (13), each bulb will get a voltage of 11 volts. The problem with this arrangement is that if one bulb burns out, no current can flow, and all the lights go out.

If the 10 bulbs are hooked up in parallel as in Figure (14), two wires have to run along the entire string. Each bulb sees the full 110 volts, but in this case, if one of the bulbs burns out, the remaining 9 stay lit.

You are more likely to encounter devices where there is one energy dissipating device powered by two or more batteries. Then the batteries that are hooked up in series to give more voltage, or in parallel to provide more current (as we saw in the ski lift analogy).

Kirchoff's Law

Kirchoff's law said that the sum of the voltage rise around a circuit is zero. Applying this to a skier on our ski slopes, we ask how much gravitational voltage gh does a skier gain when she goes up the lift, skis down, and gets back in line to go up again. Since she is back where she started from, her net height gain in one complete trip is zero meters, no matter which trail she took down the mountain. In the trip down the mountain, she had to do a number of turns to dissipate all energy she gained from the lift.

In Figure (8), the electrons flowing through a resistor R have to dissipate the energy that they got from the battery voltage V. They get no net voltage gain by going all the way around the circuit.

Energy Storage

Two devices commonly used for energy storage are the battery and the capacitor. Batteries are designed to produce a constant voltage until the battery is discharged. The design of batteries is relatively complex, involving chemical reactions of the various substances in the battery. We leave that subject to a chemistry course.

From a physics point of view, a capacitor is a much simpler energy and charge storage device. As we saw from the example of the slightly idealized parallel plate capacitor, the energy density in an electric field of strength E is

$$\text{energy density in an electric field} = \frac{\varepsilon_0}{2} E^2 \qquad (37)$$

This energy density has the dimensions of joules per cubic meter.

The practical feature of capacitors is that they can be made to store large amounts of energy that can be released rapidly in a time of the order of milliseconds or microseconds. As a result capacitors are used in the flash unit of a camera. The batteries in the camera slowly charge up the capacitor. Then to produce a flash, the energy of the capacitor is rapidly discharged through the gas in the flashbulb.

Electrical Power

*This is perhaps the most practical application of your physics course. The formula for electrical power, in **joules per second**, carried by a wire that is carrying a current (i) at a voltage V, is*

$$\boxed{\text{electric power in watts} = iV} \qquad (11)$$

*The unit of power in the MKS system is the **watt**. A **one watt** flashlight bulb uses **one joule of energy per second**. The typical 100 watt bulb uses 100 joules of energy per second.*

The formula, power = iV, tells us that there are two distinct ways to deliver electrical power. You can have a large current (i) at a low voltage V, or a small current (i) at a high voltage V. (Of course you can carry even more power with a large current i at a high voltage V.)

An example of a high current, at low voltage, is the starter motor in an automobile. The starter motor for a big engine needs a lot of power. But the voltage available is only the 12 volts from the car battery. As a result the wires from the battery to the starter motor have to carry a large current (i).

In a household in the United States, the house voltage is about 120 volts, ten times the voltage available in a car. As a result you can get the same amount of power with one tenth as much current.

Just as a big river like the Mississippi can carry much more current (gallons of water per second) than a small stream; a big fat copper wire can carry more electrical current than a skinny one. If you try to push too much current through a small wire, the wire will become hot due to resistive heating. Most electrical wires are made from copper because copper has a low electrical resistance. (So does silver, but it is too expensive to use for electrical wires.)

Most housing regulations in the United States require that the wires in a given circuit be able to carry a current of i = 20 amperes without becoming excessively warm. If you measure the wires electricians use for household wiring, you will find that copper wire has a diameter of just over 1.5 mm or 1/16 of an inch. Since the cross-sectional area of a wire is proportional to the square of the diameter, a wire with twice the diameter, 3 mm, can safely carry four times as much current, or about 80 amperes. This is enough current to run a car starter motor at 12 volts. That is why the wires from the battery to the starter motor have an effective diameter of 3 mm or even more.

If you want to power a 120 watt light bulb on a 120 volt circuit, the formula, power = iV, tells you that you only need a current (i) of one ampere. This tells you that you can run 20 such light bulbs in series, on one household circuit, before exceeding the 20 ampere rating of the wires. If you try to exceed the 20 ampere limit, houses have fuses or circuit breakers that disconnect the circuit from the power source.

In many countries outside the United States, the standard voltage is 220 volts, twice the U.S. Standard. The formula, power = iV, tells us that if you double the voltage V, you need only half the current (i) for the same power. That means that you can use thinner copper wires to carry the same power. If you travel to countries that have 220 volt wiring, you will notice that appliances have thinner power cords. Conversely, those familiar with 220 volt appliances should find that appliances in the United States have thicker power cords.

Storage of Electrical Charge

A capacitor can be thought of as a device that stores both electrical charge and electrical energy.

As a device for storing electric charge, it is slightly different in concept from a typical storage device like a reservoir for storing water or a bin for storing potatoes. There is no net electrical charge stored in a capacitor, because there are equal amounts of positive and negative charge. When we say that a capacitor is storing a charge Q, we mean that there are +Q coulombs of charge on the positive side, and −Q coulombs on the negative side.

The simplest feature of a capacitor is that the charge Q stored is proportional to the voltage V applied. We write this as

$$Q = CV \qquad (31)$$

where the proportionality constant C is called the **capacitance** of the capacitor. For the simple parallel plate capacitor we derived the formula

$$C = \frac{\varepsilon_0 A}{d} \qquad (32)$$

where A is the area of the plates and d their separation.

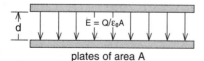

plates of area A

Figure 21
The volume occupied by the electric field E is d ×A.

A capacitor can also be a convenient place to store an electric field. If we have a parallel plate capacitor like the one shown in Figure (21), we get a uniform electric field (except at the edges). When there is a charge Q on the plates, the electric field has a strength

$$E = \frac{Q}{\varepsilon_0 A} \qquad (28)$$

where again A is the area of the plates.

We were able to calculate the work required to place a charge Q on the plates, which told us the amount of energy stored in the capacitor. Saying that all this energy was stored in the electric field E gives us the formula $\varepsilon_0 E^2/2$ for the energy density in an electric field. This is a result we will come back to in our discussion of radio waves and electromagnetic radiation.

CHAPTER EXERCISES

Chapter 23 non calculus

Magnetism

In our discussion of Coulomb's law, we saw that electric forces are very strong but in most circumstances tend to cancel. The strength of the forces is so great, but the cancellation is so nearly complete that the slightest imbalance in the cancellation leads to important effects such as molecular forces. As illustrated in Figure (17-5b) reproduced here, a positively charged proton brought up to a neutral hydrogen atom experiences a net attractive force because the negative charge in the atom is pulled closer to the proton. This net force is the simplest example of the type of molecular force called a **covalent bond**.

In this chapter we will study another way that the precise balance between attractive and repulsive electric forces can be upset. So far in our discussion of electrical phenomena, such as the flow of currents in wires, the charging of capacitors, etc., we have ignored the effects of special relativity. And we had good reason to. We saw that the conduction electrons in a wire move at utterly nonrelativistic speeds, like two

millimeters per minute. One would not expect phenomena like the Lorentz contraction or time dilation to play any observable role whatever in such electrical phenomena.

But, as we shall see, observable effects do result from the tiny imbalance in electric forces caused by the Lorentz contraction. Since these effects are not describable by Coulomb's law, they are traditionally given another name—**magnetism**. Magnetism is one of the consequences of requiring that the electrical force law and electric phenomena be consistent with the principle of relativity.

Historically this point of view is backwards. Magnetic effects were known in the time of the ancient Greeks. Hans Christian Oersted first demonstrated the connection between magnetic and electric forces in 1820 and James Clerk Maxwell wrote out a complete theory of electromagnetic phenomena in 1860. Einstein did not discover special relativity until 1905. In fact, Einstein used Maxwell's theory as an important guide in his discovery.

If you follow an historical approach, it appears that special relativity is a consequence of electricity theory, and a large number of physics texts treat it that way. Seldom is there a serious discussion of special relativity until after Maxwell's theory of electricity has been developed. This is considered necessary in order to explain the experiments and arguments that lead to the discovery of the special theory.

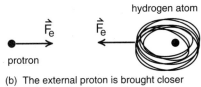

(b) The external proton is brought closer distorting the electron cloud

Figure 17-5b
The net attraction between a positive charge and a neutral atom is caused by a redistribution of charge in the atom.

But as we know today, electricity is one of but several basic forces in nature, and all of them are consistent with special relativity. Einstein's famous theory of gravity called **general relativity** *can be viewed as a repair of Newton's theory of gravity to make it consistent with the principle of relativity. (This "repair" produced only minor corrections when applied to our solar system, but has sweeping philosophical implications.) If the principle of relativity underlies the structure of all forces in nature, if all known phenomena are consistent with the principle, then it is not especially necessary to introduce special relativity in the context of its historical origins in electromagnetic theory.*

In this chapter we are taking a non-historical point of view. We already know about special relativity (from chapter one), and have just studied Coulomb's electrical force law and some simple applications like the electron gun and basic circuits. We would now like to see if Coulomb's law is consistent with the principle of relativity. In some sense, we would like to do for Coulomb's law of electricity what Einstein did to Newton's law of gravity.

Two Garden Peas

In preparation for our discussion of relativistic effects in electricity theory, let us review a homely example that demonstrates both how strong electric forces actually are, and how complete the cancellation must be for the world to act the way it does.

Suppose we had two garden peas, each with a mass of about 2 grams, separated by a distance of 1 meter. Each pea would contain about one mole (6×10^{23}) of protons in the atomic nuclei, and an equal number of electrons surrounding the nuclei. Thus each pea has a total positive charge +Q in the protons given by

$$
\left. \begin{array}{l} \text{total positive} \\ \text{charge in a} \\ \text{garden pea} \end{array} \right\} \approx 6 \times 10^{23} e
$$

$$
= 6 \times 10^{23} \times 1.6 \times 10^{-19}
$$

$$
= 10^5 \text{ coulombs}
$$

(1)

and there is an equal and opposite amount of negative charge in the electrons.

When two peas are separated by a distance of 1 meter as shown in Figure (1), we can think of there being four pairs of electric forces involved. The positive charge in pea (1) repels the positive charge in pea (2) with a force of magnitude

$$\left.\begin{array}{l}\text{repulsive force}\\\text{between positive}\\\text{charge in}\\\text{the two peas}\end{array}\right\} = \frac{QQ}{4\pi\varepsilon_0 r^2} \qquad (2)$$

which gives rise to one pair of repulsive forces. The negative charges in each pea also repel each other with a force of the same magnitude, giving rise to the second repulsive pair of electric forces. But the positive charge in pea (1) attracts the negative charge in pea (2), and the negative charge in pea (1) attracts the positive charge in pea (2). This gives us two pairs of attractive forces that precisely cancel the repulsive forces.

Let us put numbers into Equation (2) to see how big these cancelling electric forces are. Equation (2) can be viewed as giving the net force if we removed all the electrons from each garden pea, leaving just the pure positive charge of the protons. The result would be

$$|\vec{F}| = \frac{Q^2}{4\pi\varepsilon_0 r^2}$$

$$= \frac{(10^5 \text{ coulombs})^2}{4\pi \times 9 \times 10^{-12} \times (1)^2}$$

$$= 8.8 \times 10^{19} \text{ newtons} \qquad (3)$$

Figure 1

Electric forces between two garden peas. On pea #1, there is the attractive force between the protons in pea #1 and the electrons in pea #2, and between the electrons in pea #1 and the protons in pea #2. The two repulsive forces are between the electrons in the two peas and the protons in the two peas. The net force is zero.

To put this answer in a more recognizable form, note that the weight of one metric ton (1000 kg) of matter is

$$F_g \text{ (1 metric ton)} = mg$$

$$= 10^3 \text{ kg} \times 9.8 \frac{m}{\sec^2}$$

$$= 9.8 \times 10^3 \text{ newtons}$$

Expressing the force between our two positively charged peas in metric tons we get

$$\left.\begin{array}{l}\text{repulsive force}\\\text{between two}\\\text{positive peas}\\\text{1 meter apart}\end{array}\right\} = \frac{8.8 \times 10^{19} \text{ newtons}}{9.8 \times 10^3 \text{ newtons/ton}}$$

$$\approx \boxed{10^{16} \text{ tons !}}$$

$$(4)$$

If we stripped the electrons from two garden peas, and placed them one meter apart, they would repel each other with an electric force of 10^{16} tons!! Yet for two real garden peas, the attractive and repulsive electric force cancel so precisely that the peas can lie next to each other on your dinner plate.

Exercise 1

Calculate the strength of the gravitational force between the peas. How much stronger is the uncancelled electric force of Equation (3)?

With forces of the order of 10^{16} tons precisely cancelling in two garden peas, we can see that even the tiniest imbalance in these forces could lead to striking results. An imbalance of one part in 10^{16}, one part in ten million billion, would leave a one ton residual electric force. This is still huge. We have to take seriously imbalances that are thousands of times smaller. One possible source of an imbalance is the Lorentz contraction, as seen in the following thought experiment.

A THOUGHT EXPERIMENT

In our previous discussion of electric currents, we had difficulty drawing diagrams showing the electrons flowing through the positive charge. To clarify the role of the positive and negative charge, we suggested a model of a copper wire in which we think of the positive and negative charge as being attached to separate rods as shown in Figure (22-5a) repeated here. In that model the rods have equal and opposite charge to represent the fact that the copper wire is electrically neutral, and the negative rod is moving to represent the electric current being carried by a flow of the negative conduction electrons.

The point of the model in Figure (22-5) was to show that a left directed negative current, seen in (a) is essentially equivalent to a right directed positive current seen in (b). In Figure (22-5a), we drew a stick figure diagram of a person walking to the left at the same speed v as the negative rod. Figure (22-5b) is the same setup from the point of view of the stick figure person. She sees the negative rod at rest and the positive rod moving to the right as shown.

In another calculation, we saw that if a millimeter cross section copper wire carried a steady current of one ampere, the conduction electrons would have to move

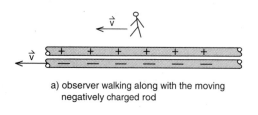

a) observer walking along with the moving
   negatively charged rod

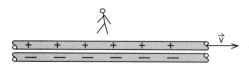

b) from the observer's point of view the negative
   rod is at rest and the positive charge is moving
   to the right

Figure 22-5 a,b
In (a) we have a left directed negative current, while in (b) we have a right directed positive current. The only difference is the perspective of the observer. (You can turn a negative current into an oppositely flowing positive one simply by moving your head.)

at the slow speed of 1/27 of a millimeter per second, a motion so slow that it would be hard to detect. As a result there should be no important physical difference between the two points of view, and a left directed negative current should be physically equivalent to a right directed positive current.

A closer examination of Figure (22-5) shows that we have left something out. The bottom figure, (22-5b) is not precisely what the moving observer sees. To show what has been left out, we have in Figure (2a) redrawn Figure (22-5a) and carefully labeled the individual charges. To maintain strict overall charge neutrality we have used charges $+Q$ on the positive rod, charges $-Q$ on the negative rod, and both sets of charges have equal separations of ℓ centimeters.

From the point of view of the moving observer in Figure (2b), the negative rod is at rest and the positive rod is moving to the right as we saw back in Figure (22-5b). But, ***due to the Lorentz contraction, the spacing between the charges is no longer*** ℓ ***!*** Since the positive rod was at rest and is now moving, the length of the positive spacing must be contracted to a distance $\ell\sqrt{1 - v^2/c^2}$ as shown.

On the other hand the negative rod was moving in Figure (2a), therefore the negative spacing must expand to $\ell/\sqrt{1 - v^2/c^2}$ when the negative rod comes to rest. *(Start with a spacing $\ell/\sqrt{1 - v^2/c^2}$ for the negative charges at rest in Figure (2b), and go up to Figure (2a) where the negative rod is moving at a speed v. There the spacing must contract by a factor $\sqrt{1 - v^2/c^2}$, and the new spacing is $\ell/\sqrt{1 - v^2/c^2} \times \sqrt{1 - v^2/c^2} = \ell$ as shown.)*

As a result of the Lorentz contraction, the moving observer will see that the positive charges on her moving rod are closer together than the negative charges on her stationary rod. (We have exaggerated this effect in our sketch, Figure (2b)). Thus the observer sees not only a right directed positive current, but also ***a net positive charge density*** on her two rods. The Lorentz contraction has changed a neutral wire in Figure (2a) into a positively charged one in Figure (2b)!

(If you are worried about conservation of electric charge, see the appendix to this chapter.)

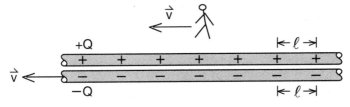

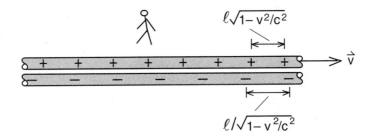

a) Observer walking along with the moving negatively charged rod.

b) Charged rods from the observer's point of view. Now that the positive charge is moving, the spacing between positive charges has **contracted** from ℓ to $\ell\sqrt{1-v^2/c^2}$. The negative rod is now at rest, the Lorentz contraction is undone, and the negative spacing has **expanded** from ℓ to $\ell/\sqrt{1-v^2/c^2}$.

Figure 2
An electric current from two points of view.

Charge Density on the Two Rods

Our next step will be to calculate the net charge density λ on the pair of rods shown in Figure (2b). Somewhat messy algebra is required for this calculation, but the result will be used in much of the remainder of the text. The effort will be worth it.

If we have a rod with charges spaced a distance d apart as shown in Figure (3), then a unit length of the rod, 1 meter, contains 1/d charges. (For example, if d = .01 meter, then there will be 1/d = 100 charges per meter.) If each charge is of strength Q, then there is a total charge Q/d on each meter of the rod. Thus the charge density is λ = Q/d coulombs per meter. Applying this result to the positive rod of Figure (2b) gives us a positive charge density

$$\lambda_+ = \frac{Q}{d_+} = \frac{Q}{\ell \sqrt{1 - v^2/c^2}} \quad \frac{coulombs}{meter} \quad (5)$$

And on the negative rod the charge density is

$$\lambda_- = \frac{-Q}{d_-} = \frac{-Q}{\ell/\sqrt{1 - v^2/c^2}} \quad \frac{coulombs}{meter}$$

$$= \frac{-Q\sqrt{1 - v^2/c^2}}{\ell} \quad (6)$$

Multiplying the top and bottom of the right side of Equation (6) by $\sqrt{1 - v^2/c^2}$, we can write λ_- as

$$\lambda_- = \frac{-Q\sqrt{1 - v^2/c^2}}{\ell} \times \frac{\sqrt{1 - v^2/c^2}}{\sqrt{1 - v^2/c^2}}$$

$$= \frac{-Q}{\ell\sqrt{1 - v^2/c^2}} \left(1 - v^2/c^2\right) \quad (7)$$

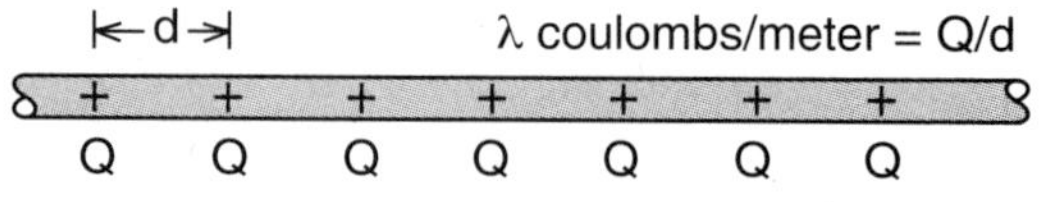

|←─d─→| λ coulombs/meter = Q/d

+   +   +   +   +   +   +

Q   Q   Q   Q   Q   Q   Q

Figure 3
If the charges are a distance d apart, then there are 1/d charges per meter of rod. (If d = .1 meters, then there are 10 charges/meter.) If the magnitude of each charge is Q, then λ, the charge per meter, is Q times as great, i.e., $\lambda = Q \times (1/d)$.

The net charge density λ is obtained by adding λ_+ and λ_- of Equations (5) and (7) to get

$$\lambda = \lambda_+ + \lambda_- = \frac{Q}{\ell\sqrt{1 - v^2/c^2}} \left\{ 1 - (1 - v^2/c^2) \right\}$$

$$\lambda = \frac{Q}{\ell\sqrt{1 - v^2/c^2}} \left\{ \frac{v^2}{c^2} \right\} = \lambda_+ \frac{v^2}{c^2} \quad (8)$$

Equation (8) can be simplified by noting that the current i carried by the positive rod in Figure (2b) is equal to the charge λ_+ on 1 meter of the rod times the speed v of the rod

$$i = \lambda_+ v \qquad \begin{array}{l} \textit{current i} \\ \textit{carried by the} \\ \textit{positive rod} \end{array} \quad (9)$$

(In one second, v meters of rod move past any fixed cross-sectional area, and the charge on this v meters of rod is λ_+v.) Using Equation (9), we can replace λ_+ and one of the v's in Equation (8) by i to get the result

$$\boxed{\lambda = \frac{iv}{c^2}} \quad (10)$$

Due to the Lorentz contraction, the moving observer in Figure (2b) sees a net ***positive charge density*** $\lambda = iv/c^2$ on the wire which from our point of view, Figure (2a) ***was precisely neutral***.

Although Equation (10) may be formally correct, one has the feeling that it is insane to worry about the Lorentz contraction for speeds as slow as 2 millimeters per minute. But the Lorentz contraction changes a precisely neutral pair of rods shown in Figure (2a), into a pair with a net positive charge density $\lambda = iv/c^2$ in Figure (2b). We have unbalanced a perfect cancellation of charge which could lead to an imbalance in the cancellation of electrostatic forces. Since we saw from our discussion of the two garden peas that imbalances as small as one part in 10^{18} or less might be observable, let us see if there are any real experiments where the charge density λ is detectable.

A PROPOSED EXPERIMENT

How would we detect the charge imbalance in Figure (2b)? If there is a net positive charge density l on the two rods in Figure (2b), repeated here again in Figure (4), then the net charge should produce a radial electric field whose strength is given by the formula

$$E = \frac{\lambda}{2\pi\varepsilon_0 r} \qquad (11), [19\text{-}36]$$

We derived this result in our discussion of Gauss' law in Chapter 19. *(Remember that the two separate rods are our model for a single copper wire carrying a current. The rods are not physically separated as we have had to draw them, the negative conduction electrons and positive nuclei are flowing through each other.)*

We can test for the existence of the electric field produced by the positive charge density $\lambda = iv/c^2$ by placing a test particle of charge q a distance r from the

wire as shown in Figure (4). This test particle should experience a force

$$\vec{F} = q\vec{E} \qquad (12)$$

which would be repulsive if the test particle q is positive and attractive if q is negative. Using Equations (10) for λ and (11) for E, Equation (12) gives for the predicted magnitude of $\vec{F}$:

$$\left|\vec{F}\right| = q\left|\vec{E}\right| = q\frac{\lambda}{2\pi\varepsilon_0 r} = \frac{q}{2\pi\varepsilon_0 r}\frac{iv}{c^2} \qquad (13)$$

Rearranging the terms on the right side of Equation (13), we can write $\left|\vec{F}\right|$ in the form

$$\left|\vec{F}\right| = qv\times\left\{\frac{i}{2\pi r\varepsilon_0 c^2}\right\} \qquad (14)$$

Why we have written Equation (14) this way will become clear shortly.

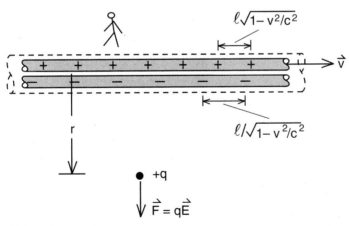

Figure 4
To test for the net charge density, as seen by the observer at rest relative to the minus charge, the observer places a test charge q a distance r from the wire as shown. If there is a net charge λ on the wire, the charge will produce an electric field $\vec{E}$, which will exert a force $\vec{F}= q\vec{E}$ on the test particle as shown.

Origin of Magnetic Forces

You might think that the next step is to put reasonable numbers into Equation (14) and see if we get a force $\vec{F}$ that is strong enough to be observed. But there is an important thought experiment we will carry out first. The idea is to look at the force on a test particle from two different points of view, one where the wire appears charged as in Figures (4 & 2b), and where the wire appears neutral as in Figure (2a). The two points of view are shown in Figure (5).

Figure (5b), on the left, is the situation as observed by the *moving observer*. She has a copper wire carrying a positive current directed to the right. Due to the Lorentz contraction, her copper wire has a charge density λ which creates an electric field $\vec{E}$. To observe $\vec{E}$, she mounts a test particle $-q$ at one end of a spring whose other end is fixed, nailed to her floor. She detects the force $\vec{F} = -q\vec{E}$ by observing how much the spring has been stretched.

Our point of view is shown in Figure (5a). It is exactly the same setup, we have touched nothing! It is just viewed by someone moving to the right relative to her.

In our point of view, the moving observer, the negative rod, and the test particle are all moving to the left at a speed v. The positive rod is at rest, the Lorentz contractions are undone, and there is *no net charge* on our rods. All we have is a negative current flowing to the left.

We can also see the test particle. It is now moving to the left at a speed v, and it is still attached to the spring.

Here is the crucial point of this discussion. We also see that the spring is stretched. We also see that the end of the spring has been pulled beyond the mark indicating the unstretched length. We also detect the force $\vec{F}$ on the test particle!

Why do we see a force $\vec{F}$ on the test particle? Our copper wire is electrically neutral; we do not have an electric field $\vec{E}$ to produce the force $\vec{F}$. Yet $\vec{F}$ is there. If we cut the spring, the test particle would accelerate toward the copper wire, and both we and the moving observer would see this acceleration.

At this point, we have come upon a basic problem. Even if the Lorentz contraction is very small and the force $\vec{F}$ in Figure (5b) is very small, we at least predict that $\vec{F}$ exists. In Figure (5a) we predict that a neutral wire, that is carrying a current but *has absolutely no net charge on it*, exerts an attractive force on a moving negative charge as shown.

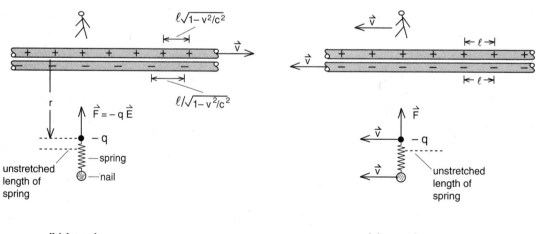

(b) her view   **(a) our view**

Figure 5

Two views of the same experiment. For the observer moving with the electrons, she sees a positively charged wire exerting an attractive force on the negative charge at rest. We see an electrically neutral wire carrying a negative current, and a moving negative charge. The spring is still stretched, meaning the attractive force is still there.

With a few modifications, the experiment shown in Figure (5a) is easy to perform and gives clear results. Instead of a negative test particle attached to a spring, we will use a beam of electrons in an electron gun as shown in Figure (6). In Figure (6a) we see the setup of our thought experiment. In Figure (6b) we have replaced the two charged rods with a neutral copper wire carrying a current –i, and replaced the test particle with an electron beam.

According to Equation (14), the force $\vec{F}$ on the test particle –q should have a strength proportional to the current i in the wire. Thus when we turn on a current (*shorting the wire on the terminals of a car storage battery to produce a healthy current*) we will see the electron beam deflected toward the wire if there is an observable force. The experimental result is shown in Figure (6c). There is a large, easily observed deflection. *The force $\vec{F}$ is easily seen*.

Exercise 2

In Figure (7) we reversed the direction of the current in the wire and observe that the electron beam is deflected away from the wire. Devise a thought experiment, analogous to the one shown in Figure (5a,b) that explains why the electron beam is repelled from the wire by this setup. (This is not a trivial problem; you may have to try several charge distributions on moving rods before you can imitate the situation shown in Figure (7a). But the effort is worth it because you will be making a physical prediction that is checked by the experimental results of Figure (7b).

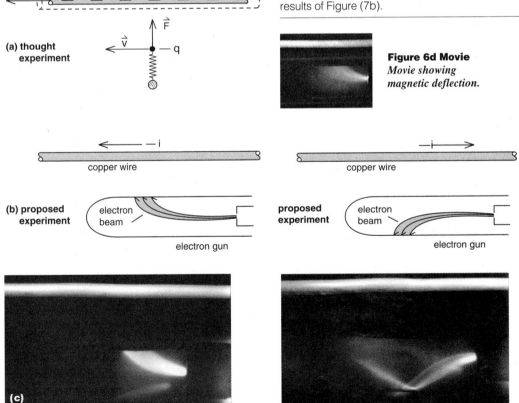

Figure 6d Movie
Movie showing magnetic deflection.

(a) thought experiment

(b) proposed experiment

electron beam

copper wire

electron gun

(c)

proposed experiment

electron beam

copper wire

electron gun

Figure 6
For an experimental test of the results of the thought experiment, we replace the moving negative charge with a beam of electrons in an electron gun. The electrons are attracted to the wire as predicted.

Figure 7
If we reverse the direction of the current in the wire, the electrons in the beam are repelled.

MAGNETIC FORCES

Historically an electric force was defined as the force between charged particles and was expressed by Coulomb's law. The force in Figure (5a) between a moving test charge and an **uncharged** wire does not meet this criterion. You might say that for historical reasons, it is not eligible to be called an electric force.

The forces we saw in Figures (6c) and (7b), between a moving charge and a neutral electric current, were known before special relativity and were called *magnetic forces*. Our derivation of the magnetic force in Figure (5a) from the electric force seen in Figure (5b) demonstrates that *electric and magnetic forces in this example are the same thing just seen from a different point of view*.

When we go from Figure (5b) to (5a), which we can do by moving our head at a speed of 2 millimeters per minute, we see essentially no change in the physical setup but we have an enormous change in perspective. We go from a right directed positive current to a left directed negative current, and the force on the test particle changes from an electric to a magnetic force.

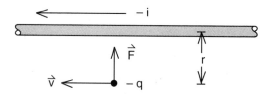

Figure 8
Force on a charge -q moving at a speed v parallel to a negative current -i a distance r away.

MAGNETIC FORCE LAW

From our Coulomb's law calculation of the electric force in Figure (5a), we were able to obtain the formula for the magnetic force in Figure (5b). The result, Equation (14) repeated here, is

$$\left|\vec{F}\right| = qv \times \left\{ \frac{i}{2\pi r\varepsilon_0 c^2} \right\} \qquad \text{(14 repeated)}$$

where q is the charge on the test particle, i the current in the wire, and r the distance from the wire to the charge as shown in Figure (8). The only thing our derivation does not make clear is whether v in Equation (14) is the speed of the test charge or the speed of the electrons in the wire. We can't tell because we used the same speed v for both in our thought experiment. A more complex thought experiment will show that the v in Equation (14) is the speed of the test particle.

The Magnetic Field B

In Equation (14) we have broken the somewhat complex formula for the magnetic force into two parts. The first part qv is related to the test charge (q is its charge and v its speed), and the second part in the curly brackets, which we will designate by the letter B

$$B \equiv \frac{i}{2\pi r\varepsilon_0 c^2} \qquad (15)$$

is related to the wire. The wire is carrying a current i and located a distance r away.

The quantity B in Equation (15) is called the magnitude of *the magnetic field of the wire*, and in terms of B the magnetic force becomes

$$\boxed{\left|\vec{F}_{magnetic}\right| = qvB} \qquad (16)$$

Equation (16) is almost a complete statement of the magnetic force law. What we have left to do for the law is to assign a direction to B, i.e., turn it into the vector $\vec{B}$, and then turn Equation (16) into a vector equation for the force $\vec{F}_{magnetic}$.

There is one more definition. In the MKS system of units, it is traditional to define the constant μ_0 by the equation

$$\mu_0 \equiv \frac{1}{\varepsilon_0 c^2}$$ *definition of μ_0*   (17)

Using this definition of μ_0 in Equation (15) for B, we get

$$B = \frac{\mu_0 i}{2\pi r}$$ *magnetic field of a wire*   (18)

as the formula for the magnetic field of a wire.

It turns out to be quite an accomplishment to get Equations (16), (17), and (18) out of one thought experiment. These equations will provide the foundation for most of the rest of our discussion of electric and magnetic (electromagnetic) theory.

By the way, we can rewrite Equation (17)

$$\mu_0 = \frac{1}{\varepsilon_0 c^2}$$

in the form

$$\mu_0 \varepsilon_0 c^2 = 1$$

$$c^2 = \frac{1}{\mu_0 \varepsilon_0}$$

$$c = 1/\sqrt{\mu_0 \varepsilon_0}$$

which is Maxwell's formula for the speed of light [see Equation (5) of Chapter 1].

Direction of the Magnetic Field

We will temporarily leave our special relativity thought experiment and approach magnetism in a more traditional way. Figure (9) is a sketch of the magnetic field of the earth. By convention the direction of the magnetic field lines are defined by the direction that a compass needle points. At the equator the magnetic field lines point north (as does a compass needle) and the field lines are parallel to the surface of the earth. As we go north from the equator the magnetic field lines begin to point down into the earth as well as north. At the north magnetic pole the magnetic field lines go straight down.

Figure (9) is drawn with the magnetic north pole at the top. The earth's rotational axis, passing through the true north pole, is at an angle of 11.5 degrees as shown. Over time the location of the earth's magnetic pole wanders, and occasionally flips down to the southern hemisphere. Currently the north magnetic pole is located in north central Canada.

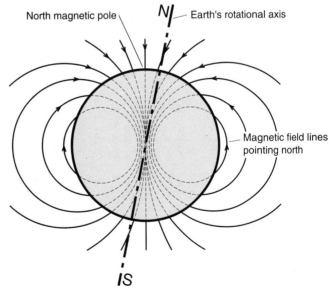

North magnetic pole   **N** — Earth's rotational axis

Magnetic field lines pointing north

IS

Figure 9
Magnetic field of the earth. The magnetic field lines show the direction a freely floating compass needle would point at any location outside the earth. For example, at the equator the compass needle would be parallel to the surface of the earth and point north. At the north magnetic pole, the compass needle would point straight down (and thus not be very useful for navigation).

As we mentioned, it is by long standing convention that the direction of the magnetic field is defined by the direction a compass needle points. We can therefore use a set of small compasses to map the direction of the magnetic field.

In 1820, while preparing a physics lecture demonstration for a class of students, Hans Christian Oersted discovered that an electric current in a wire could

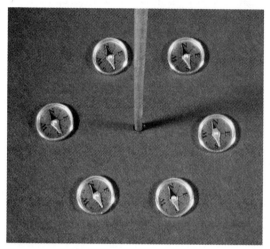

Figure 10a
With no current flowing in the wire, all the compass needles point north.

deflect a compass needle. This was the first evidence of the connection between the subject of electricity with its charges and currents, and magnetism with its magnets and compasses.

The fact that a wire carrying a current deflects a compass needle means that the current must be producing a magnetic field. We can *use the deflected compass needles to show us the shape of the magnetic field* of a wire. This is done in Figures (10a,b) where we see a ring of compasses surrounding a vertical wire. In (10a) there is no current in the wire, and all the compass needles all point north (black tips). In (10b) we have turned on an upward directed current in the wire, and the compass needles point in a circle around the wire. *Using the north pole of the compass needle to define the direction of the magnetic field*, we see that the magnetic field goes in a counterclockwise circle around the wire.

In Figure (11) we have replaced the compasses in Figure (10) with a sprinkle of iron filings. When the current in the wire is turned on, the iron filings align themselves to produce the circular field pattern shown. What is happening is that each iron filing is acting as a small compass needle and is lining up parallel to the magnetic field. While we cannot tell which way is north with iron filings, we get a much more complete

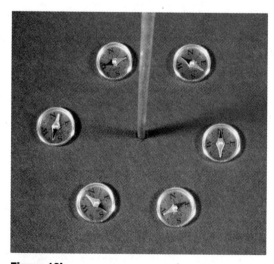

Figure 10b
When an upward directed current is turned on, the compass needles point in a counterclockwise circle about the wire.

Figure 11
Iron filings sprinkled around a current form a circular pattern. Each iron filing lines up like a compass needle, giving us a map of the magnetic field.

picture or map of the direction of the magnetic field. Figure (11) is convincing evidence that the magnetic field surrounding a wire carrying a current is in a circular field, not unlike the circular flow pattern of water around the core of a vortex.

The use of iron filings turns out to be a wonderfully simple way to map magnetic field patterns. In Figure (12), a sheet of cardboard was placed on a bar magnet and iron filings sprinkled on the cardboard. The result, with two poles or points of focus resembles what is called a *dipole field*.

In Figure (13) we have thrown iron filings at an old iron magnet and created what one young observer called a "magnet plant." Here we see the three dimensional structure of the magnetic field, not only between the pole pieces but over the top half of the magnet.

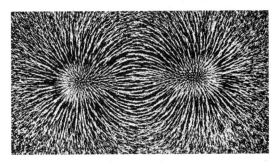

Figure 12
A sheet of cardboard is placed over the poles of a magnet and sprinkled with iron filings. From the pattern of the filings we see the shape of the more complex magnetic field of the magnet.

Figure 13
You get a three dimensional picture of the magnetic field if you pour the iron filings directly on the magnet. Our young daughter called this a **Magnet Plant.**

The Right Hand Rule for Currents

Iron filings give us an excellent picture of the shape of the magnetic field, but do not tell us which way the field is pointing. For that we have to go back to compasses as in Figure (9), where $\vec{B}$ is defined as pointing in the direction of the north tip of the compass needle. In that figure we see that when a positive current i is flowing toward us, the magnetic field goes in a counter clockwise direction as illustrated in Figure (14).

The above description for the direction may be hard to remember. A more concise description is the following. *Point the thumb of your right hand in the direction of the current* as shown in Figure (14), then *your fingers will curl in the direction of the magnetic field*. This mnemonic device for remembering the direction of $\vec{B}$ is one of the *right hand rules*. (This is the version we used in Figure (2-37) to distinguish right and left hand threads.) If we had used compasses that pointed south, we would have gotten a left hand rule.

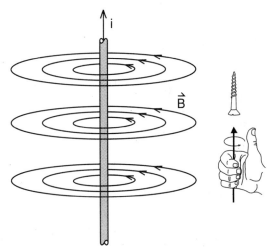

Figure 14
Right hand rule for the magnetic field of a current i. Point the thumb in the direction of the positive current and your fingers curl in the direction of the magnetic field.

Parallel Currents Attract

While we are in the business of discussing mnemonic rules, there is another that makes it easy to remember whether a charge moving parallel to a current is attracted or repelled. In Figure (6) we had a beam of negative electrons moving parallel to a negative current -i, and the electrons were attracted to the current. In Figure (7) the current was reversed and the electrons were repelled. One can work out a thought experiment similar to the ones we have done in this chapter to show that a positive charge moving parallel to a positive current as shown in Figure (15) is attracted.

The simple, yet general rule is that **parallel currents attract, opposite currents repel**. A positive charge moving in the direction of a positive current, or a negative charge moving along with a negative current are attracting parallel currents. When we have negative charges moving opposite to a negative current as in Figure (7) we have an example of opposite currents that repel.

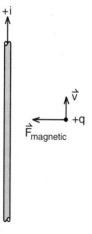

Figure 15
A positive charge, moving parallel to a positive current, is attracted by the current. Thinking of the moving positive charge as a positive upward directed current, we have the rule that parallel currents attract, opposite currents repel.

The Magnetic Force Law

Now that we have a direction assigned to the magnetic field $\vec{B}$ we are in a position to include directions in our formula for magnetic forces. In Figure (16) which is the same as (15) but also shows the magnetic field, we have a positive charge moving parallel to a positive current, and therefore an attractive force whose magnitude is given by Equation (16) as

$$\left|\vec{F}_{mag}\right| \;=\; qvB \qquad\qquad \text{(16 repeated)}$$

There are three different vectors in Equation (16), $\vec{F}_{mag}, \vec{v},$ and $\vec{B}$. Our problem is to see if we can combine these vectors in any way, so that something like Equation (16) tells us both the magnitude and the direction of the magnetic force $\vec{F}_{mag}$. That is, can we turn Equation (16) into a vector equation?

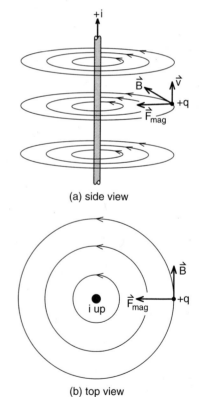

(a) side view

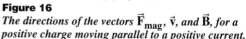

(b) top view

Figure 16
The directions of the vectors $\vec{F}_{mag}$, $\vec{v}$, and $\vec{B}$, for a positive charge moving parallel to a positive current.

The right hand side of Equation (16) involves the product of the vectors $\vec{v}$ and $\vec{B}$. So far in the text we have discussed two different ways of multiplying vectors; the dot product $\vec{A} \cdot \vec{B}$ which gives a scalar number C, and the cross product $\vec{A} \times \vec{B}$ which gives the vector $\vec{C}$. Since we want the product of $\vec{v}$ and $\vec{B}$ to give us the vector $\vec{F}_{mag}$, the cross product appears to be the better candidate. We can try

$$\vec{F}_{mag} = q\vec{v} \times \vec{B} \qquad \begin{array}{l} magnetic \\ force\ law \end{array} \qquad (19)$$

as our vector equation.

To see if Equation (19) works, look at the three vectors $\vec{v}$, $\vec{B}$, and $\vec{F}_{mag}$ of Figure (16) redrawn in Figure (17). The force $\vec{F}_{mag}$ is perpendicular to the plane defined by $\vec{v}$ and $\vec{B}$ which is the essential feature of a vector cross product. To see if $\vec{F}_{mag}$ is in the correct direction, we use the cross product right hand rule described on page (5) of Chapter 2.

Point the fingers of your **right** hand in the direction of the first vector in the cross product, in this case $\vec{v}$, and curl them in the direction of the second vector, now $\vec{B}$. Then your thumb will point in the direction of the cross product $\vec{v} \times \vec{B}$. Looking at Figure (17), we see that the thumb of the right hand sketch does point in the direction of $\vec{F}_{mag}$, therefore the direction of $\vec{F}_{mag}$ is correctly given by the cross product $\vec{v} \times \vec{B}$. (If the direction had come out wrong, we could have used $\vec{B} \times \vec{v}$ instead.)

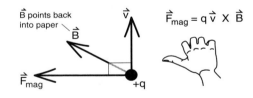

Figure 17
Right hand rule for the vector cross product $\vec{v} \times \vec{B}$.
Point the fingers of your right hand in the direction
of the first vector $\vec{v}$, and then curl them in the
direction of the second vector $\vec{B}$. Your thumb ends
up pointing in the direction of the vector $\vec{v} \times \vec{B}$.

Although the formula for $\vec{F}_{mag}$, Equation (19), was derived for a special case, the result is general. Whenever a particle of charge q is moving with a velocity $\vec{v}$ through a magnetic field $\vec{B}$, no matter what the relative directions of $\vec{v}$ and $\vec{B}$, the magnetic force is correctly given as $q\vec{v} \times \vec{B}$.

Exercise 3

Using the magnetic force law $\vec{F}_{mag} = q\vec{v} \times \vec{B}$ and the right hand rule for the magnetic field of a current, show that:

(a) An electron moving parallel to a negative current -i is attracted (Figure 6).

(b) An electron moving opposite to a negative current is repelled (Figure 7).

Lorentz Force Law

Since electric and magnetic forces are closely related, it makes sense to write one formula for both the electric and the magnetic force on a charged particle. If we have a charge q moving with a velocity $\vec{v}$ through an electric field $\vec{E}$ and a magnetic field $\vec{B}$, then the electric force is $q\vec{E}$, the magnetic force $q\vec{v} \times \vec{B}$, and the total "electromagnetic" force is given by

$$\boxed{\vec{F} = q\vec{E} + q\vec{v} \times \vec{B}} \qquad \begin{array}{l} Lorentz \\ force\ law \end{array} \qquad (20)$$

Equation (20), which is known as the *Lorentz force law*, is a complete description of the electric and magnetic forces on a charged particle, which is useful when $\vec{E}$ and $\vec{B}$ are known.

APPLYING THE MAGNETIC FORCE LAW

Dimensions of the
Magnetic Field, Tesla and Gauss

The dimensions of the magnetic field can be obtained from the magnetic force law. In the MKS system we have

$$F(newtons) = q(coulombs) \times v\left[\frac{meters}{second}\right] \times B$$

which gives us B in units of newton seconds per coulomb meter. This set of dimensions is given the name **tesla**

$$\boxed{\frac{newton\ second}{coulomb\ meter} \equiv tesla} \quad \begin{array}{l} MKS\,units \\ for \\ magnetic \\ fields \end{array} \quad (21)$$

Although most MKS electrical quantities like the volt and ampere are convenient, the tesla is too large. Only the strongest electromagnets, or the new superconducting magnets used in particle accelerators or magnetic resonance imaging apparatus, can produce fields of the order of 1 tesla or more. Fields produced by coils of wire we use in the lab are typically 100 times weaker, and the earth's magnetic field is another 100 times weaker still.

In the CGS system of units, magnetic fields are measured in gauss, where

$$\boxed{1\ gauss = 10^{-4}\ tesla} \quad (22)$$

The gauss is so much more convenient a unit that there is a major incentive to work with CGS units when studying magnetic phenomena. For example the earth's magnetic field has a strength of about 1 gauss at the earth's surface, and the magnetic field that deflected the electrons in Figures (6) and (7) has a strength of about 30 gauss at the electron beam. Refrigerator magnets have comparable strengths.

We could be pedantic, insist on using only MKS units, and suffer with numbers like .00021 tesla in discussions of the earth's magnetic field. But if someone wants you to measure a magnetic field, they hand you a "gauss meter" not a tesla meter. Magnetic-type instruments are usually calibrated in gauss.

If you worked only with tesla, you would have a hard time communicating with much of the scientific community. What we will do in this text is use either gauss or tesla depending upon which is the more convenient unit. When we come to a calculation, we will convert any gauss to tesla, just as we convert any distances measured in centimeters to meters.

UNIFORM MAGNETIC FIELDS

Using the magnetic force law $\vec{F}_{mag} = q\vec{v} \times \vec{B}$ to calculate magnetic forces is often the easy part of the problem. The hard part can be to determine the magnetic field $\vec{B}$. For a current in a straight wire, we were able to use a thought experiment and the Lorentz contraction to get Equation (20) for the strength of $\vec{B}$. But in more complicated situations, where we may have bent wires, thought experiments become too difficult and we need other techniques for calculating $\vec{B}$.

One of the other techniques, which is described in the Satellite Chapter (10), is called **Ampere's Law.** The law allows one to calculate the magnetic field of a simple current distribution in much the same way that Gauss' law allowed us to calculate the electric field of simple charge distributions. In this core text, we will confine our study of the magnetic force law to the simplest of all possible magnetic fields, the uniform magnetic field.

Figure 18
Between the poles of this magnet there is a relatively uniform magnetic field.

Working with uniform magnetic fields, fields that are constant in both magnitude and direction, is so convenient that physicists and engineers go to great lengths to construct them. One place to find a uniform field is between the flat pole pieces of a magnet, as seen in Figure (18) which is our "magnet plant" of Figure (13) with fewer iron filings.

If we bend a wire in a loop, then a current around the loop produces the fairly complex field pattern shown in Figure (19). When we use two loops as seen in Figure (20), the field becomes more complicated in some places but begins to be more uniform in the central region between the coils. With many loops, with the coil of wire shown in Figure (21a), we get a nearly uniform field inside. Such a coil is called a ***solenoid***, and is studied extensively in the Satellite Chapter (10) on Ampere's law. An iron filing map of the field of a large diameter, tightly wound solenoid is seen in Figure (21b).

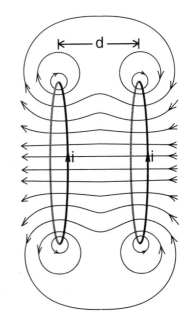

Figure 20
The magnetic field in the region between a pair of coils is relatively uniform. We can achieve the greatest uniformity by making the separation d between the coils equal to the radius of the coils. Such a setup is called a pair of **Helmholtz coils.**

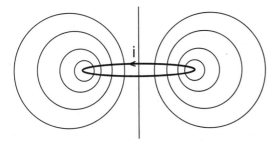

Figure 19
The magnetic field of a current loop is fairly complex.

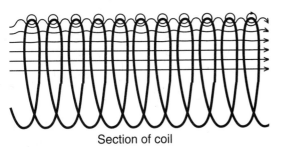

Section of coil

Figure 21a
Magnetic field in the upper half of a section of a coil of wire. When you have many closely spaced coils, the field inside can become quite uniform through most of the length of the coil.

Figure 21b
Iron filing map of the magnetic field of a large diameter coil. (Student project, Alexandra Lesk and Kirsten Teany.)

Helmholtz Coils

For now we will confine our attention to the reasonably uniform field in the central region between two coils seen in Figure (20). Helmholtz discovered that when the coils are spaced a distance d apart equal to the coil radius r, as in Figure (22), we get a maximally uniform field $\vec{B}$ between the coils. This arrangement, which is called a pair of *Helmholtz coils*, is commonly used in physics and engineering apparatus. Figure (23) shows a pair of Helmholtz coils we use in our undergraduate physics labs and which will be used for several of the experiments discussed later. An iron filing map of the field produced by these coils is seen in Figure (24a), and one of the experiments will give us a field plot similar to Figure (24b).

In our derivation of the magnetic field of a current in a straight wire, we saw that *the strength of the magnetic field was proportional to the current i in the wire*. This is true even if the wire is bent to form coils, or even twisted into a complex tangle. That means that once you have mapped the magnetic field for a given current (i) in a set of wires, doubling the current produces the same shape map with twice as strong a field.

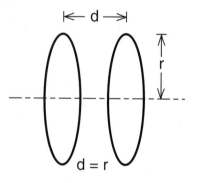

Figure 22
For Helmholtz coils, the separation d equals the coil radius r.

For the Helmholtz coils in Figure (23), it was observed that when a current of one amp flowed through the coils, the strength of the magnetic field in the central regions was 8 gauss. A current of 2 amps produced a 16 gauss field. Thus the field strength, **for these coils,** is related to the current i by

$$B(gauss) = 8i(amps)$$

for the Helmholtz coils of Fig.(23) only

In the lab we measure the strength of B simply by reading (i) from an ampmeter and multiplying by 8. Of course, if you are using a different set of coils, (i) will be multiplied by a different number. *(Do not worry about the mixed units, remember that we convert gauss to tesla before doing MKS calculations.)*

Figure 23
Helmholtz coils used in a number of lab experiments discussed in the text. Each coil consists of 60 turns of fairly heavy magnet wire.

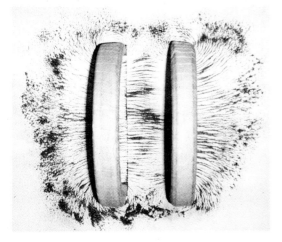

Figure 24a
Iron filing map of the magnetic field of the Helmholtz coils. (Student project, Alexandra Lesk and Kirsten Teany.)

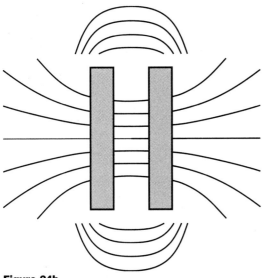

Figure 24b
Plot from a student experiment, of the magnetic field in the region between and around the coils.

MOTION OF CHARGED PARTICLES IN MAGNETIC FIELDS

In physics, one of the primary uses of magnetic fields is to control the motion of charged particles. When the magnetic field is uniform, the motion is particularly simple and has many practical applications from particle accelerators to mass spectrometers. Here we will discuss this motion and several of the applications.

The main feature of the magnetic force law,

$$\vec{F}_{magnetic} = q\vec{v} \times \vec{B} \qquad \text{(19 repeated)}$$

is that because of the cross product $\vec{v} \times \vec{B}$, the magnetic force is ***always perpendicular*** to the velocity $\vec{v}$ of the charged particle. Back in Chapter 10 on Energy, in Equation (10-26)

$$\text{work} = \text{force} \times \text{parallel distance} \qquad \text{(10-26)}$$

we pointed out that the work done by a force $\vec{F}$ was the magnitude of the force F times the distance the object moved ***in the direction parallel*** to the force. The special feature of the magnetic force is that it is always perpendicular to the motion, never parallel to the direction that the particle is moving. As a result, ***magnetic forces do no work!*** They do not add or remove energy from a particle. All they do is change the direction of motion of the particle.

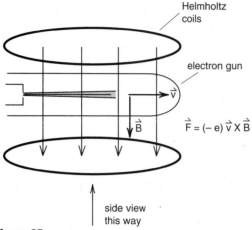

Helmholtz coils

electron gun

$\vec{v}$

$\vec{B}$

$\vec{F} = (-e)\, \vec{v} \times \vec{B}$

side view
this way

Figure 25a
Top view looking down on the electron gun placed between the Helmholtz coils. The electrons in the beam move perpendicular to the magnetic field $\vec{B}$. The magnetic force $\vec{F} = (-e)\, \vec{v} \times \vec{B}$ is directed up, out of the paper in this drawing.

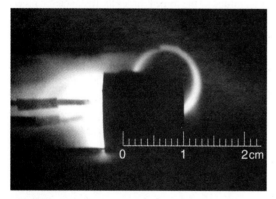

0   1   2cm

Figure 25b
Side view of the electron beam, as seen through the lower coil in Figure 25a. In this view the magnetic field is directed out of the paper toward the reader.

Figure 25d
Movie of the experiment.

MOTION IN A UNIFORM MAGNETIC FIELD

When we have a charged particle moving through a uniform magnetic field, we get a particularly simple kind of motion—the circular motion seen in Figure (25b). In Figure (25a) we sketched the experimental setup where an electron gun is placed between a pair of Helmholtz coils so that the magnetic field $\vec{B}$ is perpendicular to the electron beam as shown. Figure (25b) is a photograph of the electron beam deflected into a circular path. In Figure (25c) we have a sketch of the forces on an electron in the beam. The magnetic field B in this diagram is up out of the paper, thus $\vec{v} \times \vec{B}$ points radially out from the circle. But the electron has a negative charge, thus the magnetic force $\vec{F}_B$

$$\vec{F}_B = (-e)\, \vec{v} \times \vec{B} \qquad (23)$$

points in toward the center of the circle as shown.

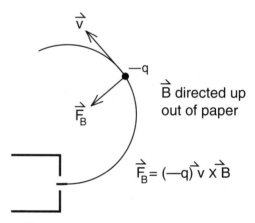

$\vec{v}$

$-q$

$\vec{F}_B$

**B directed up
out of paper**

$\vec{F}_B = (-q)\, \vec{v} \times \vec{B}$

Figure 25c
As the electrons move along a curved path, the magnetic force $\vec{F} = -q\,\vec{v} \times \vec{B}$ always remains perpendicular to the velocity and therefore cannot change the speed of the electrons. The resulting motion is uniform circular motion where the force and the acceleration are directed toward the center of the circle.

To apply Newton's second law to the electrons in Figure (25), we note that a particle moving in a circle accelerates toward the center of the circle, the same direction as $\vec{F}_{mag}$ in Figure (25c). Thus $\vec{F}_B$ and $m\vec{a}$ are in the same direction and we can use the fact that for circular motion $a = v^2/r$ to get $\left|\vec{F}_B\right| = m\left|\vec{a}\right|$ or

$$F_B = m(v^2/r)$$

$$qvB = mv^2/r \tag{24}$$

Solving for r, we predict from Equation (24) that the electron beam will be bent into a circle of radius r given by

$$r = \frac{mv}{qB} \tag{25}$$

Equation (25) is an important result that we will use often. But it is so easy to derive, and it is such good practice to derive it, that it may be a good idea not to memorize it.

Let us use the experimental numbers provided with Figure (25b) as an example of the use of Equation (25). In that figure, the strength of the magnetic field is B = 70 gauss, and the electrons were accelerated by an accelerating voltage of 135 volts. The constants m and q are the mass and charge of an electron.

The first step is to calculate the speed v of the electrons using the fact that the electrons have 135 eV of kinetic energy. We begin by converting from eV to joules using the conversion factor 1.6×10^{-19} joules per eV. This gives

$$\frac{1}{2}mv^2 = 135 \, \cancel{eV} \times 1.6 \times 10^{-19} \frac{joules}{\cancel{eV}}$$

$$v^2 = \frac{2 \times 135 \times 1.6 \times 10^{-19}}{.911 \times 10^{-30}} joules$$

$$= 47.4 \times 10^{12} \frac{meter^2}{sec^2} \tag{26}$$

$$v = 6.9 \times 10^6 \frac{meter}{sec}$$

Next convert B from gauss to the MKS tesla

$$70 \text{ gauss} = 70 \times 10^{-4} \text{ tesla} \tag{27}$$

Substituting Equations (26) and (27) in (25) gives

$$r = \frac{mv}{qB} = \frac{.911 \times 10^{-30} \times 6.9 \times 10^6}{1.6 \times 10^{-19} \times 7 \times 10^{-3}}$$

$$r = 5.6 \times 10^{-3} \text{ meter} = .56 \text{ cm} \tag{28}$$

Exercise 4

The scale of distance shown in Figure (25b) was drawn knowing the dimensions of the cap in the electron gun. Use this scale to estimate the radius of curvature of the electron beam and compare the result with the prediction of Equation (28).

Exercise 5

Use the experimental results shown in Figure (26), where B is also 70 gauss, to estimate the accelerating voltage used for the electrons in this beam. (The experimental answer is included in the homework answer section.)

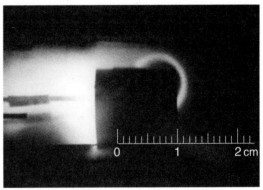

Figure 26
Use the fact that the magnetic field for this example was 70 gauss to estimate the accelerating voltage that produced the electron beam.

Particle Accelerators

Our knowledge of the structure of matter on a sub-atomic scale, where we study the various kinds of elementary particles, has come from our ability to accelerate particles to high energies in particle accelerators such as the synchrotron. In a synchrotron, an electric field $\vec{E}$ is used to give the particle's energy, and a magnetic field $\vec{B}$ is used to keep the particles confined to a circular track.

Figure (27a) is a schematic diagram of a small electron synchrotron. At the top is an electron gun that is used to produce a beam of electrons. In practice the gun is quickly turned on then off to produce a pulse of electrons.

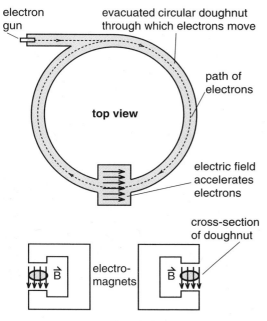

electron gun

evacuated circular doughnut through which electrons move

path of electrons

top view

electric field accelerates electrons

cross-section of doughnut

$\vec{B}$ electro-magnets $\vec{B}$

cross-sectional view

Figure 27a
Diagram of a synchrotron, in which the electrons, produced by the electron gun, travel through a circular evacuated doughnut. The electrons are accelerated by an electric field, gaining energy on each trip around. The electrons are kept in a circular orbit by an increasingly strong magnetic field produced by the electromagnets.

The pulse of electrons enter an evacuated circular track shown in the top view. To keep the pulse of electrons moving in the circular track, large electromagnets shown in the cross-sectional view are used to provide a perpendicular magnetic field. In this example the magnetic field $\vec{B}$ points downward so that the magnetic force $q\vec{v} \times \vec{B} = -e\vec{v} \times \vec{B}$ points inward toward the center of the track.

We saw that a magnetic field cannot do any work on the electrons since the magnetic force is perpendicular to the particle's velocity. Therefore to give the electrons more energy, we use an electric field $\vec{E}$. This is done by inserting into one section of the path a device that produces an electric field so that the electric force $-e\vec{E}$ points in the direction of the motion of the electrons.

One might think of using a charged parallel plate capacitor to create the electric field $\vec{E}$, but that is not feasible. Later we will see that radio waves have an electric field $\vec{E}$ associated with them, and it is a radio wave electric field in a so-called "resonant cavity" that is used to produce the required strong fields. For now it does not matter how $\vec{E}$ is produced, it is this electric field that adds energy to the electrons.

Figure 27b
The Berkeley synchrotron shown here, accelerated protons rather than electrons. It was the first machine with enough energy to create anti protons. After this machine was built, ways were devised for focusing the particle beam and using an evacuated doughnut with a much smaller cross-sectional area.

When electrons gain energy, their momentum p = mv increases. Writing Equation (25) in the form

$$r = \frac{mv}{qB} = \frac{p}{qB} \qquad (25a)$$

we see that an increase in the electron's momentum p will cause the orbital radius r to increase. The radius r will increase unless we compensate by increasing the strength B of the magnetic field. The rate at which we increase B must be synchronized with the rate at which we increase the particle's momentum p in order to keep r constant and keep the electrons in the circular path. Because of this synchronization, the device is called a *synchrotron*.

You can see that the amount of energy or momentum we can supply to the particles is limited by how strong a field B we can make. Iron electromagnets can create fields up to about 1 tesla (here the MKS unit is useful) or 10,000 gauss. The superconducting magnets, being used in the latest accelerator designs, can go up to around 5 tesla.

Noting that B is limited to one or a few tesla, Equation (25) tells us that to get more momentum or energy, we must use accelerators with a bigger radius r. This explains why particle accelerators are getting bigger and bigger. The biggest particle accelerator now operating in the United States is the proton accelerator at the Fermi National Accelerator Laboratory in Batavia, Illinois shown in Figures (28) and (29).

In Figure (28), we see a section of tunnel and the magnets that surround the 2 inch diameter evacuated pipe which carries the protons. Originally there was one ring using iron magnets (painted red and blue in the photograph). Later another ring with superconducting magnets was installed, in order to obtain stronger magnetic fields and higher proton energies. The ring of superconducting magnets (painted yellow) is beneath the ring of iron magnets.

Figure (29) is an aerial view showing the 4 mile circumference of the accelerator. Currently the largest accelerator in the world is at the European Center for Particle Physics (CERN). The 27 kilometer path of that accelerator is seen in Figure (30) on the next page.

Figure 28
The Fermi Lab accelerator has two accelerating rings, one on top of the other. In each, the evacuated doughnut is only 2 inches in diameter, and four miles in circumference. The bottom ring uses superconducting magnets (painted yellow), while the older upper ring has iron magnets (painted red and blue).

Figure 29
Aerial view of the Fermi Lab particle accelerator.

RELATIVISTIC ENERGY AND MOMENTA

Even the smallest synchrotrons accelerate electrons and protons up to relativistic energies where we can no longer use the non relativistic formula $1/2\ mv^2$ for kinetic energy. For any calculations involving the large accelerators we must use fully relativistic calculations like $E = mc^2$ for energy and $p = mv$ for momentum where $m = m_0/\sqrt{1 - v^2/c^2}$ is the relativistic mass.

Equation (25) or (25a) for a charged particle moving in a circular orbit of radius r, can be written in the form

$$p = qBr \qquad (25b)$$

where B is the strength of the uniform magnetic field and p the particle momentum. It turns out that Equation (25) is correct even at relativistic energies provided $p = mv$ is the relativistic momentum. Thus a knowl-edge of the magnetic field and orbital radius immediately tells us the momentum of the particles in the large synchrotrons.

To determine the energy of the particles in these machines, we need a relationship between a particle's energy E and momentum p. The relationship can be obtained by writing out E and p in the forms

$$p = mv = \frac{m_0}{\sqrt{1 - v^2/c^2}}\, v \qquad (29)$$

$$E = mc^2 = \frac{m_0}{\sqrt{1 - v^2/c^2}}\, c^2 \qquad (30)$$

If you add $m_0^2 c^4$ to $p^2 c^2$, you find that the result is simply

$$\boxed{E^2 = p^2 c^2 + m_0^2 c^4} \qquad \begin{array}{l}\textit{an exact}\\ \textit{relationship}\end{array} \qquad (31)$$

Figure 30
Path for the 8 kilometer circumference Super Proton Synchrotron (SPS, solid circle) and the 27 kilometer Large Electron-Positron collider (LEP, dashed circle) at CERN, on the border between France and Switzerland. The Geneva airport is in the foreground.

Exercise 6

Directly check Equation (31) by plugging in the values of p and E from Equations (29) and (30).

In the big particle accelerators, the kinetic energy supplied by the accelerators greatly exceeds the particle's rest energy m_0c^2, so that the $(m_0c^2)^2$ term in Equation (31) is completely negligible. For these "highly relativistic" particles, we can drop the $m_0^2c^4$ term in Equation (31) and we get the much simpler formula

$$\boxed{E \approx pc} \qquad \text{If } E \gg m_0c^2 \qquad (32)$$

Equation (32) is an accurate relationship between energy and momentum for **any particle** moving at a speed so close to the speed of light that its total energy E greatly exceeds its rest energy m_0c^2.

For the high energy particle accelerators we can combine Equations (25) and (32) to get

$$E = pc = qBrc \qquad (33)$$

Consider CERN's *Super Proton Synchrotron* or SPS, shown by the smaller solid circle in Figure (30), which was used to discover the particles responsible for the weak interaction. In this accelerator, the magnets produced fields of B = 1.1 tesla, and the radius of the ring was r = 1.3km (for a circumference of 8km). Thus we have

$$E = qBrc$$
$$= (1.6 \times 10^{-19} \text{ coulombs}) \times (1.1 \text{ tesla})$$
$$\times (1.3 \times 10^3 \text{meter}) \times (3 \times 10^8 \text{ meter/sec})$$
$$= 6.9 \times 10^{-8} \text{ joules} \qquad (34)$$

Converting this answer to electron volts, we get

$$E = \frac{6.9 \times 10^{-8} \text{ joules}}{1.6 \times 10^{-19} \frac{\text{joules}}{\text{eV}}} = 430 \times 10^9 \text{ eV}$$

$$= 430 \text{GeV} \qquad (35)$$

How good was our approximation that we could neglect the particle's rest energy and use the simple Equation (32)? Recall that the rest energy of a proton is about 1GeV. Thus the SPS accelerator produced protons with a kinetic energy 430 times greater! For these particles it is not much of an error to neglect the rest energy.

Exercise 7

a)   The Fermi lab accelerator, with its radius of 1 kilometer, uses superconducting magnets to produce beams of protons with a kinetic energy of 1000 GeV (10^{12}eV). How strong a magnetic field is required to produce protons of this energy?

b)   Iron electromagnets cannot produce magnetic fields stronger than 2 tesla, which is why superconducting magnets were required to produce the 1000 GeV protons discussed in part (a).   Before the ring with superconducting magnets was constructed, a ring using iron magnets already existed in the same tunnel. The iron magnets could produce 1.5 tesla fields. What was the maximum energy to which protons could be accelerated before the superconducting magnets were installed? *(You can see both rings of magnets in Figure 28.)*

Exercise 8

The *large electron-positron* (LEP) collider, being constructed at CERN, will create head on collisions between electrons and positrons. (Electrons will go around one way, and positrons, having the opposite charge, will go around the other way.) The path of the LEP accelerator, which will have a circumference of 27 km, is shown in Figure (30), superimposed on the countryside north of Geneva, Switzerland.

a)   Assuming that the LEP accelerator will use 3 tesla superconducting magnets, what will be the maximum kinetic energy, in eV, of the electrons and positrons that will be accelerated by this machine?

b)   What will be the speed of these electrons and positrons?   (How many 9's in v/c?)

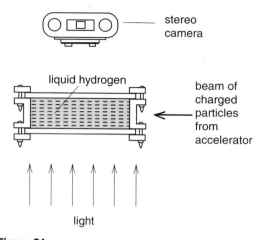

stereo camera

liquid hydrogen

beam of charged particles from accelerator

light

Figure 31a
*Schematic diagram of the Berkeley
10-inch hydrogen bubble chamber.*

Figure 31b
*The 10-inch bubble chamber at the Lawrence
Radiation Laboratory, University of California,
Berkeley. (Photograph copyright The Ealing
Corporation, Cambridge, Mass.)*

BUBBLE CHAMBERS

In the study of elementary particles, it is just as important to have adequate means of observing particles as it is to have accelerating machines to produce them. One of the more useful devices for this purpose is the bubble chamber invented by Donald Glaser in 1954.

It may not be true that Glaser invented the bubble chamber while looking at the streaks of bubbles in a glass of beer. But the idea is not too far off. When a charged particle like an electron, proton or some exotic elementary particle, passes through a container of liquid hydrogen, the charged particle tends to tear electrons from the hydrogen atoms that it passes, leaving a trail of ionized hydrogen atoms. If the pressure of the liquid hydrogen is suddenly reduced the liquid will start boiling if it has a "seed"—a special location where the boiling can start. The trail of ionized hydrogen atoms left by the charged particle provides a trail of seeds for boiling. The result is a line of bubbles showing where the particle went.

In a typical bubble chamber, a stereoscopic camera is used to record the three dimensional paths of the particles. It is impressive to look at the three dimensional paths in stereoscopic viewers, but unfortunately all we can conveniently do in a book is show a flat two dimensional image like the one in Figure (32). In that picture we see the paths of some of the now more common exotic elementary particles. In the interesting part of this photograph, sketched above, a negative π^- meson collides with a positive proton to create a neutral Λ^0 and a neutral K^0 meson. The neutral Λ^0 and K^0 do not leave tracks, but they are detected by the fact that the K^0 decayed into a π^+ and a π^- meson, and the Λ^0 decayed into a π^- and a proton p^+, all of which are charged particles that left tracks.

To analyze a picture like Figure (32) you need more information than just the tracks left behind by particles. You would also like to know the charge and the momentum or energy of the particles. This is done by placing the bubble chamber in a magnetic field so that positive particle tracks are curved one way and negatives ones the other. And, from Equation (25b), we see that the radii of the tracks tell us the momenta of the particles.

Another example of a bubble chamber photograph is Figure (33) where we see the spiral path produced by an electron. The fact that the path is spiral, that the radius of the path is getting smaller, immediately tells us that the electron is losing momentum and therefore energy as it moves through the liquid hydrogen. The magnetic field used for this photograph had a strength B = 1.17 tesla, and the initial radius of the spiral was 7.3 cm. From this we can determine the momentum and energy of the electron.

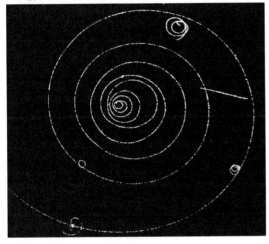

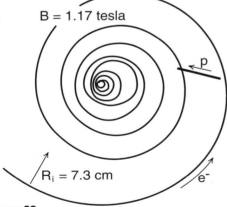

Figure 33
Spiraling electron. An electron enters the chamber at the lower left and spirals to rest as it loses momentum. The spiral track is caused by the magnetic field applied to the chamber which deflects a charged particle into a curved path with a radius of curvature proportional to the particle's momentum. The straight track crossing the spiral is a proton recoiling from a collision with a stray neutron. Because the proton has much greater mass than the electron, its track is much less curved.

Exercise 9

Calculate the energy, in eV of the electron as it entered the photograph in Figure (33). Since you do not know offhand whether the particle was relativistic or not, use the exact relation

$$E^2 = p^2c^2 + m_0^2 c^4 \tag{31}$$

to determine E from p. From your answer decide whether you could have used the non relativistic formula $KE = 1/2\,m_0 v^2$ or the fully relativistic formula $E = pc$, or whether you were in an intermediate range where neither approximation works well.

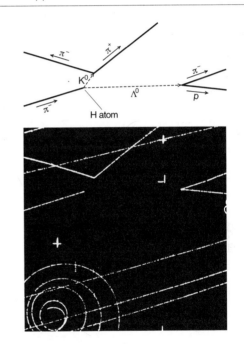

Figure 32
Bubble chamber photograph showing the creation of a K^0 meson and a Λ^0 particle, and their subsequent annihilations. We now know that the K meson is a quark/anti quark pair, and the Λ^0 particle contains 3 quarks as does a proton and a neutron. The K and Λ particles last long enough to be seen in a bubble chamber photograph because they each contain a strange quark which decays slowly via the weak interaction. (Photo copyright The Ealing Corporation Cambridge, Mass.)

The Mass Spectrometer

A device commonly seen in chemistry and geology labs is the *mass spectrometer* which is based on the circular orbits that a charged particle follows in a uniform magnetic field. Figure (34) is a sketch of a mass spectrometer which consists of a semi circular evacuated chamber with a uniform magnetic field $\vec{B}$ directed up out of the paper. The direction of $\vec{B}$ is chosen to deflect positive ions around inside the chamber to a photographic plate on the right side. The ions to be studied are boiled off a heated filament and accelerated by a negative cap in a reversed voltage electron gun shown in Figure (35). By measuring the position where the ions strike the photographic plate, we know the radius of the orbit taken by the ion. Combine this with the knowledge of the field B of the spectrometer, and we can determine the ion's momentum p if the charge q is known. The speed of the ion is determined by the accelerating voltage in the gun, thus knowing p gives us the mass m of the ions. Non relativistic formulas work well and the calculations are nearly identical to our analysis of the path of the electrons in Figure (25). (See Equations 26 to 28.)

Mass spectrometers are used to identify elements in a small sample of material, and are particularly useful in being able to separate different isotopes of an element. Two different isotopes of an element have different numbers of neutrons in the nucleus, everything else being the same. Thus ions of the two isotopes will have slightly different masses, and land at slightly different distances down the photographic plate. If an isotope is missing in one sample the corresponding line on the photographic plate will be absent. The analogy between looking at the lines identifying isotopes, and looking at a photographic plate showing the spectrum of light, suggested the name *mass spectrometer*.

Exercise 10

Suppose that you wish to measure the mass of an iodine atom using the apparatus of Figures (34) and (35). You coat the filament of the gun in Figure (35) with iodine, and heat the filament until iodine atoms start to boil off. In the process, some of the iodine atoms lose an electron and become positive ions with a charge +e. The ions are then accelerated in the gun by a battery of voltage V_b and then pass into the evacuated chamber.

(a) Assuming that V_b = 125 volts (accelerating voltage) and B = 1000 gauss (0.1 tesla), and that the iodine atoms follow a path of radius r = 18.2 cm, calculate the mass m of the iodine atoms.

(b) How many times more massive is the iodine ion than a proton? From the fact that protons and neutrons have about the same mass, and that an electron is 2000 times lighter, use your result to estimate how many nuclear particles (protons or neutrons) are in an iodine nucleus.

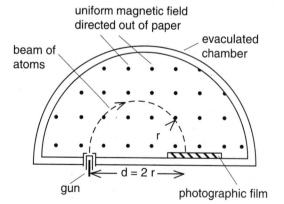

uniform magnetic field
directed out of paper

beam of atoms

evacuated chamber

r

d = 2 r

gun

photographic film

Figure 34
Top view of a mass spectrograph. A uniform magnetic field $\vec{B}$ rises directly up through the chamber. The beam of atoms is produced by the accelerating gun shown in Figure (35).

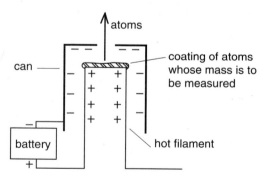

atoms

can

coating of atoms whose mass is to be measured

battery

hot filament

Figure 35
When the substance to be studied is heated by a filament, atoms evaporate and some lose an electron and become electrically charged positive ions. The ions are then accelerated by an electric field to produce a beam of ions of known kinetic energy.

Magnetic Focusing

In the magnetic force examples we have considered so far, the velocity $\vec{v}$ of the charged particle started out perpendicular to $\vec{B}$ and we got the circular orbits we have been discussing.

If we place an electron gun so that the electron beam is aimed down the axis of a pair of Helmholtz coils, as shown in Figure (36), the electron velocity $\vec{v}$ is parallel to $\vec{B}$, $\vec{v} \times \vec{B} = 0$, and there is no magnetic force.

Figure (36) is a bit too idealized for the student built electron gun we have been using in earlier examples. Some of the electrons do come out straight as shown in Figure (36), but many come out at an angle as shown in Figure (37a). In Figure (37b) we look at the velocity components $\vec{v}_\perp$ and $\vec{v}_\parallel$ of an electron emerging at an angle θ. Because $\vec{v}_\parallel \times \vec{B} = 0$, only the perpendicular component $\vec{v}_\perp$ contributes to the magnetic force

$$\vec{F}_{mag} = q\vec{v}_\perp \times \vec{B} \tag{36}$$

This force is perpendicular to both $\vec{v}_\perp$ and $\vec{B}$ as shown in the end view of the electron gun, Figure (37b). In this end view, where we can't see $\vec{v}_\parallel$, the electron appears to travel around the usual circular path.

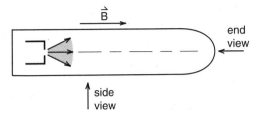

Figure 37a
In reality the electron beam spreads out when it leaves the cap. Most of the electrons are not moving parallel to $\vec{B}$, and there will be a magnetic force on them.

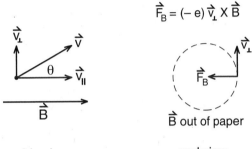

side view   end view

Figure 37b
Consider an electron emerging from the cap at an angle θ from the center line as shown in the side view above. Such an electron has a component of velocity $\vec{v}_\perp$ perpendicular to the magnetic field. This produces a magnetic force $\vec{F}_B = (-e)\vec{v}_\perp \times \vec{B}$ which points toward the axis of the gun. The magnetic force $\vec{F}_B$ can be seen in the end view above. From the end view the electron will appear to travel in a circle about the axis of the gun. The stronger the magnetic field, the smaller the radius of the circle.

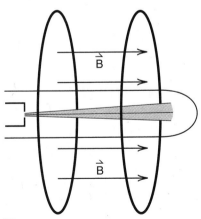

Figure 36
Electron gun inserted so that the beam of electrons moves parallel to the magnetic field of the coils. If the beam is truly parallel to $\vec{B}$, there will be no magnetic force on the electrons.

It is in the side view, Figure (38) that we see the effects of $\vec{v}_{\parallel}$. Since there is no force related to $\vec{v}_{\parallel}$, this component of velocity is unchanged and simply carries the electron at a constant horizontal speed down the electron gun. The quantity $\vec{v}_{\parallel}$ is often called the ***drift speed*** of the particle. (The situation is not unlike projectile motion, where the horizontal component v_x of the projectile's velocity is unaffected by the vertical acceleration a_y.)

When we combine the circular motion, seen in the end view of Figure (37b), with the constant drift speed $\vec{v}_{\parallel}$, down the tube seen in Figure (38a) the net effect is a helical path like a stretched spring seen in Figure (38b). The electron in effect spirals around and travels along the magnetic field line. The stronger the magnetic field, the smaller the circle in Figure (37b), and the tighter the helix.

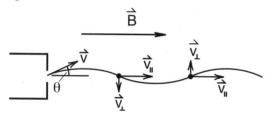

Figure 38a
In the side view of the motion of the electron, we see that $v_{\parallel}$ is unchanged, $\vec{v}_{\parallel}$ just carries the electron down the tube.

helical motion of the electron

Figure 38b
Oblique view of the helical motion of the electron. When you combine the uniform motion of the electron down the tube with the circular motion around the axis of the tube, you get a helical motion with the same shape as the wire in a stretched spring.

The tightening of the helix is seen in Figure (39) where in (a) we see an electron beam with no magnetic field. The electrons are spraying out in a fairly wide cone. In (b) we have a 75 gauss magnetic field aligned parallel to the axis of the gun and we are beginning to see the helical motion of the electrons. In (c) the magnetic field is increased to 200 gauss and the radius of the helix has decreased considerably. As B is increased, the electrons are confined more and more closely to a path along the magnetic field lines. In our electron gun, the magnetic field is having the effect of focusing the electron beam.

a) No magnetic field

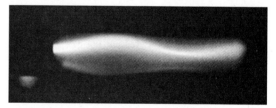

b) B = 75 gauss

c) B = 200 gauss

d) Movie

Figure 39
Focusing an electron beam with a parallel magnetic field. The beam travels along a helical path which becomes tighter as the strength of the magnetic field is increased.

SPACE PHYSICS

Even in nonuniform magnetic fields there is a tendency for a charged particle to move in a spiral path along a magnetic field line as illustrated in Figure (40). This is true as long as the magnetic field is reasonably uniform over a distance equal to the radius r of the spiral (from Equation (25), $r = mv_\perp/q\vec{v}_B$). Neglecting the spiral part of the motion, we see that the large scale effect is that charged particles tend to move or flow along magnetic field lines. This plays an important role in space physics phenomena which deals with charged particles emitted by the sun (the "solar wind") and the interaction of these particles with the magnetic field of the earth and other planets.

There are so many interesting and complex effects in the interaction of the solar wind with planetary magnetic fields that space physics has become an entire field of physics. Seldom are we aware of these effects unless a particularly powerful burst of solar wind particles disrupts radio communications or causes an Aurora Borealis to be seen as far south as the temperate latitudes. The Aurora are caused when particles from the solar wind spiral in along the earth's magnetic field lines and end up striking atoms in the upper atmosphere. The atoms struck by the solar wind particles emit light just like the residual air atoms struck by the electrons in an electron gun.

The Magnetic Bottle

If a magnetic field has the correct shape, if the field lines pinch together as shown at the left or the right side of Figure (41), then the magnetic force $\vec{F}_{mag}$ on a charged particle has a component that is directed back from the pinch. For charged particles with the correct speed, this back component of the magnetic force can reflect the particle and reverse $\vec{v}_\parallel$. If the magnetic field is pinched at both ends, as in Figure (41) the charged particle can reflect back and forth, trapped as if it were in a magnetic bottle.

In the subject of plasma physics, one often deals with hot ionized gases, particularly in experiments designed to study the possibility of creating controlled fusion reactions. These gases are so hot that they would melt and vaporize any known substance they touch. The only known way to confine these gases to do experiments on them is either do the experiments so fast that the gas does not have time to escape (inertial confinement), or use magnetic fields and devices like the magnetic bottle shown in Figure (41) (magnetic confinement).

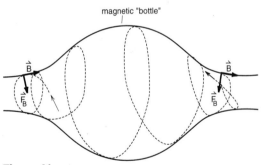

Figure 41
Magnetic bottle. When the magnetic field lines pinch together, the charged particles can be reflected back in a process called magnetic mirroring. (At the two ends of the magnetic bottle above, the magnetic force $\vec{F}_B$ has a component back into the bottle.)

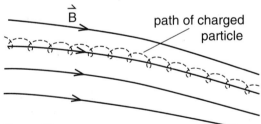

Figure 40
When charged particles from the sun enter the earth's magnetic field, they spiral around the magnetic field lines much like the electrons in the magnetic focusing experiment of Figure (39).

Van Allen Radiation Belts

The earth's magnetic field shown in Figure (9) and repeated in Figure (42) forms magnetic bottles that can trap charged particles from the solar wind. The ends of the bottles are where the field lines come together at the north and south magnetic poles, and the regions where significant numbers of particles are trapped are called the **Van Allen radiation belts** shown in Figure (42). Protons are trapped in the inner belt and electrons in the outer one.

It is not feasible to do hand calculations of the motion of charged particles in nonuniform magnetic fields. The motion is just too complicated. But computer calculations, very similar to the orbit calculations discussed in Chapter 8, work well for electric and magnetic forces. As long as we have a formula for the shape of $\vec{E}$ or $\vec{B}$, we can use the Lorentz force law (Equation 20)

$$\vec{F} = q\vec{E} + q\vec{v} \times \vec{B}$$

as one of the steps in the computer program. The computer does not care how complicated the path is, but we might have trouble drawing and interpreting the results.

In Figure (43), a student, Jeff Lelek, started with the formula for a "dipole magnetic field", namely

$$\vec{B} = -\left(\frac{B_0}{R^3}\right) * \left(\hat{Z} - 3*\left(\hat{Z}\cdot\hat{R}\right)*\hat{R}\right) \tag{37}$$

which is a reasonably accurate representation of the earth's magnetic field, and calculated some electron orbits for this field. The result is fairly complex, but we do get the feeling that the electron is spiraling around the magnetic field lines and reflecting near the magnetic poles.

To provide a simpler interpretation of this motion, the student let the calculation run for a long time, saving up the particle coordinates at many hundreds of different points along the long orbit. These points are then plotted as the dot pattern shown in Figure (44). (In this picture, the latitude of the particle is ignored, the points are all plotted in one plane so we can see the extent of the radial and north-south motion of the particles.) The result gives us a good picture of the distribution of particles in a Van Allen radiation belt..

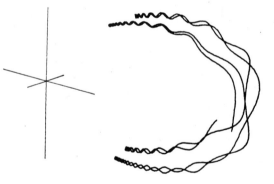

Figure 43
Computer plot of the motion of a proton in a dipole magnetic field. The formula for this field and the computer program used to calculate the motion of the proton are given in an Appendix in the calculus version of the text. As you can see, the motion is relatively complex. Not only does the proton reflect back and forth between the poles, but also precesses around the equator.

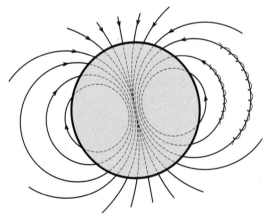

Figure 42
Charged particles, trapped by the earth's magnetic field, spiral around the magnetic field lines reflecting where the lines pinch together at the poles. The earth's magnetic field thus forms a magnetic bottle, holding the charged particles of the Van Allen radiation belts.

Auroras

Most of the electrons and protons that come to the earth from the sun do not become captured in the radiation belts. Instead they follow magnetic field lines down into the earth's atmosphere. There they excite the atoms in the atmosphere, just as the electrons in our electron gun excited air atoms in the gun, illuminating the path of the electrons. The glow created by the electrons and protons coming down through the earth's atmosphere creates an *aurora*, or what is often known as the *northern lights*. A particularly impressive aurora occurred on March 20, 2001 in the Anchorage Alaska area, which allowed Leroy Zimmerman to take the rather amazing photograph shown below.

Aurora March 20, 2001 Fairbanks Alaska
Photograph by Leroy Zimmerman at http://www.photosymphony.com/.
More aurora pictures can be found at
http://spaceweather.com/aurora/gallery_20march01.html

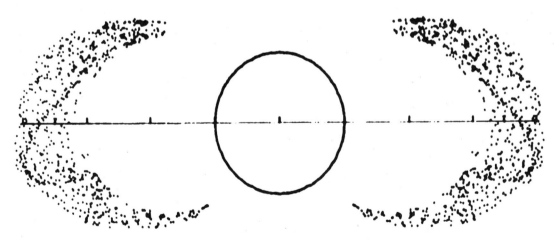

Figure 44
In this computer plot, all the data points from Figure 43 are plotted as dots in one plane. From this we see the shape of a Van Allen radiation belt emerge. (Figures (43) and (44) from a student project by Jeff Lelek.)

APPENDIX:
LORENTZ TRANSFORMATION
AND CHARGE CONSERVATION

Some people have been concerned about the derivation of the magnetic force law we used for this chapter*. They were worrying about the conservation of electric charge. Electric charge should not just appear out of nowhere. This point was raised in a letter to the editor, to appear in the magazine **The Physics Teacher**. *To show that there was no problem with conservation of electric charge, we worked out this slightly more complex thought experiment, whose results are equivalent to the earlier presentation in this chapter.*

For this new thought experiment, imagine that the two rods shown in Figure (45a) are kept in our lecture hall storage room. The shorter rod has charges +Q spaced a distance ℓ apart as shown. The longer rod has the same number of charges –Q spaced a slightly greater distance $\ell_- = \ell / \sqrt{1 - v^2/c^2}$ apart, where v is a small number compared to c. The total charge on the two rods together is zero.

For the lecture on magnetism, the rods are brought out of storage and set on the lecture bench. The setup allows the negative rod to be moved to the left at a speed v as shown in Figure (45b). Due to the Lorentz contraction, the spacing of the negative charges is seen by the class to contract to

$$\begin{align} \text{new negative} \atop \text{spacing} = \ell_- \sqrt{1 - v^2/c^2} \end{align}$$

$$= \frac{\ell \sqrt{1 - v^2/c^2}}{\sqrt{1 - v^2/c^2}} = \ell$$

which is the same spacing as the + charges on the stationary positive rod.

At the instant shown in Figure (45b), the plus and minus charges are precisely opposite each other. If we picture the two rods merged together, as a model of negative electrons flowing through stationary positive copper nuclei, we have a model of a section of an electrically neutral wire. Such a wire has no electric field.

Figure 45
A thought experiment where conservation of charge is obvious. Of the two rods with equal but opposite total charges, the negative one is slightly longer. During lecture we move the longer one at a speed so that, due to the Lorentz contraction, the rods have the same length. When merged at the instant shown, there is no electric field. To an observer moving with the negative rod, the merged rods would have the electric field shown. (The field lines emerge from the positive middle of the rod and end on the negative ends.)

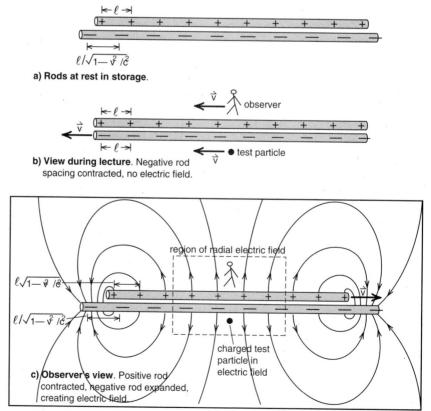

a) **Rods at rest in storage**.

b) **View during lecture**. Negative rod spacing contracted, no electric field.

c) **Observer's view**. Positive rod contracted, negative rod expanded, creating electric field.

region of radial electric field

charged test particle in electric field

To the observer shown in Figure (45b) moving along with the negative rod, the negative rod is at rest and the minus charges have returned to their longer storage room spacing $\ell_- = \ell / \sqrt{1 - v^2/c^2}$. The observer sees the positive rod moving to the right, and the plus charge spacing is reduced to $\ell_+ = \ell \sqrt{1 - v^2/c^2}$. To the observer, the positive rod is shorter than the negative rod and she sees an electric field produced by the different charge distributions.

In Figure (45c) we have drawn the electric field she would see if the two rods were merged together. In the region where the positive rod overlaps the negative rod, the greater charge density on the positive rod leads to a net charge density

$$\lambda_+ = \frac{i\,v}{c^2} \qquad \begin{array}{l}\textit{positive charge} \\ \textit{density in center}\end{array}$$

where i is the positive current being carried to the right by the positive rod. This is the same charge density we had in Figure (4) earlier in the chapter. The electric field lines emerge from this positive charge density.

What is different now is the fact that the negative rod is longer than the positive rod, and negative charge sticks out at both ends as shown. Since the total charge on the two rods is zero, all the field lines emerging from the center must go over and stop on the negative charge sticking out at the ends. We get the electric field structure shown. (We plotted this field structure using the Charges2000 program and the charge distribution shown in Figure [19-31].)

For the derivation of the magnetic force law, look at the region near the center of the rods bounded by the dashed rectangle. In this region the electric field lines go almost radially outward from the positive charge density $\lambda_+ = i\,v/c^2$ and the situation is as we showed in Figure (5) earlier in the chapter. From that figure on, all the discussion applies to Figure (45c) and we end up with the magnetic force law.

The point of this appendix is that there is no problem with conservation of electric charge. The Lorentz contraction creates an electric field simply by changing the distribution of electric charge.

Exercise 11

One possible criticism of the above thought experiment is that modeling an electric current with two finite length rods is not very realistic. One usually thinks of an electric current being in a continuous loop like the circuits in Chapter 22. This suggests the following exercise.

Picture an electrically neutral copper loop carrying a negative current as shown in Figure (46). Model the currents in the area of the dashed rectangle by positive and negative rods as we did in Figure (2a).

Then look at the situation from the point of view of an observer moving with the minus charges at the bottom of the loop. Sketch the electric fields and explain why electric charge is conserved.

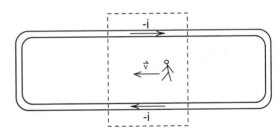

Figure 46
An electrically neutral copper loop carrying a negative current −i.

*
*When we first started teaching at Dartmouth College, a physics student pointed out that due to the Lorentz contraction, a wire carrying a neutral current becomes electrically charged if you moved along with the electrons. "What are the consequences of that?", he asked. We did not know, having not heard of the effect before. Over the following weekend we developed the derivation of the magnetic force law that appears in this chapter. We used the derivation in the 1968 **Physics 1** textbook, an earlier non calculus text.*

CHAPTER 23 REVIEW

This chapter comes in two parts. In the first part we use Coulomb's law and the Lorentz contraction to derive the magnetic force law. From this we also get the formula for the magnetic field of a straight wire carrying a current i, and we get Maxwell's formula $c = \sqrt{1/\mu_0 \varepsilon_0}$ for the speed of light.

In the second part, we begin by looking for situations where the magnetic field is uniform, and then study the circular motion of charged particles in the uniform field. Examples are our electron gun, particle accelerators, and the mass spectrograph. For non uniform magnetic fields we see that the charged particles tend to spiral around magnetic field lines, creating phenomena like the Van Allen radiation belts and the colorful auroras.

In this review we will cover the highlights of the derivation of the magnetic force law, and then focus on the circular motion of a charged particle in a uniform magnetic field.

The Magnetic Force Law

We started with two views of an electric current in a wire, summarized in Figure (5). In our view (5a) we have an electrically neutral wire with a current of moving negative charge. To an observer moving with the negative charge (5b), there is a current of positive charge moving in the other direction. This is consistent with our earlier observation (page 22-5) that a nega-tive current flowing one way is mostly equivalent to a positive current flowing the other way.

What is new here is the observation that due to the special relativity Lorentz contraction, the neutral wire in Figure (5a) becomes a positively charged wire in Figure (5b). The reason for this is that the line of positive charges are now moving, the spacing between charges contracts by a factor $\sqrt{1 - v^2/c^2}$, and the positive charge density λ_+ increases. The negative charges are no longer moving, their spacing expands by a factor $1/\sqrt{1 - v^2/c^2}$, and the negative charge density λ_- decreases. After a bit of calculation we find that the net charge density $\lambda = (\lambda_+ - \lambda_-)$ becomes simply

$$\lambda = \frac{iv}{c^2} \quad \text{net charge density} \qquad (10)$$

where i is the positive current seen in Figure (5b).

Back in our discussion of Gauss' law in Chapter (19) we derived the formula

$$E(r) = \frac{1}{2\pi\varepsilon_0 r}\lambda \qquad (19\text{-}36, \text{ page } 19\text{-}15)$$

for the radial electric field a distance r from a wire with a charge density λ. Thus in Figure (5b) our wire with a current i produces a radial electric field of magnitude

$$E(r) = \frac{1}{2\pi\varepsilon_0 r} \times \frac{iv}{c^2}$$

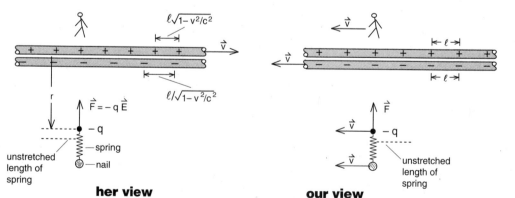

Figure 5

Two views of the same experiment. For the observer moving with the electrons, she sees a positively charged wire exerting an attractive force on the negative charge at rest. We see an electrically neutral wire carrying a negative current, and a moving negative charge. The spring is still stretched, meaning the attractive force is still there.

A negative charge $-q$ placed a distance r from the wire, as shown in Figure (5b) would feel an attractive force of magnitude

$$F(r) = qE(r) = \frac{q}{2\pi\varepsilon_0 r} \times \frac{iv}{c^2} \tag{14}$$

To "simplify" this equation, we define a new constant μ_0 (mu-naught) by the formula

$$\mu_0 \equiv \frac{1}{\varepsilon_0 c^2} \tag{17}$$

which lets us write the equation for the force $F(r)$ as

$$F = qE = qv\left(\frac{\mu_0 i}{2\pi r}\right) \tag{14a}$$

Equation (14a) is the formula for the electric force on our negative test particle seen in Figure (5b). When we go back to Figure (5a), where the wire is electrically neutral, there is no electric field, but there is still an attractive force between the test particle and the wire. We now call this force a *magnetic force*, given by the formula

$$F = qvB \tag{16}$$

$$B = \frac{\mu_0 i}{2\pi r} \tag{18}$$

We then used compasses and iron filings to turn B into the vector $\vec{B}$ that points in the direction pointed to by the north end of a compass needle. The iron filings told us that the magnetic field traveled in circles about the wire. The compass needles told us that the direction of $\vec{B}$ was given by the right hand rule. Using the vector cross product notation, we could write the magnetic force formula as

$$\vec{F}_{magnetic} = q\vec{v} \times \vec{B} \tag{19}$$

If we have both electric and magnetic fields acting on a charged particle, the formula for the net **electromagnetic** force is

$$\vec{F} = q\vec{E} + q\vec{v} \times \vec{B} \tag{20}$$

which is known as the **Lorentz force formula**.

Another result of this derivation is that, from our equation (17) for μ_0 we get

$$c^2 = \frac{1}{\mu_0 \varepsilon_0} \tag{17a}$$

It turns out that the product $\mu_0 \varepsilon_0$ can be measured in a simple experiment that does not involve light. The experiment involves measuring the rate at which electrons slosh back and forth between a capacitor and a coil of wire. The results of that experiment is

$$c = \frac{1}{\sqrt{\mu_0 \varepsilon_0}} = 3 \times 10^8 \frac{meters}{second}$$

The question Einstein dealt with was, who got to measure this value for the speed of light. His answer was—**everybody!**

From this one derivation we get

(1) The magnetic force law

$$\vec{F}_{magnetic} = q\vec{v} \times \vec{B}$$

(2) Maxwell's formula for the speed of light

$$c = \frac{1}{\sqrt{\mu_0 \varepsilon_0}}$$

(3) The formula for the strength of a magnetic field a distance r from a straight wire carrying a current i

$$B = \frac{\mu_0 i}{2\pi r}$$

Motion of Charged Particles in a Magnetic Field

The second part of the chapter discusses the motion of charged particles in a magnetic field. Most of the discussion deals with a uniform magnetic field which leads to circular motion. As shown in Figure (25c), the magnetic force is directed toward the center of the circle in the direction of the acceleration $\vec{a}$ of the particle. Equating the magnitudes of the magnetic force $F_B = qvB$ to the magnitude of the acceleration for circular motion $a = v^2/r$, we get

$$F_B = qvB = ma = mv^2/r$$

One of the factors of v cancels and we end up with

$$mv = qBr \qquad (25)$$

We have a number of exercises that use this equation in one form or another.

A special feature of Equation (25) is that if you are studying a particle like an electron or a proton whose charge is q = e, and you know the magnetic field B, then a measurement of the circular radius r immediately tells you the momentum mv of the particle. This turns out to be a fully relativistic result which is used in the interpretation of bubble chamber pictures of elementary particle tracks.

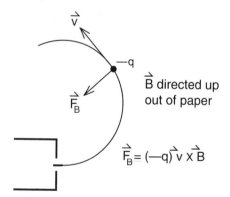

Figure 25c
As the electrons move along a curved path, the magnetic force $\vec{F} = -q\,\vec{v} \times \vec{B}$ always remains perpendicular to the velocity and therefore cannot change the speed of the electrons. The resulting motion is uniform circular motion where the force and the acceleration are directed toward the center of the circle.

CHAPTER EXERCISES

Exercise 1 On page 3
Calculate the strength of the gravitational force between the peas.

Exercise 2 On page 9
Show that the electron beam should be repelled if we reverse the direction of the current in the wire.

Exercise 3 On page 15
Use the magnetic force law and the right hand rule to show when an electron beam is attracted or repelled by a parallel current..

Exercise 4 On page 21
Analyze the electron's motion in Figure (25b).

Exercise 5 On page 21
Calculate the accelerating voltage for Figure (26).

Exercise 6 On page 25
Check the formula $E^2 = p^2c^2 + m_0^2c^4$.

Exercise 7 On page 25
Exercise on the Fermi lab accelerator.

Exercise 8 On page 25
Exercise on the LEP collider in Cern.

Exercise 9 On page 27
Calculate the energy of the electron in the bubble chamber photograph.

Exercise 10 On page 28
Exercise involving the mass spectrometer.

Exercise 11 On page 35
Special relativity exercise.

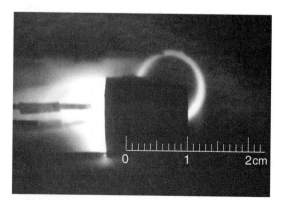

Figure 25b
Side view of the electron beam.

Essay 6 *Follows Chapter 23*

Vector Fields and Maxwell's Equations

With the introduction of the magnetic field $\vec{B}$, we now have examples of three different vector fields. We started with the velocity field $\vec{v}$ representing the flow of an incompressible fluid like water. Then we had the electric field $\vec{E}$ created by point charges like protons and electrons. And now the magnetic field which can be created by the flow of electrons in a wire.

For the electric field of point charges, we noticed that there was a mathematical analogy between the electric field and the velocity field of an incompressible fluid. Thus we could use Gauss' law and the concept of flux tubes to introduce electric field lines. Gauss' law gives us the simple rule that Q/ε_0 flux tubes or field lines start from a positive charge $+Q$ or stop on a negative charge $-Q$. Field lines never cross or start or stop in the space between the charges. These simple rules plus an intuitive feeling for symmetry allowed us to sketch field shapes like Figure (19-15) and even solve problems like calculating the electric field of a line of charge.

For the magnetic field we used iron filings or compass needles to show us the shape of the magnetic field produced by electric currents and iron magnets. In one case, where we had a current i in a straight wire, we actually calculated the strength of the magnetic field that was going in circles about the wire. The result was

$$B = \frac{\mu_0 i}{2\pi r} \tag{23-18}$$

We obtained this result, not from a general rule for calculating magnetic fields, but instead from Coulomb's law and our knowledge of Einstein's special theory of relativity.

There is also a general rule for calculating magnetic fields, a rule somewhat analogous to Gauss' law for electric fields. The rule is known as ***Ampere's law*** and is discussed in the Satellite Chapter 10.

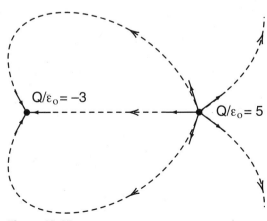

Figure 19-15
Mapping electric field lines.

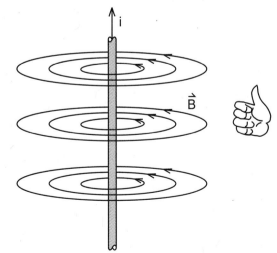

Figure 23-14
Magnetic field of a straight current.

AMPERE'S LAW

We will give a brief example of Ampere's law as it applies to the magnetic field of a straight wire, but we will not attempt to use it here to solve problems.

To introduce Ampere's law, consider the magnetic field line $\vec{B}$ going in a circle of radius r about a current i as shown in Figure (1). Writing Equation (23-18) in the form

$$B \times 2\pi r = \mu_0 i \tag{1}$$

we see that if we multiply the magnitude of B times the circumference of the circle $2\pi r$, the result is equal to a constant μ_0 times the current i flowing through the circle.

Ampere's law is a generalization of this result. It tells you to walk around a complete path, coming back to the point where you started. The circle in Figure (1) is such a path. With each step you take while walking, multiply the length of your step by the strength of the magnetic field in the direction of your step, and record the result. When you get back to your starting point and add up all your results, the sum will be the constant μ_0 times the total amount of current i flowing through your path. In the case of Figure (1), $\vec{B}$ is always pointing in the direction of the circular path, so that all we have to do is multiply B times the total length of the path $2\pi r$, to get $\mu_0 i$.

In Satellite Chapter 10 ***Vector fields and Ampere's Law***, we do a more detailed introduction to Ampere's law, and then use the law for calculating other magnetic field structures, like the field inside a coil of wire.

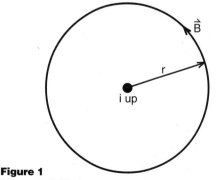

Figure 1
Magnetic field of a current.

TWO KINDS OF VECTOR FIELDS

The electric field $\vec{E}$ of a point charge, and the magnetic field $\vec{B}$ of a straight current, compared in Figure (2), are examples of two different kinds of vector fields. The electric field of a point charge is a clear example of what we call a ***diverging*** kind of vector field. The field lines diverge, or come straight out of the point charge.

The magnetic field surrounding a wire is an example of what we call a ***circulating*** vector field. Here, instead of diverging out of its source, it circulates around its source. One of the accomplishments of the mathematics of vector fields is to show that these two kinds of fields have completely distinct sources. For example, electric charges at rest produce only diverging electric fields, and electric currents produce only circulating magnetic fields.

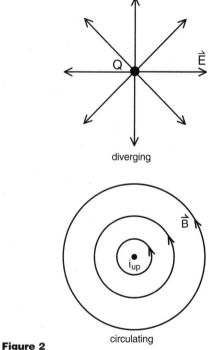

Figure 2
Two kinds of vector fields.

As a test of this idea, we can ask what kind of a vector field is the velocity field $\vec{v}$ of an incompressible fluid like water? Near the beginning of Chapter 18 on fluids we discussed the velocity field of a point source of water, seen in Figure (18-6). In that figure we imagined that water molecules were being created inside a small magic sphere. Beyond that sphere there was no more magic, and we used the continuity equation to show that the velocity field dropped off as $1/r^2$ as the fluid flowed out through larger spheres whose area increased as r^2.

The problem with that example is that for an incompressible fluid, ***there are no magic spheres***. We do not see water actually diverging outward as shown in Figure (18-6). Instead we see flow patterns like the bathtub vortex of Figures (18-25) and (18-26) or Hurricane Allen in Figure (18-27). Because there are no magic spheres creating water molecules, the only kind of velocity field we see in an incompressible fluid is a circulating velocity field $\vec{v}$. You will not see the diverging velocity field of Figure (18-6).

Figure 18-25
Bathtub vortex in a funnel. We stirred the water before letting it drain out.

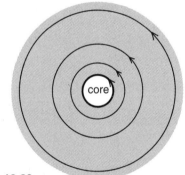

Figure 18-26
Velocity field of the bathtub vortex.

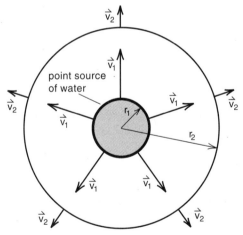

Figure 18-6
Water molecules are created inside the small magic sphere. This creates a diverging velocity field out from the small sphere.

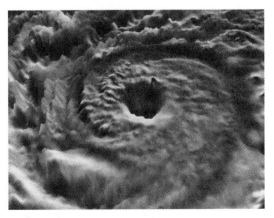

Figure 18-27
Eye of hurricane Allen viewed from a satellite.

ELECTROMAGNETIC FIELDS

We will now focus our attention on the two vector fields involved in electricity and magnetism, $\vec{E}$ and $\vec{B}$. Because each of these fields could, at least in principle, have two components, a diverging kind and a circulating kind, there are four possible electric and magnetic field types indicated in Figure (3). There is the diverging electric and circulating magnetic fields we saw in Figures (3a) and (3b). The other two possibilities are a circulating electric and a diverging magnetic field drawn in Figures (3c) and (3d).

It turns out that each kind of field has its own special kind of source and its own special law for calculating the field produced by that source. For the diverging electric field, the source is electric charge, and the law determining the field produced is Gauss' law. For the circulating magnetic field, the source is electric current and the law used to calculate the resulting magnetic field is Ampere's law.

For the diverging magnetic field shown in (3d), the source is the so called ***magnetic monopole***. Some theories of the early universe predict that magnetic monopoles should have been created shortly after the big bang. Physicists have spent years looking for a magnetic monopole, but so far have found none. Until they do find one, we have a very simple rule rule for calculating the diverging kind of magnetic field—***there is none!***

It may be a surprise, but the circulating kind of electric field not only exists, it plays a very important role in modern life. ***The source of a circulating electric field is a changing magnetic field***. The practical applications which we could not live without is the ***electric generator***. By changing the magnetic field passing through a wire loop you create an electric voltage around the loop, a voltage that can be used by a power company to provide electric voltage to your house.

The law we use to calculate the circulating kind of electric field is ***Faraday's law*** discussed in the Satellite Chapter 11. Of all the satellite chapters, this may be the one that should be included as part of the regular course, if time permits. In that chapter we discuss and carry out an important experiment that helped lead Einstein to the special theory of relativity.

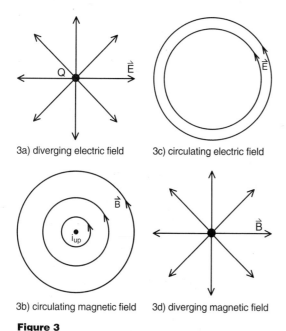

3a) diverging electric field   3c) circulating electric field

3b) circulating magnetic field   3d) diverging magnetic field

Figure 3
Four possible kinds of electric and magnetic fields.

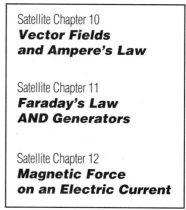

Satellite Chapter 10
***Vector Fields
and Ampere's Law***

Satellite Chapter 11
***Faraday's Law
AND Generators***

Satellite Chapter 12
***Magnetic Force
on an Electric Current***

Related satellite chapters.

MAXWELL'S EQUATIONS

The four equations governing the behavior of the four components of electric and magnetic fields are known as ***Maxwell's equations***. They are ***Gauss' law*** for diverging electric fields, ***Ampere's law*** for circulating magnetic fields, ***Faraday's law*** for circulating electric fields, and the ***absence of magnetic monopoles*** for the absence of divergent magnetic fields. Then why, with Gauss, Ampere and Faraday all preceeding Maxwell, do we call these Maxwell's equations?

The answer begins with the fact that Maxwell discovered another source for the magnetic field. We mentioned that a changing magnetic field could create a circulating electric field. Maxwell discovered that a changing electric field would act as a source of a circulating magnetic field.

At this point Maxwell saw a new possibility. Out in empty space where there are no charges or currents, he could still create electric and magnetic fields. He had an equation for how a changing magnetic field could create an electric field. The electric field being created this way could in turn create a magnetic field. The magnetic field being created this way could create an electric field ... etc. In other words, electric and magnetic fields could feed off of each other and travel in a wavelike manner through empty space. He calculated the speed of this ***electromagnetic*** wave and the result was the speed c given by

$$ c \; = \; \frac{1}{\sqrt{\mu_0 \varepsilon_0}} \; = \; 3 \times 10^8 \frac{\text{meters}}{\text{sec}} $$

which is the speed of light.

As a result, Maxwell saw that he had discovered what a light wave was—a wave of electric and magnetic fields feeding off of each other, traveling as a wave through empty space. In the next chapter we study the structure of this electromagnetic wave.

Chapter 24 non calculus

Electromagnetic Radiation

At the beginning of Chapter 1 on Special Relativity, we sketched a wave traveling down a rope in Figure (14) reproduced here. You can create such a wave on a stretched rope by flicking one end. After you do this, a bump representing the wave travels down the rope at a speed $v_{wave} = \sqrt{T/\mu}$ where T is the tension T in the rope and μ the mass per unit length of the rope.

A radio wave from an antenna is created in much the same way. Instead of a rope, we have the electric field lines coming from the charges inside the antenna. We give these charges a flick, that is, create a brief current pulse in the antenna, and a kink forms in the electric field lines. This kink, which travels out along the electric field lines, is accompanied by the magnetic field of the brief current pulse. The resulting structure of the electric field of the kink and magnetic field of the current pulse is a radio wave that moves away from the antenna at a speed $c = 1/\sqrt{\mu_0 \varepsilon_0}$, the speed of light.

In our discussion of rope waves, it is easy to see the shape of the rope wave pulse. A little more work was required to calculate its speed. In this chapter we focus on the structure of the electromagnetic waves. The only thing we leave out in this non calculus version of the text is the actual calculation of the speed of these waves.

Once we have derived the structure of the radio wave created by a simple antenna, we go on to look at the complete spectrum of electromagnetic radiation that ranges from the long wavelength radio waves, to shorter wavelength microwaves, to infra red light. Then comes visible light, ultraviolet light, x rays and the very short wavelength gamma rays. In Maxwell's theory, the only difference between all these forms of radiation is their wavelength. They all have the same structure of electric and magnetic fields.

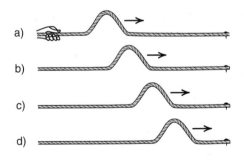

a)

b)

c)

d)

Figure 1-4
Wave traveling down a rope.

A KINK IN ELECTRIC FIELDS

You might have thought we were kidding when we said that a radio wave was a kink in the electric field lines of a charge. A kink in a rope—we can see that. But a kink in the imaginary electric field line—hard to believe!

Yet there are two basic laws governing the behavior of electric field lines that make them act in some ways like a rope.

First there is Gauss' law which says that electric field lines can start or stop only on electric charges. That means that in empty space, electric field lines cannot be broken. They have to be continuous, like an unbroken rope.

The other general law we will use is that information cannot travel faster than the speed of light. Suppose, for example, I have an electric charge that has been sitting at rest for a long time. The electric field lines come radially out as shown in Figure (1a).

Then I quickly move the charge upward a short distance in the short time Δt. During this time Δt, the information that I moved the charge can travel out from the original position of the charge only a distance cΔt. Outside a sphere of that radius, the electric field lines must be the old field lines of the undisturbed charge.

Inside the sphere cΔt, the field lines must all go to the new position of the charge. We have to bend the lines as shown in Figure (1b) to make the lines connect to the charge.

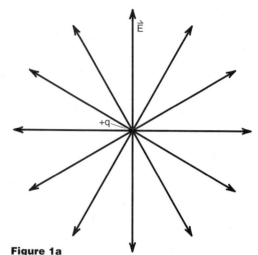

Figure 1a
Electric field of a charge at rest.

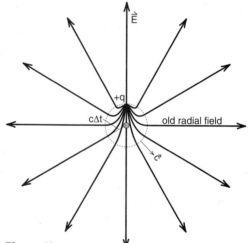

Figure 1b
We move the charge up for a short time Δt.
Outside a sphere of radius c Δt , centered on the
old position, no one knows the charge has moved.

Now I wait a while, leaving the charge at rest at the new position. If the charge has been sitting at rest for a time T, our guess is that the electric field lines out to a distance cT should be the radial field lines of a charge at rest, but centered at the new position, as shown in Figure (1c).

Out beyond a distance $c(T +\Delta t)$, there can be no information that we moved the charge. Beyond this sphere centered on the old position of the charge, the field lines must still fan radially outward. Because the lines cannot break, we have to connect the inside and outside radial lines, giving us a kink in the electric field. Maxwell's equations require that the kink travels out at the speed of light. The principle of relativity requires that the kink cannot travel faster than that.

When I moved the charge up for the short time Δt, my moving charge represents an electric current which in turn creates a magnetic field. The problem we face, however, is that it is not particularly easy to guess the structure of the magnetic field of a moving point charge.

Instead there is a distribution of electric charge whose magnetic field we already know. If we have a line of charges on a moving rod, as in our introduction to magnetism in Chapter 23, we get a circular cylinder of magnetic field surrounding the rod. Thus, we will switch our analysis from the fields and kinks generated by moving a *point* charge, to the fields and kinks generated by moving a *line* of charge. The result will be the radiation from a straight wire radio antenna.

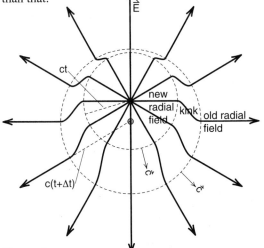

Figure 1c
The radial field at the new position expands outward. Radiation is the kink that connects the old and new radial fields.

RADIATION FROM AN ANTENNA

In Figure (2) we develop our model of the radiation from a straight wire radio antenna. In Figure (2a) we have a stationary line of positive charges. The electric field of these charges comes radially out from the charges as shown.

At time t = 0 we start moving the line of charges upward. The field lines have to stay attached to the charges that created them, but there can be no disturbance of the radial field out beyond a distance ct. Thus a kink has to form in the field lines as shown in Figure (2b).

After a short time Δt we stop moving the rod upward and leave it there at rest. New straight radial lines start moving outward at a speed c. Connecting the old lines to the new ones is a kink of width $c\Delta t$ moving at the wave speed $c = 1/\sqrt{\mu_0\varepsilon_0}$. At a time t the front of the kink has moved out a distance ct as seen in Figure (2c). (The situation is analogous to a transverse pulse traveling down our rope or Slinkey at a wave speed $v = \sqrt{T/\mu}$.)

A straight wire radio antenna has both positive charge (atomic nuclei) and negative charge (conduction electrons). To model the antenna we add in a stationary line of negative charge as shown in Figure (2d). We have also added the electric field of the negative charges. These lines come radially in, ending on the negative line of charge.

In Figure (2e) we are starting to add the outgoing electric field of the positive charge to the incoming electric field of the negative charge. Both outside

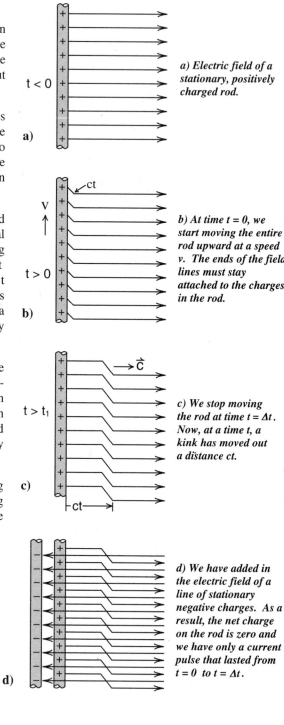

a) *Electric field of a stationary, positively charged rod.*

b) *At time t = 0, we start moving the entire rod upward at a speed v. The ends of the field lines must stay attached to the charges in the rod.*

c) *We stop moving the rod at time t = Δt. Now, at a time t, a kink has moved out a distance ct.*

d) *We have added in the electric field of a line of stationary negative charges. As a result, the net charge on the rod is zero and we have only a current pulse that lasted from t = 0 to t = Δt.*

Figures 2a-2d
Using the fact that electric field lines cannot break in empty space (Gauss' Law), and the idea that kinks in the field lines travel at the speed of light, we begin to guess the structure of an electromagnetic pulse.

and inside the kink, these fields have the same shape and strength, but precisely cancel because they are oppositely directed. All we are left with is an electric field inside the kink as shown in Figure (2f)

When we add the outward going $\vec{E}$ field of the kink to the inward $\vec{E}$ field of the negative charges, the radial components of these fields cancel, leaving only the downward pointing $\vec{E}$ field seen in Figure (2g). Since the radiated kink surrounds the entire wire, the downward directed $\vec{E}$ field in Figure (2g) also surrounds the wire in the form of a cylinder. And because the kink moves out at the speed of light, the cylinder of $\vec{E}$ field does also.

During the short time, starting at t = 0 that we were moving the positive line of charges upward, we had a positive upward directed current i. This upward directed current produces a circular magnetic field $\vec{B}$ surrounding the wire.

The circular $\vec{B}$ field cannot exist out beyond the kink because the information that we moved the rod cannot travel out faster than the speed of light. Because there is no more current after we stopped moving the positive charges, we suspect that there will be no magnetic field inside the kink. Our guess is that the magnetic field is confined to the region of the kink as shown in Figure (2h) and moves out with the kink at the speed of light. In Figure (2i) below, we show both sides of the radiated pulse. The structure shown in Figure (2i) obeys Maxwell's equations if, and only if, it moves out from the wire at the speed of light!

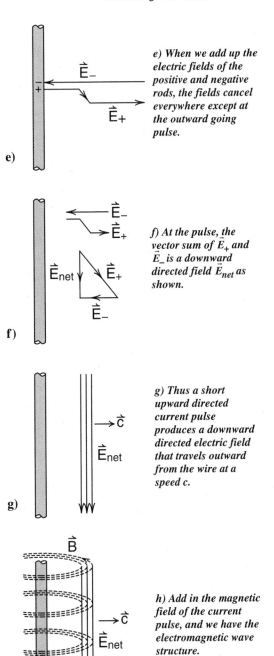

e) **When we add up the electric fields of the positive and negative rods, the fields cancel everywhere except at the outward going pulse.**

f) **At the pulse, the vector sum of $\vec{E}_+$ and $\vec{E}_-$ is a downward directed field $\vec{E}_{net}$ as shown.**

g) **Thus a short upward directed current pulse produces a downward directed electric field that travels outward from the wire at a speed c.**

h) **Add in the magnetic field of the current pulse, and we have the electromagnetic wave structure.**

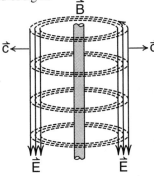

Figure 2i
Radiation from a current pulse. (Final result of Figures (2a - 2h).)

Figures 2e-2h
Except at the kink, the incoming fields of the negative charge cancel the outgoing fields of the positive charge.

A RADIO WAVE

One single pulse does not make much of a radio wave. We can more closely simulate a radio wave by having a series of pulses. First move the positive rod up to create the pulse shown in Figure (3). Let it sit at rest for a while, and then jerk the rod back down to its original position. This gives us another pulse that radiates out from the antenna.

Exercise 1

Stop and do this now. Figure out what the directions of the electric and magnetic fields $\vec{E}$ and $\vec{B}$ must be in this second radiated pulse when we move the positive rod back down. Explain your reasoning.

If you did Exercise 1, you found out that on the downward pulse of current, the electric field pointed up, and the magnetic field curled in a right hand direction when the thumb is pointing down (in the direction of i).

In Figure (3) we have sketched the electric and magnetic fields created by a series of current pulses that are graphed at the top of the diagram. The earliest electric current pulse shown (pulse #1) was

created by moving the positive rod down for a short time Δt and then letting it sit there for a longer time T_1. Then we created a positive pulse (#2) by moving the rod back up and letting it sit there for a while. Then we moved the rod down again (#3) and finally back up again (pulse #4). The reason we used a negative time axis in our current graph is so that we could draw the current pulses directly above the electric and magnetic field structure each pulse created. Note that the downward current pulses create the field structures you should have gotten as an answer to Exercise 1.)

Plane Waves

In close to the wire or antenna in Figure (3), the electric and magnetic fields are cylindrical structures surrounding the wire. As the electric and magnetic fields expand outward, the radii of the cylinders become larger and the wave becomes flatter and flatter. Far enough away from the antenna we will not notice the curvature of the magnetic field and instead see the flat waves shown in Figure (4). When the waves have become flat, they are called ***plane waves***. For the rest of this chapter we will focus on the structure of plane waves.

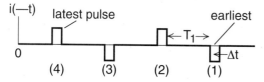

Current pulses creating the radiation fields.

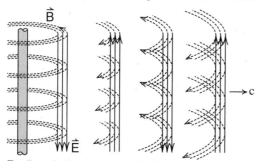

Radiated electromagnetic fields close in.

Figure 3
Electric and magnetic fields created by a series of current pulses.

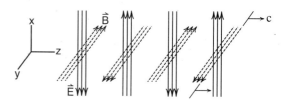

Radiated electromagnetic fields far away become plane waves. Here $\vec{E}$ and $\vec{B}$ are in the x-y plane, moving in the z direction.

Figure 4
As we go out the waves become flatter and flatter.

Sinusoidal Waves

Our final step in getting the picture we want of electromagnetic waves is to smooth out the current in the antenna. Instead of the abrupt pulses we had in Figures (3) and (4), it is more realistic to consider the plane waves created by a sinusoidal current. Instead of the pulsed structure of electric and magnetic fields, we get the sinusoidal shape shown in Figure (5b). We will use the shape in (5b) as our standard picture of an electromagnetic wave.

Wavelength

As we saw in Chapter 14 on wave motion, the wavelength of a periodic wave is the distance between similar crests. The wavelength λ of our sinusoidal electromagnetic wave is shown in Figure (5b).

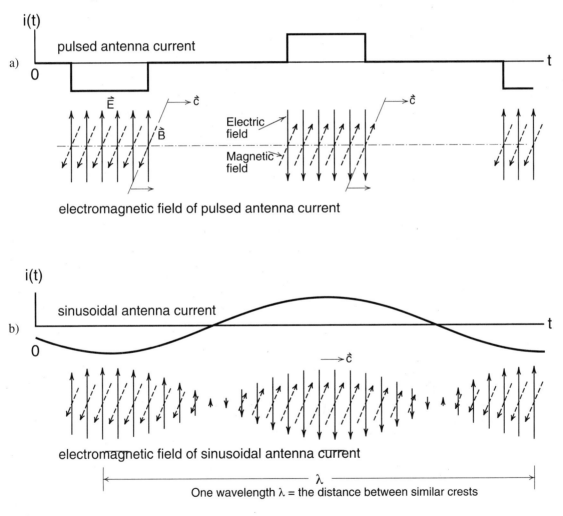

Figure 5
Changing from a pulsed wave to a sinusoidal wave. In a) the pulsed current produces a pulsed wave. When we smooth out the current into a sinusoidal wave, the radiation smooths out also.

Frequency

Because all light waves move at the speed c (in empty space), we can immediately calculate the frequency f *cycles per second* as the crests pass by us. As a reminder, we will do this calculation using dimensions. Here is how.

The frequency, the number of crests or cycles per second that pass by us, must be related to the wavelength λ *meters per cycle*, and the wave speed c *meters per second*. We could try the formula

$$f\frac{cycles}{second} = c\frac{meters}{second} \times \lambda\frac{meters}{cycle} = c\lambda\frac{meters^2}{sec\ cycle}$$

Clearly that formula does not work.

In order to get cycles upstairs, we need λ downstairs. We try

$$f\frac{cycles}{second} = c\frac{meters}{second} \times \frac{1}{\lambda\dfrac{meters}{cycle}} = \frac{c}{\lambda}\frac{cycles}{second}$$

The meters cancelled, the cycles came upstairs, and we got the right dimensions. Thus $f = c/\lambda$ is the correct formula.

We went through this exercise to remind you that you do not need to memorize a lot of formulas related to wave motion. Simply use dimensions.

(In their great wisdom, the committees who decide on the names of units, gave the name **hertz** to the dimensions cycles/sec. It is easier to write Hz rather than cycles/sec, but you lose the dimensions. When you see *Hz*, think *cycles/sec*.)

Exercise 2

The period of a repetitive wave is the number of seconds it takes each crest to pass by. Thus the period T has the dimensions T sec/cycle. Use dimensions to find formulas for the period T of an electromagnetic wave, in terms of (a) the frequency f, (b) the wavelength λ.

ELECTROMAGNETIC SPECTRUM

When Maxwell's equations are applied to our wave structure, there is no restriction on the frequency or wavelength of the pulses.

One hundred years before Maxwell it was known from interference experiments (which we will discuss in the next chapter) that light had a wave nature and that the wavelengths of light ranged from about 6×10^{-5} cm in the red part of the spectrum down to 4×10^{-5} cm in the blue part. With the discovery of Maxwell's theory of light, it became clear that there must be a complete spectrum of electromagnetic radiation, from very long down to very short wavelengths, and that visible light was just a tiny piece of this spectrum.

More importantly, Maxwell's theory provided the clue as to how you might be able to create electromagnetic waves at other frequencies. We have seen that an oscillating current in a wire produces an electromagnetic wave whose frequency is the same as that of the current. If, for example, the frequency of the current is 1030 kc (1030 kilocycles) = 1.03×10^6 cycles/sec, then the electromagnetic wave produced should have a wavelength

$$\lambda \frac{\text{meters}}{\text{cycle}} = \frac{c \text{ meters/sec}}{f \text{ cycles/sec}} = \frac{3 \times 10^8}{1.03 \times 10^6}$$

$$\lambda = 297 \text{ meters}$$

Such waves were discovered within 10 years of Maxwell's theory, and were called ***radio waves***. The frequency 1030 kc is the frequency of radio station WBZ in Boston, Mass.

Components of the Electromagnetic Spectrum

Figure (6) shows the complete electromagnetic spectrum as we know it today. We have labeled various components that may be familiar to the reader. These components, and the corresponding range of wavelengths are as follows:

Radio Waves	10^6 m to .05 mm
AM Band	500 m to 190 m
Short Wave	60 m to 15 m
TV VHF Band	10 m to 1 m
TV UHF Band	1 m to 10 cm
Microwaves	10 cm to .05 mm
Infrared Light	.05 mm to 6×10^{-7} m
Visible Light	6×10^{-7} to 4×10^{-7} m
Ultraviolet Light	4×10^{-7} m to 10^{-8} m
X Rays	10^{-8} m to 10^{-11} m
γ Rays	10^{-11} m and shorter

Exercise 3

Convert all of the above wavelengths to

a) frequencies

b) periods

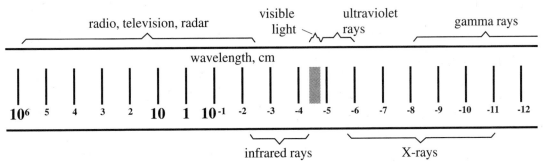

Figure 6
The electromagnetic spectrum extends from long wavelength radio waves down to short wavelength X rays and gamma rays. The visible part of the spectrum is indicated by the small box.

In each of these ranges, the most efficient way to emit or detect the radiation is to use antennas whose size is comparable to the wavelength of the radiation. For radio waves the antennas are generally some kind of a structure made from wire. In the infrared and the visible region, radiation is generally emitted by molecules and atoms. The short wavelength x rays and γ rays generally come from atomic nuclei or subatomic particles.

The longest wavelength radio waves that have been studied are the so-called "whistlers", radio waves with an audio frequency, that are produced by lightening bolts, and reflected back and forth around the earth by charged particles trapped in the earth's magnetic field. On a shorter scale of distance are the long wavelength radio waves which penetrate the ocean and are used for communications with submarines. The radio station in Cutler, Maine, shown in Figure (7), has twenty-six towers over 1000 feet tall to support the antenna to produce such waves. This station, operated by the United States Navy, is the world's most powerful.

As we go to shorter wavelengths and smaller antennas, we get to the broadcast band, short wave radio, then to the VHF and UHF television frequencies. (FM radio is tucked into the VHF band next to Channel 6). The wavelengths for VHF television are of the order of meters, while those for UHF are of the order of a foot. Those with separate VHF and UHF television antennas will be familiar with the fact that the UHF antenna, which detects the shorter wavelengths, is smaller in size.

Adjusting the rabbit ears antenna on a television set provides practical experience with the problems of detecting an electromagnetic wave. As the TV signal strikes the antenna, the electric field in the wave acts on the electrons in the TV antenna wire. If the wire is parallel to the electric field, the electrons are pushed along in the wire producing a voltage that is detected by the television set. If the wire is perpendicular, the electrons will not be pushed up and down and no voltage will be produced.

Figure 7
The world's largest radio station at Cutler, Maine. This structure, with 75 miles of antenna wire and 26 towers over 1000 ft high, generates long wavelength, low frequency radio waves for communications with submarines.

The length of the wire is also important. If the antenna were one half wavelength, then the electric field at one end would be pushing in the opposite direction from the field at the other end, the net voltage down the antenna would be zero, and you would get no signal. You want the antenna long enough to get a big voltage, but not so long that the electric field in one part of the antenna works against the field in another part. One quarter wavelength is generally the optimum antenna length.

The microwave region, now familiar from microwave communications and particularly microwave ovens, lies between the television frequencies and infrared radiation. The fact that you heat food in a microwave oven emphasizes the fact that electromagnetic radiation carries energy. One can derive that the energy density in an electromagnetic wave is given by the formula

$$\left. \begin{array}{l} \text{energy density in an} \\ \text{electromagnetic} \\ \text{wave} \end{array} \right\} = \frac{\varepsilon_0 E^2}{2} + \frac{B^2}{2\mu_0} \quad (1)$$

We have already derived the formula $\varepsilon_0 E^2/2$ for the energy density in an electric field part of the wave. [See Chapter 22, Equation (37).]

Blackbody Radiation

Atoms and molecules emit radiation in the infrared, visible and ultraviolet part of the spectrum. One of the main sources of radiation in this part of the spectrum is the so-called ***blackbody radiation*** emitted by objects because of the thermal motion of their atoms and molecules.

If you heat an iron poker in a fire, the poker first gets warm, then begins to glow a dull red, then a bright red or even, orange. At higher temperatures the poker becomes white, like the filaments in an electric light bulb. At still higher temperatures, if the poker did not melt, it would become bluish. The name *blackbody radiation* is related to the fact that an initially cold, black object emits these colors of light when heated.

There is a well studied relationship between the temperature of an object and the predominant frequency of the blackbody radiation it emits. Basically, the higher the temperature, the higher the frequency. Astronomers use this relationship to determine the temperature of stars from their color. The infrared stars are quite cool, our yellow sun has about the same temperature as the yellow filament in an incandescent lamp, and the blue stars are the hottest.

All objects emit blackbody radiation. You, yourself, are like a small star emitting infrared radiation at a wavelength corresponding to a temperature of 300K. In an infrared photograph taken at night, you would show up distinctly due to this radiation. Infrared photographs are now taken of houses at night to show up hot spots and heat leaks in the house.

Perhaps the most famous example of blackbody radiation is the 3K cosmic background radiation which is the remnant of the big bang which created the universe. We will say much more about this radiation in Chapter 26 on photons.

UV, X Rays, and Gamma Rays

When we get to wavelengths shorter than the visible spectrum, and even in the visible spectrum, we begin to run into problems with Maxwell's theory of light. These problems were first clearly displayed by Max Planck who in 1900 developed a theory that explained the blackbody spectrum of radiation. The problem with Planck's theory of blackbody radiation is that it could not be derived from Maxwell's theory of light and Newtonian mechanics. His theory involved arbitrary assumptions that would not be understood for another 23 years, until after the development of quantum mechanics.

Despite the failure of Newton's and Maxwell's theories to explain all the details, the electromagnetic spectrum continues right on up into the shorter wavelengths of ultraviolet (UV) light, then to x rays and finally to γ (gamma) rays. Ultraviolet light is most familiar from the effect it has on us, causing tanning, sunburns, and skin cancer depending on the intensity and duration of the dose. The ozone layer in the upper atmosphere, as long as it lasts, is important because it filters out much of the ultraviolet light emitted by the sun.

X rays are famous for their ability to penetrate flesh and produce photographs of bones. These rays are usually emitted by the tightly bound electrons on the inside of large atoms, and also by nuclear reactions. The highest frequency radiation, γ rays, are emitted by the smallest objects—nuclei and elementary particles.

POLARIZATION

One of the immediate tests of our picture of a light or radio wave, shown in Figure (8), is the phenomena of *polarization*. We mentioned that the reason that you had to adjust the angle of the wires on a rabbit ears antenna was that the electric field of the television signal had to have a significant component parallel to the wires in order to push the electrons up and down the wire. Polarization is a phenomena that results from the fact that the electric field $\vec{E}$ in an electromagnetic wave can have various orientations as the wave moves through space.

Although we have derived the structure of an electromagnetic wave for the specific case of a wave produced by an alternating current in a long, straight wire, some of the general features of electromagnetic waves are clearly present in our solution. The general features that are present in all electromagnetic waves are:

1) All electromagnetic waves are a structure consisting of an electric field $\vec{E}$ and a magnetic field $\vec{B}$.

2) $\vec{E}$ and $\vec{B}$ are at right angles to each other as shown in Figures (3,4,&5).

3) The wave travels in a direction perpendicular to the plane of $\vec{E}$ and $\vec{B}$.

4) The speed of the wave in a vacuum is $c = 3 \times 10^8 m/s$.

Even with these restrictions, and even if we consider only flat or plane electromagnetic waves, there are still various possible orientations of the electric field as shown in Figure (8). In Figure (8a) we see a plane wave with a vertical electrical field. This would be called a *vertically polarized* wave. In Figure (8b), where the electric field is horizontal, we have a *horizontally polarized* wave. By convention we say that the direction of polarization is the direction of the electric field in an electromagnetic wave.

Because $\vec{E}$ must lie in the plane perpendicular to the direction of motion of an electromagnetic wave, $\vec{E}$ **has only two independent components**, which we can call the vertical and horizontal polarizations, or the x and y polarizations as shown in Figures (8a) and (8b) respectively. If we happen to encounter an electromagnetic wave where $\vec{E}$ is neither vertical or horizontal, but at some angle θ, we can decompose $\vec{E}$ into its x and y components as shown in Figure (9). Thus we can consider a wave polarized at an arbitrary angle θ as a mixture of the two independent polarizations.

a) Vertical Polarization

Figure 9
We define the direction of polarization of an electromagnetic wave as the direction of the electric field.

b) Horizontal Polarization

c) Mixture

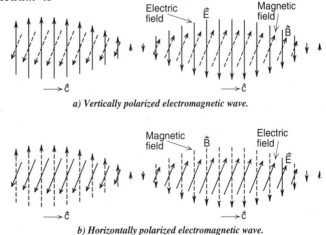

Electric field $\vec{E}$ Magnetic field $\vec{B}$

$\vec{c}$ $\vec{c}$

a) Vertically polarized electromagnetic wave.

Magnetic field $\vec{B}$ Electric field $\vec{E}$

$\vec{c}$ $\vec{c}$

b) Horizontally polarized electromagnetic wave.

Figure 8
Two possible polarizations of an electromagnetic wave.

Polarizers

A polarizer is a device that lets only one of the two possible polarizations of an electromagnetic wave pass through. If we are working with microwaves whose wavelength is of the order of a few centimeters, a frame strung with parallel copper wires, as seen in Figure (10), makes an excellent polarizer. If a vertically polarized wave strikes this vertical array of wires, the electric field $\vec{E}$ in the wave will be parallel to the wires. This parallel $\vec{E}$ field will cause electrons to move up and down in the wires, taking energy out of the incident wave. As a result the vertically polarized wave cannot get through. (One can observe that the wave is actually reflected by the parallel wires.)

If you then rotate the wires 90°, so that the $\vec{E}$ field in the wave is perpendicular to the wires, the electric field can no longer move electrons along the wires and the wires have no effect. The wave passes through without attenuation.

If you do not happen to know the direction of polarization of the microwave, put the polarizer in the beam and rotate it. For one orientation the microwave beam will be completely blocked. Rotate the polarizer by 90° and you will get a maximum transmission.

Figure 10
Microwave polarizer, made from an array of copper wires. The microwave transmitter is seen on the other side of the wires, the detector is on this side. When the wires are parallel to the transmitted electric field, no signal is detected. Rotate the wires 90 degrees, and the full signal is detected.

Light Polarizers

We can picture light from the sun as a mixture of light waves with randomly oriented polarizations. (The $\vec{E}$ fields are, of course, always in the plane perpendicular to the direction of motion of the light wave. Only the angle of $\vec{E}$ in that plane is random.) A polarizer made of an array of copper wires like that shown in Figure (10), will not work for light because the wavelength of light is so short ($\lambda \approx 5 \times 10^{-5} cm$) that the light passes between the wires. For such a polarizer to be effective, the spacing between the wires would have to be of the order of a wavelength of light or less.

A polarizer for light can be constructed by imbedding long-chain molecules in a flexible plastic sheet, and then stretching the sheet so that the molecules are aligned parallel to each other. The molecules act like the wires in our copper wire array, but have a spacing of the order of the wavelength of light. As a result the molecules block light waves whose electric field is parallel to them, while allowing waves with a perpendicular electric field to pass. (The commercial name for such a sheet of plastic is *Polaroid*.)

Since light from the sun or from standard electric light bulbs consists of many randomly polarized waves, a single sheet of Polaroid removes half of the waves no matter how we orient the Polaroid (as long as the sheet of Polaroid is perpendicular to the direction of motion of the light beam). But once the light has gone through one sheet of Polaroid, all the surviving light waves have the same polarization. If we place a second sheet of Polaroid over the first, all the light will be absorbed if the long molecules in the second sheet are perpendicular to the long molecules in the first sheet. If the long molecules in the second sheet are parallel to those in the first, most of the waves that make it through the first, make it through the second also.

In Figure (11), a smiley face was drawn on a light box, and then we placed three essentially identical Polaroid strips over the image. You can immediately see that where the strips cross at right angles, the light from the box is completely blocked. Where the strips are parallel, the image is only slightly dimmed.

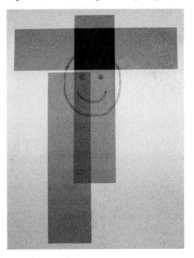

Figure 11
Three identical Polaroid strips on a lightbox. The parallel strips let light through, but where the strips cross at right angles, the light is completely blocked. (We had some difficulty finding an artist to draw the image on the surface of the light box.)

RADIATED FIELDS OF A MOVING POINT CHARGE

The way we introduced radiation in this chapter, treating electromagnetic radiation as a kink in the electric field lines, was inspired by an excellent series of short movies of computer simulation of the electric field lines of moving charges.

In the first movie, we see the electric field of a point charge at rest, as shown in Figure (12a). Then we see a charge moving at constant velocity $\vec{v}$. As the speed of the charge approaches c, the electric field scrunches up as shown in Figure (12b).

The next film segment shows what happens when we have a moving charge that stops. If the charge stopped at time t = 0, then at a distance r = ct or greater, we must have the electric field of a moving charge, because no information that the charge has stopped can reach beyond this distance. In close we have the electric field of a static charge. The expanding kink that connects the two regions is the electromagnetic wave. The result is shown in Figure (12c). The final film segment shows the electric field of an oscillating charge. Figure (12d) shows one frame of the film. This still picture does a serious injustice to the animated film. There is no substitute, or words to explain, what you see and feel when you watch this film.

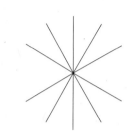

Figure 12a
Electric field of a stationary charge.

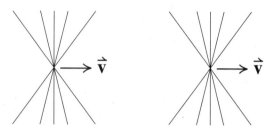
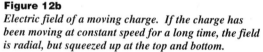

Figure 12b
Electric field of a moving charge. If the charge has been moving at constant speed for a long time, the field is radial, but squeezed up at the top and bottom.

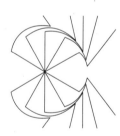

Figure 12c
Field of a charge that stopped. Assume that the charge stopped t seconds ago. Inside a circle of radius ct, we have the field of a stationary charge. Outside, where there is no information that the charge has stopped, we still have the field of a moving charge. The kink that connects the two fields is the electromagnetic radiation.

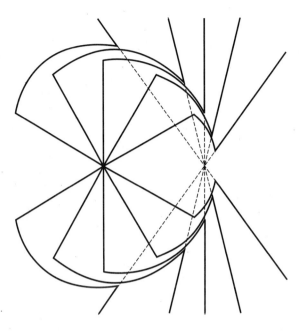

Figure 12c (enlarged)
Electric field of a charge that stopped. The dashed lines show the field structure we would have seen had the charge not stopped.

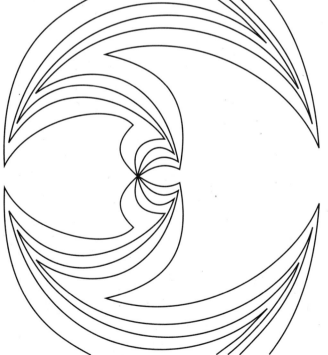

Figure 12d
Electric field of an oscillating charge.

Exercise 4

Assume that we have a supply of ping pong balls and cardboard tubes shown in Figures (13). By looking at the fields outside these objects decide what could be inside producing the fields. Explicitly do the following for each case.

i) If more than one kind of source could produce the field shown, describe both (or all) sources.

ii) If the field is impossible, explain why.

In each case, we have indicated whether the source is in a ball or tube. Magnetic fields are dashed or green lines, electric fields are solid or red lines, and the balls and tubes are surrounded by empty space.

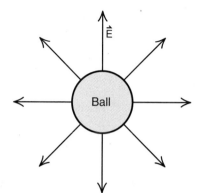

Figure 13a
Electric field emerging from ping pong ball.

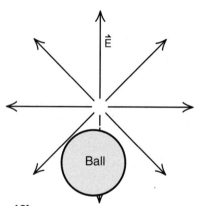

Figure 13b
Magnetic field emerging from ping pong ball.

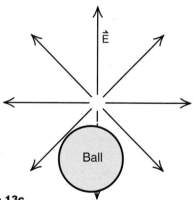

Figure 13c
Electric field emerging above ping pong ball.

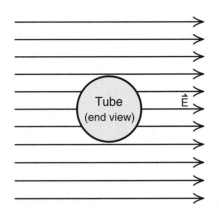

Figure 13d
Electric field passing through tube.

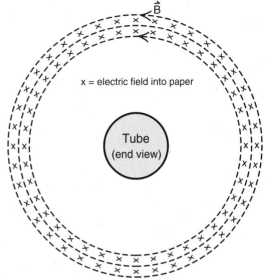

x = electric field into paper

Figure 13f
For this example, explain what is happening to the fields outside the tube, what is in the tube, and what happened inside now.

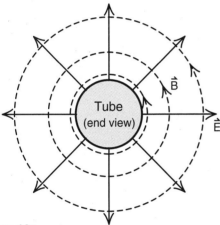

Figure 13e
There is only ONE object inside this tube. What is it? What is it doing?

CHAPTER 24 REVIEW

Vector Fields

Mathematically, there are two kinds of vector fields, a diverging kind and a circulating kind. The electric field of a point charge is the standard example of a diverging field. The magnetic field of a current in a wire and the flow fields of a vortex, are examples of circulating fields.

Since electric and magnetic fields should be able to have both diverging and circulating components, four distinct kinds of electric and magnetic fields are possible. These are (or would be) diverging electric and diverging magnetic fields, and circulation electric and circulating magnetic fields shown in Figures (3 a, b, c, d) of Essay (6), reproduced here.

Each kind of field has a distinct source. The diverging electric field is produced by electric charges. The diverging magnetic fields would be produced by the so-called magnetic monopole. Modern theories suggest that magnetic monopoles should have been created in the early universe, but none has been found so far. As a result, we have not seen any diverging magnetic fields.

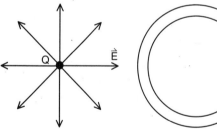

3a) diverging electric field   3c) circulating electric field

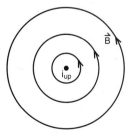 

3b) circulating magnetic field   3d) diverging magnetic field

Figure 3 of Essay 6
Four possible kinds of electric and magnetic fields.

We have seen the circulating magnetic field created by an electric current in a wire. The circulating electric field, illustrated in Figure (3c) is created by a changing magnetic field. One can create this circulating electric field, and generate a voltage in a loop of wire, by moving a magnet through the loop. This is the idea behind the electric generator.

Each kind of electric and magnetic field has a mathematical equation describing its behavior. Coulomb's law, or its equivalent, Gauss' law, governs the behavior of the diverging electric field. Since we have not yet found a magnetic monopole, the equation for the diverging magnetic field sets that field equal to zero.

The circulating magnetic field is governed by Ampere's law, and Faraday's law describes the behavior of the circulating electric field. Ampere's law and Faraday's law are mentioned in Essay (6) and discussed in detail in Satellite Chapters (10) and (11).

Maxwell's Equations

*The set of four equations governing the four kinds of electric and magnetic fields are called **Maxwell's equations**. Why is Maxwell's name used to describe the equations discovered by Coulomb, Ampere, and Faraday? The answer is that Maxwell discovered a slight generalization of Ampere's law, a result that led to Maxwell's discovery of a theory of light.*

Maxwell discovered that a changing electric field created a magnetic field, and that changing magnetic field created an electric field. A careful analysis of his equations showed that the electric and magnetic fields could feed off of each other in a wave like manner, creating a wave that traveled at a speed $c = \sqrt{1/\mu_0\varepsilon_0} = 3\times10^8$ meters per second, the speed of light. Thus Maxwell could announce that light consisted of a wave of electric and magnetic fields traveling through space.

Electromagnetic Radiation

In the calculus version of the text, we use Maxwell's equations to derive the structure of a light wave and to derive Maxwell's formula for the speed of light. Because of the explicit use of calculus in these derivations, in this non calculus text we use another, actually simpler, approach to introduce light waves.

This simpler approach is founded on two basic ideas. One is that electric field lines **cannot stop or start in empty space**. *They can only start or stop on electric charge, and thus in empty space these field lines cannot be broken. The second basic idea is that* **information cannot travel faster than the speed of light**.

To apply these ideas, we started with an electric charge that had been sitting at rest for a long time, producing straight radial electric field lines shown in Figure (1a). Then we suddenly moved the charge upward during a short time Δt.

During this time Δt, *the information that we moved the charge, can travel no farther than a distance* $c\Delta t$. *Those outside a sphere of radius* $c\Delta t$ *can only see the straight radial lines of Figure (1a). Inside the sphere the field lines have to bend so that they all stay attached to the displaced charge as shown in Figure (1b).*

If I stop the charge after I moved it for a time Δt, *the information that the charge has stopped will also travel out at a speed c. At some time t, a new radial field will be created inside a sphere of radius ct. Beyond the sphere of radius* $c(t + \Delta t)$, *centered on the old position of the charge, we must have the old radial field. Since the field lines have to be continuous, there will be an outward moving set of kinks in the electric field lines as shown in Figure (1c). The set of kinks, which move out at the speed of light, are what we call* **electromagnetic radiation**.

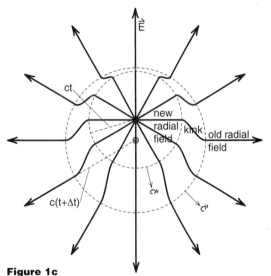

Figure 1c
The radial field at the new position expands outward. Radiation is the kink that connects the old and new radial fields.

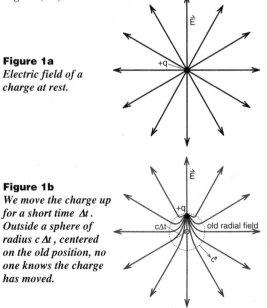

Figure 1a
Electric field of a charge at rest.

Figure 1b
We move the charge up for a short time Δt. *Outside a sphere of radius* $c\,\Delta t$, *centered on the old position, no one knows the charge has moved.*

The Antenna

It turns out to be easier to analyze the radiation from a moving line of charge rather from a point charge. In Figure (2) we imagine that we move a line of positive charge upward for a short time, and observe an outward moving kink in the radial field lines. When we add in the electric field of a similar line of negative charge, all the fields cancel except the fields in the kink. The result is a downward pointing, expanding cylinder of electric field shown in Figure (2g). Adding in the circular magnetic field produced by the moving positive charge, we end up with the expanding cylinder of the crossed electric and magnetic field shown in Figure (2h). This is the basic structure of an electromagnetic wave; crossed electric and magnetic fields moving at a speed c as shown.

If we move the positive line of charge back down to its original position, we get another expanding cylinder of electric and magnetic fields where $\vec{E}$ and $\vec{B}$ point in the opposite directions. If we move the positive charges up and down repeatedly, we get the series of cylindrical pulses shown in Figure (3). We have just described a model of a radio wave antenna.

In a real radio wave antenna, we leave the positive charges—the copper ions—at rest, and move the negative charges—the electrons—up and down. Instead of moving the electrons up and down in a jerky motion of Figure (3), it is much easier to move them up and down in a sinusoidal motion, producing the sinusoidal field structure of Figure (5b). This figure is a fairly accurate representation of the kind of electromagnetic wave produced by an antenna.

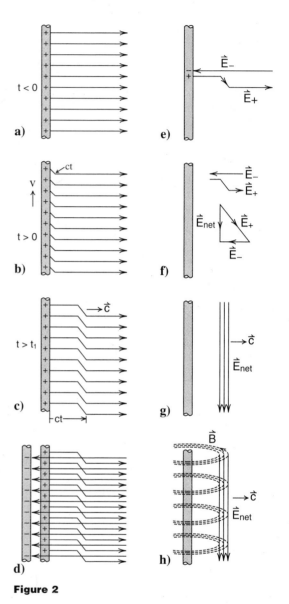

Figure 2

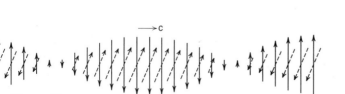

Figure 5b
An electromagnetic wave. The electric field (red) and the magnetic field (green) are perpendicular to each other, and perpendicular to the direction of motion.

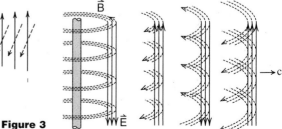

Figure 3

Electromagnetic Waves

The wave shown in Figure (5b) has a wavelength λ and is moving at a speed c. It also has a frequency f which is the number of wavelengths that pass by us each second. To calculate this frequency f, we use dimensions:

$$c \frac{meters}{second} \quad speed$$

$$\lambda \frac{meters}{cycle} \quad wavelength$$

$$t \frac{seconds}{cycle} \quad period$$

$$f \frac{cycles}{second} \quad frequency$$

To get f from c and λ we have

$$f \frac{cycles}{second} = \frac{c}{\lambda} \frac{meters/second}{meters/cycle}$$

The meters cancel and we are left with

$$f = \frac{c}{\lambda} \frac{cycles}{second}$$

As a practical example, radio station WBZ in Boston broadcasts radio waves at a frequency of 1040 kilocycles per second. Calculate the wavelength of these radio waves. We have

$$\lambda \frac{meters}{cycle} = \frac{c}{f} \frac{meters/second}{cycles/second} = \frac{c}{f} \frac{meters}{cycle}$$

For WBZ we have

$$\lambda_{WBZ} = \frac{3 \times 10^8 meters/sec}{1040 \times 10^3 cycles/sec} = 288 \frac{meters}{cycle}$$

The electromagnetic spectrum we are familiar with, consists of waves ranging from kilometers in length down to the size of an atomic nucleus. The longest wavelengths are radio waves. When we get down to a meter or so we have television and FM waves. The microwaves that cook food in the microwave ovens have wavelengths of a few centimeters. Infra red light is just regular light with too long a wavelength to see. The visible wavelengths are from 6×10^{-7} meters for red light, to 4×10^{-7} meters for blue light.

At still shorter wavelengths we have ultraviolet light, then x rays, and finally gamma rays at the shortest wavelength end of the spectrum. The surprising feature of the electromagnetic spectrum is how short the range of the visible part is.

In the recently popular terminology of nanometers [1 nanometer (nm) = 10^{-9} meter], the range of visible light is from about 600 nanometers in the red down to 400 nanometers in the blue. (A hydrogen atom has a diameter close to 0.1 nanometers.)

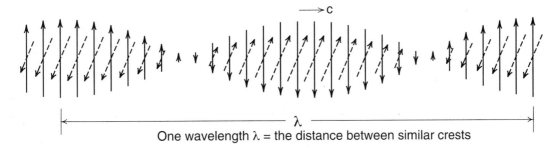

One wavelength λ = the distance between similar crests

Figure 5b (repeated)
Structure of a plane wave electromagnetic wave.

Polarization

Figure (8) shows two different polarizations of a light wave. An electromagnetic wave always consists of crossed (at right angles) electric and magnetic fields. The wave, in a vacuum, moves at a speed c in a direction perpendicular to the crossed $\vec{E}$ and $\vec{B}$ fields. We say that the direction of polarization is in the direction of the electric field $\vec{E}$. In Figure (8a) the wave is vertically polarized, while in (8b) it is horizontally polarized.

Light reflected at an angle of 53 degrees from a water surface (56 degrees for glass) is almost totally horizontally polarized. (This is called the Brewster angle.) Thus, if you wear polarized sun glasses that only allow the passage of vertically polarized light, the reflected light will be blocked. You thus eliminate the glare of the reflected light and get a clearer view of the scene.

CHAPTER EXERCISES

Exercise 1 On page 6

Figure the directions of the electric and magnetic fields when we move the charged rod down.

Exercise 2 On page 8

Use dimensions to find formulas for the period T in terms of (a) the frequency f, (b) the wavelength λ.

Exercise 3 On page 9

Convert the wavelengths of the electromagnetic spectrum to frequencies and periods.

Exercise 4 On page 18

Explain how the six field structures shown, were produced.

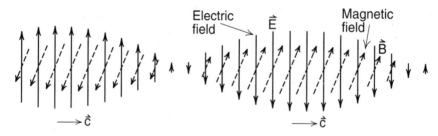

a) Vertically polarized electromagnetic wave.

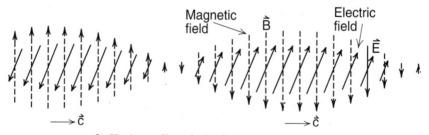

b) Horizontally polarized electromagnetic wave.

Figure 8 (repeated)
The direction of the polarization is defined as the direction of the electric field.

Chapter 25 non calculus
Light Waves

Ripples produced by rain drops. (Bill Jack Rodgers, Los Alamos Scientific Laboratory)

In the examples of wave motion we studied back in Chapter 13, like waves on a rope and sound in a gas, we could picture the wave motion as a consequence of the mechanical behavior of particles in the rope or molecules in the gas. We used Newton's laws to predict the speed these waves. When we discuss light waves, we go beyond the Newtonian behavior. Waves on a rope, on water, or in a gas are mechanical undulations of an explicit medium. Light waves travel through empty space; there is nothing to undulate, nothing to which we can apply Newton's laws. Yet, in many ways, the behavior of light waves, water waves, sound waves, and even the waves of quantum theory, are remarkably similar.

*There are general rules of wave motion that transcend the nature of the medium or type of wave. One is the principle of superposition that we used extensively in Chapter 14. It is the idea that as waves move through each other, they produce an overall wave whose amplitude is the sum of the amplitudes of the individual waves. The other is a concept we will use extensively in this chapter called the **Huygens principle**, named after its discoverer Christian Huygens, a contemporary of Isaac Newton.*

We will see that a straightforward application of the principle of superposition and the Huygens principle allows us to make detailed predictions that can be used as a test of the wave nature of the phenomena we are studying.

SUPERPOSITION OF CIRCULAR WAVE PATTERNS

When we studied the interaction of waves on a rope, it was a relatively simple process of adding up the individual waves to see what the resultant wave would be. For example, in Figure (14-2) reproduced here, we see that as a crest and a trough run into each other, for an instant they add up to produce a flat rope. At this instant the crest and the trough cancel each other. In contrast, two crests add to produce a big crest, and two troughs add to produce a deeper trough.

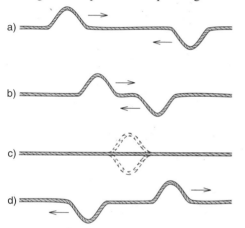

Figure 14-2
When a crest meets a trough, there is a short time when the waves cancel.

When we extend our study of wave motion to two and three dimensions, the principle of superposition works the same way, but now we have to add patterns rather than just heights along a line. For example, if we are studying wave motion on the surface of water, and two wave patterns move through each other, the resulting wave is the sum of the heights of the individual waves at every point on the surface. We do the same addition as we did for one dimensional waves, but at many more points.

An important but relatively simple example of the superposition of wave patterns, is the pattern we get when concentric circular waves from two nearby sources run into each other. The pattern is easy to set up in a ripple tank using two oscillating plungers.

Figure (1a) shows the circular wave pattern produced by a single oscillating plunger. From this picture we can easily see the circular waves emerging from the plunger. The only difficulty is distinguishing crests from troughs. We will handle this by using a solid line to represent the crest of a wave and a dashed line for a trough, as illustrated in Figure (1b).

Figure 1a,b
Circular wave pattern produced in a ripple tank by a plunger. The pattern consists of alternate crests and troughs. To diagram the circular wave pattern, we will use solid lines for crests and dashed lines for troughs.

a)

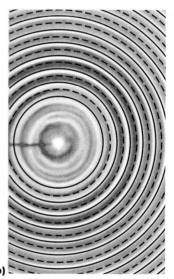

b)

In Figure (2a), we see the wave pattern produced by two plungers oscillating side by side. Each plunger sends out a circular set of waves like that seen in Figure (1). When the two sets of circular waves cross each other, we get cancellation where crests from one set meet troughs from the other set, where a solid line from one set of circles meets a dashed line from the other set of circles in Figure (2b). This cancellation occurs along lines called ***lines of nodes*** which are clearly seen in Figure (2a).

Between the lines of nodes we get beams of waves. In each beam, crests from one plunger meet crests from the other producing a higher crest. And troughs from one set meet troughs from the other producing deeper troughs. In our drawing of circles, Figures (2b) and (2c), we get beams of waves along the lines where solid circles cross solid circles and dashed circles cross dashed circles.

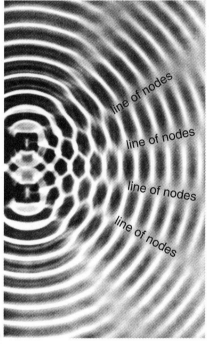

a)   b)

Figure 2a,b
Ripple tank photograph of an interference pattern.
When two sets of circular waves move through each
other, there are lines along which crests from one
set always meet troughs from the other set. These
are called **lines of nodes.** *Between the lines of*
nodes, we get beams of waves. The resulting pattern
is called an **interference pattern.**

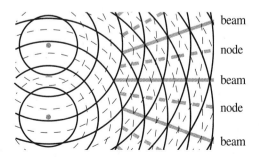

Figure 2c
We get beams of waves where crests meet crests
and troughs meet troughs. The lines of nodes are
where crests meet troughs and the waves cancel.

HUYGENS PRINCIPLE

When sunlight streams in through an open kitchen door, we see a distinct shadow on the floor. The shadow can be explained by assuming that the light beams travel in straight lines from the sun through the doorway. The whole subject of geometrical optics and lens design is based on the assumption that light travels in straight lines (except at the interface of two media of different indices of refraction).

In Figure (3) we see what happens when a wave impinges upon a slit whose width is comparable to the wavelength of the waves. Instead of there being a shadow of the slit, we see that the emerging wave comes out in all directions. The wave pattern on the right side of the slit is essentially identical to the wave pattern produced by the oscillating plunger in Figure (1a). We can explain Figure (3) by saying that the small piece of wave front that gets through the slit acts as a source of waves in much the same way that the oscillating plunger acted as a source of waves.

Christian Huygens noted this phenomena and from it developed a general principle of wave motion. His idea was that as a wave pattern evolved, each point of a wave front acts as the source of a new circular or spherical wave. To see how this principle can be applied,

consider the relatively smooth wave front shown in Figure (4). To predict the position of the wave front a short time later, we treat each point on the front of the wave as a source of circular waves. We can see the effect by drawing a series of circles at closely spaced points along the wave. The circular waves add up to produce a new wave front farther out. While you can use the same construction to figure out what is happening throughout the wave, it is much easier to see what is happening at the front.

Exercise 1

At some instant of time, the front of a wave has a sharp, right angle corner. Use Huygens principle to find the shape of the wave front at some later instant of time. [Draw a right angle corner and use the kind of construction shown in Figure (4).]

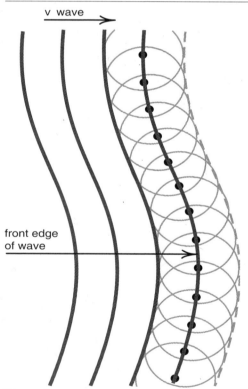

v wave →

front edge
of wave

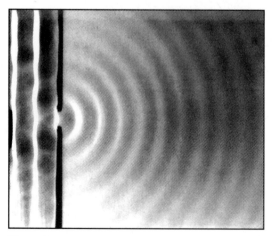

Figure 3
A wave emerging from a narrow slit spreads out in all directions, just as if the wave in the slit were a plunger.

Figure 4
Huygen's construction. The future position of a wave front can accurately be predicted by assuming that each point on the wavefront is a source of a new wave.

By using the construction of Figure (4) to predict the future shape of a wave front, we see that if we use a slit to block all but a small section of the wave front, as illustrated in Figure (5), then the remaining piece of wave front will act as a source of circular waves emerging from the other side. This is what we saw in Figure (3). Thus the Huygens construction allows us to see not only how a smooth wave travels forward intact, but also why circular waves emerge from a narrow slit as we saw in Figure (3).

The Huygens construction also provides a picture of what happens as waves go through progressively wider slits. If the slit is wider than a wavelength, then we have more sources in the slit and the waves from the sources begin to interfere with each other. In Figures (6, 7, 8) we see the wave patterns for increasingly wide slits and the corresponding Huygens constructions. For the wider slits, more of the wave goes through the center intact, but there is always a circular wave coming out at the edges. For the slit of Figure (8), the circular waves at the edges are relatively unimportant, and the edges of the slit cast a shadow. This is beginning to resemble our example of sunlight coming through the kitchen doorway. The name *diffraction* is used to describe the spreading of the waves that we see at the edges of the slits in Figures (5) through (8).

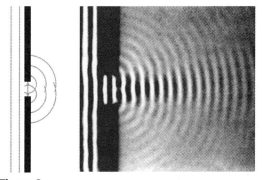

Figure 6
When the slit is about 2 wavelengths wide, the wave in the slit acts as 2 point sources.

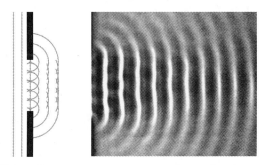

Figure 7
As the slit is widened, more of the wave comes through intact. In the center we are beginning to get a beam of waves, yet at the edges, the wave front continues to act as a source of circular waves.

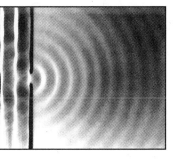

Figure 5
The small piece of wave in a narrow slit acting as a single point source.

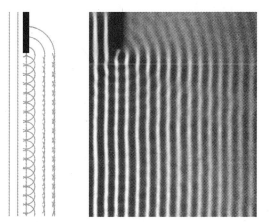

Figure 8
When the slit is wide compared to a wavelength, we get a distinct beam of waves. Yet no matter how wide the slit, there are still circular waves at the edges.

TWO SLIT
INTERFERENCE PATTERN

If a single narrow slit can produce the same wave pattern an oscillating plunger, as we saw in Figure (3), then we should expect that two slits next to each other should produce an interference pattern similar to the one produced by two oscillating plungers seen in Figure (2). That this is indeed correct is demonstrated in Figure (9). On the left we have repeated the wave pattern of 2 plungers. On the right we have a wave impinging upon two narrow slits. We see that both have the same structure of lines of nodes, with beams of waves coming out between the lines of nodes. Because the patterns are the same, we can use the same analysis for both situations.

Sending a wave through two slits and observing the resulting wave pattern is a convenient way to analyze various kinds of wave motion. But in most cases we do not see the full interference pattern, as we do for these ripple tank photographs. Instead, we observe only where the waves strike some object, and from this deduce the nature of the waves.

To illustrate what we mean, imagine a harbor with a sea wall and two narrow entrances in the wall as shown in Figure (10). Waves coming in from the ocean emerge as circular waves from each entrance and produce a two slit interference pattern in the harbor. Opposite the sea wall is a beach as shown.

If we are at point A on the beach directly across from the center of the two entrances, we are standing in the center beam of waves in the interference pattern. Here

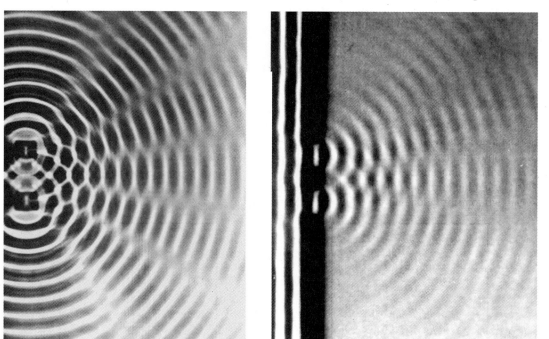

Figure 9
The wave pattern emerging from 2 slits is similar to the wave pattern produced by two plungers.

large waves wash up on the beach. Walking north along the beach we cross the first line of nodes at point B. Here the water is calm. Going farther up to point C we are again in the center of a beam of waves. We will call this the ***first maximum*** above the ***central maximum***. Farther up we cross the second line of nodes at point D and encounter the second minimum in the height of waves striking the shore.

Going south from point A we encounter the same alternate series of maxima and minima at points B', C', D', etc. If we graphed the amplitude of the waves striking the shore, we would get the pattern shown at the right side of Figure (10).

Now suppose that we walk along the beach on a calm day where there are no waves, but on the previous day there had been a storm. During the storm, the waves striking the shore eroded the beach. As you walk along the beach you notice a series of indentations, at points A, C, C', etc. where the beach was eroded. The sand was not eroded at points B, B', D and D'. If someone asked what the ocean waves were like during the storm, could you tell them?

By measuring the distance between the maximum erosions and knowing the geometry of the harbor, you can determine the wavelength of the ocean waves that struck the sea wall during the storm. Similar calculations can be made to determine the wavelength of any kind of wave striking two narrow slits producing an interference pattern on the other side. We do not have to see the actual wave pattern, we only have to note the location of the maxima and minima of the waves striking an object like the shore in Figure (10).

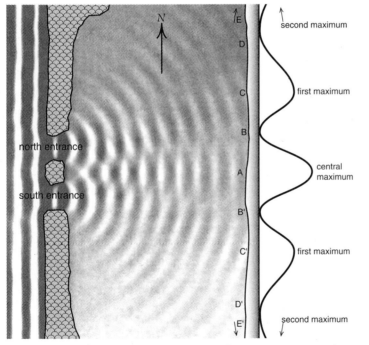

Figure 10
Hypothetical harbor with two entrances through the sea wall. If ocean waves are coming straight in toward the sea wall, there will be a 2 slit interference pattern inside the harbor, with a series of maxima and minima along the beach.

We begin our analysis of the two slit wave pattern by drawing a series of circles to represent the wave crests and troughs emerging from the two slits. The results, which are shown in Figure (11), are essentially the same as our analysis of the two plunger interference pattern in Figure (2). The maxima occur where crests meet crests and troughs meet troughs. The minima or lines of nodes are where crests meet troughs.

Exercise 2

On Figure (11), sketch the lines along which crests meet troughs, i.e., where solid and dashed circles intersect. This should be where the lines of nodes are located.

The First Maxima

The central maximum is straight across from the center of the two slits (if the incoming waves are parallel to the slits as in Figure 11). To figure out where the first maximum is located, consider the sketch in Figure (12). We have reduced the complexity of the sketch by drawing only the solid circles representing wave crests. In addition we have numbered the crests emerging

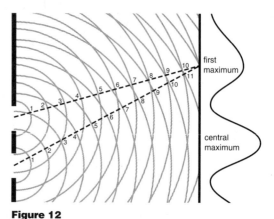

Figure 12
One more wave fits in the path from the bottom slit to the first maxima, than in the path from the top slit.

from each slit. We see that at first maximum, the 12th crest from the lower slit has run into the 11th crest from the upper slit, producing a maximum crest. ***The distance from the lower slit to the first maximum is exactly one wavelength longer than the distance from the upper slit to the first maximum.*** This is what determines the location of the first maximum.

In Figure (13) we have repeated the sketch of Figure (12), but now focus our attention on the difference in the length of the two paths from the slits to the first maximum. Since an extra wavelength λ fits into the lower path, the path length difference is λ as shown. The bottom path, with λ removed, and the upper path, both shown as dashed lines in Figure (13), are thus the same length and therefore form 2 sides of an isosceles triangle.

Let us denote by θ_1 the angle from the center of the two slits up to the first maximum. Since this line bisects the isosceles triangle formed by the two dashed lines, it is perpendicular to the base of the isosceles triangle which is the line from the center of the upper slit down to the point (a) on the lower path. As a result, the base of the isosceles triangle makes the same angle θ_1 with the plane of the slits as the line to the first maximum does with the horizontal line to the central maximum. (Picture rotating the isosceles triangle up around its base. If

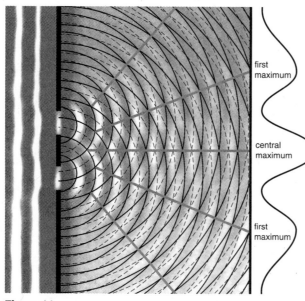

Figure 11
Analysis of the two slit wave pattern, assuming that circular waves emerge from each slit and interfere with each other. The maxima are where crests from one slit meet crests from the other. Cancellation occurs where crests meet troughs.

you rotate the isosceles triangle by an angle θ_1, its base will rotate by the same angle θ_1, thus the 2 angles labeled θ_1 in Figure (13) are the same.)

Our approximation in this analysis is that the separation d between the slits is very small compared to the distance over to where we are viewing the first maximum. If this is true, then the two paths to the first maximum are essentially parallel and the small bold triangle in Figure (13) is very nearly a right triangle. Assuming that this is a right triangle, we immediately get

$$\boxed{\sin \theta_1 = \frac{\lambda}{d}} \quad \begin{array}{l}\textit{angle to first}\\ \textit{maximum}\end{array} \quad (1)$$

In Figure (14) we have another right triangle involving the angle θ_1. If the distance from the slits to where we are viewing the maxima is D, and if we designate by Y_{max} the distance from the central to the first maximum, then the hypotenuse of this right triangle is given by the Pythagorean theorem as $\sqrt{D^2 + Y_{max}^2}$. From this triangle we have

$$\sin \theta_1 = \frac{Y_{max}}{\sqrt{D^2 + Y_{max}^2}} \quad (2)$$

Equating the two formulas for $\sin \theta_1$ and solving for λ gives

$$\boxed{\lambda = Y_{max}\frac{d}{\sqrt{D^2 + Y_{max}^2}}} \quad (3)$$

An easy way to remember this derivation is to note that the two triangles in Figures (13) and (14), drawn separately in Figure (15), are similar triangles. Thus the ratios of the small sides to the hypotenuses must be equal, giving

$$\frac{\lambda}{d} = \frac{Y_{max}}{\sqrt{D^2 + Y_{max}^2}} \quad (3')$$

The importance of Equation (3) is that it allows us to calculate the wavelength of a wave by observing the distance Y_{max} between maxima of the interference pattern. For example, in our problem of determining the character of the waves eroding the beach in Figure (10), we could use a map to determine the distance D from the breakwater to the shore and the distance d between entrances through the breakwater. Then pacing off the distance Y_{max} between erosions on the beach, we could use Equation (3) to determine what the wavelength of the waves were during the storm.

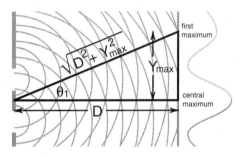

Figure 14
The angle θ_1 up to the first maxima is the same as the angle in the small triangle of Figure (13).

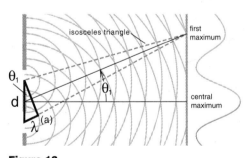

Figure 13
The path length difference to the first maximum is one wavelength λ.

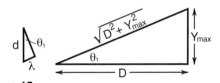

Figure 15
Since the two triangles are similar, we have $\lambda/d = Y_{max}\big/\sqrt{D^2 + Y_{max}^2}$.

Exercise 3

Repeat the derivation that led to Equation (3) except do the calculation in terms of the distance Y_{min} from the central maximum to the first minimum. (Now the path length difference is $\lambda/2$.)

Exercise 4

We will see that Equation (3) has an applicability that goes far beyond the analysis of two slit interference patterns. You will need this formula several times later in this course, and quite likely in other research work. Rather than memorizing the formula, it is much better to memorize the derivation. The best way to do this is to treat the derivation as a clean desk problem. Some time, a day or so after you have read this section, clean off your desk, take out a blank sheet of paper, and derive Equation (3). The first time you try it, you may have forgotten some steps. If that happens, review the derivation and try to do the clean desk problem a day or so later. It is worth the effort because the derivation summarizes all the formulas used in this chapter.

TWO SLIT PATTERN FOR LIGHT

Christian Huygens discovered his principle of wave motion in 1678, and developed a wave theory of light that competed with Newton's particle theory of light. It was not until 1801, over 120 years later, that Thomas Young first demonstrated the wave nature of light using a two slit interference experiment. Why did it take so long to do this demonstration?

Two major problems arise when you try to test for the wave nature of light. One is the fact that the wavelength of light is very short, on the order of one hundred thousand times shorter than the wavelengths of the water waves we observe in the ripple tank photographs. A more serious problem is that individual atoms in the sun or a light bulb emit short bursts of light that are not coordinated with each other. The result is a chopped up, incoherent beam of light that may also include a mixture of frequencies.

In our analogy of a sea wall with two entrances, it is likely that a real storm would produce a mixture of waves of different wavelengths heading in different directions. Many different interference patterns would be superimposed on the inside of the sea wall, different maxima and minima would overlap at the beach and the beach would be more or less uniformly eroded. Walking along the beach the next day, you would not find enough evidence to prove that the damage was done by ocean waves, let alone trying to determine the wavelength of the waves.

The invention of the laser by Charles Townes in 1960 eliminated the experimental problems. The laser emits a continuous coherent beam of light that more closely resembles the orderly ripple tank waves approaching the slits in Figure (10) than the confused wave motion seen in a storm. If you send a laser beam through two closely spaced slits, you cannot help but see a two slit interference pattern.

Even in a demonstration lecture, the two slit pattern produced by a laser beam can be used to measure the wavelength of the light in the beam. In Figure (16) we placed a two slit mask next to a millimeter scale on the top of an overhead projector and projected the image on a large screen. You can see that the spacing between the two slits is about 1/3 of a millimeter. In Figure (17) we aimed the red beam of a common helium neon laser through the two slits of Figure (16), onto a screen 10 meters from the slits. The resulting two slit pattern consisting of the alternate maxima and minima are easily seen by the class. Marking the separation of two maxima on a piece of paper and measuring the distance we found that the separation Y_{max} between maxima was about 2.3 cm.

In using Equation (3), $\lambda = Y_{max}d/\sqrt{D^2 + Y_{max}^2}$ to calculate the wavelength λ, we note that the 10 meter distance D is much greater than the 2.3 cm Y_{max}. Thus we can neglect the Y_{max}^2 in the square root and we get the simpler formula

$$\lambda \approx Y_{max}\frac{d}{D} \quad \text{if } D >> Y_{max} \quad (3a)$$

Putting in the numbers obtained from Figures (16) and (17), we get

$$\lambda = 2.3 \text{ cm} \times \frac{.3 \times 10^{-3}\text{m}}{10\text{m}} = 7 \times 10^{-5}\text{cm} \quad (4)$$

While this demonstration experiment gives fairly approximate results, accurate to about one significant figure, it may be somewhat surprising that a piece of apparatus as crude as the two slits seen in Figure (16) even allows us to measure something as small as $7 \times 10^{-5}\text{cm}$.

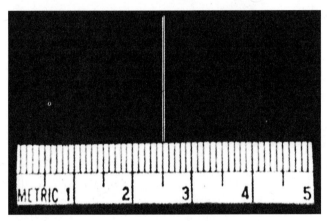

Shows that d = .3mm

Figure 16
The two slits and a plastic ruler are placed on an overhead projector and projected onto a screen 10 meters away. This is a photograph of the screen.

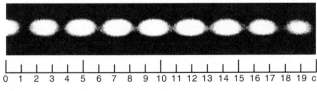

Shows that Y_{max} = 2.3 mm for D = 10 m.

Figure 17
The 2 slit laser pattern is then projected on the screen. Below is a centimeter scale, showing that the maxima are about 2.3 centimeters apart.

THE DIFFRACTION GRATING

The crudeness of our measurement of the wavelength of the laser light in our two slit experiment could be improved somewhat by a more accurate measurement of the separation of the two slits, but the improvement would not be great. There is, however, a simple way to make far more accurate measurements of the wavelength of a beam of light. The trick is simply add more slits.

To see why adding more slits gives more accurate results, we show in Figure (18) the wave patterns we get when the laser beam is sent through two slits, three slits, four slits, five slits, and seven slits. We created the slits using a Macintosh computer using the Adobe Photoshop program and a Linatronic printer to produce the film images of the slits. The Linatronic printer can draw precise lines one micron (10^{-6} meters) wide ; thus we

had excellent control over the slit width and spacing. For these images, the slits are 50 microns (50μ) wide and spaced 150 microns apart on centers.

The photographs of the interference patterns produced by the slits of Figure (18) are all enlarged to the same scale. The important point to notice is that while the maxima become sharper as we increase the number of slits, the spacing between maxima remains the same. *Adding more identical slits sharpens the maxima but does not change their spacing!* As a result the two slit formula, Equation (3), can be applied to any number of slits as long as the spacing d between slits remains constant.

If there are many slits, the device is called a ***diffraction grating***, and Equation (3), which we repeat on the next page, is known as the diffraction grating formula.

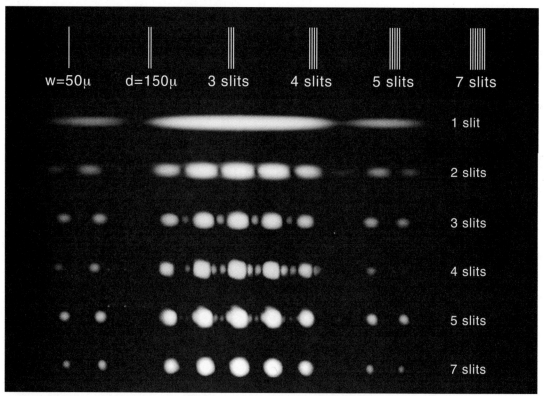

Figure 18
Interference patterns for various slit structures. If we keep the spacing between slits the same, then there is no change in the location of the maxima, no matter how many slits the laser beam passes through. Thus an analysis of the location of the maxima for 2 slits applies to any number of slits. Also note that the single slit pattern acts as an envelope for the multiple slit patterns.

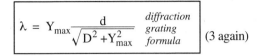

$$\lambda = Y_{max} \frac{d}{\sqrt{D^2 + Y_{max}^2}} \quad \begin{array}{l} \textit{diffraction} \\ \textit{grating} \\ \textit{formula} \end{array} \quad \text{(3 again)}$$

Exercise 5

In Figure (18) the separation of the slits is 150 microns and the separation of 10 maxima is 26.4 cm. The screen is a distance of 6.00 meters from the slits. From this determine the wavelength of the light in the laser beam

(a) using the exact formula, Equation (3).

(b) using the approximate formula, Equation (3a).

How many significant figures are meaningful in your result? To this accuracy, did it make any difference whether you used the exact Equation (3) or the approximate Equation (3a)?

Figure (18) demonstrates that the more slits you use, the sharper the maxima and the more accurately you can determine the wavelength of the light passing through the slits. In the latter part of the 1800s, the diffraction grating was recognized as an excellent tool for scientific research, and a great effort was put into producing gratings with as many closely spaced lines as possible. Fine ruling machines were developed that produced gratings on the order of 6000 lines or slits per centimeter. With so many lines, very sharp maxima are produced and very precise wavelength measurements can be made. It is possible to make inexpensive plastic replicas of fine diffraction gratings for use in all kinds of laboratory work, or even for making jewelry. It turns out that compact disks (CDs) also make superb diffraction gratings. We will not tell you the spacing of the lines on a CD for it is a nice project to figure that out for yourself. (All you need is a common helium neon laser. The wavelength of the laser beam can be gotten from Exercise 6.)

Exercise 6

In Figure (19), a laser beam is sent through a smoke filled box with a diffraction grating at the center of the box as shown in the sketch (19a). The smoke allows you to see and photograph the central laser beam and the maxima on each side. You also see maxima reflected from the back side of the grating. (When you shine a laser beam on a CD you get only the reflected maxima, no light goes through the CD.)

The grating used in Figure (19) had 15,000 lines per inch (1 inch = 2.54 cm). From this information and the photograph of Figure (19b), determine the wavelength of the laser beam used. Try both the exact Equation (3) and the approximate Equation (3a). Explain why Equation (3a) does not work well for this case.

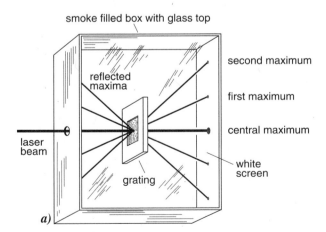

Figure 19
Laser beam passing through a diffraction grating. The beam is made visible by placing the grating in a smoke filled box. Because the lines are so close together, the maxima are widely separated. You can also see reflected maxima on the back side.

More About Diffraction Gratings

The results of Figure (18) demonstrated that the maxima got sharper but remained in the same place as we added slits. Let us now see why this happens.

The maxima of a diffraction grating occur at those points on the screen where the waves from every slit add up constructively. This can happen only when the path length difference between neighboring maxima is 0 (central maximum), λ (first maxima), 2λ (second maxima), etc. In Figure (20) we are looking at a small section of a diffraction grating where we have drawn in the paths to the first maxima. The path length differences between neighboring slits are all λ and the angle θ_1 to the first maxima is given by $\sin\theta_1 = \lambda/d$, the same results we had for the two slit problem in Figure (13). This angle does not depend upon the number of slits, thus the positions of the maxima do not change when we add slits as in Figure (18).

To see why the maxima become narrower as we add slits, let us consider the example of a 1000 slit grating illustrated in Figure (21). We have numbered the slits from 1 to 1000, and are showing the paths to a point just below the first maximum where the path length difference between neighboring slits is $(\lambda - \lambda/1000)$ instead of λ.

On the figure we are indicating, not the path length difference between neighboring slits, but instead, the path length difference between the first slit and the others. This difference is $(\lambda - \lambda/1000)$ for slit #2, $(2\lambda - 2\lambda/1000)$ for slit #3, $(3\lambda - 3\lambda/1000)$ for slit #4, etc.

When we get down to slit #501, just over half way down, the path length difference is $500\lambda - 500\lambda/1000 = 500\lambda - \lambda/2$. In other words, the waves from slit 1 and slit 501 are precisely one half a wavelength out of phase, crests exactly meet troughs, and there is precise cancellation. A similar argument shows that waves from slits #2 and #502 are $\lambda/2$ out of phase and cancel exactly. The same goes for the pairs #3 and #503, #4 and #504, all the way down to 500 and 1000. In other words, the waves all cancel in pairs and we have a minimum, complete cancellation at the point just below the first maximum where the path length difference is $\lambda - \lambda/1000$ instead of λ. With two slits we got complete cancellation half way between maxima. With 1000 slits, we only have to go approximately 1/1000 the way toward the next maxima before we get complete cancellation. The maxima are roughly 500 times sharper. You can see that with n slits, the maxima will be about n/2 times sharper than for the two slit example.

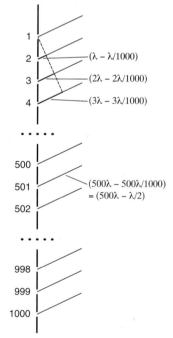

Figure 21

In a thousand slit grating, we get complete cancellation when the path length difference between neighboring slits is reduced from λ to $\lambda - \lambda/1000$.

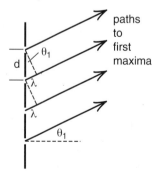

Figure 20

When the path length difference between neighboring paths is λ, then the waves from all slits add constructively and we get the first maxima.

The maxima will also be much more intense because the light is coming in from more slits. If we have n slits, the amplitude of the wave at the center of a maxima will be n times as great as the amplitude from a single slit. It turns out that the amount of energy in a wave, the intensity, or for light, the brightness, is proportional to the square of the amplitude of the wave. Thus the brightness at the center of the maxima for an n slit grating is n^2 times as bright as the brightness we would have for a single slit. The maxima for the 1000 slit grating illustrated in Figure (21) would be one million times brighter than if we let light go through only one of the slits.

(To see how the total energy works out, consider the following argument. Compared to one slit, when you have n slits, you have n times as much light energy that is compressed into a maxima that is only 1/n as wide. You get one factor of n in brightness due to the compression, and the other factor of n due to there being n slits.)

THE VISIBLE SPECTRUM

Thus far we have been using a laser beam to study the operation of a diffraction grating. Now we will reverse the process and use diffraction gratings to study the nature of beams of light.

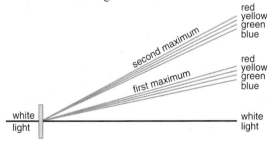

Figure 22
When white light passes through a diffraction grating, the maxima for different colors emerge at different angles. Since red light has the longest wavelength of the visible colors, it emerges at the greatest angle.

If you send a beam of white light through a diffraction grating, you get a series of maxima. In all but the central maxima light is spread out into a rainbow of colors illustrated in Figure (22). In each maxima the red light is bent the most, and blue the least. As we saw from Equation (1), $\sin \theta_1 = \lambda/d$, the longer the wavelength the greater the angle the wave is bent or diffracted. Thus red light has the longest wavelength and blue the shortest in the mixture of wavelengths that make up white light.

The longest wavelength that the human eye can see is about 7.0×10^{-5} cm, a deep red light, and the shortest is about 4.0×10^{-5} cm, a deep purple. All other visible wavelengths, the entire spectrum of visible light, lies in the range between 4.0×10^{-5} cm to 7.0×10^{-5} cm. Yellow light, for example, has a wavelength around 5.7×10^{-5} cm, and green light is near 5.0×10^{-5} cm.

As we saw in Chapter 24, visible light is just a part of the complete electromagnetic spectrum. A surprisingly small part. As radio, television, microwave ovens, infra red sensors, ultraviolet sunscreens, x ray photographs, and γ ray bursts in the sky have entered our experience of the world, we have become familiar with a much greater range of the electromagnetic spectrum. As indicated in Figure (23), AM radio waves have wavelengths in the range of 10 to 100 meters, VHF television a few meters, VHF from around 10 cm to a meter, microwaves from around a millimeter to 10 cm, infra red from less than a millimeter down to visible red light at 7.0×10^{-5} cm. At shorter wavelengths than deep blue we have ultraviolet, then x rays, and the very shortest wavelengths are called γ (gamma) rays.

Exercise 7

What are the lowest and highest frequencies of the waves in the visible spectrum? What is the color of the lowest frequency? What is the color of the highest? What is the frequency of yellow light?

Figure 23
Visible light is a tiny piece of the electromagnetic spectrum.

AM radio   FM,TV   microwaves   infra red   ultra violet   x rays   γ rays

red   yellow   green   blue

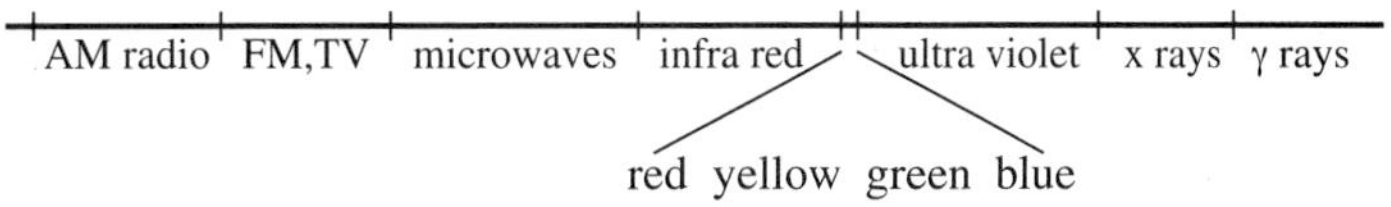

The Nanometer

In the current age of nano technology, the **nanometer (nm)** has become the popular unit for measuring short distances. ($1 \text{ nm} = 10^{-9}$ meter $= 10^{-7}$ cm.) To convert our wavelength of $\lambda(\text{red}) = 7 \times 10^{-5}$ cm to nanometers, we have

$$\lambda(\text{red}) = \frac{7 \times 10^{-5} \text{cm}}{10^{-7} \text{cm/nm}} = 700 \text{ nm}$$

Exercise 8

As we mentioned, the shortest wavelength that the human eye can see is about 4.0×10^{-5} cm, and yellow light has a wavelength around 5.7×10^{-5} cm. What are these wavelengths expressed in nanometers?

ATOMIC SPECTRA

Our main application of the diffraction grating will be to study the spectrum of light emitted by atoms. It has long been known that if you have a gas of a particular kind of atom, like nitrogen, oxygen, helium, or hydrogen, a special kind of light is emitted. You do not get the continuous blend of wavelengths seen in white light. Instead the light consists of a mixture of distinct wavelengths. Which wavelengths are involved depends upon the kind of atom emitting the light. The mixture of wavelengths provides a unique signature of that atom, better than a fingerprint, for identifying the presence of an atom in a gas. In fact, the element helium (named after the Greek word *helios* for sun) was first identified in the sun by a study of the spectrum of light from the sun. Only later was helium found here on earth.

The subject of modern astronomy is based on the study of the spectrum of light emitted by stars. Some stars consist mostly of hydrogen gas, others a mixture of hydrogen and helium, while still others contain various amounts of heavier elements. We learn the composition of the star by studying the spectrum of light emitted, and from the composition we can deduce something about the age of the star and the environment in which it was formed.

Our main reason for studying the spectrum of light emitted by atoms will be to learn something about the atoms themselves. Since Rutherford's discovery of the atomic nucleus in 1912, it has been known that atoms consist of a positively charged nucleus surrounded by negatively charged electrons. If we apply Newtonian mechanics to predict the motion of the electrons, and Maxwell's equations to predict the kind of electromagnetic radiation the moving electrons should radiate, we get the wrong answer. There is no way that we can explain the spectrum of light emitted by atoms from Maxwell's equations and Newtonian mechanics. The existence of detailed atomic spectra is a clue that something is wrong with this classical picture of the atom. It is also the evidence upon which to test new theories.

We do not have to study many kinds of atoms to find something wrong with the predictions of classical theory. The simplest of all atoms, the hydrogen atom consisting of one proton for a nucleus, surrounded by one electron, is all we need. Heated hydrogen gas emits a distinct, orderly, spectrum of light that provides the essential clues of what is going on inside a hydrogen atom. In this chapter we will focus on using a diffraction grating to learn what the spectrum of hydrogen is. In the following chapters we use the hydrogen spectrum to study the atom itself.

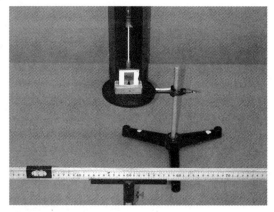

Figure 24
Apparatus to measure the hydrogen spectrum.

THE HYDROGEN SPECTRUM

The apparatus required for studying the hydrogen spectrum can be as simple as the hydrogen source, meter stick and diffraction grating shown in the photograph of Figure (24). The hydrogen source consists of a narrow glass tube filled with hydrogen gas, with metal electrodes at the ends of the tube. When a high voltage is applied to the electrodes, an electric current flows through the gas, heating it and causing it to emit light. The diffraction grating is placed in front of the hydrogen tube, and the meter stick is used to measure the location of the maxima.

The setup of the apparatus is illustrated in Figure (25) and the resulting spectrum in Figure (26). In this spectrum we are looking at the first maxima on the left side of the meter stick as shown in Figure (25). The leftmost line, the one bent the farthest, is a deep red line which is called the *hydrogen α line*, and labeled by α in the photograph. In some setups, the next line is a spurious line caused by impurities in the hydrogen tube. More to the right is a bright, swimming-pool blue line called *hydrogen β*. Much harder to see is the third line called *hydrogen γ*, a deep violet line near the short wavelength end of the visible spectrum.

The three lines α, β and γ are the only lines emitted by pure hydrogen gas in the visible part of the electromagnetic spectrum. Their wavelengths are

$$\lambda_\alpha = 6.56 \times 10^{-5}\,\text{cm} = 656 \text{ nanometers}$$

$$\lambda_\beta = 4.86 \times 10^{-5}\,\text{cm} = 486 \text{ nm}$$

$$\lambda_\gamma = 4.34 \times 10^{-5}\,\text{cm} = 434 \text{ nm} \tag{5}$$

When actually performing the experiment shown in Figure (24), there are some steps one should take to improve the accuracy of the results. As shown in Figure (27), a small arrowhead is placed on the grating itself. You then place your eye behind the meter stick and move your head and the slider on the meter stick until the point on the slider lines up with the arrowhead on the grating and with the spectral line you are trying to measure.

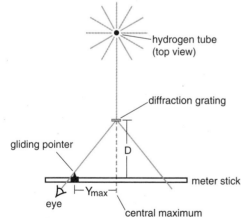

Figure 25
To determine the wavelength of light using a diffraction grating, you need to measure the distance Y_{max} to the first maximum, and the distance D shown. To measure Y_{max}, slide the pointer along the meter stick until it lines up with the first maximum.

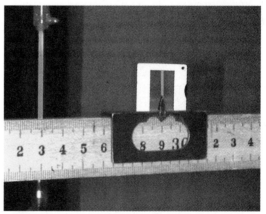

Figure 27
Looking through the grating, move your eye so that the spectral line is centered over the pointer as shown.

Figure 26
Photograph of the α, β and γ lines in the hydrogen spectrum.

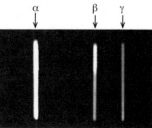

Rather than trying to measure the distance Y_{max} from the central maximum to the spectral line, it is more accurate to measure the distance $2Y_{max}$ from the first maximum on the left to the first maximum on the right, and then divide by 2. The wavelength of the line under study is then given by the diffraction grating formula, Equation (3)

$$\lambda = Y_{max}\frac{d}{\sqrt{D^2+Y_{max}^2}}$$ (3 repeated)

where d is the separation of the slits in the grating and D the distance from the grating to the meter stick.

(When you first perform this experiment you may be confused by where the central maximum is. If you look straight through the grating at the tube, all you see is the tube. But that is the central maximum. It looks like the tube because all the colors go straight through the grating. There is no separation of colors or distortion of the image. To see a spectrum you have to look through the grating but far off to the side from the tube.)

Exercise 9

Derive a formula for the wavelength λ of a spectral line in terms of the distance $Y_{2\ max}$ from the central maximum to the second maxima of the line. The second maxima of the bright lines of an atomic spectra are quite easily seen using the apparatus of Figure (24).

The Experiment on Hydrogen Spectra

You should carry out the following steps when doing the hydrogen spectrum experiment shown in Figure (25).

(1) Determine the wavelength of all the spectral lines you can see, and compare your results with those given in Equation (5). Measure distances between first maxima, not to the central maxima.

(2) Measure the distances to the second maxima for the lines you can see out there and compute the corresponding wavelengths using our results from Exercise (8). Compare these wavelengths with those you get using the first maxima.

The Balmer Series

There are many spectral lines emitted by the hydrogen atom. Only three, however, are in the visible part of the spectrum. The complete spectrum consists of a number of series of lines, and the three visible lines belong to the series called the ***Balmer series***. The red line, hydrogen α, is the longest wavelength line in the Balmer series, next comes the blue hydrogen β, then the violet hydrogen γ. Then there are many lines of the Balmer series out in the ultraviolet, which we cannot see by eye, but which we can record on photographic film.

Figure (28) shows part of the spectrum of light from a hydrogen star. These lines are in the ultraviolet and are all part of the Balmer series. Slightly different naming is used here. In the notation of Figure (28), we should call the red hydrogen α line H3, the blue β line H4, and the violet γ line H5. In Figure (28), the first 6 Balmer lines are missing. Here we see lines H9 through H40. As the lines increase in number they get closer and closer together. The whole series ends with very many, very closely spaced lines near 365 nanometers. It is called a *series* because the lines converge to a final wavelength in much the same way that many mathematical series converge to a final value.

It was the Swiss school teacher Johann Balmer who in 1885 discovered a formula for the wavelengths of the spectral lines seen in Figure (28). The wavelength of the m th line (m=3 for H3, m=4 for H4, etc.) is given by the formula

$$\lambda_m = 364.56 \text{ nm} \times \frac{m^2}{m^2 - 4} \qquad (6)$$

Equation (6) is known as the *Balmer formula*.

For m=3 we get from the Balmer formula

$$\begin{aligned} \lambda(H3) &= 364.56 \text{ nm} \times \frac{9}{9 - 4} \\ &= 656 \text{ nm} \end{aligned} \qquad (6a)$$

which agrees with Equation (5) for hydrogen α. Each higher value of m gives us the wavelength of a new line. At large values of m the factor $m^2/(m^2 - 4)$ approaches 1, and the lines get closer and closer together as seen in Figure (28). The end is at 365 nm, when m is very large.

Exercise 10

(a) Use Equation (6) to calculate the wavelengths of the β and γ lines of the hydrogen spectrum and compare the results with Equation (5).

(b) Calculate the wavelength of H40 and compare your results with Figure (28).

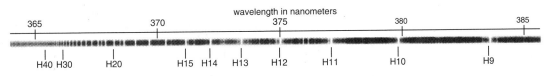

Figure 28
Spectrum of the star HD193182, showing ultraviolet hydrogen lines near the limit of the Balmer series. This series of lines begins in the visible part of the spectrum with the lines we have called α, β, and γ, (which would be called H3, H4, and H5 in this diagram), and goes on to the ultraviolet. The lines get closer and closer together, until the end just beyond the point labeled H40. The Swiss school teacher Johann Balmer discovered a formula for the wavelengths of these lines.

THE DOPPLER EFFECT

One phenomena of wave motion that is particularly easy to visualize is the **Doppler effect**. As you can see in Figure (29), if the wave source is moving, the wavelength of the waves is compressed in front of the source and stretched out behind. This result, which is obvious for water waves, also applies to sound waves in air and to light waves moving through space.

To analyze the effect, we first note that if the source is at rest, then the waves all travel out from the source at a speed v_{wave}, have a wavelength λ_0 and a period T_0 given by

$$T_0 \frac{sec}{cycle} = \frac{\lambda_0 \ cm/cycle}{v_{wave} \ cm/sec} = \frac{\lambda_0}{v_{wave}} \frac{sec}{cycle} \qquad (7)$$

If the source is moving forward at a speed v_{source}, then during one period T_0 the source will move forward a distance $x = v_{source}T_0$. But this is just the amount $\Delta\lambda$ by which the wavelength is shortened in front and stretched out in back. Thus

$$\Delta\lambda = v_{source}T_0 = v_{source}\frac{\lambda_0}{v_{wave}} \qquad (8)$$

where we used Equation (7) to replace T_0 by λ_0/v_{wave}.

As a result the wavelengths in front and back of the source are

$$\lambda_{front} = \lambda_0 - \Delta\lambda = \lambda_0 \left[1 - \frac{v_{source}}{v_{wave}} \right] \qquad (9a)$$

$$\lambda_{back} = \lambda_0 + \Delta\lambda = \lambda_0 \left[1 + \frac{v_{source}}{v_{wave}} \right] \qquad (9b)$$

If we are in front of the moving source, the wave period T_{front} we observe is the time it takes the shortened wavelength λ_{front} to pass us at a speed v_{wave}, which is

$$T_{front} = \frac{\lambda_{front}}{v_{wave}} = \frac{\lambda_0}{v_{wave}} \left[1 - \frac{v_{source}}{v_{wave}} \right]$$

$$\boxed{T_{front} = T_0 \left[1 - \frac{v_{source}}{v_{wave}} \right]} \qquad (10a)$$

where we now replaced λ_0/v_{wave} by T_0. In the back, the period is extended to

$$\boxed{T_{back} = T_0 \left[1 + \frac{v_{source}}{v_{wave}} \right]} \qquad (10b)$$

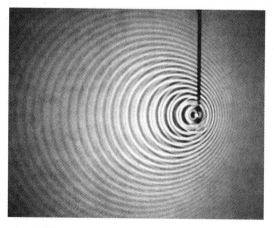

Figure 29
When the source of the wave is moving, the wavelengths are compressed in front and stretched out behind.

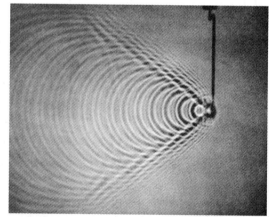

Figure 30
When the source is moving faster than the waves, the waves build up on the front edge to create a shock wave. For supersonic flight, this shock wave produces the sonic boom.

If the speed of the source approaches the speed of the wave, as in the case of a jet airplane approaching the speed of sound, the wavelength in front goes to zero. At speeds greater than the speed of the wave, as in supersonic flight, there are no waves ahead of the source; instead, the leading edge of the waves pile up as shown in Figure (30) to create what is called a ***shock wave***. This shock wave is responsible for the sonic boom we hear when a jet passes overhead at supersonic speeds.

Exercise 11

There is a simple experiment you can perform to observe the Doppler effect. Stand beside a road and have a friend drive by at about 40 mi/hr while blowing the car horn. As the car passes, the pitch of the horn will suddenly drop because the wavelength of the sound waves, which was shortened as the car approached, is lengthened after it passes. The shorter, higher-pitched sound waves change to longer, lower-pitched waves.

For this exercise, assume the car is owned by a musician, and the car horn plays the musical note A at a frequency of 440 cycles per second.

a) What is the wavelength of a 440 cycle/sec note, if the speed of sound is 300 meter/sec?

b) What is the wavelength of the note we hear if the car is approaching at a speed of 60 km/hr?

c) What is the frequency we hear if the car is approaching at 60 km/hr?

d) What is the frequency we hear when the car is going away from us at 60 km/hr?

Stationary Source and Moving Observer

If the source is at rest but we, the observer, are moving, there is also a Doppler effect. In the case of water or sound waves, if we are moving through the medium toward the source, then the wave crests pass by us at an increased relative speed $v_{rel} = v_{wave} + v_{us}$. Even though the wavelength is unchanged, the increased speed of the wave will carry the crests by faster, giving us an apparently shorter period and higher frequency.

If our velocity through the medium is small compared to the wave speed, then we observe essentially the same decrease in period and increase in frequency as in the case when the source was moving. In particular, Equation (10) is approximately correct.

On the other hand, when the waves are in water or air and the relative speed of the source and observer approaches or exceeds the wave speed, there can be a considerable difference between a moving source and a moving observer. As illustrated in Figure (31a), if the source is moving faster than the wave speed, there is a shock wave and the observer detects no waves until the source passes. But if the source is at rest as in Figure (31b), there is no shock front and the observer moves through waves before getting to the source, even if the observer is moving faster than the wave speed.

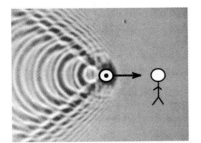

a) moving source

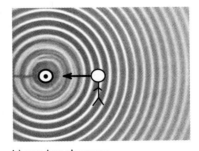

b) moving observer

Figure 31
For waves in water or air, there can be a significant difference between a moving source with a stationary observer, and a moving observer with a stationary source, even though the source and observer have the same relative velocity in the two cases. For light, the principle of relativity requires that the two cases be identical.

Doppler Effect for Light

When a source of light waves is moving toward or away from us, there is also a Doppler effect. If the source is moving toward us, the wavelengths we see are shortened. This means that the color of the light is *shifted toward the blue*. If the source is moving away, the wavelengths are stretched out, become longer, and the color *shifts toward the red*. When the speed of the source is considerably less than the speed of light, Equations (9) and (10) correctly give the observed wavelength λ and period T in terms of the source's wavelength λ_0 and period and T_0.

Principle of Relativity

There is one fundamental difference, however, between the Doppler effect for water and sound waves, and the Doppler effect for light waves. For water and sound waves we could distinguish between a source at rest with a moving observer and an observer at rest with a moving source. If the source were at rest, it was at rest *relative to the medium through which the wave moves*. We got different results depending on whether it was the source or the observer that was at rest.

In the case of light, the medium through which light moves is *space*. According to the principle of relativity, one cannot detect uniform motion relative to space. Since it is not possible to determine which one is at rest and which one is moving, we must have exactly the same Doppler effect formula for the case of a stationary source and a moving observer, or vice versa. The Doppler effect formula can depend only on the *relative velocity* of the source and observer.

One way to use the principle of relativity is to always assume that you yourself are at rest relative to space. (No one can prove you are wrong.) This suggests that we should start from Equations (9) and (10), which were derived for a stationary observer, and replace v_{wave} by the speed of light c, and interpret v_{source} as the relative velocity between the source and the observer.

Equations (9) and (10), modified this way, are correct as long as the source is not moving too fast. However if the source is moving relative to us at a speed approaching the speed of light, there is one more relativistic effect that we have to take into account. Remember that a moving clock runs slow by a factor of $\sqrt{1 - v^2/c^2}$. If the source is radiating a light wave of period T_0, then that period can be used in the construction of a clock. If we observe the source go by at a speed v_{source}, the period T_0 must appear to us to increase to T_0' given by

$$T_0' = \frac{T_0}{\sqrt{1 - v_{source}^2/c^2}} \qquad \text{(see Equation 1-11)}$$

From our point of view, the source is radiating light of period T_0'. This is the light whose wavelength is stretched or compressed, depending on whether the source is moving away from or towards us. Thus we should use T_0' instead of T_0 in Equation (10).

Replacing T_0 by T_0' in Equation (10) gives

$$T_{front} = \frac{T_0}{\sqrt{1 - v_{source}^2/c^2}} \left[1 - \frac{v_{source}}{c} \right] \qquad \text{(11a)}$$

$$T_{back} = \frac{T_0}{\sqrt{1 - v_{source}^2/c^2}} \left[1 + \frac{v_{source}}{c} \right] \qquad \text{(11b)}$$

where v_{source} is the speed of the source relative to us, and we have set $v_{wave} = c$. Equations (11) are the relativistic Doppler effect equations for light. They are applicable for any source speed, even if the source is moving relative to us at speeds approaching the speed of light. The corresponding wavelengths are

$$\lambda_{front} = c\frac{cm}{sec} \times T_{front}\frac{sec}{cycle} = cT_{front}\frac{cm}{cycle}$$

$$\begin{aligned} \lambda_{front} &= cT_{front} \\ \lambda_{back} &= cT_{back} \end{aligned} \qquad \text{(12)}$$

Exercise 12

Using Equations (12), express λ_{front} and λ_{back} in terms of λ_0, v_{source} and c.

Exercise 13

In Figure (31b), where we picture a stationary source and a moving observer, the waves pass by the observer at a speed $v_{wave} + v_{observer}$. Why can't this picture be applied to light, simply replacing v_{wave} by c and letting $v_{observer}$ be the relative velocity between the source and observer?

Doppler Effect in Astronomy

The Doppler effect has become one of the most powerful tools astronomers use in the study of the universe. Assuming that distant stars and galaxies are made up of the same matter as nearby stars, we can compare the spectral lines emitted by distant galaxies with the corresponding spectral lines radiated by elements here on earth. A general shift in the wavelengths to the blue or the red, indicates that the source of the waves is moving either toward or away from us. Using Equations (12) we can then quite accurately determine how fast this motion toward or away from us is.

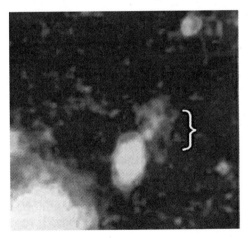

Figure 32
The most distant galaxy observed as of January 1995. This galaxy, given the romantic name 8C 1435+63, was photographed by the Keck telescope in Hawaii. The two halves of the distant galaxy are indicated by the white bracket. The galaxy is moving away from us at 95% the speed of light.

Until the 1960s astronomers did not have much need for the relativistic Doppler shift equations. The non relativistic Equations (10) were generally adequate because we did not observe stars or galaxies moving relative to us at speeds greater than 10 to 20% the speed of light. But that changed dramatically with the discovery of quasars in 1963. Quasars are now thought to be brilliant galaxies in the early stages of formation. They can be seen from great distances and are observed to move away from us at speeds as great as 95% the speed of light. To analyze such motion, the relativistic formulas, Equations (11) and (12) are clearly needed.

Exercise 14

The most rapidly receding galaxy observed by the spring of 1995 is the galaxy named 8C 1435 + 63 shown in the photograph of Figure (32) taken by the Keck telescope in Hawaii. Much of the light from this galaxy is radiated by hydrogen gas. This galaxy is moving away from us at a speed $v_{source} = .95c$.

(a) Assuming that the hydrogen in this galaxy radiates the same spectrum of light as the hydrogen gas in our discharge tube of Figure (24), what are the wavelengths of the first three Balmer series lines λ_α, λ_β, and λ_γ, by the time these waves reach us? (They will be greatly stretched out by the motion of the galaxy.)

(b) Astronomers use the letter z to denote the relative shift of the wavelength of light due to the Doppler effect. I.e.,

$$z = \frac{\Delta\lambda}{\lambda_0} = \frac{\lambda - \lambda_0}{\lambda_0} \quad \begin{array}{l} \text{astronomers} \\ \text{notation for} \\ \text{the red shift} \end{array} \quad (13)$$

where λ_0 is the wavelength of the unshifted spectral line, and λ is the Doppler shifted wavelength we see. What is z for galaxy 8C 1435 + 63?

Update:

As of 2007, the most distant known galaxy, observed by the Subaru telescope in Hawaii, was traveling away from us at a speed of 96.9% the speed of light.

The Red Shift and the Expanding Universe

In 1917 Albert Einstein published his relativistic theory of gravity, known as *General Relativity*. In applying his theory of gravity to the behavior of the stars and galaxies in the universe, he encountered what he thought was a serious problem with the theory. Any model of the universe he constructed was unstable. The galaxies tended either to collapse in upon themselves or fly apart. He could not find a solution to his equations that represented the stable unchanging universe everyone knew was out there.

Einstein then discovered that he could add a new term to his gravitational equations. By properly adjusting the value of this term, he could construct a model of the universe that neither collapsed or blew up. This term, that allowed Einstein to create a static model of the universe, became known as the *cosmological constant*.

In later life, Einstein said that his introduction of the cosmological constant was the greatest mistake he ever made. The reason is that the universe is not static. Instead it is *expanding*. The galaxies are all flying apart like the debris from some gigantic explosion. The expansion, or at least instability of the universe, could have been considered one of the predictions of Einstein's theory of gravity, had Einstein not found his cosmological constant. (Later analysis showed that the static model, obtained using the cosmological constant, was not stable. The slightest perturbation would cause it to either expand or contract.)*

* *Einstein's cosmological constant, instead of being a mistake, may be one of his great discoveries. It may have played a crucial role in the first tiny fraction of a second in the life of the universe, and may be a dominant factor in the future of the universe. We will return to this topic.*

That the universe is not static was discovered by Doppler shift measurements. In the 1920s, the astronomer Edwin Hubble observed that spectral lines from distant galaxies were all shifted toward the red, and that the farther away the galaxy was, the greater the red shift. Interpreting the red shift as being due to the Doppler effect meant that the distant galaxies were moving away from us, and the farther away a galaxy was, the faster it was moving.

Hubble was the first astronomer to develop a way to measure the distance out to other galaxies. Thus he could compare the red shift or recessional velocity to the distance the galaxy is away from us. He found a simple rule known as Hubble's law. *If you look at galaxies twice as far away, they will be receding from us twice as fast*. Roughly speaking, he found that a galaxy .1 billion light years away would be receding at 1% the speed of light; a galaxy .2 billion light years away at 2% the speed of light, etc. In the 1930s, construction of the 200 inch Mt. Palomar telescope was started. It was hoped that this telescope (completed in 1946) would be able to observe galaxies as far away as 2 billion light years. Such galaxies should be receding at the enormous speeds of approximately 20% the speed of light.

With the discovery of quasars, we have been able to observe much more distant galaxies, with far greater recessional velocities. As we have just seen, the galaxy 8C 1435+63, photographed by the 10 meter (400 inch) telescope in Hawaii, is receding from us at a speed of 95% the speed of light. To analyze the Doppler effect for such a galaxy, the fully relativistic Doppler effect formula, Equation (12) is needed; non relativistic approximations will not do.

Hubble's law raises several interesting questions. First, it sounds as if we must be at the center of everything, since the galaxies in the universe appear to all be moving away from us. But this is simply a consequence of a uniform expansion. Someone in a distant galaxy will also observe the same Hubble law.

To see how a uniform expansion works, mark a number of equally spaced dots on a partially blown up balloon. Select any one of the dots to represent our galaxy, and then start blowing up the balloon to represent the expansion of the universe. You will notice that dots twice as far away move away twice as fast, no matter which dot you selected. Hubble's law is obeyed from the point of view of any of the dots on the balloon. (You can see this expansion in Figure (33), where we started with an array of (black or red) dots, and uniformly expanded the array to get the (gray or blue) dots.)

Another interesting question is related to nature's speed limit c. We cannot keep looking out twice as far to see galaxies receding twice as fast, because we cannot have galaxies receding faster than the speed of light. Something special has to happen when the recessional speeds approach the speed of light, as they have in the case of 8C 1435 + 63. This appears to place a limit on the size of the universe we can observe.

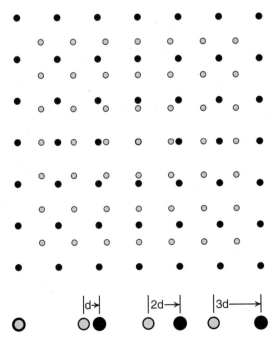

Figure 33
During a uniform expansion, neighboring galaxies move a certain distance away (d), galaxies twice as far away move twice as far (2d), etc. This is Hubble's law for the expanding universe.

One of the things to remember when we look at distant galaxies is that we are not only looking far away, but we are also looking back in time. When we look at a galaxy 10 billion light years away, we are looking at light emitted 10 billion years ago, when the universe was 10 billion years younger. Recent studies have clearly shown that galaxies 10 billion years away look different than nearby galaxies. Over the past 10 billion years the universe has evolved; galaxies have aged, becoming more symmetric and less violent.

To predict what we will find as we look back in time, look at ever more distant galaxies, imagine that we take a moving picture of the universe and run the moving picture backwards.

If we reverse the moving picture of expanding galaxies, we see contracting galaxies. They are all contracting back to one point in space and time. Go back to that point and run the movie forward, and we see all of the universe rushing out of that point, apparently the consequence of a gigantic explosion. This explosion has become known as the ***Big Bang***. (The name Big Bang was a derisive expression coined by the astronomer Fred Hoyle who had a competing theory of the origin of the universe.)

The idea that the universe started in a big bang, provides a simple picture of the Hubble law. From our point of view, galaxies emerged at various speeds in all directions from the Big Bang. Those that were moving away from us the fastest just after the explosion are now the farthest away from us. Galaxies moving away twice as fast are now twice as far away.

In the next chapter we will have more to say about the origin of the universe and evidence for the Big Bang. We will also introduce another way to interpret the Doppler effect and its relationship to the expansion of the universe.

A CLOSER LOOK AT INTERFERENCE PATTERNS

Our focus so far in this chapter has been on the application of the wave properties of light to the study of physical phenomena such as atomic spectra and the expansion of the universe. We now want to turn our attention to a more detailed study of the wave phenomena itself, by taking a closer look at the single slit diffraction pattern that serves as the envelope of the multiple slit patterns we saw back in Figure (18).

Single Slit Diffraction Pattern

In the 1600s, Francesco Maria Grinaldi discovered that light going through a fine slit cannot be prevented from spreading on the other side. He named this phenomenon **diffraction**. Independently Robert Hook, of Hook's law fame, made the same observation and provided a wave like explanation. The clearest explanation comes from the Huygens construction illustrated in Figures (3) through (8).

In Figure (3) reproduced here, we have a deceptively simple picture of the single slit diffraction pattern. In the photograph, a wave is impinging upon a slit whose width is less than one wavelength, with the result that we get a simple circular wave emerging on the other side. As the slit gets wider than a wavelength, the pattern becomes more complex. If you carefully look at Figure (6), reproduced below, you can see lines of nodes coming out of the slit that is about 2 wavelengths wide.

In Figure (34) on the next page, we have the diffraction pattern produced by a laser beam passing through a 50 micron wide single slit and striking a screen 10 meters away. This is a reproduction of the single slit pattern that acts as an envelope for the multiple slit patterns seen in Figure (18). A 50 micron slit is 50×10^{-6} meters or 50,000 nm wide. This is nearly a hundred times greater than the 640 nm wavelength of the laser light passing through the slit. Thus we are dealing with slits that nearly about 100 wavelengths wide.

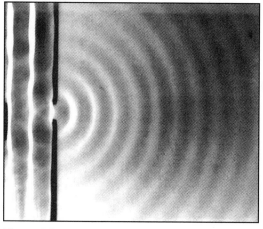

Figure 3 (repeated)
The simple diffraction pattern you get when the slit is narrow compared to a wavelength.

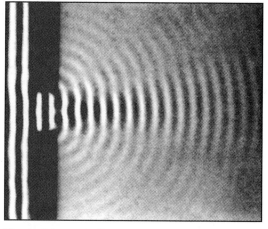

Figure 6 (repeated)
The pattern becomes more complex when the slit is wider than a wavelength. Here you can begin to see lines of nodes emerging from the slit.

The fact that the diffraction pattern was photographed 10 meters from the slits means that we are looking at the pattern nearly 20 million wavelengths away from the slits. Thus the ripple tank photographs showing diffraction patterns within a few wavelengths of the slits, are not a particularly relevant guide as to what we could expect to see 20 million wavelengths away.

The general features of the diffraction pattern in Figure (34) are that we have a relatively broad central maximum, with nodes on either side. Then there are dimmer and narrower maxima on either side. There is a series of these side maxima that extend out beyond the photograph of Figure (34).

If the slit were narrow compared to a wavelength, if the wave spread out as in Figure (3), then we would get just one broad central maxima. Only when the slit is wider than a wavelength do we get the minima we see in Figure (34). These minima result from the interference and cancellation of waves from different parts of the slit. What we wish to do now is to show how this cancellation occurs and predicts where the minima will be located.

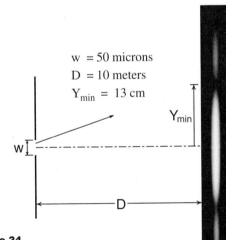

w = 50 microns
D = 10 meters
$Y_{min} = 13$ cm

Y_{min}

W

D

Figure 34
For this single slit laser beam diffraction pattern, the slit was about 100 wavelengths wide (w), and the screen was about 20 million wavelengths away (D).

Analysis of the Single Slit Pattern

In our discussion of diffraction gratings, we estimated the width of the maxima by determining how far from the center of the maxima the intensity first went to zero, where we first got complete cancellation. This occured where light from pairs of slits cancelled. In our example of Figure (21), light from slit 1 cancelled that from slit 501, from slit 2 with slit 502, etc., all the way down to slits 500 and 1000.

We can use a similar analysis for the single slit pattern, except the one big slit is broken up, *conceptually*, into many narrow slits, as illustrated in Figure (35). Suppose, for example, we think of the one wide slit of width w as being broken up into 1000 neighboring individual slits. The individual slits are so narrow that each piece of wave front in them should act as a source of a pure circular wave as shown back in Figure (3).

Now consider the light heading out in such a direction that the wave from the first conceptual slit is half a wavelength $\lambda/2$, in front of the wave from the middle slit, number 501. When the waves from these two "slits" strike the screen they will cancel. Similarly waves from slits 2 and 502 will cancel, as will those from 3 and 503, etc., down to 500 and 1000. Thus this is the direction where the path length difference from the edge to the center of the opening is half a wavelength $\lambda/2$. Between the two edges of the opening, the path length difference to this minimum is λ, as shown.

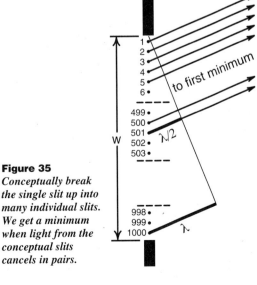

to first minimum

1
2
3
4
5
6
·
499
500
501
W   502 $\lambda/2$
503

998
999
1000 λ

Figure 35
Conceptually break the single slit up into many individual slits. We get a minimum when light from the conceptual slits cancels in pairs.

From Figure (36), we can calculate the height of the first minimum using the familiar similar triangles we have seen in a previous analysis. The small right triangle near the slit has a short side of length λ and a hypotenuse equal to the slit width w. The big triangle has a short side equal to Y_{min} and a hypotenuse given by the Pythagorean theorem as $\sqrt{D^2 + Y_{min}^2}$. Usually Y_{min} will be much smaller than the distance D, so that we can replace $\sqrt{D^2 + Y_{min}^2}$ by D, to get

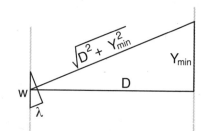

Figure 36
Similar triangles for calculating the distance to the first minimum of a single slit diffraction pattern.

$$\frac{\lambda}{w} = \frac{Y_{min}}{\sqrt{D^2 + Y_{min}^2}} \approx \frac{Y_{min}}{D}$$

or

$$\boxed{Y_{min} \approx \frac{\lambda D}{w}} \quad \begin{array}{l}\textit{distance to the}\\\textit{first minima of}\\\textit{a single slit}\\\textit{diffraction pattern}\end{array} \quad (14)$$

Exercise 15

To obtain the single slit diffraction pattern seen in Figure (34), we used a slit 50 microns wide located 10 meters from the screen. The distance Y_{min} to the first minimum was about 13 cm. Use this result to determine the wavelength of the laser light used. Compare your answer with your results from Exercises 5 and 6, where the same wavelength light was used.

CHAPTER 25 REVIEW

This chapter can be viewed as a study of the applications of the Huygens' principle, that each piece of a wavefront acts as a source of a new circular or spherical wave. This is best illustrated in Figure (3) where we see circular waves emerging from a narrow slit.

Figure 3
Huygens' principle illustrated.

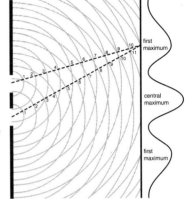

Figure 12
One more wave fits in the path from the bottom slit to the first maxima, than in the path from the top slit.

Another important rule we use in this chapter is the principle of superposition, where if we have two distinct sources of wave, as in the case of two oscillating plungers in Figure (9a) or two slits as in (9b), the resulting pattern is simply the sum of the individual wave patterns.

The theory discussed in this chapter is the analysis of the two slit pattern in Figure (9b). The main feature of the two slit pattern is that we get beams of waves separated by lines of nodes. The beams are where crests meet crests and troughs meet troughs producing high waves. The lines of nodes are where crests meet troughs and the waves cancel.

The analysis of the two slit pattern involves determining the angles at which the beams emerge. In Figure (12), we have drawn the wave crests emerging from the two slits and approaching a boundary on the right side. We have focused on the beams of waves headed for the first maximum.

The first maximum is located at the point where one more wave fits in the path from the bottom slit than the path from the top slit. Figure (13-14) shows the geometry used to calculate the angle to the first maximum. The idea is that the lower path is one wavelength λ longer than the upper path. In this diagram, d is the separation between the slits, D the distance from the slits to the screen where we are viewing the maximum, and θ_1 the angle to that maximum.

The key to determining the angle θ_1 is to find the two triangles that both involve that angle. One is the small triangle shown by bold lines with sides λ, d, and angle θ_1. The other triangle is the big triangle that starts at the center between the slits, goes a distance D over to the screen, and then up a distance Y_{max} to the first maximum.

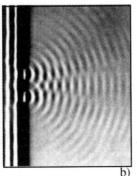

a)

b)

Figure 9
Two plungers produce the same interference pattern as the waves emerging from two slits.

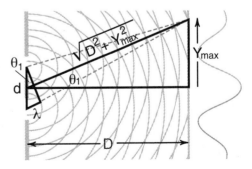

Figure 13-14 combined
The path length difference to the first maximum is one wavelength λ.

In all our examples, the screen distance D will be much greater than the slit separation d. This means that the small triangle in Figure (13-14) is a right triangle, and that the two triangles with an angle θ_1 are similar triangles. Equating the ratio of corresponding sides gives

$$\frac{\lambda}{d} = \frac{Y_{max}}{\sqrt{D^2 + Y^2_{max}}} \quad \begin{array}{l} \textit{diffaction} \\ \textit{grating} \\ \textit{formula} \end{array} \qquad (3)$$

Equation (3) is the key result of this chapter. It applies not only to the two slit interference pattern, but also locates the first maxima Y_{max} for a diffraction grating. The reason that the same formula works for both two slits and the thousands of slits in a diffraction grating, is that adding more slits makes the maxima sharper but does not change the angle θ_1.

In the case of two slits, where we usually have D much greater than Y_{max}, we can replace $\sqrt{D^2 + Y^2_{max}}$ by D giving

$$\lambda = Y_{max}\frac{d}{D} \qquad (4)$$

This made it easy to determine the wavelength of a red laser beam by sending the beam through two small slits, whose separation d we measured in a lecture.

The best review we can think of for this chapter is to clean off your desk, take a clean sheet of paper, and derive the diffraction grating formula (3). If you can do this without looking back at the text, you understand the theory of this chapter. Then make sure that you get to use a diffraction grating to actually measure the wavelength of light.

In the absence of any special lab equipment, you can use a CD for a diffraction grating, and one of the now very inexpensive red lasers for a source of pure color light. You can turn the experiment around and use the fact that the common red lasers have a wavelength of 670 nanometers in order to predict the spacing of the lines on your CD. You can also compare the spacing of the lines on a DC, a DVD, and a Blu-Ray disk if you have one.

CHAPTER EXERCISES

Exercise 1 On page 4
Graphical work with the Huygens construction.

Exercise 2 On page 8
Locate lines of nodes in a ripple tank photograph.

Exercise 3 On page 10
Analyze the 2 slit pattern using y_{min} instead of y_{max}.

Exercise 4 On page 10
Derive Equation (3) as a clean desk problem.

Exercise 5 On page 13
Determine the wavelength of the light in a laser beam, using the slits of Figure (18).

Exercise 6 On page 13
Determine the wavelength of the light in a laser beam, using the diffraction grating of Figure (19).

Exercise 7 ·On page 15
Calculate the frequencies of various light beams.

Exercise 8 On page 16
Express various wavelengths in terms of nanometers.

Exercise 9 On page 18
Derive the diffraction grating formula using the second maxima.

Exercise 10 On page 19
Calculate the wavelengths of the β and γ lines of the hydrogen spectrum.

Exercise 11 On page 21
Study the Doppler effect experimentally.

Exercise 12 On page 23
Relativistic Doppler effect problem.

Exercise 13 On page 23
Explain why Figure (31) cannot be directly applied to a relativistic situation.

Exercise 14 On page 23
Apply the relativistic Doppler effect formulas to light from receding galaxies.

Exercise 15 On page 28
Determine the wavelength of the laser light used in the experiment of Figure (34).

Chapter 26 non calculus
Photons

The effort to determine the true nature of light has been a fitful process in the history of physics. Newton and Huygens did not agree on whether light was a wave or consisted of beams of particles. That issue was apparently settled by Thomas Young's two-slit experiment performed in 1801, nearly three quarters of a century after Newton's death. Young's experiment still did not indicate what light was a wave of. That insight had to come from Maxwell's theory of 1864 which showed that light was a wave of electric and magnetic fields.

In the late 1800s there were dramatic confirmations of Maxwell's theory. In 1888 Heinrich Hertz observed radio waves, the expected low frequency component of the electromagnetic spectrum. The electric and magnetic fields in a radio wave can be measured directly.

But as the nineteenth century was ending, not all predictions of Maxwell's theory were as successful. Applications of Maxwell's equations to explain the light radiated by matter were not working well. No one understood why a heated gas emitted sharp spectral lines, and scientists like Boltzman were unable to explain important features of light radiated by hot solid objects. The fact that Boltzman could get some features right, but not others, made the problem more vexing. Even harder to understand was the way beams of light could eject electrons from the surface of a piece of metal, a phenomenon discovered in 1897 by Hertz.

Many of these problems were cleared up by a picture developed by Max Planck and Einstein, a picture in which light consisted of beams of particles which became known as photons. The photon picture immediately explained the ejection of electrons from a metal surface and the spectrum of radiation from a heated solid object. In the past few years, the observation of photons coming in uniformly from all directions in space has led to a new, and surprisingly well confirmed, picture of the origin of the universe.

In this chapter we will discuss the properties of photons and how discovering the particle nature of light solved some outstanding problems of the late nineteenth century. We will finish with a discussion of what photons have told us about the early universe.

What we will not discuss in this chapter is how to reconcile the two points of view about light. How could light behave as a wave in Thomas Young's experiment, and as a particle in experiments explained by Einstein? How could Maxwell's theory work so well in some cases and fail completely in others? These questions, which puzzled physicists for over a quarter of a century, will be the subject of the chapters on quantum mechanics.

BLACKBODY RADIATION

When we studied the spectrum of hydrogen, we saw that heated hydrogen gas emits definite spectral lines, the red hydrogen α, the blue hydrogen β, and the violet hydrogen γ. Other gases emit definite but different spectral lines. But when we look through a diffraction grating at the heated tungsten filament of a light bulb, we see something quite different. Instead of sharp spectral lines we see a continuous rainbow of all the colors of the visible spectrum. Another difference is that the color of the light emitted by the filament changes as you change the temperature of the filament. If you turn on the light bulb slowly, you first see a dull red, then a brighter red, and finally the filament becomes white hot, emitting the full spectrum seen in white light. In contrast, if you heat hydrogen gas, you see either no light, or you see all three spectral lines at definite unchanging wave lengths.

Some complications have to be dealt with when studying light from solid objects. The heated burner on an electric stove and a ripe McIntosh apple both look red, but for obviously different reasons. The skin of the McIntosh apple absorbs all frequencies of visible light except red, which it reflects. A stove burner, when it is cool, looks black because it absorbs all wavelengths of light equally. When the black stove burner is heated, the spectrum of light is not complicated by selective absorption or emission properties of the surface that might enhance the radiation at some frequencies. The light emitted by a heated black object has universal characteristic properties that do not depend upon what kind of black substance is doing the radiating. The light from such objects is called *blackbody radiation*.

One reason for studying blackbody radiation is that you can determine the temperature of an object from the light it emits. For example, Figure (1) shows the intensity of light radiated at different wavelengths by a tungsten filament at a temperature of 5800 kelvins. The greatest intensity is at a wavelength of 500 nm, the middle of the visible spectrum at the color yellow. If we plot intensities of the various wavelengths radiated by the sun, you get essentially the same curve. As a result we can conclude that the temperature of the surface of the sun is 5800 kelvins. It would be hard to make this measurement any other way.

There are a few simple rules governing blackbody radiation. One is that the wavelength of the most intense radiation, indicated by λ_{max} in Figure (1), is inversely proportional to the temperature. The explicit formula, known as *Wein's displacement law* turns out to be

$$\lambda_{max} = \frac{2.898}{T}mmK = \frac{2.898 \times 10^6}{T}nmK \quad (1)$$

where λ_{max} is in millimeters (mm) or nanometers (nm) and the temperature T is in kelvins. For T = 5800K, Equation (1) gives

$$\lambda_{max}(5800K) = \frac{2.898 \times 10^6}{5800K}nmK$$
$$= 500 \text{ nm}$$

which is the expected result.

While λ_{max} changes with temperature, the relative shape of the spectrum of radiated intensities does not. Figure (1) is a general sketch of the blackbody radiation spectrum. To determine the blackbody spectrum for another temperature, first calculate the new value of λ_{max} using Equation (1) then shift the horizontal scale in Figure (1) so that λ_{max} has this new value.

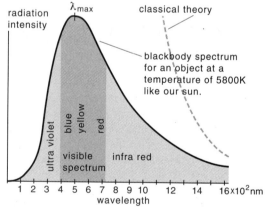

Figure 1

Blackbody spectrum at 5800 degrees on the kelvin scale. The solid line is the experimental curve, the dotted line represents the prediction of Newtonian mechanics combined with Maxwell's equations. The classical theory agrees with the experimental curve only at long wavelengths.

Knowledge of the blackbody spectrum is particularly useful in astronomy. Most stars radiate a blackbody spectrum of radiation. Thus a measurement of the value of λ_{max} determines the temperature of the surface of the star. There happens to be quite a variation in the surface temperature and color of stars. This may seem surprising at first, because most stars look white. But this is due to the fact that our eyes are not color sensitive in dim light. The variation in the color of the stars can show up much better in a color photograph.

As an example of the use of Equation (1), suppose you observe a red star that is radiating a blackbody spectrum with $\lambda_{max} = 700$ nm. The surface temperature should then be given by

$$T = \frac{2.898 \times 10^6 \text{nmK}}{700 \text{ nm}} = 4140 \text{ K (kelvin)}$$

Exercise 1

(a) What is the surface temperature of a blue star whose most intense wavelength is $\lambda_{max} = 400$ nm?

(b) What is the wavelength λ_{max} of the most intense radiation emitted by an electric stove burner that is at a temperature of 600° C (873K)?

(c) What is the wavelength of the most intense radiation emitted by you?

Another feature of blackbody radiation is that the intensity of the radiation increases rapidly with temperature. You see this when you turn up the voltage on the filament of a light bulb. Not only does the color change from red to white, the bulb also becomes much brighter.

The net amount of radiation you get from a hot object is the difference between the amount of radiation emitted and the amount absorbed from the surroundings. If the object is at the same temperature as its surroundings, it absorbs just as much radiation as it emits, with the result that there is no net radiation. This is why you cannot feel any heat from an electric stove burner before it is turned on. But after the burner is turned on and its temperature rises above the room temperature, you begin to feel heat. Even if you do not touch the burner you feel infrared radiation which is being emitted faster than it is being absorbed. By the time the burner becomes red hot, the amount of radiation it emits greatly exceeds the amount being absorbed.

In 1879, Joseph Stefan discovered that the total intensity, the total energy emitted per second in blackbody radiation was proportional to the fourth power of the temperature, to T^4 where T is in kelvins. Five years later Ludwig Boltzman explained the result theoretically. This result is thus known as the Stefan-Boltzman law.

As an example of the use of the Stefan-Boltzman law, suppose that two stars are of the same size, the same surface area, but one is a red star at a temperature of 4,000K while the other is a blue star at a temperature of 10,000K. How much more rapidly is the hot blue star radiating energy than the cool red star?

The ratio of the rates of energy radiation is equal to the ratio of the fourth power of the temperatures. Thus

$$\frac{\text{energy radiated by blue star}}{\text{energy radiated by red star}} = \frac{T_{blue}^4}{T_{red}^4} = \left(\frac{10,000K}{4,000K}\right)^4$$

$$= 2.5^4 \approx 40$$

We see that the blue star must be burning its nuclear fuel 40 times faster than the red star.

Planck Blackbody Radiation Law

Boltzman used a combination of Maxwell's equations, Newtonian mechanics, and the theory of statistics to show that the intensity of blackbody radiation increased as the fourth power of intensity. But neither he nor anyone else was able to derive the blackbody radiation spectrum shown in Figure (1). There was some success in predicting the long wavelength side of the curve, but no one could explain why the intensity curve dropped off again at short wavelengths.

In 1900 Max Planck tried a different approach. He first found an empirical formula for a curve that matched the blackbody spectrum. Then he searched for a derivation that would lead to his formula. The idea was to see if the laws of physics, as they were then known, could be modified in some way to explain his empirical blackbody radiation curve.

Planck succeeded in the following way. According to Maxwell's theory of light, the amount of radiation emitted or absorbed by a charged particle was related to the acceleration of the particle, and that could vary continuously. Planck found that he could get his empirical formula if he assumed that the electrons in a solid emitted or absorbed radiation only in discrete packets. The energy in each packet had to be proportional to the frequency of the radiation being emitted and absorbed. Planck wrote the formula for the energy of the packets in the form

$$E \ = \ hf \tag{2}$$

where f is the frequency of the radiation. The proportionality constant **h** became known as **Planck's constant**.

For over two decades physicists had suspected that something was wrong either with Newtonian mechanics, Maxwell's equations, or both. Maxwell was unable to derive a formula that explained the specific heat of gases (except the monatomic noble gases), and no one had the slightest idea why heated gases emitted sharp spectral lines. Planck's derivation of the blackbody radiation formula was the first successful derivation of a phenomena that could not be explained by Newtonian mechanics and Maxwell's equations.

But what did it mean that radiation could be emitted or absorbed only in discrete packets or **quanta** as Planck called them? What peculiar mechanism lead to this **quantization** of the emission and absorption process? Planck did not know.

THE PHOTOELECTRIC EFFECT

1905 was the year in which Einstein cleared up several outstanding problems in physics. We have seen how his focus on the basic idea of the principle of relativity lead to his theory of special relativity and a new understanding of the structure of space and time. Another clear picture allowed Einstein to explain why light was emitted and absorbed in discrete quanta in blackbody radiation. The same idea also explained a process called the ***photoelectric effect***, a phenomenon first encountered in 1887 by Heinrich Hertz.

In the photoelectric effect, a beam of light ejects electrons from the surface of a piece of metal. This phenomenon can be easily demonstrated in a lecture, using the kind of equipment that was available to Hertz. You start with a gold leaf electrometer like that shown in Figure (2), an old but effective device for measuring the presence of electric charge. (This is the apparatus we used in our initial discussion of capacitors.) If a charged object is placed upon the platform at the top of the electrometer, some of the charge will flow down to the gold leaves that are protected from air currents by a glass sided container. The gold leaves, each receiving the same sign of charge, repel each other and spread apart as shown. Very small amounts of charge can be detected by the spreading of the gold leaves.

To perform the photoelectric effect experiment, clean the surface of a piece of zinc metal by scrubbing it with steel wool, and charge the zinc with a negative charge. We can be sure that the charge is negative by going back to Ben Franklin's definition. If you rub a rubber rod with cat fur, a negative charge will remain on the rubber rod. Then touch the rubber rod to the piece of zinc, and the zinc will become negatively charged. The presence of charge will be detected by the spreading of the gold leaves.

Now shine a beam of light at the charged piece of zinc. For a source of light use a carbon arc that is generated when an electric current jumps the narrow gap between two carbon electrodes. The arc is so bright that you do not need to use a lens to focus the light on the zinc. The setup is shown in Figure (3).

When the light is shining on the zinc, the gold leaves start to fall toward each other. Shut off or block the light and the leaves stop falling. You can turn on and off the light several times and observe that the gold leaves fall only when the light is shining on the zinc. Clearly it is the light from the carbon arc that is discharging the zinc.

Figure 2
The gold leaf electrometer.
This is the same apparatus we
used back in Figure (21-27)
on page 21-14, in our study of
capacitors.

Figure 3
Photoelectric effect experiment.

carbon arc
light source

A simple extension to the experiment is to see what happens if the zinc is given a positive charge. Following Ben Franklin's prescription, we can obtain a positive charge by rubbing a glass rod with a silk cloth. Then touch the positively charged glass rod to the zinc and again you see the gold leaves separate indicating the presence of charge. Now shine the light from the carbon arc on the zinc and nothing happens. The leaves stay spread apart, and the zinc is not discharged by the light.

When we charge the zinc with a negative charge, we are placing an excess of electrons on the zinc. From Gauss's law we know that there cannot be any net charge inside a conductor, thus the excess negative charge, the extra electrons, must be residing in the surface of the metal. The light from the carbon arc, which discharges the zinc, must therefore be knocking these extra electrons out of the metal surface. When we gave the zinc a positive charge, we created a deficiency of electrons in the surface, and no electrons were knocked out.

In the context of Maxwell's equations, it is not particularly surprising that a beam of light should be able to knock electrons out of the surface of a piece of metal. According to Maxwell's theory, light consists of a wave of electric and magnetic fields. An electron, residing on the surface of the zinc, should experience an oscillating electric force when the light shines on the zinc. The frequency of oscillation should be equal to the frequency of the light wave, and the strength of the electric field should be directly related to the intensity of the light. (We saw earlier that the intensity of the light should be proportional to the square of the magnitude of the electric field.)

The question is whether the electric force is capable of ejecting an electron from the metal surface. A certain amount of energy is required to do this. For example, in our electron gun experiment we had to heat the filament in order to get an electron beam. It was the thermal energy that allowed electrons to escape from the filament. We now want to know whether the oscillating electric force of the light wave can supply enough energy to an electron for the electron to escape.

There are two obvious conclusions we should reach. One is that we do not want the frequency of oscillation to be too high, because the direction of the electric field reverses on each half cycle of the oscillation. The electron is pushed one way, and then back again. The longer the time it is pushed in one direction, the lower the frequency of the oscillation, the more time the electron has to pick up speed and gain kinetic energy. If the frequency is too high, just as the electron starts to move one way, it is pushed back the other way, and it does not have time to gain much kinetic energy.

The second obvious conclusion is that we have a better chance of ejecting electrons if we use a more intense beam of light. With a more intense beam, we have a stronger electric field which should exert a stronger force on the electron, producing a greater acceleration and giving the electron more kinetic energy. An intense enough beam might supply enough kinetic energy for the electrons to escape.

In summary, we expect that light might be able to eject electrons from the surface of a piece of metal if we use a low enough frequency and an intense enough beam of light. An intense beam of red light should give the best results.

These predictions, based on Maxwell's equations and Newtonian mechanics, are completely wrong!

Let us return to our photoelectric effect demonstration. During a lecture, a student suggested that we make the light from the carbon arc more intense by using a magnifying glass to focus more of the arc light onto the zinc. The more intense beam of light should discharge the zinc faster.

When you use a magnifying glass, you can make the light striking the zinc look brighter. But something surprising happens. The zinc stops discharging. The gold leaves stop falling. Remove the magnifying glass and the leaves start to fall again. *The magnifying glass prevents the discharge.*

You do not have to use a magnifying glass to stop the discharge. A pane of window glass will do just as well. Insert the window glass and the discharge stops. Remove it, and the gold leaves start to fall again.

How could the window glass stop the discharge? The window glass appears to have no effect on the light striking the zinc. The light appears just as bright. It was brighter when we used the magnifying glass, but still no electrons were ejected. The prediction from Maxwell's theory that we should use a more intense beam of light does not work for this experiment.

What the window glass does is block *ultraviolet radiation*. It is ultraviolet radiation that tans your skin (and can lead to skin cancer). It is difficult to get a tan indoors from sunlight that has gone through a window, because the glass has blocked the ultraviolet component of the sun's radiation. Similarly the pane of window glass, or the glass in the magnifying lens, used in the photoelectric effect experiment, prevents ultraviolet radiation from the carbon arc from reaching the zinc. It is the high frequency ultraviolet radiation that is ejecting electrons from the zinc, not the lower frequency visible light. This is in direct contradiction to the prediction of Maxwell's theory and Newton's laws.

Einstein's explanation of the photoelectric effect is simple. He assumed that Newton was right after all, in that light actually consisted of beams of particles. The photoelectric effect occurred when a particle of light, a *photon*, struck an electron in the surface of the metal. All the energy of the photon would be completely absorbed by the electron. If this were enough energy the electron could escape, if this were not enough energy the electron could not escape.

The idea that light actually consisted of particles explains why Planck had to assume that in blackbody radiation, light could only be emitted or absorbed in quantum units. What was happening in blackbody radiation was that photons were being emitted or absorbed. As a result, Planck's formula for the energy of the quanta of emitted and absorbed radiation, must also be the formula for the energy of a photon. Thus Einstein concluded that a photon's energy is given by the equation

$$E_{photon} = hf \qquad \text{\textit{Einstein's photoelectric effect formula}} \qquad (3)$$

where again f is the frequency of the light and h is Planck's constant. Equation (3) is known as Einstein's *photoelectric effect formula*.

With Equation (3), we can begin to understand our photoelectric effect demonstration. It turns out that visible photons do not have enough energy to knock an electron out of the surface of zinc. There are other metals that require less energy and for these metals visible light will produce a photoelectric effect. But for zinc, visible photons do not have enough energy. Even making the visible light more intense using a magnifying glass does not help. It is only the higher frequency, more energetic, ultraviolet photons that have enough energy to kick an electron out of the surface of zinc. We blocked these energetic photons with the window glass and the magnifying glass.

In 1921, Einstein received the Nobel prize, not for the special theory of relativity which was still controversial, nor for general relativity, but for his explanation of the photoelectric effect.

PLANCK'S CONSTANT h

Planck's constant h, the proportionality constant in Einstein's photoelectric effect formula, appears nowhere in Newtonian mechanics or Maxwell's theory of electricity and magnetism. As physicists were to discover in the early part of the twentieth century, Planck's constant appears just when Newtonian mechanics and Maxwell's equations began to fail. Something was wrong with the nineteenth century physics, and Planck's constant seemed to be a sign of this failure.

The value of Planck's constant is

$$h = 6.63 \times 10^{-34} \text{ joule seconds} \qquad (4)$$

where the dimensions of h have to be an energy times a time, as we can see from the photoelectric formula

$$E = hf = h(\text{joule } \cancel{\text{seconds}}) \times f\left(\frac{\text{cycles}}{\cancel{\text{second}}}\right)$$

The seconds cancel, and cycles are dimensionless, leaving energy in joules.

$$E = hf(\text{joules})$$

We can get the dimensions of (h) in terms of kilograms, meters and seconds by using

$$E = mc^2 \left(kg\frac{\text{meter}^2}{\text{second}^2}\right)$$

to get

$$h(\text{joule}) \times \text{second} = h\left(kg\frac{\text{meter}^2}{\text{second}^2}\right) \times \text{second}$$

$$= h\left(kg\frac{\text{meter}^2}{\text{second}}\right) \qquad (5)$$

It is not hard to see that Planck's constant also has the dimensions of angular momentum. Recall that the angular momentum L of an object is equal to the object's linear momentum p = mv times its lever arm $r_\perp$ about some point. Thus the formula for angular momentum is

$$L = pr_\perp = m(kg)v\left(\frac{\text{meter}}{\text{second}}\right) \times r_\perp(\text{meter})$$

$$= mvr_\perp\left(kg\frac{\text{meter}^2}{\text{second}}\right)$$

which is the same result we got for the dimensions of (h) that we saw in Equation (5).

A fundamental constant of nature with the dimensions of angular momentum is not something to be expected in Newtonian mechanics. It suggests that there is something special about this amount of angular momentum, $6.63 \times 10^{-34}(\text{kg m}^2/\text{sec})$ of it, and nowhere in Newtonian mechanics is there any reason for any special amount. It would be Neils Bohr in 1913 who first appreciated the significance of this amount of angular momentum.

PHOTON ENERGIES

Up to a point we have been describing the electromagnetic spectrum in terms of the frequency or the wavelength of the light. Now with Einstein's photoelectric formula, we can also describe the radiation in terms of the energy of the photons in the radiation. This can be convenient, for we often want to know how much energy photons have. For example, do the photons in a particular beam of light have enough energy to kick an electron out of the surface of a given piece of metal, or to break a certain chemical bond?

For visible light and nearby infrared light, the frequencies are so high that describing the light in terms of frequency is not particularly convenient. We are more likely to work in terms of the light's wavelength and the photon's energy, and want to go back and forth between the two. Using the formula

$$f \frac{\text{cycles}}{\text{sec}} = \frac{c \text{ meters/sec}}{\lambda \text{ meters/cycle}} = \frac{c}{\lambda} \frac{\text{cycles}}{\text{sec}}$$

which we can get from dimensions, we can write the photoelectric formula in the form

$$E = hf = \frac{hc}{\lambda} \qquad (6)$$

Using MKS units in Equation (6) for h, c, and λ, we end up with the photon energy expressed in joules. But a joule, a huge unit of energy compared to the energy of a visible photon, is also inconvenient to use. A far more convenient unit is the ***electron volt***. To see why, let us calculate the energy of the photons in the red hydrogen α line, whose wavelength was 656 nm or 6.56×10^{-7}m. First calculating the energy in joules, we have

$$E(H_{\alpha \text{ line}}) = \frac{hc}{\lambda_{\alpha}}$$

$$= \frac{6.63 \times 10^{-34}\text{joule sec} \times 3 \times 10^8 \text{m/sec}}{6.56 \times 10^{-7}\text{m}}$$

$$= 3.03 \times 10^{-19}\text{joules}$$

Converting this to electron volts, we get

$$E(H_{\alpha \text{ line}}) = \frac{3.03 \times 10^{-19}\text{joules}}{1.6 \times 10^{-19}\text{joules/eV}}$$

$$E(H_{\alpha \text{ line}}) = 1.89 \text{ eV} \qquad (7)$$

That is a convenient result. It turns out that the visible spectrum ranges from about 1.8 eV for the long wavelength red light to about 3.1 eV for the shortest wavelength blue photons we can see. It requires just more than 3.1 eV to remove an electron from the surface of zinc. You can see immediately that visible photons do not have quite enough energy. You need ultraviolet photons with an energy greater than 3.1 eV.

Exercise 2

The blackbody spectrum of the sun corresponds to an object whose temperature is 5800 kelvin. The predominant wavelength λ_{max} for this temperature is 500 nm as we saw in the calculation following Equation (1). What is the energy, in electron volts, of the photons of this wavelength?

Exercise 3

The rest energy of an electron is .51MeV = 5.1×10^5 eV . What is the wavelength, in nanometers, of a photon whose energy is equal to the rest energy of an electron?

We can greatly simplify calculating photon energies in eV, if we convert directly from a photon's wavelength λ in nanometers to its energy E in electron volts. This is most easily done by starting with the formula $E = hc/\lambda$ and using conversion factors until E is in electron volts when λ is in nanometers.

First, we will convert (h) from joule sec to eV sec

$$h = \frac{6.63 \times 10^{-34} \text{ joule sec}}{1.6 \times 10^{-19} \text{joule/eV}}$$

$$= 4.14 \times 10^{-15} \text{ eV sec}$$

The product (hc) becomes

$$hc = 4.14 \times 10^{-15} \text{ eV sec} \times 3 \times 10^8 \frac{\text{meter}}{\text{sec}}$$

$$= 1.24 \times 10^8 \text{ eV meter} \times 10^9 \frac{\text{nm}}{\text{meter}}$$

$$= 1240 \text{ eV nm}$$

Thus the formula $E = hc/\lambda$ can be written as

$$\boxed{E_{photon}(\text{in eV}) = \frac{hc}{\lambda} = \frac{1240 \text{ eV nm}}{\lambda(\text{in nm})}} \quad (8)$$

As an example in the use of Equation (8), let us recalculate the energy of the H_α photons whose wavelength is 656 nm. We get immediately

$$E_{H\alpha} = \frac{1240 \text{ eV nm}}{656 \text{ nm}} = 1.89 \text{eV}$$

which is our previous result.

Exercise 4
The range of wavelengths of light in the visible spectrum is from 700 nm in the red down to 400 nm in the blue. What is the corresponding range of photon energies?

Exercise 5
(a) It requires 2.20 eV to eject an electron from the surface of potassium. What is the longest wavelength light that can eject electrons from potassium?

(b) You shine blue light of wavelength 400 nm at potassium. What is the maximum kinetic energy of the ejected electrons?

Exercise 6
The human skin radiates blackbody radiation corresponding to a temperature of 32°C. (Skin temperature is slightly lower than the 37°C internal temperature.)

What is the predominant energy, in eV of the photons radiated by a human? (This is the energy corresponding to λ_{max} for this temperature.)

Exercise 7
A 100 watt bulb uses 100 joules of energy per second. For this problem, assume that all this energy went into emitting yellow photons at a wavelength of 588 nm..

(a) What is the energy, in eV and joules, of one of these photons?

(b) How many of these photons would the bulb radiate in one second?

(c) From the results of part (b), explain why it is difficult to detect individual photons in a beam of light.

Exercise 8
Radio station WBZ in Boston broadcasts at a frequency of 1050 kilocycles at a power of 50,000 watts.

(a) How many photons per second does this radio station emit?

(b) Should these photons be hard to detect individually?

Exercise 9
In what part of the electromagnetic spectrum will photons of the following energies be found?

(a) 1 eV   (e) 5 eV

(b) 2.1 eV   (f) 1000 eV

(c) 2.5 eV   (g) $.51 \times 10^6$eV (.51 MeV)

(d) 3 eV   (h) 4.34×10^{-9}eV

(The rest energy of the electron is .51 MeV.)

Exercise 10
(a) Calculate the energy, in eV, of the photons in the three visible spectral lines in hydrogen

$$\lambda_\alpha(\text{red}) = 656 \text{ nm}$$

$$\lambda_\beta(\text{blue}) = 486 \text{ nm}$$

$$\lambda_\gamma(\text{violet}) = 434 \text{ nm}$$

It requires 2.28 eV to eject electrons from sodium.

(b) The red H_α light does not eject electrons from sodium. Explain why.

(c) The H_β and H_γ lines do eject electrons. What is the maximum kinetic energy, in eV, of the ejected electrons for these two spectral lines?

PARTICLES AND WAVES

We gain two different perspectives when we think of the electromagnetic spectrum in terms of wavelengths and in terms of photon energies. The wavelength picture brings to mind Young's two slit experiment and Maxwell's theory of electromagnetic radiation. In the photon picture we think of electrons being knocked out of metals and chemical bonds being broken. These pictures are so different that it seems nearly impossible to reconcile them. Reconciling these two pictures will, in fact, be the main focus of the remainder of the text.

For now we seek to answer a more modest question. How can the two pictures coexist? How could some experiments, like our demonstration of the photoelectric effect exhibit only the particle nature and completely violate the predictions of Maxwell's equations, while other experiments support Maxwell's equations and give no hint of a particle nature?

In Figure (4) we show the electromagnetic spectrum both in terms of wavelengths and photon energies. It is in the low energy, long wavelength region, from radio waves to light waves, that the wave nature of the radiation tends to dominate. At shorter wavelengths and higher photon energies, from visible light through γ rays, the particle nature tends to dominate. The reason for this was well illustrated in Exercise 8.

In Exercise 8 you were asked to calculate how many photons were radiated per second by radio station WBZ in Boston. The station radiates 50,000 watts of power at a frequency of 1.05 megacycles. To solve the problem, you first had to calculate the energy of a 1.05

megacycle photon using Einstein's formula $E_{photon} = hf$. This turns out to be about 7×10^{-28} joules. The radio station is radiating 50,000 joules of energy every second, and thus emitting 7×10^{31} photons per second. It is hard to imagine an experiment in which we can detect individual photons when so many are being radiated at once. Any experiments should detect some kind of average effect, and that average effect is given by Maxwell's equations.

When we get up to visible photons, whose energies are in the 2-3 eV range and wavelengths of the order of 500 nm, it is reasonably easy to find experiments that can detect either the particle or the wave nature of light. With a diffraction grating we have no problem measuring wavelengths in the range of 500 nm. With the photoelectric effect, we can easily detect individual photons in the 2-3 eV range.

As we go to shorter wavelengths, individual photons have more energy and the particle nature begins to dominate. To detect the wave nature of x rays, we need something like a diffraction grating with line spacing of the order of the x ray wavelength. It turns out that the regular lines and planes of atoms in crystalline materials act as diffraction gratings allowing us to observe the wave nature of x ray photons. But when we get up into the γ ray region, where photons have energies comparable to the rest energies of electrons and protons, all we observe experimentally are particle reactions. At these high energies, the wave nature of the photon is basically a theoretical concept used to understand the particle reactions.

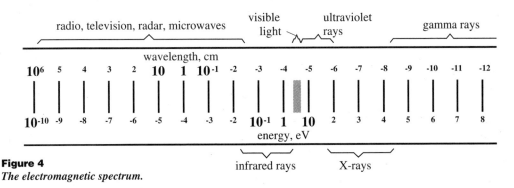

Figure 4
The electromagnetic spectrum.

While it is a rule of thumb that at wavelengths longer than visible light, the wave nature of electromagnetic radiation dominates, there are important exceptions. The individual photons in the WBZ radio wave can be detected! You might ask, what kind of experiment can detect an object whose energy is only 7×10^{-28} joules. This, however, happens to be the amount of energy required to flip the spin of an electron or a nucleus in a reasonably sized magnetic field. This spin flip process for electrons is called *electron spin resonance* and for nuclei, *nuclear spin resonance*. In the Satellite Chapter (15) we discuss an electron spin resonance experiment that is easily performed in the lab. Nuclear spin resonance, as you may be aware, is the basis of magnetic resonance imaging, an increasingly important medical diagnostic tool.

PHOTON MASS

The basic idea behind Einstein's famous formula $E = mc^2$ is that energy is mass. The factor c^2 is a conversion factor to go between energy measured in grams and energy measured in joules. If we had used a different set of units, for example, measuring distances in feet, and time in nanoseconds, then the numerical value of c would be 1, and Einstein's equation would be $E = m$, the more revealing statement.

Photons have energy, thus they have mass. If we combine the photoelectric formula $E = hf$ with $E = mc^2$, we can solve for the mass m of a photon of frequency f. The result is

$$E = hf = m_{photon}c^2$$

$$m_{photon} = \frac{hf}{c^2} \tag{10}$$

We can also express the photon mass in terms of the wavelength λ, using $f/c = 1/\lambda$

$$m_{photon} = \frac{hf}{c^2} = \frac{h}{c}(f/c) = \frac{h}{c\lambda} \tag{11}$$

The idea that photons have mass presents a certain problem. In our earliest discussions of mass in Chapter 6, we saw that the mass increased with velocity, increasing without bounds as the speed of the object approached the speed of light. The formula that described this increase in mass was

$$m = \frac{m_0}{\sqrt{1 - v^2/c^2}} \tag{6-14}$$

where m_0 is the mass of the particle at rest and m its mass when traveling at a speed v.

The obvious problems with photons is that they are light—and therefore travel *at* the speed of light. Applying Equation (6-14) to photons gives

$$m_{photon} = \frac{m_0}{\sqrt{1 - c^2/c^2}} = \frac{m_0}{\sqrt{1 - 1}} = \frac{m_0}{0} \tag{12}$$

a rather embarrassing result. The divisor in Equation (12) is exactly zero, not approximately zero. Usually division by 0 is a mathematical disaster.

There is only one way Equation (12) can be salvaged. The numerator m_0 must also be identically zero. Then Equation (12) gives m = 0/0, an undefined, but not disastrous result. The numerical value of 0/0 can be anything you want. In other words, if the rest mass m_0 of a photon is zero, Equation (12) says nothing about what the actual mass m_{photon} is. Equation (12) only tells us that the rest mass of a photon must be zero.

Stop a photon and what do you have left? Heat! In the daytime many billions of photons strike your skin every second. But after they hit nothing is left except the warmth of the sunlight. When a photon is stopped it no longer exists—only its energy is left behind. That is what is remarkable about photons. Only if they are moving *at* the speed of light do they exist, carry energy and have mass. This distinguishes them from all the particles that have rest mass and cannot get up to the speed of light.

PHOTON MOMENTUM

While photons have no rest mass, and do not obey Newton's second law, they do obey what turns out to be a quite simple set of rules of mechanics. Like their massive counterparts, photons carry energy, linear momentum, and angular momentum all of which are conserved in interactions between particles. The formulas for these quantities can all be obtained straightforwardly from Einstein's photoelectric formula $E = hf$ and energy formula $E = mc^2$.

We have already combined these two equations to obtain Equation (11) for the mass of a photon

$$m_{photon} = \frac{h}{\lambda c} \tag{11a}$$

To find the momentum of the photon, we multiply its mass by its velocity. Since all photons move at the same speed c, the photon momentum p_{photon} is given by

$$\boxed{p_{photon} = m_{photon}c = \frac{h}{\lambda}} \tag{13}$$

In the next few chapters, we will find that Equation (13) applies to more than just photons. *It turns out to be one of the most important equations in physics.*

One of the consequences of photons carrying momentum, is that if a beam of light is absorbed by a surface, it must be exerting a force on that surface. The force $\vec{F}$ is equal to the amount of momentum being delivered per second by the photons.

This is not an unfamiliar concept. Hold your hand in a stream of water, and you will feel that the stream is exerting a force on your hand. From Newton's second law, you find that the force you feel is equal to the rate at which the stream delivers linear momentum to your hand.

When you shine a beam of light at an object, if the photons in the beam actually carry momentum $p = h/\lambda$ then the beam should exert a force equal to the rate at which momentum is being absorbed by the object. If the object, like a black surface, absorbs the photon, the momentum delivered is just the momentum of the photons. If it is a reflecting surface, then we have to include the photon recoil, and the momentum transferred is twice as great.

The Radiometer

There is a common toy called a radiometer that has a 4 vane structure balanced on the tip of a needle as shown in Figure (5). One side of each vane is painted black, while the other side is reflecting. If you shine a beam of light at the vanes, they start to rotate. If, however, you look at the apparatus for a while, you will notice that the vanes rotate the wrong way. They move as if the black side were being pushed harder by the beam of light than the reflecting side.

In the toy radiometers, it is not the force exerted by the light, but the fact that there are some air molecules remaining inside the radiometer, that causes the vanes to rotate. When the light strikes the vanes, it heats the black side more than the reflecting side. Air molecules striking the black side are heated, gain thermal energy, and bounce off or recoil from the vane with more speed than molecules bouncing off the cooler reflecting side. It is the extra speed of the recoil of the air molecules from the black side that turns the vane. This thermal effect is stronger than the force exerted by the light beam itself.

Figure 5
The radiometer.

PRESSURE OF LIGHT & COMPTON SCATTERING

We can see from the example of the radiometer that the measurement of the force exerted by a beam of light, measuring the so-called *pressure of light*, must be done in a good vacuum during a carefully controlled experiment. That measurement was first made by Nichols and Hull at Dartmouth College in 1901. While Maxwell's theory of light also predicts that a beam of light should exert a force, we can now interpret the Nichols and Hull experiment as the first experimental measurement of the momentum carried by photons.

The first experiments to demonstrate that individual photons have momentum, were carried out by Arthur Compton in 1923. In what is now known as the *Compton scattering* or the *Compton effect*, x ray photons are aimed at a thin foil of metal. In many cases the x ray photons collide with and scatter an electron rather than being absorbed as in the photoelectric effect. Both the struck electron and the scattered photon emerge from the back side of the foil as illustrated in Figure (6).

The collision of the photon with the electron in the metal foil is in many ways similar to the collision of the two steel balls studied in Chapter 7, Figures (1) and (2). The energy of the x ray photons used by Compton were of the order of 10,000 eV while the energy of the electron in the metal is of the order of 1 or 2 eV. Thus the x ray photon is essentially striking an electron at rest, much as the moving steel ball struck a steel ball at rest in Figure (7-2).

In both the collision of the steel balls and in the Compton scattering, both energy and linear momentum are conserved. In particular the momentum carried in by the incoming x ray photon is shared between the scattered x ray and the excited electron. This means that the x ray photon loses momentum in the scattering process. Since the photon's momentum is related to its wavelength by $p = h/\lambda$, a loss in momentum means an increase in wavelength. Thus, if the photon mechanics we have developed applies to x ray photons, then the scattered x rays should have a slightly longer wavelength than the incident x rays, a result which Compton observed.

In contrast, Maxwell's theory of light predicts that the scattered x rays should have the same wavelength as the incident wave, a result which is not in agreement with experiment.

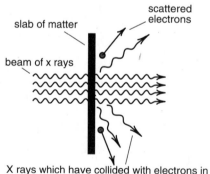

X rays which have collided with electrons in the slab are scattered out of the main beam. These x rays lose momentum, with the result that their wavelength is longer than those that were not scattered.

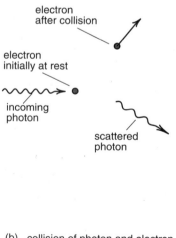

Figure 6   (a) observation of Compton scattering
Compton scattering.

(b) collision of photon and electron resulting in Compton scattering

STELLAR EVOLUTION

While the experiments we have just discussed involved delicate measurements in order to detect the photon momentum, in astronomy the momentum of photons and the pressure of light can have dramatic effects. In about 5 billion years our sun will finish burning the hydrogen in its core. The core will then cool and start to collapse. In one of the contradictory features of stellar evolution, the contracting core releases gravitational potential energy at a greater rate than energy was released by burning hydrogen. As a result the core becomes hotter and much brighter than it was before.

The core will become so bright, emit so much light, that the pressure of the escaping light will lift the surface of the sun out into space. As a result the sun will expand until it engulfs the orbit of the earth. At this point the sun will have become what astronomers call a *red giant* star. Because of its huge surface area it will become thousands of times brighter than it is now.

The red giant phase does not last long, only a few million years. If the sun were bigger than it is, the released gravitational potential energy would be enough to ignite helium and nuclear fusion would continue. But the red giant phase for the sun will be near the end of the road. The sun will gradually cool and shrink, becoming a white dwarf star about the size of the earth, and finally a black ember of about the same size.

The pressure of light played an even more important role in the evolution of the early universe. The light from the big bang explosion that created the universe was so intense that for the first 1/3 of a million years, it knocked the particles of matter around and prevented the formation of atoms, stars, and galaxies. But a dramatic event occurred when the universe reached an age of 1/3 of a million years. That was the point where the universe had cooled enough to become transparent. At that point the light from the big bang decoupled from matter and atoms, matter was no longer ruled by light pressure, and stars, and galaxies began to form. We will discuss this event in more detail shortly.

ANTIMATTER

The fact that photons have no rest mass and travel only at the speed of light makes them seem quite different from particles like an electron or proton that have rest mass and make up the atoms and molecules. The distinction fades somewhat when we consider a process in which a photon is transformed into two particles with rest mass. The two particles can be any particle-antiparticle pair. Figure (7) is a bubble chamber photograph of the creation of an electron-positron pair by a photon.

In 1926 Erwin Schrödinger developed a wave equation to describe the behavior of electrons in atoms. The first equation he tried had a serious problem; it was a relativistic wave equation that appeared to have two solutions. One solution represented the ordinary electrons he was trying to describe, but the other solution appeared to represent a particle with a negative rest mass. Schrödinger found that if he went to the non relativistic limit, and developed an equation that applied only to particles moving at speeds much less than the speed of light, then the negative rest mass solutions did not appear. The non relativistic equation was adequate to describe most chemical phenomena, and is the famous Schrödinger equation.

A year later, Paul Dirac developed another relativistic wave equation for electrons. The equation was specifically designed to avoid the negative mass solutions, but the technique he used did not work. Dirac's equation correctly predicted some important relativistic phenomena, but as Dirac soon found out, the negative mass solutions were still present.

Usually one ignores undesirable solutions to mathematical equations. For example, if you want to solve for the hypotenuse of a triangle, the Pythagorean theorem tells you that $c^2 = a^2 + b^2$. This equation has two solutions, $c = \sqrt{a^2 + b^2}$ and $c = -\sqrt{a^2 + b^2}$. Clearly you want the positive solution. It is difficult to imagine a negative length hypotenuse!

The problem Dirac faced was that he could not ignore the negative mass solution. If he started with a collection of positive mass particles and let them interact, the equation predicted that negative mass particles would be created. He could not avoid them.

Through a rather incredible trick, Dirac was able to reinterpret the negative mass solutions as positive mass solutions of another kind of matter—antimatter. In this interpretation, every elementary particle has a corresponding antiparticle. The antiparticle had the same rest mass but opposite charge from its corresponding particle. Thus a particle-antiparticle pair could be created or annihilated without violating the law of conservation of electric charge.

In 1927, when Dirac proposed his theory, no one had seen any form of antimatter, and no one was sure of exactly what to look for. The proton had the opposite charge from the electron, but its mass was much greater, and therefore it could not be the electron's antiparticle. If the electron antiparticle existed, it would have to have the same positive charge as the proton, but the same mass as an electron. In 1932 Carl Anderson at Caltech found just such a particle among the cosmic rays that rain down through the earth's atmosphere. That particle is the **positron** which is shown being created in the bubble chamber photograph of Figure (7).

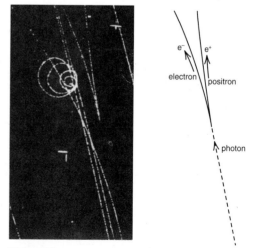

Figure 7
Creation of positron-electron pair. A photon enters from the bottom of the chamber and collides with a hydrogen nucleus. The nucleus absorbs some of the photon's momentum, allowing the photon's energy to be converted into a positron-electron pair. Since a photon is uncharged, it leaves no track in the bubble chamber; the photon's path is shown by a dotted line. (Photograph copyright The Ealing Corporation, Cambridge, Mass.)

(In the muon lifetime moving picture, discussed in Chapter 1, positively charged muons were stopped in the block of plastic, emitting the first pulse of light. When a positive muon decays, it decays into a positron and a neutrino. It was the positron that made the second flash of light that was used to measure the muon's lifetime.)

In the early 1950s, the synchrotron at Berkeley, the one shown in Figure (23-27b) on page 23-22, was built just large enough to create antiprotons, and succeeded in doing so. Since then we have created antineutrons, and have observed antiparticles corresponding to all the known elementary particles. Nature really has two solutions—matter and antimatter.

The main question we have now concerning antimatter is why there is so little of it around at the present time. In the very early universe, temperatures were so high that there was a continual creation and annihilation of particles and antiparticles, with roughly equal but not exactly equal, numbers of particles and antiparticles. There probably was an excess of particles over antiparticles in the order of about one part in 10 billion. In a short while the universe cooled to the point where annihilation became more likely than creation, and the particle-antiparticle pairs annihilated. What was left behind was the slight excess of matter particles, the particles that now form the stars and galaxies of the current universe.

In 1964, James Cronin and Val Fitch, while working on particle accelerator experiments, discovered interactions that lead to an excess of particles over antiparticles. It could be that these interactions were active in the very early universe, creating the slight excess of matter over antimatter. But on the other hand, there may not have been time for known processes to create the observed imbalance. We do not yet have a clear picture of how the excess of matter over antimatter came about.

Exercise 11

Since an electron and a positron have opposite charge, they attract each other via the Coulomb electric force. They can go into orbit forming a small atom-like object called *positronium*. It is like a hydrogen atom except that the two particles have equal mass and thus move about each other rather than having one particle sit at the center. The positronium atom lasts for about a microsecond, whereupon the positron and electron annihilate each other, giving off their rest mass energy in the form of photons. The rest mass energy of the electron and positron is so much greater than their orbital kinetic energy, that one can assume that the positron and electron were essentially at rest when they annihilated. In the annihilation both momentum and energy are conserved.

(a) Explain why the positron and electron cannot annihilate, forming only one photon. (What conservation law would be violated by a one photon annihilation?)

(b) Suppose the positronium annihilated forming two photons. What must be the energy of each photon in eV? What must be the relative direction of motion of the two photons?

The answer to part (b) is that each photon must have an energy of .51 MeV and the photons must come out in exactly opposite directions. By detecting the emerging photons you can tell precisely where the positronium annihilated. This phenomenon is used in the medical imaging process called *positron emission tomography* or *PET* scans.

INTERACTION OF PHOTONS AND GRAVITY

Because photons have mass, we should expect that photons should interact with gravity. But we should be careful about applying the laws of Newtonian gravity to photons, because Newtonian gravity is a nonrelativistic theory, while photons are completely relativistic particles.

If we apply the ideas of Newtonian gravity to photons, which we will do shortly, we will find that we get agreement with experiment if the photons are moving parallel to the gravitational force, for example, falling toward the earth. But if we do a Newtonian type of calculation of the deflection of a photon as it passes a star, we get half the deflection predicted by Einstein's general theory of relativity. It was in Eddington's famous eclipse expedition of 1917 where the full deflection predicted by Einstein's theory was observed. This observation, along with measurements of the precession of Mercury's orbit, provided the first experimental evidence that Newton's theory of gravity was not exactly right.

In 1960, R. V. Pound and G.A. Rebka performed an experiment at Harvard that consisted essentially of dropping photons down a well. What they did was to aim a beam of light of precisely known frequency down a vertical shaft about 22 meters long, and observed that the photons at the bottom of the shaft had a slightly higher frequency, i.e., had slightly more energy than when they were emitted at the top of the shaft.

The way you can use Newtonian gravity to explain their results is the following. If you drop a rock of mass m down a shaft of height h, the rock's gravitational potential energy mgh at the top of the shaft is converted to kinetic energy at the bottom. For a rock, the kinetic energy shows up in the form of increased velocity, and is given by the formula $1/2\, mv^2$. For a photon, all of whose energy is kinetic energy anyway, the kinetic energy gained from the fall shows up as an increased frequency of the photon.

Using Einstein's formula $E = hf$ for the kinetic energy of a photon, we predict that the photon energy at the bottom is given by

$$E_{bottom} = hf_{bottom} = hf_{top} + m_{photon}gy \quad (14)$$

where we are assuming that the same formula mgy for gravitational potential energy applies to both rocks and photons.

Since $m_{photon} = hf/c^2$, the mass of the photon changes slightly as the photon falls. But for a 22 meter deep shaft, the change in frequency is very small and we can quite accurately use hf_{top}/c^2 for the mass of the photon in Equation (14). This gives

$$hf_{bottom} = hf_{top} + \left(\frac{hf_{top}}{c^2}\right)gy$$

Cancelling the h's, we get

$$f_{bottom} = f_{top}\left(1 + \frac{gy}{c^2}\right) \quad (15)$$

as the formula for the increase in the frequency of the photon. This is in agreement with the results found by Pound and Rebka.

Exercise 12

(a) Show that the quantity gy/c^2 is dimensionless.

(b) What is the percentage increase in the frequency of the photons in the Pound-Rebka experiment? (Answer: 2.4×10^{-13}%. This indicates how extremely precise the experiment had to be.)

To calculate the sideways deflection of a photon passing a star, we could use Newton's second law to calculate the rate at which a sideways gravitational force added a sideways component to the momentum of the photon. The result, as we have mentioned, is half the deflection predicted by Einstein's theory of gravity and half that observed during Eddington's eclipse expedition.

The gravitational deflection of photons, while difficult to detect in 1917, has recently become a useful tool in astronomy. In 1961, Allen Sandage at Mt. Palomar Observatory discovered a peculiar kind of object that seemed to be about the size of a star but which emitted radio waves like a radio galaxy. In 1963 Maarten Schmidt photographed the spectral lines of a second radio star and discovered that the spectral lines were all shifted far to the red. If this red shift were caused by the Doppler effect, then the radio star would be moving away from the earth at a speed of 16% the speed of light.

If the motion were due to the expansion of the universe, then the radio star would have to be between one and two billion light years away. An object that far away, and still visible from the earth, would have to be as bright as an entire galaxy.

The problem was the size of the object. The intensity of the radiation emitted by these radio stars was observed to vary significantly over times as short as weeks to months. This virtually guarantees that the object is no bigger than light weeks or light months across, because the information required to coordinate a major change in intensity cannot travel faster than the speed of light. Thus Schmidt had found an object, not much bigger than a star, radiating as much energy as the billions of stars in a galaxy. These rather dramatic objects, many more of which were soon found, became known as *quasars*, which is an abbreviation for *quasi stellar objects*.

It was hard to believe that something not much bigger than a star could be as bright as a galaxy. There were suggestions that the red shift detected by Maarten Schmidt was due to something other than the expansion of the universe. Perhaps quasars were close by objects that just happened to be moving away from us at incredible speeds. Perhaps they were very massive objects so massive that the photons escaping from the object lost a lot of their energy and emerged with lower frequencies and longer wavelengths. (This would be the opposite effect than that seen in the Pound-Rebka experiment where photons falling toward the earth gained kinetic energy and increased in frequency.)

Over the years, no explanation other than the expansion of the universe satisfactorily explained the huge red shifts seen in quasars, but there was this nagging doubt about whether the quasars were really that far away. Everything seemed to fit with the model that red shifts were caused by an expanding universe, but it would be nice to have direct proof.

The direct proof was supplied by gravitational lensing, a consequence of the sideways deflection of photons as they pass a massive object. In 1979, a photograph revealed two quasars that were unusually close to each other. Further investigation showed that the two quasars had identical red shifts and emitted identical spectral lines. This was too much of a coincidence. The two quasars had to be two images of the same quasar.

How could two images of a single quasar appear side by side on a photographic plate? The answer is illustrated in Figure (8). Suppose the quasar were directly behind a massive galaxy, so that the light from the quasar to the earth is deflected sideways as shown. Here on earth we could see light coming from the quasar from 2 or more different directions. The telescope forms images as if the light came in a straight line. Thus in Figure (8), light that came around the top side of the galaxy would look like it came from a quasar located above the actual quasar, while light that came around the bottom side would look as if it came from another quasar located below the actual quasar.

This gravitational lensing turned out to be a more common phenomena than one might have expected. Many examples of gravitational lensing have been discovered in the past decade. Figure (9), an image produced by the repaired Hubble telescope, shows a quasar surrounded by four images of itself. The four images were formed by the gravitational lensing of an intermediate galaxy.

The importance of gravitational lensing is that it provides definite proof that the imaged objects are more distant than the objects doing the imaging. The quasar in Figure (9) must be farther away from us than the galaxy that is deflecting the quasar's light. This proved that the quasars are distant objects and that the red shift is definitely due to the expansion of the universe.

Evidence over the years has indicated that quasars are the cores of newly formed galaxies. Quasars tend to be distant because most galaxies were formed when the universe was relatively young. If all quasars we see are very far away, the light from them has taken a long time to reach us, thus they must have formed a long time ago. The fact that we see very few nearby quasars means that most galaxy formation has already ceased.

Although we have photographed galaxies for over a hundred years, we know surprisingly little about them, especially what is at the core of galaxies. Recent evidence indicates that at the core of the galaxy M87 there is a black hole whose mass is of the order of millions of suns. The formation of such a black hole would produce brilliant radiation from a very small region of space, the kind of intense localized radiation seen in quasars. In recent years we have gathered evidence that many galaxies have massive black holes at their centers.

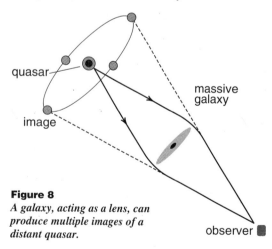

Figure 8
A galaxy, acting as a lens, can produce multiple images of a distant quasar.

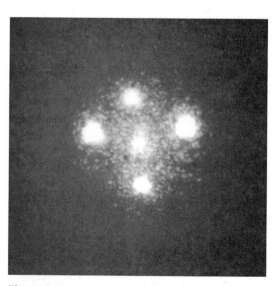

Figure 9
Hubble telescope photograph of a distant quasar surrounded by 4 images of the quasar. This is known as the **Einstein cross**.

EVOLUTION OF THE UNIVERSE

The two basic physical ideas involved in understanding the early universe are its expansion, and the idea that the universe was in thermal equilibrium. Before we see how these concepts are applied, we wish to develop a slightly different perspective of these two concepts. First we will see how the red shift of light can be interpreted in terms of the expansion of the universe. Then we will see that blackbody radiation can be viewed as a gas of photons in thermal equilibrium. With these two points of view, we can more easily follow the evolution of the universe.

Red Shift and the Expansion of the Universe

The original clue that we live in an expanding universe was from the red shift of light from distant galaxies. We have explained this red shift as being caused by the Doppler effect. The distant galaxies are moving away from us, and it is the recessional motion that stretches the wavelengths of the radiated waves, as seen in the ripple tank photograph back in Figure (25-29) reproduced here.

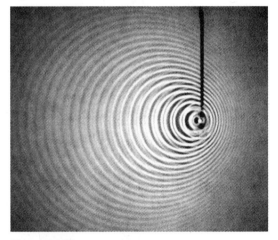

Figure 25-29
The Doppler effect. If we are looking at light from a receding galaxy, the light reaching us will have a longer, stretched out wavelength.

There is another way to view the red shift that gives the same results but provides a more comprehensive picture of the evolution of the universe. Consider a galaxy that is, for example, receding from us at 10% the speed of light. According to the Doppler effect, the wavelength of the light from that galaxy will be lengthened by a factor of 10%.

Where is that galaxy now? If the galaxy were moving away from us at 10% the speed of light, it has traveled away from us 1/10th as far as the light has traveled in reaching us. In other words the galaxy is 10% farther away now than when it emitted the light. If the recessional motion of the galaxy is due to the expansion of the universe, then the universe is now 10% bigger than it was when the galaxy emitted the light.

In this example, the universe is now 10% bigger and the wavelength of the emitted light is 10% longer. We can take the point of view that *the wavelength of the light was stretched 10% by the expansion of the universe.*

In other words it makes no difference whether we say that the red shift was caused by the 10% recessional velocity of the galaxy, or the 10% expansion of the universe. Both arguments give the same answer. When we are studying the evolution of the universe, it is easier to use the idea that the universe's expansion stretches the photon wavelengths. This is especially true for discussions of the early universe where recessional velocities are close to the speed of light and relativistic Doppler calculations would be required.

ANOTHER VIEW OF BLACKBODY RADIATION

The surface of the sun provides an example of a hot gas more or less in thermal equilibrium. Not only are the ordinary particles, the electrons, the protons, and other nuclei in thermal equilibrium, so are the photons, and this is why the sun emits a blackbody spectrum of radiation. Blackbody radiation at a temperature T can be viewed as a gas of photons in thermal equilibrium at that temperature.

In our derivation of the ideal gas law, we were surprisingly successful using the idea that the average gas molecule had a thermal kinetic energy 3/2 kT. In a similar and equally naïve derivation, we can explain one of the main features of blackbody radiation from the assumption that the average or typical photon in blackbody radiation also has a kinetic energy 3/2 kT.

The main feature of blackbody radiation, that could not be explained using Maxwell's theory of light, was the fact that there was a peak in the blackbody spectrum. There is a predominant wavelength which we have called λ_{max} that is inversely proportional to the temperature T. The precise relationship given by Wein's displacement law is

$$\lambda_{max} = \frac{2.898}{T} mmK \qquad \text{(1) repeated}$$

a result we stated earlier. The blackbody radiation peaks around λ_{max} as seen in Figure (1) reproduced here.

If blackbody radiation consists of a gas of photons in thermal equilibrium at a temperature T, we can assume that the average photon should have a kinetic energy like 3/2 kT. (The factor 3/2 is not quite right for relativistic particles, but close enough for this discussion.) Some photons should have more energy, some less, but there should be a peak in the distribution of photons around this energy. Using Einstein's photoelectric effect formula we can relate the most likely photon energy to a most likely wavelength λ_{max}.

We have

$$E_{photon} = \frac{3}{2}kT$$

$$E_{photon} = \frac{hc}{\lambda_{max}}$$

Combining these equations gives

$$\frac{hc}{\lambda_{max}} = \frac{3}{2}kT$$

$$\lambda_{max} = \frac{2hc}{3kT}$$

Putting in numbers gives

$$\lambda_{max} = \frac{2 \times 6.63 \times 10^{-34} joule\ sec \times 3 \times 10^{8}\frac{m}{s}}{3 \times 1.38 \times 10^{-23}\frac{joule}{K} \times T}$$

$$= \frac{.0096\ meter \cdot K}{T}$$

Converting from meters to millimeters gives

$$\lambda_{max} = \frac{9.60}{T} mmK \qquad \begin{array}{l}\textit{our estimate}\\ \textit{for } \lambda_{max}\end{array} \qquad (16)$$

While this is not the exact result, it gives us the picture that there should be a peak in the blackbody spectrum around λ_{max}. The formula gives the correct temperature dependence, and the constant is only off by a factor of 3.3. Not too bad a result considering that we did not deal with relativistic effects and the distribution of energies in thermal equilibrium. None of these results can be understood without the photon picture of light.

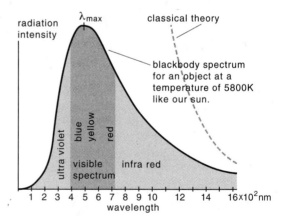

Figure 1 (repeated)
Blackbody radiation spectrum showing the peak at λ_{max}. (The classical curve goes up to infinity at $\lambda = 0$.)

MODELS OF THE UNIVERSE

As we saw in Chapter 25, Hubble was able to combine his new distance scale for stars and galaxies with Doppler shift measurements to discover that the universe is expanding, that the farther a galaxy is away from us, the faster it is moving away from us. Another property of the interaction of light with matter, the blackbody spectrum discussed at the beginning of this chapter, provided a critical clue to the role of this expansion in the history of the universe. To see why, it is instructive to look at the evolution of our picture of the universe, to see what led us to support or reject different models of its large scale structure.

Powering the Sun

In the 1860s, Lord Kelvin, for whom the absolute temperature scale is named, did a calculation of the age of the sun. Following a suggestion by Helmholtz, Kelvin assumed that the most powerful source of energy available to the sun was its gravitational potential energy. Noting the rate at which the sun was radiating energy, Kelvin estimated that the sun was no older than half a billion years. This was a serious problem for Darwin, whose theory of evolution required considerably longer times for the processes of evolution to have taken place. During their lifetimes neither Darwin or Kelvin could explain the apparent discrepancy of having fossils older than the sun.

This problem was overcome by the discovery that the main source of energy of the sun was not gravitational potential energy, but instead the nuclear energy released by the fusion of hydrogen nuclei to form helium nuclei. In 1938 Hans Bethe worked out the details of how this process worked. The reaction begins when two protons collide with sufficient energy to overcome the Coulomb repulsion and get close enough to feel the very strong, but short range, attractive nuclear force. Such a strong collision is required to overcome the Coulomb barrier, that fusion is a rare event in the lifetime of any particular solar proton. On the average, a solar proton can bounce around about 30 million years before fusing. There are, of course, many protons in the sun, so that many such fusions are occurring at any one time.

Just after two protons fuse, electric potential energy is released when one of the protons decays, via the weak interaction, into a neutron, electron, and a neutrino. The electron and neutrino are ejected, leaving behind a deuterium nucleus consisting of a proton and a neutron. This reaction is the source of the neutrinos radiated by the sun.

Within a few seconds of its creation, the deuterium nucleus absorbs another proton to become a helium 3 nucleus. Since helium 3 nuclei in the sun are quite rare, it is on the average several million years before the helium 3 nucleus collides with another helium 3 nucleus. The result of this collision is the very stable helium 4 nucleus and the ejection of 2 protons. The net result of all these steps is the conversion of 4 protons into a helium 4 nucleus with the release of .6% of the proton's rest mass energy in the form of neutrinos and photons.

Not only did Beta's theory provide an explanation for the source of the sun's energy, it also demonstrated how elements can be created inside a star. It raised the question of whether all the elements could be created inside stars. Could you start with stars initially containing only hydrogen gas and end up with all the elements we see around us?

Abundance of the Elements

From studies of minerals in the earth and in meteorites, and as a result of astronomical observations, we know considerable detail about the abundances of the elements around us. As seen in the chart of Figure (10), hydrogen and helium are the most abundant elements, followed by peaks at carbon, oxygen, iron and lead. There is a noticeable lack of lithium, beryllium and boron, and a general trailing off of the heavier elements. Is it possible to explain not only how elements could be created in stars, but also explain these observed abundances as being the natural result of the nuclear reactions inside stars?

The first problem is the fact that there are no stable nuclei with 5 or 8 nucleons. This means you cannot form a stable nucleus either by adding one proton to a helium 4 nucleus or fusing two helium 4 nuclei. How, then, would the next heavier element be formed in a star that consisted of only hydrogen and helium 4? The answer was supplied by E. E. Salpeter in 1952 who showed that two helium 4 nuclei could produce an unstable beryllium 8 nucleus. In a dense helium rich stellar core, the beryllium 8 nucleus could, before decaying, collide with another helium 4 nucleus forming a stable carbon 12 nucleus. One result is that elements between helium and carbon are skipped over in the element formation process, explaining the exceptionally low cosmic abundances of lithium, beryllium and boron seen in Figure (10).

The biggest barrier to explaining element formation in stars is the fact that the iron 56 nucleus is the most stable of all nuclei. Energy is released if the small nuclei fuse together to create larger ones, but energy is also released if the very largest nuclei split up (as in the case of the fission of uranium in an atomic bomb or nuclear reactor). To put it another way, when making nuclei up to iron, energy is released. But it costs energy to build nuclei larger than iron. Iron is the ultimate ash of nuclear reactions. How, then, could elements heavier than iron be created in the nuclear furnaces of stars?

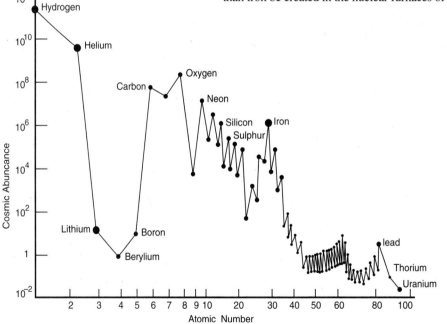

Figure 10
Abundance of the elements.

In 1956 the element technetium 99 was identified in the spectra of a certain class of stars. Technetium 99, heavier than iron, is an unstable element with a half life of only two hundred thousand years. On a cosmic time scale, this element had to have been made quite recently. Thus elements heavier than iron are now being created in some kind of a process.

Soon after the observation of technetium, the British astronomer Geoffrey Burbidge, looking over recently declassified data from the Bikini Atoll hydrogen bomb tests, noticed that one of the elements created in the explosion, californium 254, had a half life of 55 days. Burbidge realized that this was also the half life of the intensity of a recently observed supernova explosion. This suggested that the light from the supernova was powered by decaying californium 254. That meant that it was the supernova explosion itself that created the very heavy californium 254, and probably all the other elements heavier than iron.

In 1957 Geoffrey and Margaret Burbidge, along with the nuclear physicist William Fowler at Caltech and the British astronomer Fred Hoyle, published a famous paper showing how the fusion process in stars could explain the abundances of elements up to iron, and how supernova explosions could explain the formation of elements heavier than iron. This was one of the important steps in the use of our knowledge of the behavior of matter on a small scale, namely nuclear physics, to explain what we see on a large scale—the cosmic abundance of the elements.

The Steady State Model of the Universe

A model of the universe, proposed in 1948 by Fred Hoyle, Herman Bondi and Thomas Gold, fit very well with the idea that all the elements in the universe heavier than hydrogen, were created as a result of nuclear reactions inside stars. This was the so-called *steady state* model.

Knowing that the universe is expanding, it seems to be a contradiction to propose that the universe is steady state—i.e., that on the average, it is unchanging. If the universe is expanding and galaxies are flying apart, then in a few billion years the galaxies will be farther separated from each other than they are today. This is hardly a steady state picture.

The steady state theory got around this problem by proposing that matter was continually being created to replace that being lost due to the expansion. Consider, for example, a sphere a billion light years in diameter, centered on the earth. Over the next million years a certain number of stars will leave the sphere due to the expansion. To replace this matter flowing out of the sphere, the steady state theory assumed that hydrogen atoms were continually being created inside the sphere. All that was needed was about one hydrogen atom to be created in each cubic kilometer of space every year.

The advantage of constructing a model like the steady state theory is that the model makes certain definite predictions that can be tested. One prediction is that all the matter around us originated in the form of the hydrogen atoms that are assumed to be continually created. This implies that the heavier elements we see around us must be created by ongoing processes such as nuclear reactions inside stars. This provided a strong incentive for Hoyle and others to see if nuclear synthesis inside stars, starting from hydrogen, could explain the observed abundance of elements.

Another prediction of the steady state model is that galaxies far away must look much like nearby galaxies. When you look far away, you are also looking back in time. If you look at a galaxy one billion light years away, you are seeing light that started out a billion years ago. Light reaching us from a galaxy 10 billion light years away started out 10 billion light years ago. If the universe is really in a steady state, then galaxies 10 billion years ago should look much like galaxies do today.

THE BIG BANG MODEL

The discovery of the expansion of the universe suggests another model of the universe, namely that the universe started in one gigantic explosion, and that the expansion we now see is the result of the pieces from that explosion flying apart.

To see why you are led to the idea of an explosion, imagine that you take a motion picture of the expanding universe and then run the motion picture backwards. If the expansion is uniform, then in the reversed motion picture we see a uniform contraction. The particles in this picture are the galaxies which are getting closer and closer together. There is a time, call it t = 0, when all the galaxies come together at a point. Now run the motion picture forward and the galaxies all move out as if there were an explosion at that point.

The explosion of the universe was first proposed by the Belgian priest and mathematician Georges Lemaître in the late 1920s. It was, in fact, Lemaître who explained Hubble's red shift versus distance data as evidence for the expansion of the universe. In the late 1920s not much was known about nuclear physics, even the neutron had not yet been discovered. But in the 1940s after the development of the atomic fission bomb and during the design of the hydrogen fusion bomb, physicists gained considerable experience with nuclear reactions in hot, dense media, and some, George Gamov in particular, began to explore the consequences of the idea that the universe started in an initial gigantic explosion.

A rough picture of the early universe in the explosion model can be constructed using the concepts of the Doppler effect and thermal equilibrium. Let us see how this works.

We have seen that the red shift of the spectral lines of light from distant galaxies can be interpreted as being caused by the stretching of the wavelengths of the light due to the expansion of the universe. In a reverse motion picture of the universe, distant galaxies would be coming toward us and the wavelengths of the spectral lines would be blue shifted. We would say that the universe was contracting, shrinking the wavelength of the spectral lines. The amount of contraction would depend upon how far back toward the t = 0 origin we went. If we went back to when the universe was 1/10

as big as it is now, wavelengths of light would contract to 1/10 their original size.

In the Einstein photoelectric effect formula, $E_{photon} = hf = hc/\lambda$, the shorter the photon wavelength, the more energetic the photons become. This suggests that as we compress the universe in the time reversal moving picture, photon energies increase. If there is no limit to the compression, then there is no limit to how much the photon energies increase.

Now introduce the idea of thermal equilibrium. If we go back to a very small universe, we have very energetic photons. If these photons are in thermal equilibrium with other forms of matter, as they are inside of stars, then all of the matter has enormous thermal energy, and the temperature is very high. Going back to a zero sized universe means going back to a universe that started out at an infinite temperature. Fred Hoyle thought that this picture was so ridiculous that he gave the explosion model of the universe the derisive name the "Big Bang" model. The name has stuck.

The Helium Abundance

In the mid 1950s the cosmological theory taken seriously by most physicists was the steady state theory. In the late 1940s George Gamov had suggested that the elements had been created in the big bang when the universe was very small, dense and hot. But the work of Hoyle and Fowler was showing that the abundance of the elements could much more satisfactorily be explained in terms of nuclear synthesis inside of stars. This nuclear synthesis also explained the energy source in stars and the various stages of stellar evolution. What need was there to propose some gigantic, cataclysmic explosion?

Hoyle soon found a need. Most of the energy released in nuclear synthesis in stars results from the burning of hydrogen to form helium. By observing how much energy is released by stars, you can estimate how much helium should be produced. By the early 1960s Hoyle began to realize that nuclear synthesis could not produce enough helium to explain the observed cosmic abundance of 25%. In a 1964 paper with R. J. Taylor, Hoyle himself suggested that perhaps much of the helium was created in an initial explosion of the universe.

Cosmic Radiation

In a talk given at Johns Hopkins in early 1965, Princeton theoretician P. J. E. Peebles suggested that the early universe must have contained a considerable amount of radiation if the big bang model were correct. If there were little radiation, any hydrogen present in the early universe would have quickly fused to form heavier elements, and no hydrogen would be left today. This directly contradicts the observation that about 75% of the matter we see today consists of hydrogen. If, however, there were a large amount of radiation present in the early universe, the energetic photons would bust up the larger nuclei as they formed, leaving behind hydrogen.

Peebles proposed that this radiation, the cosmic photons which prevented the fusion of hydrogen in the early universe, still exists today but in a very altered form. There should have been little change in the number of photons, but a great change in their energy. As the universe expanded, the wavelength of the cosmic photons should be stretched by the expansion, greatly reducing their energy. If the photons were in thermal equilibrium with very hot matter in the early universe, they should still have a thermal blackbody spectrum, but at a much lower temperature. He predicted that the temperature of the cosmic radiation should have dropped to around 10 kelvin. His colleagues at Princeton, P. G. Roll and D .T. Wilkinson were constructing a special antenna to detect such radiation. All of this work had been suggested by R. H. Dicke, inventor of the key microwave techniques needed to detect ten degree photons.

Peebles was not the first to suggest that there should be radiation left over from the big bang. That was first suggested in a 1948 paper by George Gamov and colleagues Ralph Alpher and Robert Herman in a model where all elements were to be created in the big bang. A more realistic model of the big bang proposed by Alpher and Herman in 1953 also led to the same prediction of cosmic radiation. In both cases, it was estimated that the thermal radiation should now have a temperature of 5 kelvin. In the early 1950s, Gamov, Alpher and Herman were told by radio astronomers that such radiation could not be detected by equipment then available, and the effort to detect it was not pursued. Peebles was unaware of these earlier predictions.

THE THREE DEGREE RADIATION

In 1964, two radio astronomers working for Bell Labs, Arno Penzias and Robert Wilson, began a study of the radio waves emitted from parts of our galaxy that are away from the galactic plane. They expected a faint diffuse radiation from this part of the galaxy and planned to use a sensitive low noise radio antenna shown in Figure (11), an antenna left over from the *Echo Satellite* experiment. (In that early experiment on satellite communication, a reflecting balloon was placed in orbit. The low noise antenna was built to detect the faint radio signals that bounced off the balloon.)

Since the kind of signals Penzias and Wilson expected to detect would look a lot like radio noise, they had to be careful that the signals they recorded were coming from the galaxy rather than from noise generated by the antenna or by electronics. To test the system, they looked for signals at a wavelength of 7.35 cm, a wavelength where the galaxy was not expected to produce much radiation. They found, however, a stronger signal than expected. After removing a pair of pigeons that were living in the antenna throat, cleaning out the nest and other debris which Wilson referred to as "a white dielectric material", and taking other steps to eliminate noise, the extra signal persisted.

Figure 11
Penzias and Wilson, and the Holmdel radio telescope.

If the 7.35 cm wavelength signal were coming from the galaxy, there should be regions of the galaxy that produced a stronger signal than other regions. And the neighboring galaxy Andromeda should also be a localized source of this signal. However Penzias and Wilson found that the 7.35 cm signal was coming in uniformly from all directions. The radiation had to be coming in from a much larger region of space than our galaxy.

Studies of the signal at still shorter wavelengths showed that if the signal were produced by a blackbody spectrum of radiation, the effective temperature would be about 3.5 kelvin. Penzias talked with a colleague who had talked with another colleague who had attended Peebles' talk at Johns Hopkins on the possibility of radiation left over from the big bang. Penzias and Wilson immediately suspected that the signal they were detecting might be from this radiation.

Penzias and Wilson could detect only the long wavelength tail of the three degree radiation. Three degree radiation should have a maximum intensity at a wavelength given by the Wein formula, Equation (1),

$$\lambda_{max} = \frac{2.898 \text{ mm K}}{T}$$
$$= \frac{2.898 \text{ mm K}}{3 \text{ K}} \approx 1 \text{ mm} \tag{17}$$

Radiation with wavelengths in the 1 mm region cannot get through the earth's atmosphere. As a result Penzias and Wilson, and others using ground based antennas, could not verify that the radiation had a complete blackbody spectrum. From 1965 to the late 1980s, various balloon and rocket based experiments, which lifted antennas above the earth's atmosphere, verified that the radiation detected by Penzias and Wilson was part of a complete blackbody spectrum of radiation at a temperature of 2.74 kelvin.

In 1989, NASA orbited the **COBE** (Cosmic Background Explorer) satellite to make a detailed study of the cosmic background radiation. The results from this satellite verified that this radiation has the most perfect blackbody spectrum ever seen by mankind. The temperature is 2.735 kelvin with variations of the order of one part in 100,000. The questions we have to deal with now are not whether there is light left over from the big bang, but why it is such a nearly perfect blackbody spectrum.

Thermal Equilibrium of the Universe

That the cosmic background radiation has nearly a perfect blackbody spectrum tells us that at some point in its history, the universe was in nearly perfect thermal equilibrium, with everything at one uniform temperature. That is certainly not the case today. The cosmic radiation is at a temperature of 2.735 kelvin, Hawaii has an average temperature of 295 kelvin, and the temperature inside of stars ranges up to billions of degrees. There must have been a dramatic change in the nature of the universe sometime in the past. That change occurred when the universe suddenly became transparent at an age of about 300,000 years.**

To see why the universe suddenly became transparent, and why this was such an important event, it is instructive to reconstruct what the universe must have been like at still earlier times.

** The universe today is just under 14 billion years old. To get a feeling for how far back 300,000 years is in the life of the universe, we would like to quote a statement from the website **Smoot's astrophysics program.** *"Put in human terms, if the universe were a middle aged person today, then the epoch (seen in the 2.7 degree radiation) corresponds to an image of an embryo at 10 hours age."*

THE EARLY UNIVERSE

Imagine that we have a videotape recording of the evolution of the universe. We put the tape in our VCR and see that the tape has not been rewound. It is showing our current universe with stars, galaxies and the cosmic radiation at a temperature of 2.735 k. You can calculate the density of photons in the cosmic radiation, and compare that with the average density of protons and neutrons (nucleons) in the stars and galaxies. You find that the photons outnumber the nucleons by a factor of about 10 billion to 1. But the energy of a three degree photon is much less than the rest energy of a proton or neutron. As a result, the total rest energy of all the stars and galaxies is about 100 times greater than the total energy in the cosmic radiation.

Leaving the VCR on play, we press the rewind button. The picture is not too clear, but we can see general features of the contracting universe. The galaxies are moving together and the wavelength of the cosmic radiation is shrinking. Since the energy of the cosmic photons is given by Einstein's formula $E = hc/\lambda$, the shrinking of the photon wavelengths increases their energy. On the other hand the rest mass energy of the stars and galaxies is essentially unchanged by the contraction of the universe. Consequently the energy of the cosmic photons is becoming a greater and greater share of the total energy of the universe. When the universe has contracted to about 1/100th of its present size, when the universe is about 1/2 million years old, the cosmic photons have caught up to the matter particles. At earlier times, the cosmic photons have more energy than other forms of matter.

The Very Early Universe

As the tape rewinds our attention is diverted. When we look again at the screen, we see that the tape is showing a very early universe. The time indicated is .01 seconds! The temperature has risen to 100 billion degrees, and the thermal photons have an average energy of 40 million electron volts! We obviously missed a lot in the rewind. Stopping the tape, we then run it forward to see what the universe looks like at this very early stage.

There is essentially the same number of nucleons in this early universe as there are today. Since the thermal energy of 40 MeV is much greater than the 1.3 MeV mass difference between neutrons and protons, there is enough thermal energy to freely convert protons into neutrons, and vice versa. As a result there are about equal numbers of protons and neutrons. There is also about the same number of thermal photons in this early universe as there are today, about 100 billion photons for each nucleon.

While there is not much change from today in the number of nucleons or photons in our .01 second universe, there is a vastly different number of electrons. The thermal photons, with an average energy of 40 MeV, can freely create positron and electron pairs. The rest energy of a positron or an electron is only .5 MeV, thus only 1 MeV is required to create a pair. The result is that the universe at this time is a thermal soup of photons, positrons and electrons—about equal numbers. There are also many neutrinos left over from an earlier time. All of those species outnumber the few nucleons by a factor of about 100 billion to one.

Excess of Matter over Antimatter

If you look closely and patiently count the number of positrons and electrons in some region of space, you will find that for every 100,000,000,000 positrons, there are 100,000,000,001 electrons. The electrons outnumber the positrons by 1 in 100 billion. In fact, the excess number of negative electrons is just equal to the number of positive protons, with the result that the universe is electrically neutral.

The tiny excess of electrons over positrons represents an excess of matter over antimatter. In most particle reactions we study today, if particles are created, they are created in particle, antiparticle pairs. The question is then, why does this early universe have a tiny excess of matter particles over antimatter particles? What in the still earlier universe created this tiny imbalance? There is a particle reaction, caused by the weak interaction, that does not treat matter and antimatter symmetrically. This reaction, discovered by Val Fitch in 1964, could possibly explain how this tiny imbalance came about. It is not clear whether there was enough time in the very early universe for Fitch's reaction to create the observed imbalance.

An excellent guidebook for our video tape is Steven Weinberg's *The First Three Minutes*. Weinberg was one of the physicists who discovered the connection between the weak interaction and electromagnetism. Weinberg breaks up the first three minutes of the life of the universe into five frames. We happened to have stopped the tape recording at Weinberg's frame #1. To see what we missed in our fast rewind, we will now run the tape forward, picking up the other four frames in the first three minutes as well as important later events.

Frame #2 (.11 seconds)

As we run the tape forward, the universe is now expanding, the wavelength of the thermal photons is getting longer, and their temperature is dropping. When the time counter gets up to t = .11 seconds, the temperature has dropped to 30 billion kelvin and the average energy of the thermal photons has dropped to 10 MeV. Back at frame #1, when the thermal energy was 40 MeV, there were roughly equal numbers of protons and neutrons. However, the lower thermal energy of 10 MeV is not sufficiently greater than the 1.3 MeV proton-neutron mass difference to maintain the equality.

In the many rapid collisions where protons are being converted into neutrons and vice versa (via the weak interaction), there is a slightly greater chance that the heavier neutron will decay into a lighter proton rather than the other way around. As a result the percentage of neutrons has dropped to 38% by the time t = .11 seconds.

Frame #3 (1.09 seconds)

Aside from the drop in temperature and slight decrease in the percentage of neutrons, not much else happened as we went from frame #1 at .01 seconds to frame #2 at .11 seconds. Starting up the tape player again, we go forward to t = 1.09 seconds, Weinberg's third frame. The temperature has dropped to 10 billion kelvin, which corresponds to a thermal energy of 4 MeV. This is not too far above the 1 MeV threshold for creating positron electron pairs. As a result the positron electron pairs are beginning to annihilate faster than they are being created. Also by this time the percentage of neutrons has dropped to 24%.

Frame #4 (13.82 seconds)

At a time of 13.82 seconds, Weinberg's fourth frame, the temperature has dropped to 3 billion kelvin, corresponding to an average thermal energy of 1 MeV per particle. With any further drop in temperature, the average thermal photon will not have enough energy to create positron electron pairs. The result is that vast numbers of positrons and electrons are beginning to annihilate each other. Soon there will be equal numbers of electrons and protons, and the only particles remaining in very large numbers will be neutrinos and thermal photons.

By this fourth frame, the percentage of neutrons has dropped to 17%. The temperature of 3 billion degrees is low enough for helium nuclei to survive, but helium nuclei do not form because of the deuterium bottleneck. When a proton and neutron collide, they can easily form a deuterium nucleus. Although deuterium is stable, it is weakly bound. At a temperature of 3 billion kelvin, the thermal protons quickly break up any deuterium that forms. Without deuterium, it is not possible to build up still larger nuclei.

Frame #5 (3 minutes and 2 seconds)

Going forward to a time of 3 minutes and 2 seconds, the universe has cooled to a billion kelvin, the positrons and most electrons have disappeared, and the only abundant particles are photons, neutrinos and antineutrinos. The neutron proton balance has dropped to 14% neutrons. While tritium (one proton and two neutrons) and helium 4 are stable at this temperature, deuterium is not, thus no heavier nuclei can form.

A short time later, the temperature drops to the point where deuterium is stable. When this happens, neutrons can combine with protons to form deuterium and tritium, and these then combine to form helium 4. Almost immediately the remaining nearly 13% neutrons combine with an equal number of protons to form most of the 25% abundance of cosmic helium we see today. This is where the helium came from that Hoyle could not explain in terms of nuclear synthesis inside of stars.

Because there are no stable nuclei with 5 or 8 nucleons, there is no simple route to the formation of still heavier elements. At a temperature of a billion degrees, the universe is only about 70 times hotter than the core of our sun, cooler than the core of hot stars around today that are fusing the heavier elements. As a result, nuclear synthesis in the early universe stops at helium 4 with a trace of lithium 7. One of the best tests of the big bang theory is a rather precise prediction of the relative abundances of hydrogen, deuterium, helium 4 and lithium 7, all left over from the early universe. When the formation of these elements is complete, the universe is 3 minutes and 46 seconds old.

Decoupling (300,000 years)

Continue running the tape forward, and nothing of much interest happens for a long time. The thermal photons still outnumber the nucleons and electrons by a factor of about 10 billion to one, and the constant collisions between these particles prevent the formation of atoms. What we see is a hot, ionized, nearly uniform plasma consisting of photons, charged nuclei and separate electrons. As time goes on, the plasma is expanding and cooling.

When you look at the sun, you see a round ball with an apparently sharp edge. But the sun is not a solid object with a well defined surface. Instead, it is a bag of mostly hydrogen gas held together by gravity. It is hottest at the center and cools off as you go out from the center. At what appears to us to be the surface, the temperature has dropped to about 3,000 kelvin.

At a temperature above 3,000 kelvin, hydrogen gas becomes ionized, a state where an appreciable fraction of the electrons are torn free from the proton nuclei. When the gas is ionized, it is opaque because photons can interact directly with the free charges present in the gas. Below a temperature of 3,000 kelvin, hydrogen consists essentially of neutral atoms which are unaffected by visible light. As a result the cooler hydrogen gas is transparent. The apparent surface of the sun marks the abrupt transition from an opaque plasma, at temperatures above 3,000K, to a transparent gas at temperatures below 3,000K.

A similar transition takes place in the early universe. By the age of about 700,000 years, the universe cools to a temperature of 3,000K. Before that, the universe is an opaque plasma like the inside of the sun. The photons in thermal equilibrium with the matter particles have enough energy to bust up any complete atoms and any gravitational clumps that are trying to form.

When the universe drops to a temperature below 3,000 kelvin, the hydrogen gas forms neutral atoms and becomes transparent. (The 25% helium had already become neutral some time earlier). As a result the universe suddenly becomes transparent, and the thermal photons decouple from matter.

From this decoupling on, there is essentially no interaction between the thermal photons and any form of matter. All that happens to the photons is that their wavelength is stretched by the expansion of the universe. This stretching preserves the blackbody spectrum of the photons while lowering the effective blackbody temperature. This blackbody spectrum is now at the temperature of 2.73 kelvin, as observed by the 1992 COBE satellite.

When the matter particles are decoupled, freed from the constant bombardment of the cosmic photons, gravity can begin the work of clumping up matter to form stars, globular clusters, black holes and galaxies. All these structures start to form after the decoupling, after the universe is 300,000 years old. It is this formation of stars and galaxies that we see as we run the tape forward to our present day.

Looking out with ever more powerful telescopes is essentially equivalent to running our videotape backwards. The farther out we look, the farther back in time we see. Images from the Hubble telescope are giving us a view back toward the early universe when galaxies were very much younger and quite different than they are today. The most distant galaxy we have identified so far emitted light when the universe was 5% of its current size.

What happens when we build still more powerful telescopes and look still farther back? When we look out so far that the universe is only 300,000 years old, we are looking at the universe that has just become transparent. *We can see no farther!* To look farther is like trying to look down inside the surface of the sun.

In fact we do not need a more powerful telescope to see this far back. The three degree cosmic background radiation gives us a fantastically clear, detailed photograph of the universe at the instant it went transparent.

The horn antenna used by Penzias and Wilson was the first device to look at a small piece of this photograph. The COBE satellite looked at the whole photograph, but with rather limited resolution. COBE detected some very tiny lumpiness, temperature variations of about one part in 100,000. This lumpiness may have been what gravity needed to start forming galaxies. A higher resolution photograph will be needed to tell for sure.

Update

The small temperature variations have been the subject of intense study in the 18 years since the first COBE satellite. One of the discoveries is that the variations arose mostly from resonant acoustic oscillations in the very early universe. The oscillations are caused by a competition between photon pressure trying to push particles apart, and gravity trying to pull them together.

From these studies, we have learned some amazing details. For example, in 1990, it was known that the age of the universe was somewhere between 11 billion and 20 billion years. Now our best estimate for the age of the universe is $13.7 \pm .2$ billion years. What an improvement!

Guidebooks

We ran the videotape quite rapidly without looking at many details. Our focus has been on the formation of the elements and the three degree radiation, two of the main pieces of evidence for the existence of a big bang. We have omitted a number of fascinating details such as how dense was the early universe, when did the neutrinos decouple from matter, and what happened before the first frame? There are excellent guidebooks that accompany this tape where you can find these details. There is Weinberg's *The First Three Minutes* which we have mentioned. The 1993 edition has an addendum that introduces some ideas about the very, very early universe, when the universe was millions of times younger and hotter than the first frame. Perhaps the best guidebook to how mankind came to our current picture of the universe is the book by Timothy Ferris *Coming of Age in the Milky Way*. Despite the title, this is one of the most fascinating and readable accounts available. In our discussion we have drawn much from Weinberg and Ferris.

CHAPTER 26 REVIEW

In the previous chapter we used the two slit experiment and diffraction gratings to demonstrate that light was a wave phenomenon. In this chapter we find that light consists of particles called photons that have an energy given by Einstein's photoelectric effect formula

$$E = hf = \frac{hc}{\lambda} \tag{3,6}$$

where h is Planck's constant, f is the frequency and λ the wavelength of the light wave. How light could have both a wave and a particle nature is the subject of the next seven chapters.

Photon Mass

From Einstein's formula $E = mc^2$ we deduce that the mass of a photon is given by

$$E_{photon} = \frac{hc}{\lambda} = m_{photon}c^2$$

$$m_{photon} = \frac{h}{\lambda c} \tag{10}$$

This raises an interesting question about the rest mass of a photon. Einstein's mass formula

$$m = \frac{m_0}{\sqrt{1 - v^2/c^2}} \tag{6-14}$$

*implies that an object moving **at** the speed of light (v = c) should have a mass*

$$m = \frac{m_0}{\sqrt{1 - 1}} = \frac{m_0}{0} \tag{12}$$

which is usually an infinite number. The only way to avoid the infinity is if the photon's rest mass m_0 is also zero, giving

$$m_{photon} = \frac{(m_0)_{photon}}{0} = \frac{0}{0}$$

a ratio that can be any number you want. Thus the Einstein mass formula does not cause a problem if the photon's rest mass is exactly zero.

Photon Momentum

That photons carry momentum was demonstrated in the Compton Scattering experiment discussed on page 26-14, where a photon collided with an electron, and linear momentum was conserved in the collision. The formula for the photon's momentum is simply its mass $m_{photon} = h/\lambda c$ times its speed c giving us

$$\boxed{p_{photon} = \frac{h}{\lambda}} \tag{13}$$

This will turn out to be a very important result.

Calculating Photon Energies

To use the Einstein photon energy formula $E = hf = hc/\lambda$, it is often more convenient to replace joules and meters with electron volts (eV) for energy and nanometers (nm) for length. When we convert $E = hc/\lambda$ to eV and nanometers, we get

$$E_{photon}(in\ eV) = \frac{1240\ eV\ nm}{\lambda(in\ nm)} \tag{8}$$

As an example of using Equation (8), we found that the red line in the hydrogen spectrum had a wavelength λ = 656 nanometers. Thus the photons in that red light had an energy

$$E_{red\ hydrogen\ photons} = \frac{1240\ eV\ nm}{656\ nm} = 1.89\ eV$$

All visible photons have energies in the range from about 1.8 eV in the red up to about 3 eV in the blue.

If a photon is particularly energetic, about 100 million eV, it can do things like creating an electron-positron pair, an example of which was shown in Figure (7) on page 26-16.

Photons and Gravity

Because photons have mass, they are affected by gravity. In an experiment performed at Harvard University in 1960, photons were dropped down a vertical shaft 22 meters high. As the photons fell, they gained energy much like a falling rock. A rock falling down a shaft gains speed and increases its kinetic energy $1/2\,mv^2$. Since a photon always travels at the same speed c, the gravitational potential energy $m_{photon}gy$ released by the falling photon goes, instead, into increasing the photon's frequency f.

Photons passing the rim of a star can be deflected sideways, a phenomenon leading to the gravitational lensing seen in Figure (9) on page 26-20.

Black Body Radiation and the Early Universe

Plank's constant h, which appears in Einstein's formula $E = hf$ was first introduced by Max Planck to explain the blackbody spectrum. (This is the spectrum of light radiated by a heated object.)

The subject of blackbody radiation has taken on special significance in the study of the early universe. When the universe, which consists mostly of hydrogen, was hotter than 3000 degrees Centigrade, it was opaque like the inside of the sun. At an age of 1/3 of a million years the universe cooled to below 3000 degrees, becoming transparent. At that point, the photons in the universe had a blackbody spectrum corresponding to 3000 degree radiation.

Since that time, the expansion of the universe has stretched the wavelength of this radiation, i.e., cooled the photons, so that they now represent blackbody radiation at a temperature of 2.73 kelvin. A study of this radiation is telling us about the universe when it was a tiny fraction of a second old.

CHAPTER EXERCISES

Exercise 1 0n page 3
Calculate the temperature of a blue star from λ_{max}, then calculate λ_{max} for a stove.

Exercise 2 0n page 9
Calculate the energy of photons from the sun, at λ_{max}.

Exercise 3 0n page 9
Calculate the wavelength of a photon whose energy is the same as the rest mass energy of an electron.

Exercise 4 0n page 10
Calculate the range of energies of the visible photons.

Exercise 5 0n page 10
Exercises on the photoelectric effect.

Exercise 6 0n page 10
What is the energy, in eV, of the predominant photons radiated by human skin?

Exercise 7 0n page 10
Analyze the photons radiated by a 100 watt light bulb.

Exercise 8 0n page 10
How many photons are radiated per second by the radio station WBZ in Boston.?

Exercise 9 0n page 10
Where in the electromagnetic spectrum do we find photons of various energies.

Exercise 10 0n page 10
Calculate the energy, in eV, of the photons in the three visible lines in the hydrogen spectrum.

Exercise 11 0n page 17
Questions on electron-positron annihilation.

Exercise 12 0n page 18
Studying the change in energy of photons dropped down a vertical shaft.

Weighing Photons Using Bathroom Scales, a Thought Experiment

Our article, to appear in THE PHYSICS TEACHER magazine fall, 2009.

Jay Orear, in his introductory physics text[1], defined the weight of a person as the reading one gets when standing on a (properly calibrated) bathroom scales. Here we will use Jay's definition of weight in a thought experiment to measure the weight of a photon. The thought experiment uses the results of the Pound-Rebka-Snider[2,3] experiments and the Compton scattering experiments.

Imagine that we construct two identical cubes made from perfectly reflecting mirrors. The reflecting surface is on the inside. Place the cubes on identical bathroom scales. Leave one cube empty, and in the other cube, insert the photon that is bouncing up and down as shown in Fig.(1).

The results of the Pound-Rebka experiment tell us that when the photon is at the bottom of the cube its frequency will be greater than its frequency at the top by an amount

$$\Delta \nu = \frac{\nu_{top} g y}{c^2} \tag{1}$$

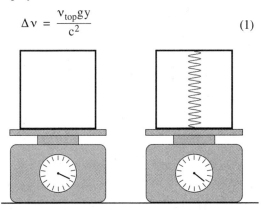

Fig. 1. Two identical cubes made from mirrors are set on identical bathroom scales. A photon is bouncing up and down in one of the cubes.

where ν_{top} is the frequency of the photon at the top of the cube, g the acceleration due to gravity and y the height of the cube. The Pound-Rebka-Snider experiments verified Eq.(1) to an accuracy of 1% in experiments on photons traveling down and up a seven story high shaft.

The Compton effect experiments demonstrate that a photon of frequency ν carries a momentum $p = h\nu/c$. When the photon bounces perpendicularly off a reflecting surface, it transfers an amount of momentum Δp given by

$$\Delta p = \frac{2h\nu}{c}$$

Since the photon bouncing in our cube has a slightly higher frequency when bouncing off the bottom surface, it will transfer slightly more momentum to the bottom surface than the top surface. The net momentum transferred to the cube in one complete bounce up and down is

$$\Delta p_{net} = \frac{2h\nu_{bottom}}{c} - \frac{2h\nu_{top}}{c}$$

$$= \frac{2h\Delta\nu}{c}$$

The time Δt for one complete bounce up and down is

$$\Delta t = \frac{2y}{c}$$

Thus the average momentum per second the photon transfers to the cube is

$$\frac{\Delta p}{\Delta t} = \frac{2h\Delta\nu}{c} \times \frac{c}{2y} = \frac{h\Delta\nu}{y} \tag{2}$$

By Newton's second law, this average momentum transfer per second is the average downward force F_g that the photon exerts on the cube. We use the subscript g to represent the fact that this average force is caused by the effect of gravity acting on the photon. This force F_g is the additional force the bathroom scales should measure due to the presence of the photon, and thus by Orear's definition, the weight of the photon.

Using Eqs. (1) and (2) and Newton's second law, we get

$$F_g = \frac{\Delta p}{\Delta t} = \frac{h\Delta \nu}{y}$$

$$= \frac{h}{y} \frac{\nu_{top} g y}{c^2} = h\nu_{top}\left(\frac{g}{c^2}\right)$$

$$F_g = \left(\frac{E_{top}}{c^2}\right) g \qquad (3)$$

where $E_{top} = h\nu_{top}$ is the photon energy at the top of the cube.

If we say that the weight F_g is equal to the gravitational mass m_g times g, Eq. (3) tells us that the photon's gravitational mass is

$$m_g = \frac{E_{top}}{c^2} g \; ; \quad E_{top} = m_g c^2 \qquad (4)$$

In the equations $E = mc^2$ and $p = mv$, the m is the inertial mass of the object. Thus we have just seen that for a photon, an object that is pure kinetic energy, its inertial and gravitational masses are equal. This equality was the essential result of the Eötvos experiments.

References

1. Jay Orear, *Physics.* (John Wiley & Sons., New York, 1961.)

2. Pound, R. V.; Rebka Jr. G. A. *Physical Review Letters* **3** (9): 439-441 (November 1959).

3. Pound, R. V.; Snider J. L. *Physical Review Letters* **13** (18): 539-540 (November 1964).

4. For a related discussion of weight caused by momentum transfer, see the analysis of the weight of an hourglass in Ian H. Redmount and Richard H. Price, "The Weight of Time," *Phys. Teach.* **36** 432-434 (October 1998).

NOTE

In Essay 3, following Chapter 11, we introduced the momentum form of Newton's second law. The result, given in Equation (3-3) was

$$\vec{F}_{net} = \frac{\vec{p}_2 - \vec{p}_1}{\Delta t} = \frac{\Delta\vec{p}}{\Delta t} \qquad (3)$$

where $\vec{F}_{net}$ is the amount of momentum $(\vec{p}_2 - \vec{p}_1)$ transferred in the time Δt.

Chapter 27 non calculus

Bohr Theory of Hydrogen

The hydrogen atom played a special role in the history of physics by providing the key that unlocked the new mechanics that replaced Newtonian mechanics. It started with Johann Balmer's discovery in 1884 of a mathematical formula for the wavelengths of some of the spectral lines emitted by hydrogen. The simplicity of the formula suggested that some understandable mechanisms were producing these lines.

The next step was Rutherford's discovery of the atomic nucleus in 1912. After that, one knew the basic structure of atoms—a positive nucleus surrounded by negative electrons. Within a year Neils Bohr had a model of the hydrogen atom that "explained" the spectral lines. Bohr introduced a new concept— the **energy level**. The electron in hydrogen had certain allowed energy levels, and the sharp spectral lines were emitted when the electron jumped from one energy level to another. To explain the energy levels, Bohr developed a model in which the electron had certain allowed orbits, and the jump between energy levels corresponded to the electron moving from one allowed orbit to another.

Bohr's allowed orbits followed from Newtonian mechanics and the Coulomb force law, with one small but crucial modification of Newtonian mechanics. The angular momentum of the electron could not vary continuously, it had to have special values, be quantized in units of Planck's constant divided by 2π, namely $h/2\pi$. In Bohr's theory, the different allowed orbits corresponded to orbits with different allowed values of angular momentum.

Again we see Planck's constant appearing at just the point where Newtonian mechanics is breaking down. There is no way one can explain, from Newtonian mechanics, why the electrons in the hydrogen atom could have only specific quantized values of angular momentum. While Bohr's model of hydrogen represented only a slight modification of Newtonian mechanics, it represented a major philosophical shift. Newtonian mechanics could no longer be considered the basic theory governing the behavior of particles and matter. Something had to replace Newtonian mechanics, but from the time of Bohr's theory in 1913 until 1924, no one knew what the new theory would be.

In 1924, a French graduate student, Louis de Broglie, made a crucial suggestion that was the key that led to the new mechanics. This suggestion was quickly followed up by Schrödinger and Heisenberg who developed the new mechanics called **quantum mechanics**. In this chapter we will focus on Bohr's theory, with de Broglie's hypothesis being the subject of the next chapter.

A CLASSICAL PICTURE OF THE HYDROGEN ATOM

With Rutherford's discovery of the atomic nucleus in 1912, it became clear that the hydrogen atom consisted of a negative electron and a much more massive positive particle that later became known as the proton. Because a complete hydrogen atom is electrically neutral, if we call the charge on the electron (–e), then the charge on the proton must be +e. As a result these particles should attract each other with a force of magnitude F_e given by Coulomb's law in Equation (17-1). The result is

$$F_e = K\frac{Q_{electron}Q_{proton}}{r^2} = K\frac{e^2}{r^2} \qquad (17\text{-}1)$$

where K is the electrical force constant and r is the separation of the particles.

Because of the close analogy between the Coulomb force in Equation (17-1) and Newton's law of gravity $F_g = Gm_1m_2/r^2$, we should expect that the electron should be in a Kepler orbit about the massive proton in much the same way that the planets move in Kepler orbits about the massive sun.

We talked about this analogy back in Chapter 17 when we introduced Coulomb's law. We pointed out that in the hydrogen atom, we did not have to deal with complex distributions of electrical charge. Here we had an example of a pure Coulomb force between two point-like particles. We made the analogy to a gravitational system in Figure (17-3) reproduced here,

where we compare Jupiter in its nearly circular orbit about the sun with an electron in a circular orbit about a proton.

However, there is a problem with the analogy shown in Figure (17-3). To see what the problem is, compare the front and side views of the electron in its circular orbit, as shown in Figure (1). In the side view we have the proton sitting essentially at rest while the electron oscillates up and down. This picture is not too dissimilar to Figures (24-2) and (24-3) that we drew back in Chapter 24, showing a radio wave antenna. There we saw that a negative charge oscillating up and down in a wire would radiate an electromagnetic wave. This was a direct consequence of Maxwell's equations.

If we apply Maxwell's equations to the oscillating electron in Figure (1b), we make the same prediction. Each time the electron appears to go up and down once, it should radiate one wavelength of an electromagnetic wave as the oscillating charge did in Figure (24-5). As a result, the frequency of the radiated wave should be the same as the frequency of the oscillation or rotation of the electron in its orbit.

This leads to a problem with this classical picture of the hydrogen atom. A radio station has to supply energy to keep its antenna broadcasting, because the emitted radio waves carry out energy. Similarly, the electron in hydrogen should radiate a wave that should suck energy out of the electron.

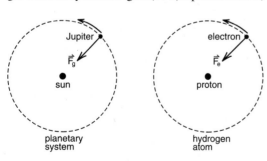

planetary system   hydrogen atom

Figure 17-3
Classical picture of the hydrogen atom.

a) electron in circular orbit   b) side view of circular orbit

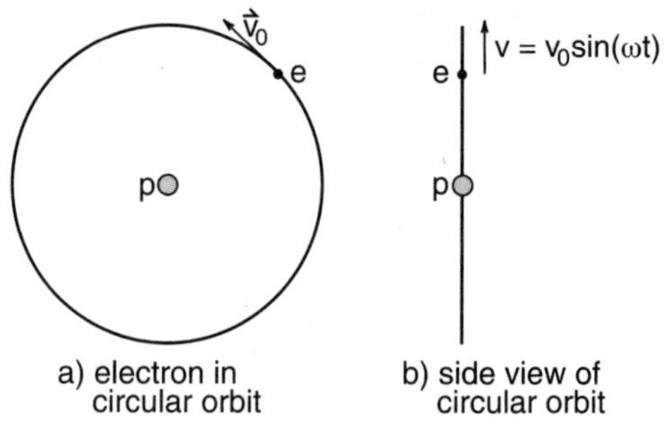

Figure 1
The side view of circular motion is an up and down oscillation.

To see what should happen to the electron if it continually loses energy, consider the analogy to a satellite in low earth orbit. If the orbit is too low, the satellite is moving through the earth's thin upper atmosphere, and starts losing energy due to friction. As the satellite loses energy, it falls down to a lower orbit where it encounters a more dense atmosphere and loses energy at a faster rate. This process continues until the satellite either burns up or crashes into earth.

A similar fate awaits the electron in the hydrogen atom, if Maxwell's equations apply. As the electron radiates energy, it should spiral down closer and closer to the proton, orbiting faster and faster, radiating higher and higher frequency light. There has to come a time when the electron crashes into the proton and we no longer have a hydrogen atom.

Thus the *very existence of hydrogen* atoms, where the electron has not crashed, is a conclusive demonstration that Newtonian mechanics together with Maxwell's theory does not work for hydrogen.

This classical theory is not completely wrong. Hydrogen atoms do radiate light. We saw that light in our experiment in Chapter 25 where we studied the hydrogen spectrum shown in Figure (25-26) reproduced here. But that experiment raises two problems with the classical theory. First of all, we had to heat the hydrogen to get it to radiate light. We saw no light when the hydrogen tube cooled to room temperature. Even harder to explain was the fact that we saw three discrete spectral lines. Nowhere in the classical theory is there any way to explain why the atom radiates these distinct frequencies.

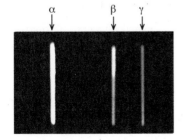

Figure 25-26
Visible spectrum of hydrogen.

OUTLINE OF THE BOHR THEORY

Within a year of the time Rutherford discovered the atomic nucleus, Neils Bohr in 1913 came up with a theory that explained many features of the hydrogen atom. Basically what Bohr did was to see how he could modify classical physics in order to explain the behavior of the hydrogen atom.

His first step was to assume that the electron could exist only in certain allowed orbits that had definite energies. When an electron was in an allowed orbit, it did not radiate light. Only when an electron fell from a higher energy orbit to a lower energy orbit did it radiate light. The light was emitted as a single photon whose energy was precisely equal to the energy lost in the fall to a lower energy orbit. This scheme provides an explanation of why the electron radiates distinct spectral lines. The photons coming out of the atom could only have energies corresponding to the energy differences between allowed orbits.

One of the most successful parts of Bohr's theory is that the formula for the electron energies in the allowed orbits is so simple. Expressed in terms of electron volts (eV), it is

$$E_n = \frac{-13.6}{n^2} \text{ eV} \tag{1}$$

where n is an integer starting at n = 1, then n = 2, on up to as large a value as you want.

The lowest, most negative, energy orbit is the n = 1 orbit with an energy

$$E_1 = \frac{-13.6}{1^2} = -13.6 \text{ eV} \tag{2}$$

This is the orbit occupied by all the hydrogen atoms in a cold bottle of hydrogen.

To get the atoms to radiate light, you have to heat them so that some atoms are kicked up into a higher energy orbit. Then light is radiated as the electrons fall back down into lower energy orbits.

Let us consider an example. The three orbits with the lowest energy, have energies

$$E_1 = \frac{-13.6}{1^2} = -13.6 \text{ eV}$$

$$E_2 = \frac{-13.6}{2^2} = -3.40 \text{ eV}$$

$$E_3 = \frac{-13.6}{3^2} = -1.51 \text{ eV} \qquad (3)$$

Suppose an electron is kicked up into the E_3 orbit with an energy –1.51 eV. There are two ways this electron can lose energy. One is to fall all the way down to the –13.6 eV orbit. The other is to stop at the –3.40 eV orbit.

For this example, suppose the electron stops at the E_2, –3.40 eV orbit. The energy it loses in falling from the E_3 to the E_2 orbit is

$$E\,(3 \rightarrow 2) = E_3 - E_2$$
$$= -1.51 \text{ eV} - (-3.40 \text{ eV})$$
$$= (+3.40 - 1.51) \text{ eV}$$
$$= 1.89 \text{ eV} \qquad (4)$$

Back in our discussion of photons in Chapter 26, we gave you the homework exercise to use Einstein's photoelectric formula

$$E_{photon} = hf = \frac{hc}{\lambda} \qquad (26\text{-}6)$$

or the more convenient formula, in terms of eV and nanometers (nm),

$$E_{photon}(\text{in eV}) = \frac{hc}{\lambda} = \frac{1240 \text{ eV nm}}{\lambda(\text{in nm})} \qquad (26\text{-}8)$$

to calculate the energies of the photons in the three spectral lines whose wavelengths were observed to be

$$\lambda_\alpha \quad (\text{red}) = 656 \text{ nm}$$
$$\lambda_\beta \quad (\text{blue}) = 486 \text{ nm}$$
$$\lambda_\gamma \quad (\text{violet}) = 434 \text{ nm} \qquad (25\text{-}5)$$

The answers you should have gotten immediately from Equation (26-8), were

$$E_\alpha = 1.89 \text{ eV} \quad (\text{red})$$
$$E_\beta = 2.55 \text{ eV} \quad (\text{blue}) \qquad (5)$$
$$E_\gamma = 2.86 \text{ eV} \quad (\text{violet})$$

Comparing the photon energies in Equation (5) with the predicted photon energy in Equation (4), we see that when the electron falls from the E_3 orbit to the E_2 orbit, it emits the red photon we saw in the hydrogen spectra.

Exercise 1

Calculate the energy of the photon the electron radiates when the electron falls from the second E_2 orbit down to the lowest energy E_1 orbit. Explain why we do not see these photons. (Hint, we can barely see the violet photon whose energy is only 2.86 eV. What part of the electromagnetic spectrum do you find photons with still more energy?).

Exercise 2

Use Bohr's energy formula $E_n = -13.6/n^2 \text{ eV}$ to tell what orbital jumps explain hydrogen's blue line with a wavelength $\lambda_\beta = 486 \text{ nm}$, and hydrogen's violet line with a wavelength $\lambda_\gamma = 434 \text{ nm}$.

In the next section on hydrogen energy levels, we take a look at all possible jumps the electron can make if the allowed energies are given by Bohr's formula $E_n = -13.6/n^2 \text{ eV}$. There are many spectral lines radiated by hydrogen. We saw some of them in the spectrum of a hydrogen star in Figure (25-28). It turns out that Bohr's formula explains every line.

Bohr went beyond his energy formula to find out how Newtonian mechanics had to be modified in order to get his allowed orbits. (He had already modified Maxwell's theory by saying that electrons in allowed orbits do not radiate.) In the last part of this chapter, we will see that the modification to Newtonian mechanics involved the electron's angular momentum.

BOHR'S ENERGY LEVEL DIAGRAM

Figure (2) is a sketch showing the five lowest energy, smallest radius, Bohr orbits. On this sketch we have drawn arrows showing the three jumps that produce the three visible spectral lines radiated by hydrogen. If you did Exercise (1) correctly, you found that the blue hydrogen line was emitted in a jump from the $E_4 = -.850$ eV to the $E_2 = -3.40$ eV level. The violet line resulted from a jump from the E_5 to the E_2 level.

You can also see the problems involved in trying to draw all the allowed orbits. To explain the three visible lines, we have to draw five orbits. Imagine how many orbits you would have to draw to explain all the spectral lines radiated by the hydrogen star whose spectra was shown back in Figure (25-28).

Instead of trying to draw the orbits, it is easier to draw what we call an *energy level diagram*. This is a diagram where the vertical axis represents the electron energy, and short horizontal lines are placed at the energies of the allowed orbits. Figure (3) is the energy level diagram that represents Bohr's energy formula $E_n = -13.6/n^2$ eV .

The lowest energy level E_1 is down at –13.6 eV. The level E_2 is at $-13.6/4 = -3.40$ eV. As we go up, the energy levels get closer together. We have an infinite series of them ending up at $E_\infty = 0$. Above the zero energy level, when the electron's total energy has become positive, the electron has escaped from the hydrogen atom and there are no more allowed orbits.

The three jumps producing the visible spectral lines are again shown as arrows in Figure (3). The advantage of the energy level diagram is that now the length of the arrows represents the amount of energy the electron loses and the photon carries out. Thus energy level diagrams make it easy to relate allowed energy levels to the spectra of the radiated photons.

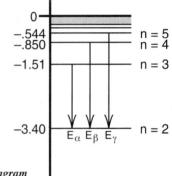

Figure 3
Energy level diagram for the hydrogen atom. All the energy levels are given by the formula $E_n = -13.6/n^2 eV$. The 3 jumps shown give rise to the three visible hydrogen lines.

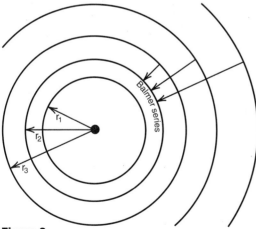

Figure 2
The Bohr orbits are determined by calculating the orbital radius of an electron in a circular classical orbit of energy $E_n = -13.6/n^2$.

The Balmer Series

The three visible hydrogen lines are part of the series of lines that end at the n = 2 energy level as shown in Figure (4). These lines are called the ***Balmer series*** because the Swiss school teacher, Johann Balmer, deduced a formula for the wavelengths of this set of lines. Balmer's formula, given in Equation (25-6) is somewhat complex and a bit hard to explain. But with Bohr's energy level diagram, the explanation is simple. All you need is the formula $E_n = -13.6/n^2 \, eV$ and the statement that all of Balmer's lines correspond to jumps down to the second, n = 2 energy level.

In Figure (25-28), showing the spectrum of a hydrogen star, we see ultraviolet photon lines labeled from H9 up to H40. The H9 line, at a wavelength of 384 nanometers results from the jump down from the n = 9 to the n = 2 energy level. Similarly the H10 line, with a wavelength of 380 nm results from a jump down from the n = 10 to the n = 2 level.

Exercise 3

(a) In the hydrogen spectrum, the spectral lines get closer and closer together as we approach the H40 line. Calculate the energy of the H40 line (a jump from n = 40 to n = 2), convert that to nanometers, and see how close your result comes to the experimental value shown in the hydrogen spectrum of Figure (25-28).

(b) Explain why the lines get closer and closer together as we approach H40 in the hydrogen star spectrum.

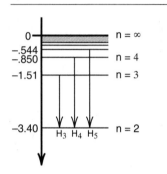

Figure 4
The Balmer Series.

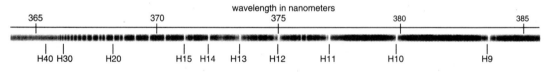

wavelength in nanometers

Figure 25-28
Spectrum of the star HD193182, showing ultraviolet hydrogen lines near the limit of the Balmer series.

The Lyman and Paschen Series

From our discussions of the Balmer series, we know that when the hydrogen atom emits one of the visible lines, it leaves the electron up in the n = 2 energy level. Once we shut off the power to the hydrogen tube, and the hydrogen inside has cooled, all the atoms are in their lowest energy n = 1, or –13.6 eV, level. This is called the ***ground state***. To get to the ground state from the n = 2, –3.40 eV level, the electron must emit a photon whose energy is

$$\left.\begin{array}{l}\text{energy from}\\ \text{n = 2 \ to}\\ \text{n = 1 \ jump}\end{array}\right\} \begin{array}{l}= (13.6 - 3.40)\,\text{eV}\\[4pt] = 10.2\,\text{eV}\end{array}$$

Since the highest energy photon we can see is the violet 3 eV photon, these photons have much too much energy to see, and lie in what we call the ***ultraviolet*** part of the spectrum.

Figure (5) shows some of the jumps directly down to the ground state. The series of spectral lines we get from these jumps is called the ***Lyman Series***. You can see that all the photons emitted in these jumps have an energy equal to or greater than 10.2 eV, and thus are ultraviolet.

In Figure (6) we show some of the jumps down to the n = 3 level. Photons emitted in these jumps produce spectral lines in what is called the ***Paschen Series***. All of these jumps are shorter than any Balmer Series jumps, and the corresponding photons have lower energy and longer wavelengths than the longest wavelength red light we can see. As a result, all of the lines are in the invisible ***infrared*** part of the spectrum.

Jumps down to higher levels such as n = 4, 5, etc. are still shorter jumps, and produce less energetic photons that have longer infrared wavelengths.

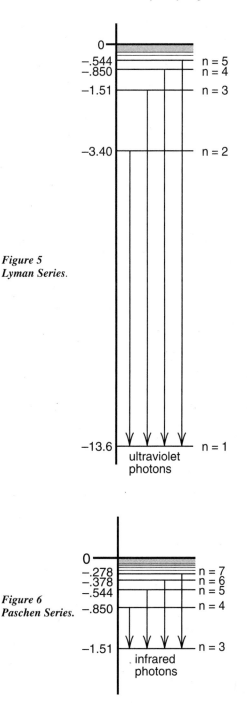

Figure 5
Lyman Series.

Figure 6
Paschen Series.

BOHR ORBITS

To find a reason for the allowed energy levels $E_n = -13.6/n^2$ eV, Bohr went back to a simple mechanical model. That was the picture of an electron in a circular orbit about the nucleus, in analogy to the nearly circular orbits of the planets about the sun, as shown in Figure (17-3). The electric force binding the electron to the nucleus has a magnitude

$$F_e = \frac{KQ_1Q_2}{r^2} = \frac{Ke^2}{r^2} \qquad \text{(17-1 and 17-13)}$$

where r is the radius of the orbit and e is the magnitude of the charge on both the nucleus (proton) and the electron. The analogous gravitational force is

$$F_g = \frac{GM_1M_2}{r^2} \qquad \text{(8-10)}$$

Due to the similarity of the two force laws, we only have to replace GM_1M_2 by KQ_1Q_2 to translate a result from a gravitational calculation to an electric calculation. We did this in the appendix to Chapter 17 and found that the total energy of an electron in a circular orbit around a proton was given by the formula

$$E_{total} = -\frac{Ke^2}{2r} \qquad \text{(17-18)}$$

where the total energy is the sum of the electron's positive kinetic energy and negative potential energy. The fact that the electron's total energy is negative tells us that an electron in a circular orbit does not have enough kinetic energy to overcome the negative potential energy and escape from the atom.

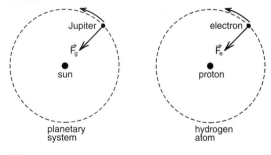

Figure 17-3 (repeated)
Classical picture of the hydrogen atom.

The Ground State

If you have a bottle of cold (room temperature) hydrogen gas, all the atoms are in their lowest energy state which is called the ***ground state***. In Bohr's theory, this is when the electron is in its smallest orbit where its total energy is –13.6 eV. If we convert –13.6 eV to joules, and use the MKS value of K, Equation (17-18) should allow us to calculate the radius r, in meters, of the lowest energy orbit. This should give us an estimate of the size of a ground state hydrogen atom. We will have you do this exercise now.

Exercise 4

The MKS values of the electrical force constant K and the electron charge e are

$$K = 9.00 \times 10^9$$

$$e = 1.60 \times 10^{-19}$$

and the conversion factor from electron volts to joules is

$$1.60 \times 10^{-19} \frac{\text{joules}}{\text{eV}}$$

Use these values in Equation (17-18) to calculate the radius of the smallest Bohr orbit.

The Bohr Radius

If you just did Exercise (4) you should have found that the radius of the –13.6 eV orbit, a distance called the ***Bohr radius***, has the value

$$\boxed{\begin{array}{l} \textit{Bohr} \\ \textit{radius} \end{array} \quad r_{Bohr} = .529 \times 10^{-10} \text{ meters}} \qquad (6)$$

If you double the Bohr radius you find that the diameter of the Bohr orbit is about 10^{-10} meters or 0.1 nanometers. (The length 10^{-10} meters is also called an angstrom, denoted by the symbol Å.) This turns out to be approximately the size of all ground state atoms. This tells you that the current nanotechnology, which is working with objects as small as 10 nanometers, involves objects only about 100 atoms across!

The Other Bohr Orbits

Bohr's formula $E_n = E_1/n^2$ tells us that there should be a whole series of orbits with less negative energy than the ground state. To see what these orbits are, we start with the energy formulas

$$E_1 = -\frac{Ke^2}{2r_1}; \quad E_n = -\frac{Ke^2}{2r_n} \quad (7)$$

Then the relationship $E_n = E_1/n^2$ becomes

$$E_n = \frac{E_1}{n^2}$$

$$-\frac{Ke^2}{2r_n} = -\frac{1}{n^2}\frac{Ke^2}{2r_1} \quad (8)$$

Most of the terms cancel in Equation (8) and we are left with

$$r_n = n^2 r_1 \quad (9)$$

Thus we see that the higher energy Bohr orbits increase in size as n^2. The second orbit is 4 times as large as the first, the third 9 times larger, etc. This is the way we should have drawn the orbits back in Figure (2), but we did not have room to do so.

While the Bohr orbit picture is not the current picture of atomic structure, the result that the size of the excited states of hydrogen increase rapidly in size is a correct result.

Angular Momentum

Perhaps the most important result of the Bohr theory comes when we calculate the angular mometum of the electron in the various orbits. The result, which is particularly simple, takes several steps to calculate. The answer is that if L_1 is the electron's angular momentum in the lowest energy, smallest orbit, then the angular momentum L_n in the n'th orbit is

$$\boxed{L_n = nL_1} \quad (10)$$

This implies that L_1 is some kind of a basic unit of angular momentum, and the allowed orbits are those that have multiple numbers of this basic unit.

To derive Equation (10). we go back to Chapter 7 where we found that the formula for the angular momentum of a particle of mass m, traveling at a speed v in a circle of radius r was

$$L = mvr \quad (7\text{-}11)$$

which is the momentum (mv) times the lever arm (r).

To calculate the angular momentum, we need to know the electron's speed v. We can get this directly from Newton's second law $\vec{F} = m\vec{a}$ with the magnitude of $\vec{F}$ being the coulomb force $F_e = Ke^2/r^2$ and $\vec{a}$ having a magnitude $a = v^2/r$ for a particle moving in a circle. Since both $\vec{F}$ and $\vec{a}$ point toward the center of the circle, we can equate magnitudes getting

$$F_e = ma; \quad \frac{Ke^2}{r^2} = \frac{mv^2}{r} \quad (11)$$

One of the r's cancels and we are left with

$$mv^2 = \frac{Ke^2}{r}; \quad v = \sqrt{\frac{Ke^2}{mr}} \quad (12)$$

Equation (12) tells us that as the orbital radius r increases, the speed v decreases. If an electron is in the nth orbit, its speed v_n will be

$$v_n = \sqrt{\frac{Ke^2}{mr_n}} \quad (13)$$

But $r_n = n^2 r_1$, thus v_n is

$$v_n = \sqrt{\frac{Ke^2}{m(n^2 r_1)}} = \frac{1}{n}\sqrt{\frac{Ke^2}{mr_1}}$$

$$v_n = \frac{v_1}{n} \quad (14)$$

and we see that the orbital speeds decrease as $1/n$.

When we use $v_n = v_1/n$, and $r_n = n^2 r_1$ in a formula for the angular momentum $L_n = mv_n r_n$, we get

$$L_n = mv_n r_n = m\frac{v_1}{n}(n^2 r_1) \quad (15)$$

One of the factors of n cancels and we are left with

$$L_n = n(mv_1 r_1) \quad (16)$$

Since $(mv_1 r_1)$ is the electron's ground state orbital angular momentum L_1 we get our predicted result

$$\boxed{L_n = nL_1} \quad (10)$$

This is such an important result, that we do not mind putting it in a box twice.

As we mentioned, Equation (10) tells us that the orbital angular momentum increases in steps of size L_1 as we go to larger orbits. There are no orbits except those that have an integer number of this angular momentum L_1. For some reason, other values of angular momentum do not appear.

THE UNIT OF ANGULAR MOMENTUM

Equation (10) tells us that there is something special about the angular momentum L_1 of the electron in its smallest orbit. Let us calculate the magnitude of L_1 to see if we can find something special about its value. We have you do that in the following exercise.

Exercise 5

Using the formula for v_1

$$v_1 = \sqrt{\frac{Ke^2}{mr_1}} \qquad (14a)$$

where r_1 is the Bohr radius calculated in Exercise (4), and using the MKS values

$K = 9.00 \times 10^9$

$e = 1.60 \times 10^{-19} \dfrac{\text{joules}}{\text{eV}}$

$m = 9.11 \times 10^{-31} \text{kg}$ (electron mass)

calculate L_1.

The answer to Exercise (5) is

$$L_1 = 1.05 \times 10^{-34} \frac{\text{kg meters}^2}{\text{second}} \qquad (17)$$

where the dimensions (kg meters^2/second) come from $L_1 = m(kg) \times v_1(\text{meter/sec}) \times r_1(\text{meter})$.

At first sight you may think that the number 10^{-34} is ridiculously small. Is there any other quantity in physics that small? The answer is, yes! It is Planck's constant h.

$$h = 6.63 \times 10^{-34} \text{ joule seconds} \qquad (26\text{-}4)$$

which appeared in Einstein's formula for the energy of a photon of frequency f

$$E_{photon} = hf \qquad (26\text{-}3)$$

As we showed in Chapter 26 (page 26-8), the dimensions (joule seconds) is the same as the dimensions of angular momentum (kg meters^2/second). Thus there is a quantity in physics, that has the dimensions of angular momentum, and is nearly as small as Bohr's unit of angular momentum L_1.

Exercise 6

Show that the formula E = hf gives (joule seconds) for the dimensions of h. Then show that (joule seconds) is the same as (kg meters^2/second).

We have seen that L_1 and h are close. Is there a simple precise relationship between them? The answer is

$$L_1 = \frac{h}{2\pi} = \frac{6.63 \times 10^{-34}}{6.28} = 1.05 \times 10^{-34} \qquad (18)$$

The quantity $h/2\pi$ appears so often in physics that it is denoted by a special symbol, namely h with a bar over it, $\hbar$, called **h bar**.

SUMMARY

The easiest way to explain Bohr's model of hydrogen is to say that the electron in hydrogen obeys Newton's laws, except that the electron's angular momentum is restricted to integer values of $\hbar$. Or using a more modern terminology, the electron's orbiting angular momentum is **quantized** in units of size $\hbar$. The main problem with the model is that it gives no explanation of why the angular momentum is quantized. That explanation was provided eleven years later by the graduate student Louis de Broglie. De Broglie's explanation is the subject of the next chapter.

It is worth noting that Bohr's model was the third example of a successful modification or correction to nineteenth century physics. The first was Planck's formula for blackbody radiation which Planck introduced in 1900. Then in 1905 Einstein explained the photoelectric effect. And in 1913 Bohr explained the hydrogen spectrum. In all three cases, classical physics failed, and all three corrections involved Planck's constant h or $\hbar$. The appearance of Planck's constant had become a clear indicator that something new was involved.

CHAPTER 27 REVIEW

There are a few basic steps in the Bohr theory. The first was Bohr's observation that the entire spectrum of hydrogen could be explained in terms of a simple set of allowed energy levels E_n given by the formula

$$E_n = -\frac{13.6\ eV}{n^2}$$

In ordinary room temperature hydrogen gas, the electrons in all the atoms are in the lowest energy $n = 1$ state with a total energy of –13.6 eV

When you heat hydrogen, some of the electrons are kicked up into a higher energy state, like the $n = 2$ state with an energy $E_2 = E_1/2^2 = -3.40 eV$, or the $n = 3$ state with an energy $E_3 = E_1/3^2 = -1.51 eV$.

Hydrogen emits light when an electron falls from a higher to a lower energy state, emitting a photon that carries out the energy lost by the electron. For example, when the electron falls from the E_3 to the E_2 state, the electron's energy drops from –1.51 eV to –3.40 eV, losing (3.40 – 1.51) eV = 1.89 eV. This is the energy of the red photons in the hydrogen H_α line we saw in the hydrogen spectrum. All the lines in the Balmer series spectra correspond to electron jumps down to the $E_2 = -3.40$ eV energy level.

*The photons emitted in jumps down to the ground state $E_1 = -13.6$ eV, all have energies too great to be visible and are thus in the **ultraviolet** part of the spectrum. Photons emitted in jumps down to the $E_3 = -1.51$ eV level, or to a higher level, have too little energy to be visible and are in the **infrared** part of the spectrum.*

In an attempt to explain the hydrogen energy levels, Bohr worked out a classical model of the electron in hydrogen. In the simplest model, the electrons could move only in certain allowed circular orbits. Using classical Newtonian formulas for orbits whose energy was given by $E_n = E_1/n^2$, Bohr found that the allowed orbits were those whose angular momentum L_n was an integer multiple of the angular momentum L_1 in the smallest orbit. For some reason the electron's angular momentum was quantized in units of size L_1 which turned out to be Planck's constant h divided by 2π, or $\hbar$.

For eleven years no one knew why the electron's angular momentum was quantized in units of $\hbar$. The answer to that puzzle was provided by the graduate student Louis de Broglie, as we shall see in the next chapter.

CHAPTER EXERCISES

Exercise 1 On page 4
Explain the blue and violet lines in the hydrogen spectrum.

Exercise 2 On page 4
Calculate the energy of a photon falling from the E_2 orbit down to the E_1 orbit. Is it visible?

Exercise 3 On page 6
Explain the crowding of spectral lines near the H40 line.

Exercise 4 On page 8
Calculate the Bohr radius.

Exercise 5 On page 10
Calculate the electron's angular momentum in the smallest Bohr orbit.

Exercise 6 On page 10
Show that (joule seconds) is the same as (kg meters^2/second).

Chapter 28 non calculus
The de Broglie Hypothesis

Bohr's theory of hydrogen, which explains so many features and details of the hydrogen spectrum, is a theory that can be fully described in just a few sentences. First, there is the idea that the electron in hydrogen can exist in only certain allowed orbits. The electron emits light, a photon, when it jumps or falls from one allowed orbit to a lower energy orbit. The hydrogen spectral lines result from the fact that the energy of the emitted photon is precisely equal to the energy the electron loses falling down to the lower energy orbit. What ties this whole theory together is that you can calculate the allowed orbits by using Newtonian mechanics with one simple modification. The allowed orbits are those whose angular momentum comes in units of Planck's constant h divided by 2π, a constant which we denote by the symbol $\hbar$.

Despite its success in explaining the hydrogen atom, Bohr's approach did not work for atoms with two or more electrons. All atoms radiate spectral lines, but only single electron atoms like hydrogen or ionized helium have a recognizable series of lines like the Balmer series. In the decade following Bohr's 1913 theory, scientists tried without success to find an explanation of the spectral lines of the more complex atoms.

But a deeper problem was the way in which Bohr's theory explained the hydrogen spectra. It was by assuming that the allowed orbits in hydrogen had angular momenta quantized in units of $\hbar = h/2\pi$.

For two centuries Newtonian mechanics had represented a complete, constant scheme, applicable without exception. Special relativity did not harm the integrity of Newtonian mechanics. Relativistic Newtonian mechanics is more generally consistent with the principle of relativity. Even Einstein's general relativity with its concept of curved space left Newtonian mechanics intact in a consistent but slightly altered form.

However, the framework of Newtonian mechanics could not be modified to include the concept of quantized angular momentum. Bohr, Sommerfield, and others tried during the decade following the introduction of Bohr's model, but without success.

In Paris in 1924, a graduate student named Louis de Broglie defended his doctoral thesis. The thesis itself was unusually short for a Ph.D. thesis in physics. For a theoretical thesis it contained few calculations and only one main result—a new way to explain Bohr's quantized orbits. It was a simple idea that changed the history of physics.

Here we will present a simularly short chapter on de Broglie's hypothesis.

DE BROGLIE WAVELENGTH

In his Ph.D. thesis de Broglie presented an idea. He noted that light had a wave nature, seen in the 2-slit experiment and Maxwell's theory, and a particle nature seen in Einstein's explanation of the photoelectric effect. Physicists could not explain how light could behave as a particle in some experiments, and a wave in others. This problem seemed so incongruous that it was put on the back burner, more or less ignored for nearly 20 years.

De Broglie's idea was that, if light can have both a particle and a wave nature, *perhaps electrons can too!* Perhaps the quantization of the angular momentum of an electron in the hydrogen atom was due to the wave nature of the electron.

The main question de Broglie had to answer was how do you determine the wavelength of an electron wave?

An analogy to photons might help. There is, however, a significant difference between electrons and photons. Electrons have a rest mass energy and photons do not, thus there can be no direct analogy between the total energies of the two particles.

But both particles have mass and carry linear momentum, and the amount of momentum can vary from zero on up, for both particles. Thus photons and electrons could have similar formulas for linear momentum.

Back in Chapter 26 on photons we saw that photons carried linear momentum. Combining Einstein's energy formula $E = mc^2$ with his photoelectric effect formula $E_{photon} = hf = hc/\lambda$ we found that the formula for the photon's linear momentum should be

$$p_{photon} = \frac{h}{\lambda} \qquad (26\text{-}13)$$

The derivation of the photon momentum formula is worth reviewing. Equating the Einstein energy formulas $E = mc^2$ and $E = hf = hc/\lambda$, we get

$$E_{photon} = m_{photon}c^2 = h\frac{c}{\lambda}$$

$$m_{photon} = \frac{h}{\lambda c} \qquad (26\text{-}11)$$

$$p_{photon} = m_{photon}v_{photon}$$

$$= m_{photon}c$$

$$= \frac{h}{\lambda c} \times c$$

The factors of c cancel and we get

$$p_{photon} = \frac{h}{\lambda}$$

$$\boxed{\lambda = \frac{h}{p} \quad \begin{array}{l}\textit{de Broglie} \\ \textit{wavelength}\end{array}} \qquad (1)$$

De Broglie assumed that this same relationship also applied to electrons. An electron with a linear momentum p would have a wavelength $\lambda = h/p$. This is now called the *de Broglie wavelength*. This relationship applies not only to photons and electrons, but as far as we know, to all particles, even you!

Exercise 1

What is the de Broglie wavelength of a 50 kg student running at a speed of 5 meters per second.

With a formula for the electron wavelength, de Broglie was able to construct a simple model explaining the quantization of angular momentum in the hydrogen atom. In de Broglie's model, one pictures an electron wave chasing itself around a circle in the hydrogen atom. If the circumference of the circle, $2\pi r$, did not have an exact integral number of wavelengths, then the wave, after going around many times, would eventually cancel itself out as illustrated in Figure (1).

But if the circumference of the circle were an exact integral number of wavelengths as illustrated in Figure (2), there would be no cancellation. This would therefore be one of Bohr's allowed orbits shown back in Figure (27-2).

Suppose that (n) wavelengths fit around a particular circle of radius r_n. Then we have

$$n\lambda = 2\pi r_n \tag{2}$$

Using the de Broglie formula $\lambda = h/p$ for the electron wavelength, we get

$$n\lambda = n\frac{h}{p} = 2\pi r_n \tag{3}$$

Multiplying through by p and gives

$$nh = 2\pi p r_n$$

Then dividing by 2π we get

$$pr_n = n\frac{h}{2\pi} = n\hbar \tag{4}$$

Now pr_n is the angular momentum L_n (momentum times lever arm) of the electron

$$L_n = pr_n \tag{5}$$

Thus Equation (4), $pr_n = n\hbar$, becomes

$$\boxed{L_n = n\hbar} \tag{6}$$

Equation (6) tells us that for the allowed orbits, the orbits in which the electron wave does not cancel, the angular momentum comes in integer amounts of the angular momentum $\hbar$. The quantization of angular momentum is thus due to the wave nature of the electron, a concept completely foreign to Newtonian mechanics.

When a graduate student does a thesis project, typically the student does a lot of work under the supervision of a thesis advisor, and comes up with some new, hopefully verifiable, results. What do you do with a student who comes up with a strange idea, completely unverified by experiment, that can be explained in a few pages of algebra? Einstein happened to be passing through Paris in the summer of 1924 and was asked if de Broglie's thesis should be accepted. Although doubtful himself about a wave nature of the electron, Einstein recommended that the thesis be accepted, for *de Broglie just might be right!*

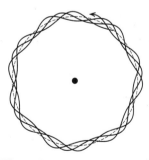

Figure 1
de Broglie picture of an electron wave cancelling itself out.

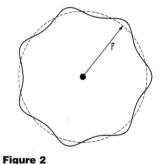

Figure 2
If the circumference of the orbit is an integer number of wavelengths, the electron wave will go around without any cancellation.

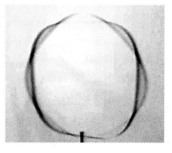

Figure 2a--Movie
The standing waves on a circular metal band nicely illustrate de Broglie's waves.

Experimental verification

In 1925, two physicists at Bell Telephone Laboratories, C. J. Davisson and L. H. Germer were studying the surface of nickel by scattering electrons from the surface. The point of the research was to learn more about metal surfaces in order to improve the quality of switches used in telephone communication. After heating the metal target to remove an oxide layer that had accumulated following a break in the vacuum line, they discovered that the electrons scattered differently. The metal had crystallized during the heating, and the peculiar scattering had occurred as a result of the crystallization. Davisson and Germer then prepared a target consisting of a single crystal, and studied the peculiar scattering phenomena extensively. Their apparatus is illustrated schematically in Figure (3), and

their experimental results are shown in Figure (4). For their experiment, there was a marked peak in the scattering when the detector was located at an angle of 50° from the incident beam.

Davisson presented these results at a meeting in London in the summer of 1927. At that time there was a considerable discussion about de Broglie's hypothesis that electrons have a wave nature. Hearing of this idea, Davisson recognized the reason for the scattering peak. The atoms of the crystal were diffracting electron waves. The enhanced scattering at 50° was a diffraction peak, a maximum similar to the reflected maxima we saw back in Figure (25-19) when light goes through a diffraction grating. Davisson had the experimental evidence that de Broglie's idea about electron waves was correct after all.

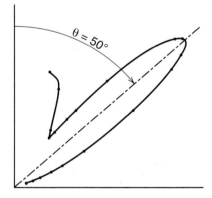

Figure 4
Plot of intensity vs. angle for electrons scattered by a nickel crystal, as measured by Davisson and Germer. The peak in intensity at 50° was a diffraction peak like the ones produced by diffraction gratings. (The intensity is proportional to the distance out from the origin.)

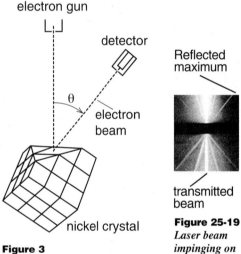

Figure 3
Scattering electrons from the surface of a nickel crystal.

Figure 25-19
Laser beam impinging on a diffraction grating.

EXERCISE 2 AND CHAPTER REVIEW

We are going to have the reader do the chapter review by doing the following clean desk problem (i.e. try to do this without looking back at the text).

a) Starting from Einstein's two formulas, $E = mc^2$ and $E = hf$, derive a formula for the momentum $p = mv$ of a photon

b) Explain how de Broglie concluded that the electron's orbital angular momentum had to come on multiples of Planck's constant $h/2\pi = \hbar$.

Try out your explanation on a friend who is stuck in a physics course that does not include modern physics.

CHAPTER EXERCISES

Exercise 1 On page 2

Calculate the de Broglie wavelenth of a student runner.

Chapter 29 non calculus
Scattering of Waves

As we just saw, it was the scattering of electron waves from the surface of a nickel crystal that provided the first experimental evidence of the wave nature of electrons. Earlier experiments, involving the scattering of x rays, had begun to yield detailed information about the atomic structure of crystals.

Our main focus in this chapter will be an experiment developed in the early 1960s by Harry Meiners at R.P.I., which made it easy for students to study electron waves and work with de Broglie's formula $\lambda = h/p$. The apparatus involved the scattering of electrons from a graphite crystal. The analysis of the resulting diffraction pattern requires nothing more than a combination of the de Broglie wavelength formula with the diffraction grating formula discussed in Chapter 25. We will use Meiners' experiment as our main demonstration of the wave nature of the electron.

Unfortunately, new versions of Meiners' apparatus are not currently available. We have been told that the 6000 volts needed to accelerate the electrons exceeds government regulations for instructional equipment. Hopefully this restriction can be overcome in the future. In the meantime, we have a good set of photographs of the diffraction patterns that we can use.

SCATTERING OF A WAVE BY A SMALL OBJECT

The first step in studying the scattering of waves by atoms is to see what happens when a wave strikes a small object—an object smaller in size than the wavelength of the wave. The result can be seen in the ripple tank photographs shown in Figure (1). In (1a), an incident wave is passing over a small object. You can see scattered waves emerging from the object. In (1b), the incident wave has passed, and you can see that the scattered waves are a series of circular waves, the same pattern you get when you drop a stone into a quiet pool of water.

If the scattering object is smaller in size than the wavelength of the wave, as in Figure (1), the scattered waves contain essentially no information about the shape of the object. For this reason, you cannot study the structure of something that is much smaller than the wavelength of the wave you are using for the study. Optical microscopes, for example, cannot be used to study viruses, because most viruses are smaller than the wavelength of visible light. (Very clever work with optical microscopes allows one to see down to about 1/10th of the wavelength of visible light, to see objects like microtubules.)

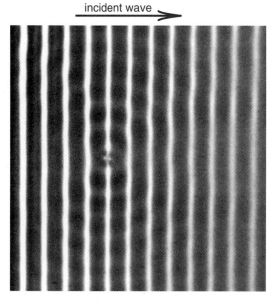

a) Incident and scattered wave together.

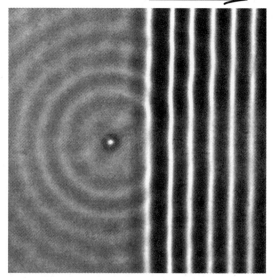

b) After the incident wave has passed.

Figure 1
If the scattering object is smaller than a wavelength, we get circular scattered waves that contain little or no information about the shape of the object.

REFLECTION OF LIGHT

Using the picture of scattering provided by Figure (1), we can begin to understand the reflection of visible light from a smooth metal surface. Suppose we have a long wavelength wave impinging on a metal surface represented by a regular array of atoms, as illustrated in Figure (2). As the wave passes over the array of atoms, circular scattered waves emerge. As seen in Figure (2a), the scattered waves add up to produce a reflected wave coming back out of the surface. The angles labeled θ_i and θ_r in Figure (2b) are what are called the *angle of incidence* and *angle of reflection* , respectively. Since the scattered waves emerge at the same speed as the incident wave enters, it is clear from the geometry that the angle of incidence is equal to the angle of reflection. That is the main rule governing the reflection of light.

What happens inside the material depends upon details of the scattering process. Note that the scattered wavefront inside the material coincides with the incident wave. For a metal surface, the phases of the scattered waves are such that the scattered wave inside just cancels the incident wave and there is no wave inside. All the radiation is reflected. For other types of material that are not opaque, the incident and scattered waves do not cancel. Instead they add up to produce a new, transmitted wave whose crests move slower than the speed of light. This apparent slowing of the speed of light, due to the interference of transmitted and scattered waves, leads to the bending of a beam of light as it enters or leaves a transparent medium. *It is this bending that allows one to construct lenses and optical instruments.*

Exercise 1

Using Figure (2), explain why the angle of incidence equals the angle of reflection.

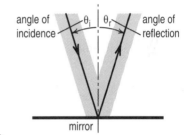

Figure 2b
When light reflects from a mirror, the angle of incidence equals the angle of reflection.

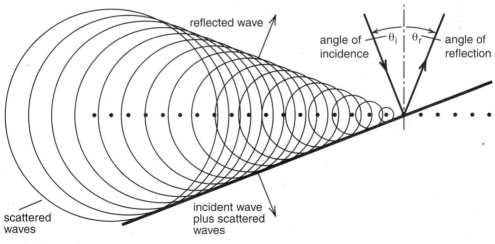

Figure 2a
A reflected wave is produced when the incident wave is scattered by many atoms. From this diagram, you can see why the angle of incidence equals the angle of reflection.

X RAY DIFFRACTION

If the wavelength of the light striking a crystal becomes comparable to the spacing between atoms, we get a new effect. The scattered waves from adjacent atoms begin to interfere with each other and we get diffraction patterns.

The spacing between atoms in a crystal is of the order of a few angstroms. (An angstrom, abbreviated Å, is 10^{-10} meters or .1 nm[nanometers]. An angstrom is essentially the diameter of a hydrogen atom.) Light with this wavelength is in the x ray region. Using Einstein's formula $E = hf = hc/\lambda$, but in the form

$$E\ (in\ eV) = \frac{1240\ eV\ nm}{\lambda\ (in\ nm)} \qquad (26\text{-}8)$$

we see that photons with a wavelength of 2 Å or .2 nm have an energy

$$E\ ^{photon\ with\ 2\mathring{A},}_{.2\ nm\ wavelength} = \frac{1240\ eV\cdot nm}{.2 nm}$$

$$= 6{,}200\ eV \qquad (1)$$

This is a considerably greater energy than the 2 to 3 eV of visible photons.

When a beam of x rays is sent through a crystal structure, the x rays will reflect from the planes of atoms within the crystal. The process, called **Bragg reflection**, is illustrated for the example of a cubic lattice in Figure (3). The dotted lines connect lines of atoms, which are actually planes of atoms if you consider the depth of the crystal. An incident wave coming into the crystal can be reflected at various angles by various planes, with the angle of incidence equal to the angle of reflection in each case.

When the wavelength of the incident radiation is comparable to the spacing between atoms, we get a strong reflected beam when the reflected waves from one plane of atoms are an integral number of wavelengths behind the reflected waves from the plane above, as illustrated in Figure (4). If it is an exact integral wavelength, then the reflected light from all the parallel planes will interfere constructively giving us an intense reflected wave. If, instead, there is a slight mismatch, then light from relatively distant planes will cancel in pairs and we will not get constructive interference. The argument is similar to the one used to find the maxima in a diffraction grating.

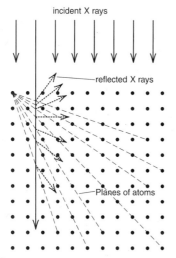

Figure 3
Planes of atoms act like mirrors reflecting x rays.

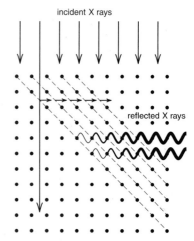

Figure 4
When the incident x ray wavelength equals the spacing between one of the sets of planes, the reflected waves add up to produce a maxima. We can call these diffracted rays.

Thus with Bragg reflection you get an intense reflection only from planes of atoms, and only if the wavelength of the x ray is just right to produce the constructive interference described above. As a result, if you send an x ray beam through a crystal, you get a diffraction pattern consisting of a series of dots surrounding the central beam, like those seen in Figure (5). Figure (5a) is a sketch of the setup, (5b) is the resulting diffraction pattern for x rays passing through a silver bromide crystal, whose structure is shown in (5c).

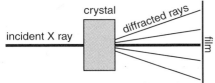

a) An incident beam of x rays is diffracted by the atoms of the crystal.

b) X ray diffraction pattern produced by a silver bromide crystal. (Photograph courtesy of R. W. Christy.)

c) The silver bromide crystal is a cubic array with alternating silver and bromine atoms.

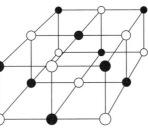

Figure 5
X ray diffraction study of a silver bromide crystal.

The main use of x ray diffraction has been to determine the structure of crystals. From the location of the dots in the x rays' diffraction photograph, and a knowledge of the wavelength of the x rays, you can figure out the orientation of and spacing between the planes of atoms. By using various wavelength x rays, striking the crystal at different angles, it is possible to decipher complex crystal structures. Figure (6) is one of many x ray diffraction photographs taken by J. C. Kendrew of a crystalline form of myoglobin. Kendrew used these x ray diffraction pictures to determine the structure of the myoglobin molecule shown in Figure (16-3). Kendrew was awarded the 1962 Nobel prize in chemistry for this work.

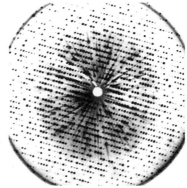

Figure 6
One of the x ray diffraction photographs used by Kendrew to determine the structure of the myoglobin molecule.

Figure 16-3
The myoglobin molecule, whose structure was determined by x ray diffraction studies.

Diffraction by Thin Crystals

The diffraction of waves passing through relatively thin crystals can also be analyzed using the diffraction grating concepts discussed in Chapter 25. Suppose for example, we had a thin crystal consisting of a rectangular array of atoms as shown in Figure (7a). The edge view of the array is shown in (7b). Here each dot represents the end view of a line of atoms.

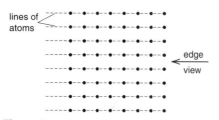

Figure 7a
Front view of a rectangular array of atoms in a thin crystal.

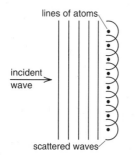

Figure 7b
Edge view with an incident wave. Each dot now represents one of the lines of atoms in Fig.(7a). The lines of atoms produce cylindrical waves.

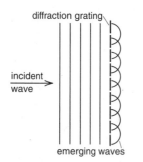

Figure 8
The waves emerging from a diffraction grating have a structure similar to the waves scattered by a line of atoms.

Now suppose a beam of waves is impinging upon the crystal as indicated in Figure (7b). The impinging waves will scatter from the lines of atoms, producing an array of cylindrical waves as shown.

Compare this with Figure (8), a sketch of waves emerging from a diffraction grating. The scattered waves from the lines of atoms, and the waves emerging from the narrow slits have a similar structure and therefore should produce similar diffraction patterns.

There is one major difference between the array of atoms in Figure (7) and the diffraction grating of Figure (8). In the crystal structure there are numerous sets of lines of atoms, some of which are indicated in Figure (9). Each of these sets of lines of atoms should act as an independent diffraction grating, producing its own diffraction pattern. The main sets of lines are horizontal and vertical, thus the main diffraction pattern we should see should look like that produced by two diffraction gratings crossed at right angles.

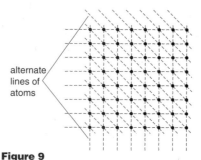

Figure 9
Various lines of atoms can imitate slits in a diffraction grating.

Sending a laser beam through two crossed diffraction gratings produces the image shown in Figure (10). In Figure (10a), the laser beam is sent through a single grating. In (10b) we see the effect of adding another grating crossed at right angles.

Figure 10a
A laser beam sent through a single grating. The lines of the grating were 25 microns wide, spaced 150 microns apart.

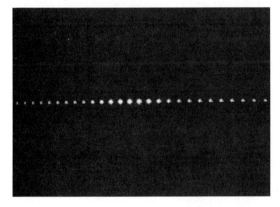

Figure 10b
A laser beam sent through crossed diffraction gratings. Again the lines of the grating were 25 microns wide, spaced 150 microns apart.

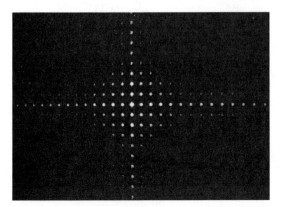

Exercise 2

In Figure (10a) the maxima seen in the photograph are 1.68 cm apart and the distance from the grating to the screen is 4.00 meters. The wavelength of the laser beam is 6.3×10^{-5} cm. What is the spacing between the slits of the diffraction grating?

Exercise 3

In Figure (11), a laser beam is sent through two crossed diffraction gratings of different spacing. Which image, (a) or (b) is oriented correctly? (What happens to the spacing of the maxima when you make the grating lines closer together?)

Figure 11
Two diffraction gratings with different spacing are crossed. As shown, the vertical lines are farther apart than the horizontal ones. Which of the two images of the resulting diffraction pattern has the correct orientation?

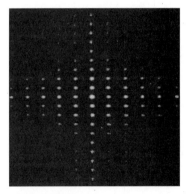

a)

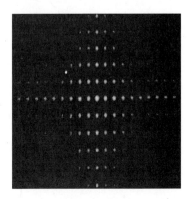

b)

THE ELECTRON DIFFRACTION EXPERIMENT

One of the main differences between the scattering of x rays and of electrons is that x ray photons interact less strongly with atoms, with the result that x rays can penetrate deeply into matter. This enables doctors to photograph through flesh to observe broken bones, or engineers to photograph through metal looking for hidden flaws. Electrons interact strongly with atoms, do not penetrate nearly as deeply, and therefore are well suited for the study of the structure of surfaces or thin crystals, where you get considerable scattering from a few layers of atoms.

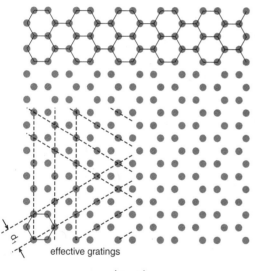

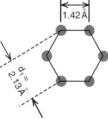

Figure 12
The hexagonal array of atoms in one layer of a graphite crystal. Lines of atoms in this crystal act as crossed diffraction gratings.

The Graphite Crystal

Graphite makes an ideal substance to study by electron scattering because graphite crystals come in thin sheets. A graphite crystal consists of a series of planes of carbon atoms. Within one plane the atoms have the hexagonal structure shown in Figure (12), reminiscent of the tiles often seen on bathroom floors. The spacing between neighboring atoms in each hexagon is 1.42 Å, as indicated at the bottom of Figure (12).

The atoms within a plane are very tightly bound together. The hexagonal array forms a strong framework. The planes themselves are stacked on top of each other at the considerable distance of 3.63 Å as indicated in Figure (13). The forces between these planes are weak, allowing the planes to easily slide over each other. The result is that graphite is a slippery substance, making an excellent dry lubricant. In contrast, the strength within a plane makes graphite an excellent strengthening agent for epoxy. The resulting carbon filament epoxies, used for constructing racing boat hulls, light airplanes and stayless sailboat masts, is one of the strongest plastics available.

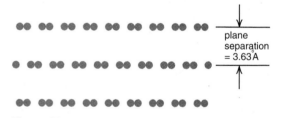

Figure 13
Edge view of the graphite crystal, showing the planes of atoms. The planes can easily slide over each other, making the substance slippery.

In the last few years, we have discovered that a single layer of graphite can be rolled up into a seamless tube about 10 angstroms or 1 nanometer in diameter. This is called a ***carbon nanotube***. A few years earlier, it was discovered that the graphite sheet could fold into a 60 carbon atom ball. These are commonly called ***buckeyballs*** because they have the same structure as one of Buckmeister Fuller's geodesic domes.

The Electron Diffraction Tube

The electron diffraction experiment where we send a beam of electrons through a graphite crystal, can be viewed either as an experiment to demonstrate the wave nature of electrons or as an experiment to study the structure of a graphite crystal. Perhaps both.

The apparatus, shown in Figure (14), consists of an evacuated tube with an electron gun at one end, a graphite target in the middle, and a phosphor screen at the other end. A finely collimated electron beam can be aimed to strike an individual flake of graphite, producing a single crystal diffraction pattern on the phosphor screen. Usually you hit more than one crystal and get a multiple image on the screen, but with some adjustment you can usually obtain a single crystal image.

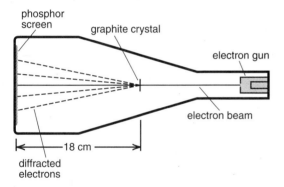

Figure 14
Electron diffraction apparatus. An electron beam, produced by an electron gun, strikes a graphite crystal located near the center of the evacuated tube. The original beam and the scattered electrons strike a phosphor screen located at the end of the tube.

Electron Wavelength

The accelerating voltage required to produce a good diffraction pattern is in the range of 6,000 volts. As our first step in the analysis, let us use the de Broglie wavelength formula to calculate the wavelength of 6,000 eV electrons.

The rest energy of an electron is .51 MeV, or 510,000 eV, far greater than the 6,000 eV we are using in this experiment. Since the 6,000 eV kinetic energy is much less than the rest energy, we can use the non relativistic formula $1/2\, mv^2$ for kinetic energy. First converting 6,000 eV to joules, we can equate that to $1/2\, mv^2$ to calculate the speed v of the electron. We get

$$6000\ eV \times 1.6 \times 10^{-19}\frac{\text{jouls}}{\text{eV}} = 1/2\ m_e v^2 \quad (2)$$

With the electron mass $m_e = .911 \times 10^{-27}$gm , we get

$$v^2 = \frac{2 \times 6000 \times 1.6 \times 10^{-19}\text{jouls}}{9.11 \times 10^{-31}\text{kg}}$$

$$= 21.1 \times 10^{14}\frac{\text{meter}^2}{\text{sec}^2}$$

$$v = 4.59 \times 10^7 \text{meter/sec} \quad (3)$$

which is slightly greater than 10% the speed of light.

The next step is to calculate the momentum of the electron for use in de Broglie's formula. We have

$$p = mv$$

$$= 9.11 \times 10^{-31}\text{kg} \times 4.59 \times 10^7\frac{\text{meter}}{\text{sec}}$$

$$= 4.18 \times 10^{-23}\frac{\text{kg meter}}{\text{sec}} \quad (4)$$

Finally using de Broglie's formula we have

$$\lambda = \frac{h}{p} = \frac{6.63 \times 10^{-34}\text{kg meter}^2/\text{sec}}{4.18 \times 10^{-23}\text{kg meter/sec}}$$

$$\boxed{\lambda_{\text{electron}} = 1.59 \times 10^{-11}\text{meter} = .159\ \overset{\circ}{A}} \quad (5)$$

Thus the wavelength of the electrons we are using in this experiment is about one tenth the spacing between atoms in the hexagonal array.

Exercise 4

Calculate the wavelength of a 6000 eV photon. What causes such a difference in the wavelengths of a photon and an electron of the same energy?

Figure 15a
Single grating diffraction pattern.

Figure 15b
Two grating diffraction pattern.

Figure 15c
Diffraction pattern from three crossed gratings.

The Diffraction Pattern

What should we see when a beam of waves is diffracted by the hexagonal array of atoms in a graphite crystal? Looking back at the drawing of the graphite crystal, Figure (12), we see that there are prominent sets of lines of atoms in the hexagonal array. To make an effective diffraction grating, the lines of atoms have to be equally spaced. We have marked three sets of equally-spaced lines of atoms, each set being at an angle of 60° from each other. We expect that these lines of atoms should produce a diffraction pattern similar to three crossed diffraction gratings.

In Figure (15), we are looking at the diffraction we get when a laser beam is sent through three crossed diffraction gratings. In (15a), we have one diffraction grating. In (15b) a second grating at an angle of 60° has been added. In (15c) we have all three gratings, and see a hexagonal array of dots surrounding the central beam, the central maximum.

Figure (16) is the electron diffraction pattern photographed from the face of the electron diffraction tube shown in Figure (14). We clearly see an hexagonal array of dots expected from our diffraction grating analysis. On the photograph we have superimposed a centimeter scale so that measurements may be made from this photograph.

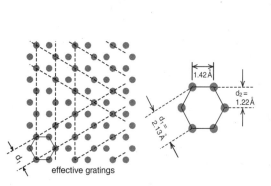

Figure 12 (cropped)
Three sets of lines of atoms act as three crossed diffraction gratings with 2.13 angstrom spacing.

Figure 16
Diffraction pattern produced by a beam of electrons passing through a single graphite crystal. The energy of the electrons was 6000 eV.

The electron diffraction apparatus allows us to move the beam around, so that we can hit different parts of the target. In Figure (16), we have essentially hit a single crystal. When the electron beam strikes several graphite crystals at the same time, we get the more complex pattern seen in Figure (17).

Analysis of the Diffraction Pattern

Let us begin our analysis of the diffraction pattern by selecting one set of dots in the pattern that would be produced by one set of lines of atoms in the crystal. The dots and the corresponding lines of atoms are shown in Figure (18). In (18a) we see that the spacing Y_{max} between the dots on the screen is 1.33 cm. These horizontal dots correspond to the maxima for a vertical set of lines of atoms indicated in (18c). In (18b) we are reminded that the distance from the target to the screen is 18 cm. Using the diffraction grating formula, we can calculate the wavelength of the electron waves that produce this set of maxima.

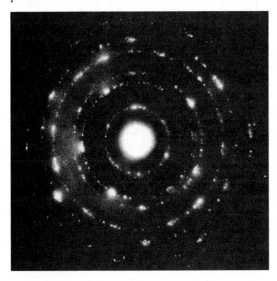

Figure 17
Diffraction pattern produced by a beam of electrons passing through multiple graphite crystals.

Using the diffraction formula, Equation (25-3), and noting that $Y_{max} \ll D$, we have

$$\lambda = Y_{max}\frac{d}{\sqrt{D^2 + Y^2_{max}}} \approx Y_{max}\frac{d}{D}$$

$$= 1.33 \text{ cm}\ \frac{2.13 \times 10^{-10}\text{meter}}{18 \text{ cm}}$$

$$(6)$$

$$\boxed{\lambda = 1.57 \times 10^{-11}\text{meter} = .157\ \overset{\circ}{\text{A}}}$$

which closely agrees well with Equation (5), the calculation of the electron wavelength using the de Broglie wavelength formula.

Figure 18a
The diffraction grating maxima from one set of lines in the graphite crystal. You can see that $3y_{max} = 4cm$, so that $y_{max} = 1.33$ cm.

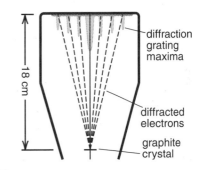

Figure 18b
Top view of the electron diffraction apparatus.

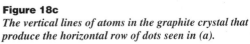

Figure 18c
The vertical lines of atoms in the graphite crystal that produce the horizontal row of dots seen in (a).

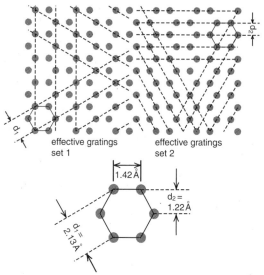

effective gratings
set 1

effective gratings
set 2

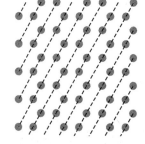

1.42 Å

$d_2 =$
1.22 Å

$d_1 =$
2.13 Å

Figure 19
*It is easy to find a second set of effective
gratings, rotated 30° from the first set,
and with a narrower spacing.*

Figure 20
*We have highlighted the
maxima produced by this
set of lines. Note that the
more narrowly spaced
lines produce more
widely spaced maxima.*

Other Sets of Lines

With a careful analysis of the lines of atoms in the
hexagonal ray of atoms, one can explain all the dots of
the diffraction pattern of Figure (16). For example, in
Figure (19) we see that there is another set of lines that
are rotated at an angle of 30° and more closely spaced
than our original set. In Figure (20), we have highlighted a set of dots in the diffraction pattern that are
rotated by an angle of 30° and more widely spaced than
the dots we have been analyzing. Since more closely
spaced lines in a grating produce more widely spaced
maxima, we should suspect that the highlighted maxima
result from this new set of lines. The point of Exercise
(5) is to see if this is true.

Exercise 5

(a) Explain why more closely spaced atoms should
produce more widely spaced dots in the diffraction
pattern.

(b) Assuming that the dots highlighted in Figure (20) are
produced by the lines of atoms shown by dotted lines in
set 2 of the effective gratings, calculate the wavelength
of the waves producing the dots. Compare your results
with our previous analysis.

Exercise 6

Suppose that a beam of neutrons rather than electrons
were fired at the graphite crystal. Assuming that neutrons also obey the de Broglie relationship $\lambda = h/p$, what
should be the kinetic energy, in eV, of the neutrons in
order to produce the same diffraction pattern with the
same spacing between dots?

STUDENT PROJECT

In our discussion of the diffraction of waves by the atoms of a crystal, we pointed out that waves should emerge from a line of atoms in much the same way that they do from the slits of a diffraction grating. The two situations are illustrated in Figures (7b) and (8) repeated here.

That a slit and a line produce similar diffraction patterns was clearly illustrated in a project by Gwendylin Chen. While working with a laser, she observed that when the beam passed over a strand of hair, it produced a single slit diffraction pattern superimposed on the image of the beam itself. Here we have reproduced Gwendylin's experiment. Figure (21) is a photograph of a slit made from two scapel blades, and a strand of Gwendylin's hair. We tried to make the width of the slit the same as the width of the hair. The two circles indicate where we aimed the laser for the two diffraction patterns.

The results are seen in Figure (22).The diffraction patterns are almost identical. The only difference is that when the beam passes over the hair, the beam continues on, landing in the center of the diffraction pattern.

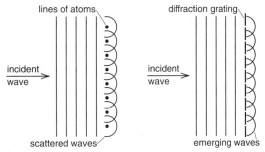

Figure 7b
Edge view of a thin crystal with an incident wave. Each dot now represents one of the line of atoms in the crystal.

Figure 8
The waves emerging from a diffraction grating have a structure similar to the waves scattered by a line of atoms.

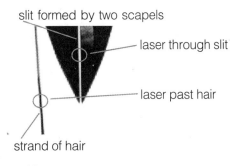

Figure 21
Slit and hair used to produce diffraction patterns. The circles indicate where we aimed the laser.

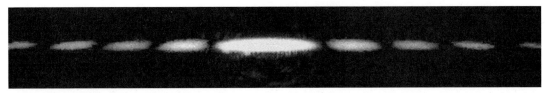

a) single slit diffraction pattern

b) diffraction pattern produced by strand of hair

Figure 22
Comparison of diffraction patterns.

CHAPTER 29 REVIEW

The purpose of this chapter is to study the wave nature of the electron. This is done with an experiment where a beam of electron waves is diffracted by the atoms in a graphite crystal.

To analyze the experiment, we first showed that when a wave passed through a thin crystal, the lines of atoms in the crystal acted like slits in a diffraction grating. This allowed us to use the diffraction grating formula to study the resulting diffraction pattern.

The graphite crystal consists of layers of carbon atoms in hexagonal arrays as shown in Figure (12). As shown by the dotted lines, the lines of atoms should imitate three diffraction gratings crossed at angles of 60 degrees. The similarity of the diffraction pattern by a laser passing through three gratings, Figure (15c), and the electron diffraction pattern from graphite seen in Figure (16) supports this analysis.

The main focus of the experiment was to apply the diffraction grating formula $\lambda = Y_{max}d/D$ to determine the wavelength of the electrons for d equal to the line spacing of 2.13 angstroms, D equal to the target distance of 18 cm, and Y_{max} equal to 1.33 cm. The resulting wavelength was $\lambda = .157$ angstroms.

Then we used our knowledge of the accelerating voltage of 6000 volts to calculate the speed and momentum of the electrons. This allowed us to use the de Broglie formula $\lambda = h/p$ to calculate the electron wavelength which turned out to be $\lambda = .159$ angstroms, in very good agreement with the diffraction grating analysis.

The best review for this chapter is to do the following two calculations on a clean sheet of paper.

(a) Calculate the wavelength of a 6000 eV electron. The constants you need are

$$m_{electron} = 9.11 \times 10^{-31} \, kg$$
$$h = 6.63 \times 10^{-34} \, joule \ sec$$

and the conversion factor

$$1.60 \times 10^{-19} \, joules/eV$$

(b) Calculate the electron wavelength using the diffraction grating formula.

CHAPTER EXERCISES

Exercise 1 0n page 3
Show that the angle of incidence equals the angle of reflection.

Exercise 2 0n page 7
Use the analysis of a laser diffraction pattern to determine the spacing of the slits in a diffraction grating.

Exercise 3 0n page 7
For crossed gratings of different spacing, which is the correct diffraction pattern?

Exercise 4 0n page 9
Calculate the wavelength of 6000 eV photons and electrons.

Exercise 5 0n page 12
Explain the electron diffraction pattern.

Exercise 6 0n page 12
What kinetic energy should neutrons have to give the same diffraction pattern as the electrons in Figure (16)?

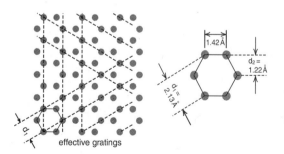

Figure 12 (cropped)
Three sets of lines of atoms act as three crossed diffraction gratings with 2.13 angstrom spacing.

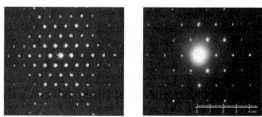

Figures 15c & 16
Diffraction pattern produced by 3 crossed diffraction gratings and by a beam of electrons passing through a graphite crystal.

Chapter 30 non calculus

Lasers, a Model Atom and Zero Point Energy

In an address to the American Physical Society in 1976, *FELIX BLOCK* commented:

"Once at the end of a colloquium I heard Debye saying something like: 'Schrödinger, you are not working right now on very important problems...why don't you tell us some time about that thesis of de Broglie, which seems to have attracted some attention?' So in one of the next colloquia, Schrödinger gave a beautifully clear account of how de Broglie associated a wave with a particle, and how he could obtain the quantization rules ... by demanding that an integer number of waves should be fitted along a stationary orbit. When he had finished, Debye casually remarked that he thought this way of talking was rather childish ... To deal properly with waves, one had to have a wave equation."

Schrödinger took Debye's advice, and in the following months devised a wave equation for the electron wave, an equation from which one could calculate the electron energy levels. The structure of the hydrogen atom was a prediction of the equation without arbitrary assumptions like those needed for the Bohr theory. The wave nature of the electron turned out to be the key to the new mechanics that was to replace Newtonian mechanics as the fundamental theory.

In the satellite chapter on Atoms and Chemistry, we take a look at some of the electron wave patterns determined by Schrödinger's equation, and see how these patterns, when combined with the Pauli exclusion principle and the concept of electron spin, begin to explain the chemical properties of atoms and the structure of the periodic table.

The problem one encounters when discussing the application of Schrödinger's equation to the hydrogen atom, is that relatively complex mathematical steps are required in order to obtain the solutions. These steps are usually beyond the mathematical level of most introductory physics and chemistry texts, with the result that students must simply be shown the solutions without being told how to get them. We will have to do the same in the satellite chapter.

In this chapter we will study a model atom, one in which we can see how the particle-wave nature of the electron leads directly to quantized energy levels and atomic spectra. The basic idea, which we illustrate with the model atom, is that whenever you have a wave confined to some region of space, there will be a set of allowed standing wave patterns for that wave. Whether the patterns are complex or simple depends upon the way the wave is confined. If the wave is also a particle, like an electron or photon, you can then use the particle-wave nature to calculate the energy of the particle in each of the allowed standing wave patterns. These energy values are the quantized energy levels of the particle.

An example of a set of simple standing waves that are easily analyzed is found in the laser. It is essentially the laser standing wave patterns that we use for our model atom. For this reason we begin the chapter with a discussion of the laser and how the photon standing waves are established. In the model atom the photon standing waves of the laser are replaced by electron standing waves.

An analysis of the model atom shows why any particle, when confined to some region of space, must have a non zero kinetic energy. The smaller the region of space, the greater this so-called **zero point** kinetic energy. When these ideas are applied to the atoms in liquid helium, we see why helium does not freeze even at absolute zero. We also see why the entropy definition of temperature must be used at these low temperatures.

THE LASER AND STANDING LIGHT WAVES

The laser, the device that is at the heart of your CD player and fiber optics communications, provides a common example of a standing light wave. In most cases a laser consists of two parallel mirrors with standing light waves trapped between the mirrors as illustrated in Figure (1). The light comes from radiation emitted by excited atoms that are located within the standing wave.

How the light radiated by the excited atoms ends up in a standing wave is a story in itself. An atom excited to a high energy level can drop down to a lower level by emitting a photon whose energy is the difference in energy of the two levels. This photon will have the wavelength of the spectral line associated with those two levels.

Spectral lines are not absolutely sharp. For example, due to the Doppler effect, thermal motion slightly shifts the wavelength of the emitted radiation. If the atom is moving toward you when it radiates, the wavelength is shifted slightly towards the blue. If moving away, the shift is toward the red. In addition the photons are radiated in all directions, and waves from different photons have different phases. Even in a sharp spectral line the light is a jumble of directions and phases, giving what is called *incoherent* light.

In contrast, the light in a laser beam travels in one direction, the phases of the waves are lined up and there is almost no spread in photon energies. This is the beam of *coherent* light which made it so easy for us to study interference effects like those we saw in the two slit and multiple slit diffraction patterns. These patterns would be much more difficult to observe if we had to use incoherent light.

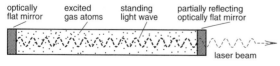

optically flat mirror   excited gas atoms   standing light wave   partially reflecting optically flat mirror

laser beam

Figure 1
Laser consisting of two parallel mirrors with standing light waves trapped between the mirrors.

The purity of the light in a laser beam depends upon the standing light wave pattern created by the two mirrors, and upon a quantum mechanical effect discovered by Einstein in 1915.

Einstein found that there were two distinct ways an excited atom could radiate light, either by *spontaneous emission* or *stimulated emission*. An example of spontaneous emission is when an excited atom is all by itself and eventually drops down to a lower energy level. The emitted photon can come out in any direction and can be Doppler shifted.

If, however, a photon with the right energy passes by the excited atom, there is some chance that the atom will emit a photon *exactly* like the one passing by. This is called stimulated emission. (The energy of the passing photon has to be close to the energy the atom would naturally radiate.)

It is the process of stimulated emission that can lead to a laser beam. Suppose we have a gas of excited atoms located between parallel mirrors. At first the atoms radiate spontaneously in all directions. (We assume that there is some mechanism to excite the atoms). After a while, one of the photons hits a mirror straight on and starts reflecting back and forth between the parallel mirrors. As the photon moves back and forth, it passes by an excited atom, stimulating that atom to emit an identical photon.

Now there are two identical photons bouncing back and forth. Each is likely to stimulate another atom to emit an identical photon, and we have four identical photons, etc. Soon there are so many identical photons moving through the excited atoms that there is little chance that an atom can radiate spontaneously. All the radiation is stimulated and all the photons are identical to the one that started bouncing back and forth between the mirrors.

The mirrors on the ends of the laser are not perfect reflectors. A few percent of the photons striking the mirror pass through, forming the beam produced by the laser. The photons lost to the laser beam are continually replaced by new identical photons being emitted by stimulated emission. One of the tricky technical parts of constructing a laser is to maintain a continuous supply of excited atoms. There are various ways of doing this that we need not discuss here.

Photon Standing Waves

The photons bouncing back and forth between the mirrors in a laser are in an allowed standing wave pattern. Back in Chapter 14, in our discussion of standing waves on a guitar string, we saw that only certain standing wave patterns are allowed. The allowed patterns, shown in Figure (14-8), are those with an integral or half integral number of wavelengths between the ends of the string. For photons trapped between two mirrors, the allowed standing wave patterns are also those with an integral or half integral number of wavelengths between the mirrors, as indicated schematically in Figure (2).

Because of the simple geometry, we do not need to solve a wave equation to determine the shape of these standing light waves. The waves are sinusoidal, and the allowed wavelengths are given by the same formula as for the allowed waves on a guitar string, namely

$$\lambda_n = \frac{2D}{n} \quad \begin{array}{l}\textit{wavelength of the} \\ \textit{nth standing wave}\end{array} \quad (1)$$

where D is the separation between the mirrors.

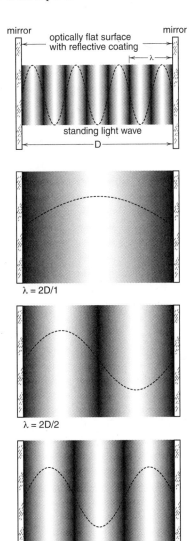

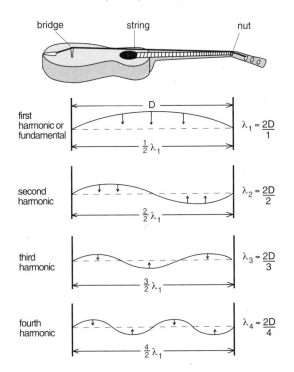

Figure 14-8 (reproduced)
On a guitar string only certain standing wave patterns which have an integral or half integral number of wavelengths between the ends of the string are allowed.

Figure 2
Three longest wavelength standing wave patterns for a light beam trapped between two mirrors.

Photon Energy Levels

The special feature of the standing light wave is that the light has both a wave and a particle nature. Equation (1), which tells us the allowed wavelengths, is all we need to know about the wave nature of the light. The particle nature is described by Einstein's photoelectric effect formula $E = hf = hc/\lambda$. Applying this formula to the photons in the standing wave, we find that a photon with an allowed wavelength λ_n has a corresponding energy E_n given by

$$E_n = \frac{hc}{\lambda_n} \tag{2}$$

Because only certain wavelengths λ_n are allowed, only certain energy photons, those with an energy E_n are allowed between the mirrors. We can say that the photon energies are quantized. If the separation of the mirrors is D, then from Equation (1) ($\lambda_n = 2D/n$), and Equation (2) ($E_n = hc/\lambda_n$), we find that the quantized values of E_n are

$$E_n = \frac{hc}{\lambda_n} = \frac{hc}{\dfrac{2D}{n}}$$

$$\boxed{E_n = n\frac{hc}{2D}} \tag{3}$$

From Equation (3) we can construct an energy level diagram for the photons trapped between the mirrors. In contrast to the energy level diagram for the hydrogen atom, the photon energies start at zero because there is no potential energy. We see that the levels are equally spaced, a distance hc/2D apart.

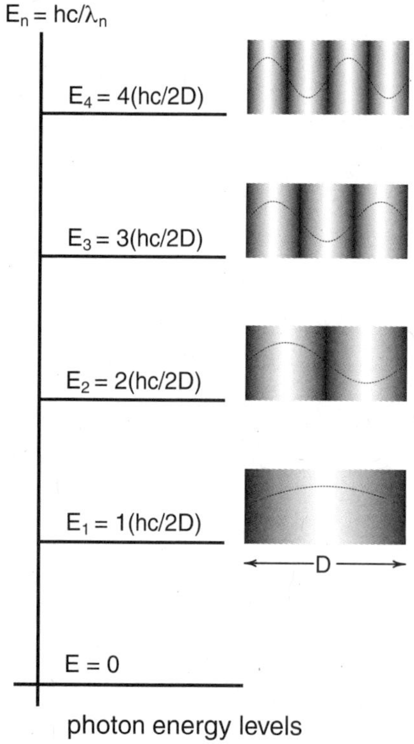

Exercise 1

If you could have two mirrors 1Å apart (the size of a hydrogen atom) what would be the energy, in eV, of the lowest 5 energy levels for a photon trapped between the mirrors?

$E_n = hc/\lambda_n$

$E_4 = 4(hc/2D)$

$E_3 = 3(hc/2D)$

$E_2 = 2(hc/2D)$

$E_1 = 1(hc/2D)$

←——— D ———→

$E = 0$

photon energy levels

Figure 3
Energy level diagram for a photon trapped between two mirrors.

A MODEL ATOM

Now imagine that we replace the photons trapped between two mirrors with an electron between parallel walls located a distance D apart, as shown in Figure (4). For this model, the allowed standing wave patterns are again similar to the guitar string standing waves. The allowed electron wavelengths are

$$\lambda_n = \frac{2D}{n} \quad \begin{array}{l} \textit{allowed wavelength} \\ \textit{of an electron trapped} \\ \textit{between two walls} \end{array} \tag{1a}$$

The difference between having a photon trapped between mirrors and an electron between walls, is the formula for the energy of the particle. If the energy of the electron is non relativistic, then the formula for its

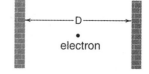

←-------- D --------→

• electron

Figure 4
Electron trapped between two walls.

kinetic energy is $1/2 \, mv^2$, not the Einstein formula $E = hc/\lambda$ that applies to photons. The difference arises because the electron has a rest mass while the photon does not.

For the electron trapped between walls, there is no electric potential energy like there was in the hydrogen atom. Thus we can take $1/2 \, mv^2$ as the formula for the electron's total energy, ignoring the electron's rest mass energy as we usually do in non relativistic calculations.

To relate the kinetic energy to the electron's allowed wavelength λ_n, we use de Broglie's formula $p = h/\lambda$. The easy way to do this is to express the energy $1/2 \, mv^2$ in terms of the electron's momentum $p = mv$. We get

$$E = 1/2 \, mv^2 = \frac{1}{2m}(mv)^2$$

$$E = \frac{p^2}{2m} \tag{4}$$

Next use the de Broglie formula $p = h/\lambda$ to give us

$$E_n = \frac{(h/\lambda_n)^2}{2m} = \frac{h^2}{2m\lambda_n^2} \tag{5}$$

as the formula for the energy of an electron of wavelength λ_n.

Finally use Equation (1), $\lambda_n = 2D/n$, for allowed electron wavelengths to get

$$E_n = \frac{h^2}{2m\left(\frac{2D}{n}\right)^2}$$

$$\boxed{E_n = n^2\left(\frac{h^2}{8mD^2}\right)} \tag{6}$$

This is our equation for the energy levels of an electron trapped between two plates separated by a distance D. The corresponding energy level diagram is shown in Figure (5). The energy levels go up as n^2 instead of being equally spaced as they were in the case of a photon trapped between two mirrors.

If the electron is in one of the higher levels and falls to a lower one, it will get rid of its energy by emitting a photon whose energy is equal to the difference in the energy of the two levels. Thus the trapped electron should emit a spectrum of radiation with sharp spectral lines, where the lines correspond to energy jumps between levels just as in the hydrogen atom. Thus the electron trapped between plates is effectively a model atom, complete with an energy level diagram and spectral lines.

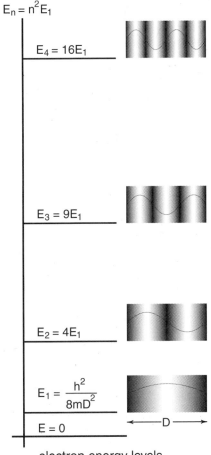

$$E_n = n^2 E_1$$

$E_4 = 16 E_1$

$E_3 = 9 E_1$

$E_2 = 4 E_1$

$E_1 = \frac{h^2}{8mD^2}$

$E = 0$

electron energy levels

Figure 5

Energy level diagram for an electron trapped between two walls.

Our model atom is not just a fantasy. With the techniques used to fabricate microchips, it has been possible to construct tiny boxes, the order of a few angstroms across, and trap electrons inside. An electron microscope photograph of these *quantum dots* as they are called, is shown in Figure (6). The allowed standing wave patterns are reasonably well represented by the sine wave patterns of Figure (5), where D is the smallest dimension of the box. Thus we predict that electrons trapped in these boxes should have allowed energies E_n close to those given by Equation (6), and emit discrete line spectra like an atom. This is precisely what they do. (Some of the low energy jumps are shown in Figure 7.)

In calculating with the model atom we have not fudged the theory in any way, either by modifying Newtonian mechanics or even picturing a wave chasing itself around in a circle. We see a spectrum resulting purely from a combination of the particle nature and the wave nature of electrons and photons, where the connection between the two points of view is de Broglie's formula $p = h/\lambda$.

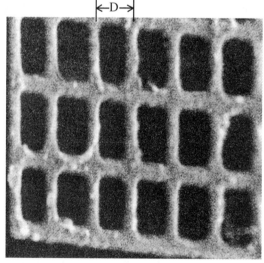

Figure 6
Grid of quantum dots. These cells are made on a silicon wafer with the same technology used in making electronic chips. An electron trapped in one of these cells has energy levels similar to those of our model atom. (See Scientific American, Jan. 1993, p118.)

Exercise 2

Assume that an electron is trapped between two walls a distance D apart. The distance D has been adjusted so that the lowest energy level is $E_1 = 0.375\,eV$.

(a) What is D?

(b) What are the energies, in eV, of the photons in the six longest wavelength spectral lines radiated by this system? Draw the energy level diagram for this system and show the electron jumps corresponding to each spectral line.

(c) What are the corresponding wavelengths, in cm and nm, of these six spectral lines?

(d) Where in the electromagnetic spectrum (infra red, visible, or ultra violet) do each of these spectral lines lie? If any of these lines are visible, what color are they? (Partial answer: the photon energies are 1.125, 1.875, 2.625, 3.00, 3.375, and 4.125 eV)

Exercise 3

Explain why an electron, confined in a box, cannot sit at rest. This is an important result whose consequences will be discussed next. Try to answer it now.

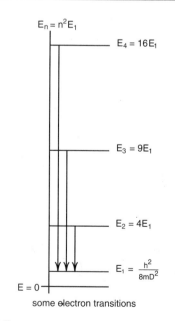

$E_n = n^2 E_1$

$E_4 = 16E_1$

$E_3 = 9E_1$

$E_2 = 4E_1$

$E_1 = \dfrac{h^2}{8mD^2}$

$E = 0$

some electron transitions

Figure 7
When an electron falls from one energy level down to another, the energy of the photon it emits equals the energy lost by the electron.

ZERO POINT ENERGY

One of the immediate consequences of the particle-wave nature of the electron is that a confined electron can never be at rest. The smaller the confinement, the greater the kinetic energy the electron must have. This follows from the fact that at least half a wavelength of the electron's wave must fit within the confining region. If D is the length of the smallest dimension of the confining region, then the electron's wavelength cannot be greater than 2D. But the smaller D is, the shorter the electron's wavelength, and the greater its kinetic energy.

The de Broglie wavelength formula $\lambda = h/p$ applies not only to photons and electrons, but to any particle, even an entire atom. As a result, an atom confined to a region of size D should have a wavelength no greater than $\lambda_1 = 2D$, and thus a minimum kinetic energy

$$E_{min} = \frac{h^2}{8m_{atom}D^2} \qquad (7)$$

where we simply replaced the electron's mass by the atom' mass in Equation (7). Equation (7) is somewhat approximate if the atom is confined on all sides in a three dimensional box, but it is reasonably accurate if D is the smallest dimension of the box.

An atom in a solid or a liquid is an example of a particle confined in a box. The atom is confined by its neighboring atoms as illustrated in Figure (8). We may think of its neighbors as forming a box of size D where D is the average spacing between atoms. Thus atoms in solids or liquids have a minimum kinetic energy given by Equation (7), and the atoms must be in continual motion *no matter how low the temperature*! Cooling the solid cannot get rid of this so-called *zero point energy*.

Figure 8
A helium atom in liquid helium is confined by its neighbors. As a result it has a zero point energy like an electron confined between walls.

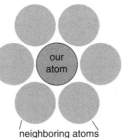

neighboring atoms

Exercise 4

In liquid helium, the helium atoms are about 3Å apart and the atoms have a mass essentially equal to 4 times the mass of a proton.

(a) what is the zero point energy, in ergs, of helium atoms in liquid helium?

(b) at what temperature T is the helium atom's thermal kinetic energy 3/2 kT equal to the zero point energy calculated in part (a)? [Answer: (a) 9.1×10^{-16}ergs, (b) 4.4 kelvin.]

Helium is an especially interesting substance to study at low temperatures because it is the only substance that remains a liquid all the way down to absolute zero. The only way you can freeze helium is to take it down to very low temperatures, and then squeeze it at relatively high pressure.

In all other substances, at low enough temperatures the atoms settle down to a solid array. To melt the solid, you have to add enough thermal energy to disrupt the molecular bonds that hold the atoms in a more or less fixed array.

Why can't helium atoms be cooled to the point where molecular forces dominate and the atoms form a solid array? Part of the answer is that the molecular forces between helium atoms are very weak, the weakest there is between any atoms. Consequently you have to go to very low temperatures before helium gas even becomes a liquid. At atmospheric pressure, helium becomes a liquid at 4.5 kelvins. To turn liquid helium into a solid you should have to go to still lower temperatures.

From Exercise 4, you saw that, in one sense, you cannot get helium to a lower temperature, at least as far as the kinetic energy of the atoms is concerned. The zero point energy of the atoms is as big as the thermal energy that the atoms would have at a few kelvin— 4.4 kelvin by our rough estimate in Exercise 4. As a result, cooling the helium further cannot remove enough kinetic energy to allow the helium liquid to freeze. Helium thus remains a liquid all the way down to absolute zero.

Definition of Temperature

This discussion raises interesting questions about the very concept of temperature. Our initial experimental definition of temperature was the ideal gas thermometer, which is based on the thermal kinetic energy of the particles. The simple idea of absolute zero was, that it was the point where all the thermal kinetic energy was gone and the atoms were at rest. Now we see that no matter how much thermal kinetic energy we try to remove, zero point or *quantum kinetic energy* remains. This is not a problem at ordinary temperatures, but it can significantly affect the behavior of matter at temperatures close to absolute zero.

At low temperatures, the ideal gas thermometer is not adequate, and a new definition of temperature is needed. That new definition is provided by the efficiency of Carnot's heat engine. As we suggested in the Entropy Essay, this gives us a definition of temperature based, not on the kinetic energy of the molecules, but upon the degree of randomness or disorder. A system at absolute zero is as perfectly ordered as it can be. If zero point energy is required by the particle wave nature of the atoms, if it cannot be removed, then the most organized, least disordered state of the system must include this zero point energy. Helium can go to its most ordered state at absolute zero, retain its zero point energy, and remain a liquid.

TWO DIMENSIONAL STANDING WAVES

In our discussion of percussion instruments in Chapter 15, we saw that a drumhead has a set of allowed standing wave patterns somewhat like the standing waves on a guitar string. On a guitar string we have one dimensional waves, while the drumhead has the two dimensional wave patterns. The six lowest frequency patterns are shown in Figure (15-28) repeated here. We could excite and observe individual standing waves using the apparatus shown in Figure (15-27).

That we get the same kind of standing wave patterns on an atomic scale is seen in Figure (9), which is a recent tunneling microscope image of an electron standing wave on the surface of a copper crystal. The standing wave, which is formed inside a corral of 48 iron atoms, has the same shape as one of the allowed standing waves on a drumhead. (This particular standing wave pattern is excited because the average wavelength in the standing wave is closest to the wavelength of the conduction electrons at the surface of the copper.)

A colleague Geoff Nunes, who works with scanning microscopes, describes the image: "The incredible power of today's personal computers has been made possible by our ability to make smaller and smaller transistors. The smallest transistor one could imagine building would be made up of single atoms. In a dramatic series of experiments at IBM, Don Eigler and his co-workers have shown how to use a tunneling microscope to move and arrange single atoms."

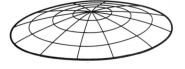
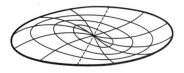
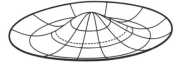
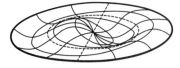

Figure 15-28 repeated
Standing waves on a drumhead.

"This picture (Figure 9) shows a ridge of 48 iron atoms arranged in a circle on the surface of a copper crystal. Electrons in the copper are reflected from these iron atoms much as the waves on the surface of a pond are reflected from anything at the surface: rocks, weeds, the shoreline. Inside the ring, the electron waves form a beautifully symmetric pattern. This pattern occurs often in the physical world. For example it is the shape that the head of a drum forms when struck. You can easily observe a similar pattern by gently skidding the base of a Styrofoam cup full of coffee across the surface of a table."

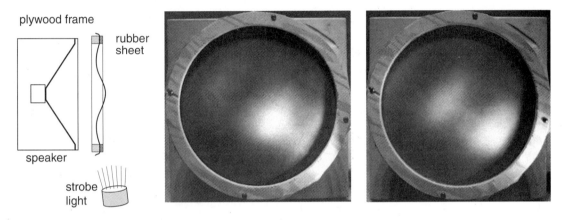

Figure 15-27
Exciting and observing the standing waves on a drumhead.

Figure 9
Conduction electrons on the surface of a copper crystal, forming a standing wave inside a corral of 48 iron atoms. The shape is the same as one of the symmetric standing waves on a drumhead. (Photo credits: Crommie and Eigler/IBM.)

CHAPTER 30 REVIEW

Once de Broglie pointed out that the electron's wave nature could explain the allowed orbits in Bohr's theory, it was not long before Schrödinger developed a wave equation that could be solved for a detailed picture of the hydrogen atom. We show much of that picture in Satellite Chapter 14 on Atoms and Chemistry.

The problem is that Schrödinger's wave equation involves mathematical techniques that go beyond even those we discuss in the calculus version of this text. Thus we are limited to showing results of calculations rather than actually doing the calculations. This may leave the impression that working with the particle-wave nature of matter is a difficult subject.

That is not an accurate impression. What is difficult about the hydrogen atom is its spherical geometry. Here in this chapter we deal with a model atom that has the much simpler rectangular geometry. It involves the same basic physics as the hydrogen atom, but uses the familiar wave patterns we first observed on a guitar string.

In our model atom, an electron or a photon is trapped between parallel walls separated by a distance d. The allowed wave patterns which we show in Figure (10) are analogous to the four longest wavelength patterns on a guitar string. The relationship between the wall spacing d and wavelength λ is

$$\lambda = \frac{2D}{n}$$

where n = 1, 2, 3 and 4 for these waves.

When we use de Broglie's formula $p = h/\lambda$, we find that the magnitude of the momenta of the trapped particle becomes

$$p_n = \frac{h}{\lambda_n} = \frac{nh}{2D} \quad (8)$$

A formula that applies to both electrons and photons.

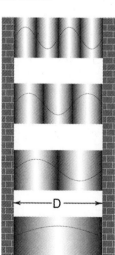

Figure 10
The allowed wave patterns for a particle (electron or photon) trapped between two walls.

The difference between electrons and photons shows up when we calculate the energy levels of the trapped particles. For a photon, the relationship between its energy E and momentum p is always

$$\boxed{E = pc} \quad \text{photon energy}$$

which we get from $E = hf = hc/\lambda = (h/\lambda)c = pc$. For a non relativistic electron we can use the kinetic energy formula

$$\boxed{E = \frac{p^2}{2m}} \quad \text{electron kinetic energy}$$

which we get from $E = mv^2/2 = m^2v^2/2m = p^2/2m$.

When we use these two formulas for energy, the photon energy levels become

$$\boxed{E_{photons} = p_n c = n\frac{hc}{2D}}$$

and the electron energy levels become

$$E_{electrons} = \frac{p^2}{2m} = \frac{1}{2m}\left[\frac{nh}{2D}\right]^2$$

$$\boxed{E_{electrons} = n^2\left[\frac{h^2}{8mD^2}\right]}$$

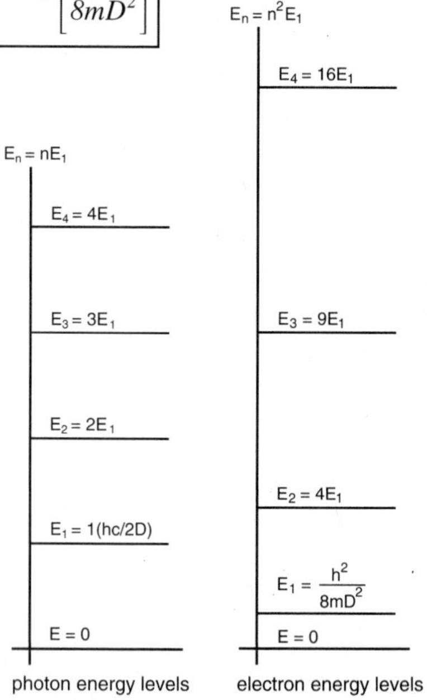

Figure 11
Comparison of the photon and electron energy levels for a particle trapped between two walls.

photon energy levels:

$E_n = nE_1$

$E_4 = 4E_1$

$E_3 = 3E_1$

$E_2 = 2E_1$

$E_1 = 1(hc/2D)$

$E = 0$

electron energy levels:

$E_n = n^2E_1$

$E_4 = 16E_1$

$E_3 = 9E_1$

$E_2 = 4E_1$

$E_1 = \frac{h^2}{8mD^2}$

$E = 0$

CHAPTER EXERCISES

By far the most important exercise you can do for this chapter is to start with a clean desk and a blank sheet of paper, and derive the energy level diagrams for both photons and electrons trapped between two walls. If you can do this without looking at the text, you have a good grasp of the material of this chapter!

Exercise 1 0n page 4

Calculate the 5 lowest energy levels for a photon trapped between two mirrors one angstrom apart.

Exercise 2 0n page 6

Analyze an electron trapped between two walls.

Exercise 3 0n page 6

Explain why an electron confined in a box cannot sit at rest.

Exercise 4 0n page 7

Zero point energy of an atom in liquid helium.

Chapter 31 non calculus

Quantum Mechanics I
Probability Interpretation

That light had both a particle and a wave nature became apparent with Einstein's explanation of the photoelectric effect in 1905. One might expect that such a discovery would lead to a flood of publications speculating on how light could behave both as a particle and a wave. But no such response occurred. The particle-wave nature was not looked at seriously for another 18 years, when de Broglie proposed that the particle-wave nature of the electron was responsible for the quantized energy levels in hydrogen. Even then there was great reluctance to accept de Broglie's proposal as a satisfactory thesis topic.

Why the reluctance? Why did it take so long to deal with the particle-wave nature, first of photons, then of electrons? What conceptual problems do we encounter when something behaves both as a particle and as a wave? How are these problems handled? That is the subject of the three quantum mechanics chapters which follow.

TWO SLIT EXPERIMENT

Of all the experiments in physics, it is perhaps the 2 slit experiment that most clearly, most starkly, brings out the problems encountered with the particle-wave nature of matter. For this reason we will use the 2 slit experiment as the basis for much of the discussion of this chapter.

Let us begin with a review of the 2 slit experiment for water and light waves. Figure (1) shows the wave pattern that results when water waves emerge from 2 slits. The lines of nodes are the lines along which the waves from one slit just cancel the waves coming from the other. Figure (2) shows our analysis of the 2 slit pattern. The path length difference to the first minimum must be half a wavelength $\lambda/2$. This gives us the two similar, shaded, triangles shown in Figure (2).

If y_{min} is much less than D, which it is for most 2 slit experiments, then the hypotenuse of the big triangle is approximately D, and equating corresponding sides of the similar triangles gives us the familiar relationship

$$\frac{\lambda/2}{d} = \frac{y_{min}}{D}$$

$$\boxed{\lambda = \frac{2y_{min}d}{D}} \tag{1}$$

Figure (3a) is the pattern we get on a screen if we shine a laser beam through 2 slits. To prove that the dark bands are where the light from one slit cancels the light from the other, we have in Figure (3b) moved a razor blade in front of one of the slits. We see that the dark bands disappear, and we are left with a one slit pattern. The dark bands disappear because there is no longer any cancellation of the waves from the 2 slits.

Figure 3a
Two slit interference pattern for light. The closely spaced dark bands are where the light from one slit cancels the light from the other.

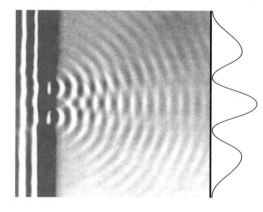

Figure 1
Water waves emerging from two slits.

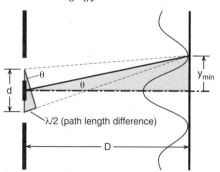

Figure 2
Analysis of the two slit pattern. We get a minimum when the path length difference is half a wavelength.

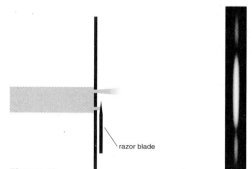

Figure 3b
Move a razor blade in front of one of the slits, and the closely spaced dark bands disappear. There is no more cancellation.

In 1961, Claus Jönsson did the 2 slit experiment using electrons instead of light, with the results shown in Figure (4). Assuming that the electron wavelength is given by the de Broglie formula $p = h/\lambda$, the dark bands are located where one would expect waves from the 2 slits to cancel. The 2 slit experiment gives the same result for light and electron waves.

The Two Slit Experiment from a Particle Point of View

In Figure (3a), the laser interference patterns were recorded on a photographic film. The pattern is recorded when individual photons of the laser light strike individual silver halide crystals in the film, producing a dark spot where the photon landed. Where the image is bright in the positive print, many photons have landed close together exposing many crystal grains.

In a more modern version of the experiment one could use an array of photo detectors to count the number of photons landing in each small element of the array. The number of counts per second in each detector could then be sent to a computer and the image reconstructed on the computer screen. The result would look essentially the same as the photograph in Figure (3a).

The point is that the image of the two slit wave pattern for light is obtained by counting particles, not by measuring some kind of wave height. When we look at the two slit experiment from the point of view of counting particles, the experiment takes on a new perspective.

Figure 4
Two slit experiment using electrons. (By C. Jönsson)

Imagine yourself shrunk down in size so that you could stand in front of a small section of the photographic screen in Figure (3a). Small enough that you want to avoid being hit by one of the photons on the laser beam. As you stand at the screen and look back at the slits, you see photons being sprayed out of both slits as if two machine guns were firing bullets at you, but you discover that there is a safe place to stand. There are these dark bands where the particles fired from one slit cancel the particles coming from the other.

When one of the slits is closed, there is no more cancellation, the dark bands disappear as seen in Figure (3b). There is no safe place to stand when particles are being fired at you from only one slit. It is hard to imagine in our large scale world how it would be safe to have two machine guns firing bullets at you, but be lethal if only one is firing. It is hard to visualize how machine gun bullets could cancel each other. But the particle-wave nature of light seems to require light particles to do so. No wonder the particle nature of light remained an enigma for nearly 20 years.

Two Slit Experiment— One Particle at a Time

You might object to our discussion of the problems involved in interpreting the two slit experiment. After all, Figure (1) shows water waves going through two slits and producing an interference pattern. The waves from one slit cancel the waves from the other at the lines of nodes. Yet water consists of particles—water molecules. If we can get a two slit pattern for water molecules, what is the big deal about getting a two slit pattern for photons ? Couldn't the photons somehow interact with each other the way water molecules do, and produce an interference pattern?

Photons do not interact with each other the way water molecules do. Two laser beams can cross each other with no detectable interaction, while two streams of water will splash off of each other. But one still might suspect that the cancellation in the two slit experiment for light is caused by some kind of interaction between the photons. This is even more likely in the case of electrons, which are strongly interacting charged particles.

a) 10 dots

b) 100 dots

c) 1000 dots

d) 10000 dots

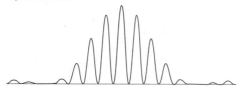

e) Predicted pattern

f) Experimental results by C. Jönsson

Figure 5
Computer simulation of the 2 slit electron diffraction experiment, as if the electrons had landed one at a time.

In an earlier text, we discussed the possibility of an experiment in which electrons would be sent through a two slit array, one electron at a time. The idea was to eliminate any possibility that the electrons could produce the two slit pattern by bouncing into each other or interacting in any way. Since the experiment had not yet been done, we drew a sketch of what the results should look like. That sketch appears in several introductory physics texts.

When he saw the sketch, Lawrence Campbell of the Los Alamos Scientific Laboratories did a computer simulation of the experiment. We will first discuss Campbell's simulation, and then compare the simulation with the results of the actual experiment which was performed 20 years later in 1989.

It is not too hard to guess some of the results of sending electrons through two slits, one at a time. After the first electron goes through, you end up with one dot on the screen showing where the electron hit. The single dot is not a wave pattern. After two electrons, two dots; you cannot make much of a wave pattern out of two dots.

If, after many thousands of electrons have hit the screen, you end up with a two slit pattern like that shown in Figure (5f), that means that none of the electrons land where there will eventually be a dark band. You know where the first dot, and the second dot, cannot be located. Although two dots do not suggest a wave pattern, some aspects of the wave have already imposed themselves by preventing the dots from being located in a dark band.

To get a better idea of what is happening, let us look at Campbell's simulation in Figure (5). In (5a), and (5b) we see 10 dots and 100 dots respectively. In neither is there an apparent wave pattern, both look like a fairly random scatter of dots. But by the time there are 1000 dots seen in (5c), a fairly distinctive interference pattern is emerging. With 10,000 dots of (5d), we see a close resemblance between Campbell's simulation and Jönsson's experimental results. Figure (5e) shows the wave pattern used for the computer simulation.

Although the early images in Figure (5) show nearly random patterns, there must be some order. Not only do the electrons not land where there will be a dark band, but they must also accumulate in greater numbers where the brightest bands will eventually be. If this were a roulette type of game in Las Vegas, you should put your money on the center of the brightest band as being the location most likely to be hit by the next electron.

Campbell's simulation was done as follows. Each point on the screen was assigned a probability. The probability was set to zero at the dark bands and to the greatest value in the brightest band. Where each electron landed was randomly chosen, but a randomness governed by the assigned probability.

How to assign a probability to a random event is illustrated by a roulette wheel. On the wheel, there are 100 slots, of which 49 are red, 49 black and 2 green. Thus where the ball lands, although random, has a 49% chance of being on red, 49% on black, 2% on green, and 0% on blue, there being no blue slots.

In the two slit simulation, the probability of the electron landing at some point was proportional to the intensity of the two slit wave pattern at that point. Where the wave was most intense, the electron is most likely to land. Initially the pattern looks random because the electrons can land with roughly equal probability in any of the bright bands. But after many thousands of electrons have landed, you see the details of the two slit wave pattern. The dim bands are dimmer than the bright ones because there was a lower probability that the electron could land there.

Figure (6) shows the two slit experiment performed in 1989 by Akira Tonomura and colleagues. The experiment involved a novel use of a superconductor for the two slits, and the incident beam contained so few electrons per second that no more than one electron was between the slits and the screen at any one time. The screen consisted of an array of electron detectors which recorded the time of arrival of each electron in each detector. From this data the researchers could reconstruct the electron patterns after 10 electrons (6a), 180 electrons (6b), 3000 electrons (6c), 20,000 electrons (6d) and finally after 70,000 electrons in Figure (6e). Just as in Campbell's simulation, the initially random looking patterns emerge into the full two slit pattern when enough electrons have hit the detectors.

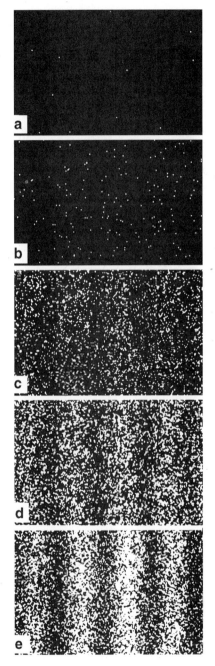

Figure 6
Experiment in which the 2 slit electron interference pattern is built up one electron at a time. (A. Tonomura, J. Endo, T. Matsuda, T. Kawasaki, American Journal of Physics, Feb. 1989. See also Physics Today, April 1990, Page 22.)

BORN'S INTERPRETATION OF THE PARTICLE WAVE

In 1926, while calculating the scattering of electron waves, Max Born discovered an interpretation of the electron wave that we still use today. In Born's picture, the electron is actually a particle, but it is the electron wave that governs the behavior of the particle. The electron wave is a probability wave governing the probability of where you will find the electron.

To apply Born's interpretation to the two slit electron experiment, we do what Campbell did in the simulation of Figure (5). We first calculate what the wave pattern at the screen would be for a wave passing through the two slits. It is the two slit interference pattern we have seen for water waves, light waves and electron waves. ***We then interpret the intensity of the pattern at some point on the screen as being proportional to the probability that the electron will land at that point.*** We cannot predict where any given electron will actually land, any more than we can predict where the ball will end up on the roulette wheel. But we can predict what the pattern will look like after many electrons have landed. If we repeat the experiment, the electrons will not land in the same places, but eventually the same two slit pattern will result.

Exercise 1

Figure (29-16) reproduced here, shows the diffraction pattern produced when a beam of electrons is scattered by the atoms of a graphite crystal. Explain what you would expect to see if the electrons went through the graphite crystal one at a time and you could watch the pattern build up on the screen. Could you market this apparatus in Las Vegas, and if so, how would you use it?

Figure 29-16
Diffraction pattern produced by electrons passing through a graphite crystal.

PHOTON WAVES

Both electrons and photons have a particle-wave nature related by the de Broglie formula $p = h/\lambda$, and both produce a two slit interference pattern. Thus one would expect that the same probability interpretation should apply to electron waves and light waves.

We have seen, however, that a light wave, according to Maxwell's equations, consists of a wave of electric and magnetic fields $\vec{E}$ and $\vec{B}$. These are vector fields that at each point in space have both a magnitude and a direction. Since probabilities do not point anywhere, we cannot directly equate $\vec{E}$ and $\vec{B}$ to a probability.

To see how to interpret the wave nature of a photon, let us first consider something like a radio wave or a laser beam that contains many billions of photons. In our discussion of capacitors in Chapter 22, we saw that the energy density in a classical electric field was given by

$$\left.\begin{array}{l} \textit{energy density in} \\ \textit{an electric field} \end{array}\right\} = \frac{\varepsilon_0 E^2}{2} \qquad (22\text{-}37)$$

where $E^2 = \vec{E} \cdot \vec{E}$. In an electromagnetic wave there are equal amounts of energy in the electric and the magnetic fields. Thus the energy density in a classical electromagnetic field is twice as large as that given by Equation (22-37), and we have

$$\left.\begin{array}{l} \textit{energy density in an} \\ \textit{electromagnetic wave} \end{array}\right\} = \varepsilon_0 E^2 \frac{joules}{meter^3}$$

If we now picture the electromagnetic wave as consisting of photons whose energy is given by Einstein's photoelectric formula

$$E_{photon} = hf \frac{joules}{photon}$$

then the density of photons in the wave is given by

$$n = \frac{\varepsilon_0 E^2 \, joules/meter^3}{hf \;\; joules/photon}$$

$$n = \frac{\varepsilon_0 E^2}{hf} \frac{photons}{meter^3} \quad \begin{array}{l} \textit{density of photons} \\ \textit{in an electromagnetic} \\ \textit{wave of frequency f} \end{array} \quad (2)$$

where f is the frequency of the wave.

(In Exercise 2, we have you estimate the density of photons one kilometer from the antenna of the student AM radio station at Dartmouth College. The answer is around .25 billion photons per cm^3— so many photons that it would be hard to detect them individually.)

Exercise 2

To estimate the density of photons in a radio wave, we can, instead of calculating $\vec{E}$ for the wave, simply use the fact that we know the power radiated by the station. As an example, suppose that we are one kilometer away from a 1000 watt radio station whose frequency is 1.4×10^6 Hz. A 1000 watt station radiates 1000 joules of energy per second or 10^{-6} joules in a nanosecond. In one nanosecond the radiated wave moves out one foot or about 1/3 of a meter. If we ignore spatial distortions of the wave, like reflections from the ground, etc., then we can picture this 10^{-6} joules of energy as being located in a spherical shell 1/3 of a meter thick, expanding out from the antenna.

(a) What is the total volume of a spherical shell 1/3 of a meter thick and 1 kilometer in radius?

(b) What is the average density of energy, in joules/m³ of the radio wave 1 kilometer from the antenna?

(c) What is the energy, in joules, of one photon of frequency 1.4×10^6 Hz?

(d) What is the average density of photons in the radio wave 1 kilometer from the station? Give the answer first in photons/m³ and then photons per cubic centimeter. (The answer should be about .25 billion photons/cm³.)

Now imagine that instead of being one kilometer from the radio station, you were a million kilometers away. Since the volume of a spherical shell 1/3 of a meter thick increases as r^2, [the volume being $(1/3) \times 4\pi r^2$] the density of photons would decrease as $1/r^2$. Thus if you were 10^6 times as far away, the density of photons would be 10^{-12} times smaller. At one million kilometers, the average density of photons in the radio wave would be

$$\left.\begin{array}{l} \text{number of photons} \\ \text{per cubic centimeter} \\ \text{at 1 million kilometers} \end{array}\right\} = \frac{\text{number at 1km}}{10^{12}}$$

$$= \frac{.25 \times 10^9}{10^{12}}$$

$$= .00025 \ \frac{\text{photons}}{\text{cm}^3}$$

In the classical picture of Maxwell's equations, the radio wave has a continuous electric and magnetic field even out at 1 million kilometers. You could calculate the value of $\vec{E}$ and $\vec{B}$ out at this distance, and the result would be sinusoidally oscillating fields whose structure is that shown back in Figure (24-5). But if you went out there and tried to observe something, all you would find is a few photons, on the order of .25 per liter (about one per gallon of space). If you look in 1 cubic centimeter of space, chances are you would not find a photon.

So how do you use Maxwell's equations to predict the results of an experiment to detect photons a million kilometers from the antenna? First you use Maxwell's equation to calculate $\vec{E}$ at the point of interest, then evaluate the quantity $(\varepsilon_0 E^2/hf)$, and finally interpret the result as the probability of finding a photon in the region of interest. If, for example, we were looking in a volume of one liter (1000cm³), the probability of finding a photon there would be about .25 or 25%.

This is an explicit prescription for turning Maxwell's theory of electromagnetic radiation into a probability wave for photons. If the wave is intense, as it was close to the antenna, then $(\varepsilon_0 E^2/hf)$ represents the density of photons. If the wave is very faint, then $(\varepsilon_0 E^2/hf)$ becomes the probability of finding a photon in a certain volume of space.

Exercise 3

The laser we used to create the patterns in Figure (3) is a 1 milliwatt (10^{-3} watts) laser. That means that the laser emits 10^{-3} joules of energy every second. The wavelength of the laser beam is 660 nanometers, as we found in Exercise (5) on page (25-13). How maqny photons are in 1 foot (1/3 meter) of the beam? (Hint: how long is the laser beam if you aim the laser up into a clear sky and turn it on for one second?)

REFLECTION AND FLUORESCENCE

An interesting example of the probability interpretation of light waves is provided by the phenomena of reflection and of fluorescence.

When a light beam is reflected from a metal surface, the angle of reflection, labeled θ_r in Figure (7a), is equal to the angle of incidence θ_i. The reason for this is seen in Figure (7b). The incident light wave is scattered by many atoms in the metal surface. The scattered waves add up to produce the reflected wave as shown in Figure (7b). Any individual photon in the incident wave must have an equal probability of being scattered by all of these atoms in order that the scattered probability waves add up to the reflected wave shown in (7b).

When you have a fluorescent material, you see a rather uniform eerie glow rather than a reflected wave. The light comes out in all directions as in Figure (8a).

The wavelength of the light from a fluorescent material is not the same wavelength as the incident light. What happens is that a photon in the incident beam strikes and excites an individual atom in the material. The excited atom then drops back down to the ground state radiating two or more photons to get rid of the excitation energy. (Ultraviolet light is often used in the incident beam, and we see the lower energy visible photons radiated from the fluorescing material.)

The reason that fluorescent light emerges in many directions rather than in a reflected beam is that an individual photon in the incident beam is absorbed by and excites one atom in the fluorescent material. There is no probability that it has struck any of the other atoms. The fluorescent light is then radiated as a circular wave from that atom, and the emerging photon has a more or less equal probability of coming out in all directions above the material.

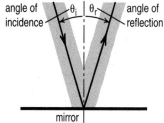

Figure 7a
When a light wave strikes a mirror, the angle of incidence equals the angle of reflection.

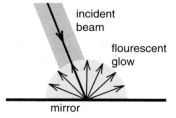

Figure 8a
When a beam of light strikes a fluorescent material, we see an eerie glow rather than a normal reflected light.

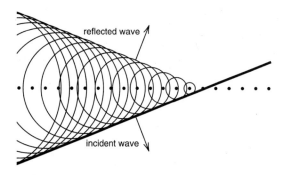

Figure 7b
The reflected wave results from the scattering of the incident wave by many atoms. If the incident wave contains a single photon, that photon must have an equal probability of being scattered by many atoms in order to emerge in the reflected wave.

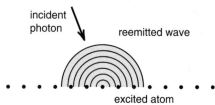

Figure 8b
Fluorescence occurs when an individual atom is excited and radiates its extra energy as two distinct photons. Since there is no chance that the radiation came from other atoms, the radiated wave emerges only from the excited atom.

CHAPTER 31 REVIEW

In a lecture demonstration we sent a laser beam through two closely spaced slits and observed the two slit interference pattern on a distant wall. In the pattern there is a series of regularly spaced dark bands which are caused by the cancellation of the waves from the two slits. We demonstrate this cancellation by sliding a razor blade in front of one of the slits as shown in Figure (3). The result is that the dark bands disappear and we see only the single slit diffraction pattern.

You can do a similar demonstration with water waves in a ripple tank. What were the dark bands in the laser beam demonstration are now the lines of nodes that emerge from the two slits as seen in Figure (25-9). Close one of the slits and the lines of nodes will disappear.

In 1961, Claus Jönsson sent a beam of electrons through two slits and got the interference pattern shown in Figure (4). The dark bands were located just where you would expect if the electrons behaved as a wave with a wavelength given by de Broglie's formula $p = h/\lambda$.

Did we feel that Jönsson's two slit electron wave pattern was a complete demonstration of the particle-wave nature of the electron? Not quite.

After all, water waves consist of particles, water molecules. And the two slit pattern in a ripple tank is not a demonstration of the wave nature of water molecules. Instead the two slit pattern results from the beams of waves from the two slits interacting with each other, cancelling at the lines of nodes. One could wonder if the dark lines in Jönsson pattern resulted from a similar interaction between beams of electrons emerging from the two slits.

To prevent such an interpretation, we proposed an experiment in which the electrons would be sent through the slits one at a time. In such an experiment there would be no possibility of the beams of electrons from one slit interacting with beams from the other slit. If, after many electrons had finally gone through, we still ended up with a two slit interference pattern, we would have direct experimental evidence that the electron's wave went through both slits even though the electron itself may have gone through only one of the slits. This would be a demonstration of the fundamental problem one faces with the particle-wave nature of matter.

When Jönsson did the electron two slit experiment, the equipment needed to do the experiment one electron at a time was not available. Thus for a textbook we drew sketches of what to expect as the electron interference pattern built one dot at a time. Initially we should see a random pattern of dots. After enough electrons have landed, the two slit pattern should emerge. The initial pattern cannot be completely random, because no electron can land where there will eventually be a dark band in the two slit pattern.

Larry Campbell at Los Alamos Laboratories cleaned up our crude sketches with the computer plots that are shown in Figure (5). He had the computer plot white dots one at a time, with a probability based program. The probability of a dot being drawn at any point on the screen was proportional to the intensity of the two slit pattern. There is a high probability of the electron or dot landing in one of the bright bands, and zero probability of it landing in the center of a dark band.

Twenty years later the experiment was actually performed with the results shown in Figure (6). There is an excellent match between the experimental results of Figure (6) and the probability analysis of Figure (5). This provides strong evidence supporting Max Born's interpretation the electron wave as a probability wave.

Review Continued
Quantum Mechanics

It is the probability interpretation of the particle wave that lies at the core of quantum mechanics. The rule for doing calculations in quantum mechanics is to first calculate the wave pattern you expect for some given experimental situation. That could be the two slit pattern we have just discussed, the wave pattern we described in our model atom of the last chapter or the electron wave patterns in atoms. Once you have solved for the wave pattern, you interpret the intensity of the wave pattern as being proportional to the probability of finding the particle at that point in the wave.

For example, the electron clouds which chemists call orbitals, are the calculated allowed standing wave patterns in the various atoms and molecules. Once the wave pattern has been calculated using Schroedinger's equation for electrons, you square the wave amplitude to get the intensity and interpret that to be the probability of finding an electron there. Basically this is how you do Quantum Mechanics.

CHAPTER EXERCISES

Exercise 1   0n page 6

Probability interpretation of the electron diffraction pattern produced by electrons passing through a graphite crustal.

Exercise 2   0n page 7

Calculating the density of photons in a radio wave.

Exercise 3   0n page 7

Calculating the number of photons in a one foot length of a laser beam.

Chapter 32 non calculus

Quantum Mechanics II
The Uncertainty Principle –
Position and Momentum

*In the last chapter, we studied the two slit interference pattern produced by electrons going through two slits, one at a time. We found that we could explain the way the pattern emerged by assuming that the probability of an electron landing at a point on the screen was proportional to the intensity of the wave pattern formed by a wave passing through **both slits**, even if we assume that the particle itself went through only one of the slits.*

The results of this two slit experiment are consistent with Max Born's interpretation of an electron wave as a probability wave, whose intensity at some point is proportional to the probability of finding the electron at that point.

Not all physicists were happy with the probability interpretation. Einstein himself was known for the comment that "God does not play dice".

We begin this chapter with a thought experiment designed to show that the probability interpretation of an electron wave might lead to inconsistent, unreasonable results. The idea is to do a delicate experiment in which we observe the electrons as they go through the slits. If we know which slit each electron went through, the entire probability wave must have gone through the same slit and we should get a single slit pattern. The thought experiment ends by showing that such an attempt must fail if all matter has a particle-wave nature obeying the de Broglie relationship $p = h/\lambda$.

*In physics, when we absolutely cannot do something, we turn that failure into a basic physical law. The principle of relativity tells us that we cannot do any experiment that allows us to detect our motion relative to empty space. The failure of the thought experiment we discuss in this chapter, is a consequence of a basic law called the **uncertainty principle.***

There are two mathematically equivalent forms of the uncertainty principle. One, which involves the simultaneous measurement of the position and momentum of an object, is the main focus of this chapter. The other form involves the measurement of the energy in a short time. That is the focus of the next chapter.

A CLOSER LOOK AT THE TWO SLIT EXPERIMENT

While the probability interpretation of electron and photon waves provides a reasonable explanation of some phenomena, the interpretation is not without problems. To illustrate what these problems are, consider the following thought experiment.

Imagine that we have a large box with two slits at one end and a photographic film at the other end, as shown in Figure (1). Far from the slits is an electron gun that produces a weak beam of electrons, so weak that on the average only one electron per hour passes through the slits and strikes the film. For simplicity we will assume that the electrons go through the slits on the hour, there being the 9:00 AM electron, the 10:00 AM electron, etc.

The electron gun is one of the simple electron guns we discussed back in Chapter 21. The beam is so spread out that there is no way it can be aimed at one slit or the other. Our beam covers both slits, meaning that each of the electrons has an equal chance of going through the top or bottom slit.

We will take the probability interpretation of the electron wave seriously. If the electron has an equal probability of passing through either slit, then an equally intense probability wave must emerge from both slits. When the probability waves get to the photographic film, there will be bands along which waves from one slit cancel waves from the other, and we should eventually build up a two slit interference pattern on the film.

Suppose that on our first run of the thought experiment, we do build up a two slit pattern after many hours and many electrons have hit the film.

We will now repeat the experiment with a new twist. We ask for a volunteer to go inside the box, look at the slits, and see which one each electron went through. John volunteers, and we give him a sheet of paper to write down the results. To make the job easier, we tell him to just look at the bottom slit on the hour to see if the electron went through that slit. If, for example, he sees an electron come out of the bottom slit at 9:00 AM, then the 9:00 AM electron went through the bottom slit. If he saw no electron at 10:00 AM, then the 10:00 AM electron must have gone through the upper slit.

If John does his job carefully, what kind of a pattern should build up on the film after many electrons have gone through? If the 9:00 AM electron was seen to pass through the bottom slit, then there is no probability that it went through the top slit. As a result, a probability wave can emerge only from the bottom slit, and there can be no cancellation of probability waves at the photographic film. Since the 10:00 AM electron did not go through the bottom slit, the probability wave must have emerged only from the top slit and there again can be no cancellation of waves at the photographic film.

If John correctly determines which slit each electron went through, there can be no cancellation of waves from the two slits, and we have to end up with a one slit pattern on the film. Just the knowledge of which slit each electron went through has to change the two slit pattern into a one slit pattern. With Born's probability interpretation of electron waves, ***knowledge*** of which slit the electrons go through ***changes the result of the experiment***. Does this really happen, or have we entered the realm of metaphysics?

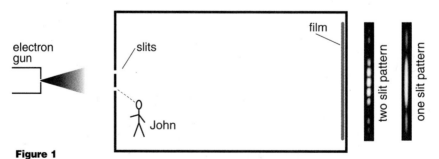

Figure 1
In this thought experiment, we consider the possibility that someone is looking at the two slits to see which slit each electron comes through.

Let us return to our thought experiment. John has been in the box for a long time now, so that a number of electrons have hit the film. We take the film out, develop it, and clearly see a two slit interference pattern emerging. There are the dark bands along which waves from one slit cancel the waves from the other slit.

Then we go over to the door on the side of the box, open it and let John out, asking to see his results. We look at his sheet of paper and nothing is written on it. "What were you doing all of that time?" we ask. "What do you mean, what was I doing? How could I do anything? You were so careful sealing up the box from outside disturbances that it was dark inside. I couldn't see a thing and just had to wait until you opened the door. Not much of a fun experiment."

"Next time," John said, "give me a flashlight so I can see the electrons coming through the slits. Then I can fill out your sheet of paper."

"Better be careful," Jill interrupts, "about what kind of a flashlight you give John. A flashlight produces a beam of photons, and John can only see a passing electron if one of the flashlight's photons bounces off the electron."

"Remember that the energy of a photon is proportional to its frequency. If the photons from John's flashlight have too high a frequency, the photon hitting the passing electron will change the motion of the electron and mess up the two slit pattern. Give John a flashlight that produces low frequency, low energy photons, so he won't mess up the experiment."

"But," Bill responds, "a low frequency photon is a long wavelength photon. Remember that demonstration where waves were scattered from a tiny object? The scattered waves were circular, and contained no information about the shape of the object [Figure (29-1)]. You can't use waves to study details that are much smaller than the wavelength of the wave. That is why optical microscopes can't be used to study viruses that are smaller than a wavelength of visible light."

"If John's flashlight," Bill continues, "produced photons whose wavelength was longer than the distance between the two slits, then even if he hit the electron with one of the photons in the wave, John could not tell which slit the electron came through."

"Let us do some calculations," the professor says. "The most delicate way we can mess up the experiment is to hit an electron sideways, changing the electron's direction of motion so that if it were heading toward a maxima, it will instead land in a minima, filling up the dark bands and making the pattern look like a one slit pattern. Here is a diagram for the situation [Figure (2)]."

Figure 29-1 (reproduced)
If an object is smaller than a wavelength, the scattered waves are circular and do not contain information about the shape of the object.

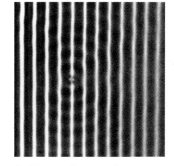

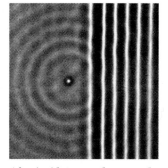

Incident and scattered wave.   *After incident wave has passed.*

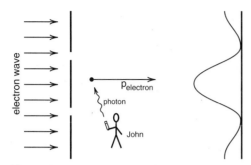

Figure 2a
In order to see the electron, John uses a flashlight, and strikes the electron with a photon.

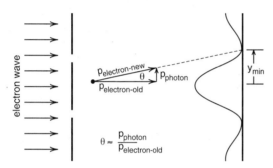

Figure 2b
Assume the photon's momentum has been absorbed by the electron. This could deflect the electron's path by an angle θ.

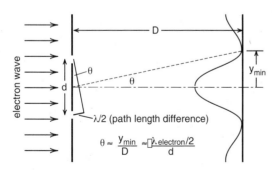

Figure 2c
Analysis of the two slit pattern. The angle to the first minimum is determined by using similar triangles. If the angle θ is small, then sin θ ≈ θ.

"In the top sketch (2a), John is shining his flashlight at an electron that has just gone through the slit and is heading toward the central maximum. In the middle sketch (2b), the photon has knocked the electron sideways, so that it is now headed toward the first minimum in the diffraction pattern. Let us assume that all the photon's momentum $\vec{p}_{photon}$ has been transferred to the electron, so that the electron's new momentum is now

$$\vec{p}_{electron-new} = \vec{p}_{electron-old} + \vec{p}_{photon} \qquad (1)$$

The angle θ by which the electron is deflected is approximately given by

$$\theta \approx \frac{p_{photon}}{p_{electron}} = \frac{h/\lambda_{photon}}{h/\lambda_{electron}}$$

$$\theta \approx \frac{\lambda_{electron}}{\lambda_{photon}} \qquad (2)$$

where we used the de Broglie formula for the photon and electron momenta."

"In the bottom sketch we have the usual analysis of a two slit pattern. If the angle θ to the first minimum is small, which it usually is for a two slit experiment, then by similar triangles we have

$$\theta \approx \frac{y_{min}}{D} = \frac{\lambda_{electron}/2}{d} \qquad (3)$$

Equating the values of θ from Equations (3) and (2), we get

$$\theta = \frac{\lambda_{electron}}{2d} = \frac{\lambda_{electron}}{\lambda_{photon}} \qquad (4)$$

"Look!" Bill says, "$\lambda_{electron}$ cancels and we are left with "

$$\boxed{\lambda_{photon} = 2d} \qquad (5)$$

"I told you," Jill interrupts, "that you had to be careful about what wavelength photons John could use. Here we see that if John's photons have a wavelength of 2d or less, his photons will carry enough of a punch, enough momentum, to destroy the two slit pattern. Be sure John's photons have a wavelength longer than 2d so that they will be incapable of knocking an electron from a maxima to a minima."

"No way," responds Bill. "A wavelength of 2d is already too big. John cannot use photons with a wavelength any greater than the slit separation d if he wants to see which slit the electron went through. And you want him to use photons with a wavelength greater than 2d!"

"That's the dilemma," the professor replies. "If John uses photons whose wavelength is short enough to see which slit the electron went through, he is likely to mess up the experiment and destroy the two slit pattern."

"It looks like the very act of getting information is messing up the experiment," Jill muses.

"It messes it up if we use photons," Bill responds." Let us work out a better experiment where we do a more delicate measurement to see which slit the electron went through. Do the experiment so delicately that we do not affect the motion of the electron, but accurately enough to see which slit the electron went through."

"How would you do that?" Jill asks.

"Maybe I would put a capacitor plate on one of the slits," Bill responds, "and record the capacitor voltage. If the electron went through that slit, the electric field of the electron should affect the voltage on the capacitor and leave a blip on my oscilloscope screen. If I don't see a blip, the electron went through the other slit."

"Would this measurement affect the motion of the electron?" Jill asks.

"I don't see why," Bill responds.

"Think about this," the professor interrupts. "We are now interpreting the electric and magnetic fields of a light wave as a probability wave for photons. In this view, all electric and magnetic phenomena are ultimately caused by photons. The electric and magnetic fields we worked with earlier in the course are now to be thought of as a way of describing the behavior of the underlying photons."

"That's crazy," Bill argues. "You mean, for example, that the good old $1/r^2$ coulomb force law that holds the hydrogen atom together, is caused by photons? I don't see how."

"It's hard to visualize," the professor replies, "but you can use a photon picture to explain every detail of the interaction between the electron and proton in the hydrogen atom. That calculation was actually done back in 1947. The modern view is that all electric and magnetic phenomena are caused by photons."

"If all electric and magnetic phenomena are caused by photons," Jill observes, "then Bill's capacitor plate and voltmeter, which uses electromagnetic phenomena, is based on photons. Since photons obey the de Broglie relationship, the photons in Bill's experiment should have the same effect as the photons from John's flashlight. If John's photons mess up the experiment, Bill's should too!"

"I have an idea." Bill says. "Aren't there such a things as gravitational waves?"

"Yes," replies the professor. "They are very hard to make, and very hard to detect. We have not been able to make or detect them yet in the laboratory. But back in the 1970s Joe Taylor at the University of Massachusetts discovered a pair of binary neutron stars orbiting about each other. Since the stars eclipse each other, Taylor could accurately measure the orbital period."

"According to Einstein's theory of gravity, the orbiting neutron stars should radiate gravitational waves and lose energy. Joe Taylor has conclusively shown that the pair of stars are losing energy just as predicted by Einstein's theory. Taylor got the Nobel prize for this work in 1993."

"Is Einstein's theory a quantum theory?" Bill asks.

"What do you mean by that?" Jill asks.

"I mean," Bill responds, "in Einstein's theory, do gravitational waves have a particle-wave nature like electromagnetic waves? Are there particles in a gravitational wave like there are photons in a light wave?"

"Not in Einstein's theory," the professor replies. "Einstein's theory is strictly a classical theory. No particles in the wave."

"Then if Einstein's theory is correct," Bill continues, "I should be able to make a gravitational wave with a very short wavelength and very little energy."

"Couldn't I then use this short wavelength, low energy, gravitational wave to see which slit the electron went through? I would make the wavelength much shorter than the slit spacing d so that there would be no doubt about which slit the electron went through. But I would use a very low energy, delicate wave so that I would not affect the motion of the electron."

"You could do that if Einstein's theory is right," the professor replies.

"But," Bill responds, "that allows me to tell which slit the electron went through without destroying the two slit pattern. What happens to the probability interpretation of the electron wave? If I know which slit the electron went through, the probability wave must have come from that slit, and we must get a one slit pattern. If John used gravitational waves instead of light waves in his flashlight, he could observe which slit the electron went through without destroying the two slit pattern."

"You have just stumbled upon one of the major outstanding problems in physics," the professor replies. "As far as we know there are four basic forces in nature. They are: gravity, the electromagnetic force, the weak interaction, and the so-called gluon force that holds quarks together. I listed these in the order in which they were discovered."

"Now three of these forces, all but gravity, are known to have a particle-wave nature like light. All the particles obey the de Broglie relation $p = h/\lambda$."

"As a result, if we perform our two slit electron experiment, trying to see which slit the electron went through, and we use apparatus based on non gravitational forces, we run into the same problem we had with John's flashlight. The only chance we have for detecting which slit the electron went through without messing up the two slit pattern, is to use gravity."

"Could Einstein be wrong?" Jill asks. "Couldn't gravitational waves also have a particle nature? Couldn't the gravitational particles also obey the de Broglie relation?"

"Perhaps," the professor replies. "For years, physicists have speculated that gravity should have a particle-wave nature. They have even named the particle—they call it a *graviton*. One problem is that gravitons should be very, very, hard to detect. The only way we know that gravitational waves actually exist is from Joe Taylor's binary neutron stars. There are various experiments designed to directly observe gravitational waves, but no waves have yet been seen in these experiments."

"In the case of electromagnetism, we saw electromagnetic radiation—i.e., light—long before photons were detected in Hertz's photoelectric effect experiment. After gravitational waves are detected, then we will have to do the equivalent of a photoelectric effect experiment for gravity in order to see the individual gravitons. The main problem here is that the gravitational radiation we expect to see, like that from massive objects such as neutron stars, is very low frequency radiation. Thus we would be dealing with very low energy gravitons which would be hard to detect individually."

"And there is another problem," the professor continues, "no one has yet succeeded in constructing a consistent quantum theory of gravity. There are mathematical problems that have yet to be overcome. At the present time, the only consistent theory of gravity we have is Einstein's classical theory."

"It looks like two possibilities," Jill says. "If the probability interpretation of electron waves is right, then there has to be a quantum theory of gravity, gravitons have to exist. If Einstein's classical theory is right, then there is some flaw in the probability interpretation."

"That is the way it stands now," the professor replies.

THE UNCERTAINTY PRINCIPLE

We have just seen that, for the probability interpretation of particle-waves to be a viable theory, there **must** be no way we can detect which slit the electron went through without destroying the two slit pattern. Also we have seen that if every particle and every force have a particle-wave nature obeying the de Broglie relationship $\lambda = h/p$, then there **is** no way we can tell which slit the electron went through without destroying the two slit pattern.

Both the particle-wave nature of matter, and the probability interpretation of particle waves, lead to a basic limitation on our ability to make experimental measurements. This basic limitation was discovered by Werner Heisenberg shortly before Schrödinger developed his wave equation for electrons. Heisenberg called this limitation the **uncertainty principle**.

When you cannot do something, when there is really no way to do something, physicists give the failure a name, and call it a basic law of physics. We began the text with the observation that you cannot detect uniform motion. Michaelson and Morley thought they could, repeatedly tried to do so, and failed. This failure is known as the principle of relativity which Einstein used as the foundation of his theories of relativity. Throughout the text we have seen the impact of this simple idea. When combined with Maxwell's theory of light, it implied that light traveled at the same speed relative to all observers. That implied moving clocks ran slow, moving lengths contracted, and the mass of a moving object increased with velocity. This led to the relationship $E = mc^2$ between mass and energy, and to the connections between electric and magnetic fields. The simple idea that you cannot measure uniform motion has an enormous impact on our understanding of the way matter behaves.

Now, with the particle-wave nature of matter, we are encountering an equally universal restriction on what we can measure, and that restriction has an equally important impact on our understanding of the behavior of matter. Our discussion of the uncertainty principle comes at the end of the text rather than at the beginning only because it has taken a while to develop the concepts we need to explain this restriction. With the principle of relativity we could rely on the student's experience with uniform motion, clocks and meter sticks. For the uncertainty principle, we need some understanding of the behavior of particles and waves, and as we shall see, Fourier analysis plays an important role.

There are two forms of the uncertainty principle, one related to measurements of position and momentum, and the other related to measurements of time and energy. They are not separate laws, one can be derived from the other. The choice of which to use is a matter of convenience. Our discussion of the two slit experiment and the de Broglie relationship naturally leads to the position-momentum form of the law, while Fourier analysis naturally introduces the time-energy form.

POSITION-MOMENTUM FORM OF THE UNCERTAINTY PRINCIPLE

In our two slit thought experiment, in the attempt to see which slit the electron went through, we used a beam of photons whose momenta was related to their wavelength by $p = h/\lambda$. The wave nature of the photon is important because we cannot see details smaller than a wavelength λ when we scatter waves from an object. When we use waves of wavelength λ, the uncertainty in our measurement is at least as large as λ. Let us call the uncertainty in the position measurement Δx.

However when we use photons to locate the electron, we are slugging the electron with particles, photons of momentum $p_{photon} = h/\lambda$. Since we do not know where the photons are within a distance λ, we do not know exactly how the electron was hit and how much momentum it absorbed from the photon. The electron could have absorbed the full photon momentum p_{photon} or none of it. If we observe the electron, we make the electron's momentum uncertain by an amount at least as large as p_{photon}. Calling the uncertainty in the electron's momentum $\Delta p_{electron}$ we have

$$\Delta p_{electron} = p_{photon} = \frac{h}{\lambda} = \frac{h}{\Delta x} \qquad (6)$$

multiplying through by Δx gives

$$\Delta p \Delta x = h \qquad (7)$$

In Equation (7), Δp and Δx represent the smallest possible uncertainties we can have when measuring the position of the electron using photons. To allow for the fact that we could get much greater uncertainties using poor equipment or sloppy techniques, we will write the equation in the form

$$\boxed{\Delta p \Delta x \geq h} \qquad \begin{array}{l} \textit{position–momentum} \\ \textit{form of the} \\ \textit{uncertainty principle} \end{array} \qquad (8)$$

indicating that the product of the uncertainties is at least as large as Planck's constant h.

If all forces have a particle nature, and all particles obey the de Broglie relationship, then the fact that we derived Equation (8) using photons makes no difference. We have to get the same result using any particle, in any possible kind of experiment. Thus Equation (8) represents a fundamental limitation on the measurement process itself!

Equation (8) is not like any formula we have previously dealt with in the text. It gives you an estimate, not an exact value. Often you will see the formula written $\Delta p \Delta x \geq \hbar$ with $\hbar = h/2\pi$, rather than h, appearing on the right side. Whether you use h or $\hbar$ depends upon how you wish to define the uncertainties Δp and Δx. But it is not necessary to be too precise. The important point is that the product $\Delta p \Delta x$ must be at least of the order of magnitude h. It cannot be h/100 or something smaller.

The gist of the uncertainty principle is that the more accurately you measure the position of the particle, the more you mess up the particle's momentum. Or, the more accurately you measure the momentum of a particle, the less you know about the particle's position.

Equation (8) is not quite right, because it turns out that an accurate measurement of the x position of a particle does not necessarily mess up the particle's y component of momentum, only its x component. A more accurate statement of the uncertainty principle is

$$\Delta p_x \Delta x \geq h \qquad (9a)$$

$$\Delta p_y \Delta y \geq h \qquad (9b)$$

$$\Delta p_z \Delta z \geq h \qquad (9c)$$

where Δp_x is the uncertainty in the particle's x component of momentum due to a measurement of its x position, Δp_y is the uncertainty in the y component of momentum resulting from a y position measurement, etc. The quantities Δx, Δy, and Δz are the uncertainty in the x y and z measurements respectively.

In the next section we will see an explicit example of Equation (9b) in our analysis of the single slit diffraction experiment.

SINGLE SLIT EXPERIMENT

In our two slit thought experiment, we measured the position of the electron by hitting it with a photon. Another way to measure the position of a particle is to send it through a slit. For example, suppose a beam of particles impinges on a slit of width (W) as illustrated in Figure (3). We know that any particle which makes it to the far side of the slit had, at one time, been within the slit. At that time we knew its y position to within an uncertainty Δy equal to the width (W) of the slit.

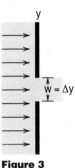

Figure 3
When a particle goes through the slit, its y position is known to within an uncertainty $\Delta y = W$.

$$\Delta y = W \qquad (10)$$

This is an example of a position measurement with a precisely known uncertainty Δy .

According to the uncertainty principle, the particle's y component of momentum is uncertain by an amount Δp_y given by Equation (9b) as

$$\Delta p_y \geq \frac{h}{\Delta y} = \frac{h}{W} \qquad (11)$$

Equation (11) tells us that the smaller Δy , i.e., the narrower the slit, the bigger the uncertainty Δp_y that we create in the particle's y momentum.

In Figure (4), we see waves passing through two different width slits. The narrower the slit, the more the wave spreads out on the other side.

If the wave represents a particle that is initially moving in the x direction with no y momentum, this spreading represents y momentum that the particle gained by going through the slit. Since the wave spreads both up and down, the y momentum can point up or down, and any y momentum gained represents an uncertainty Δp_y . Thus we see that Δp_y increases as we make the slit width and Δy smaller, as predicted by the uncertainty principle.

On the next page, we calculate the spreading, and see that the uncertainty in y momentum is accurately given by the formula $\Delta p_y \Delta y = h$.

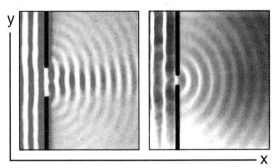

Figure 4
Waves passing through a single slit. The narrower the slit, the more the wave spreads out.

Back at the end of Chapter 25 we analyzed the single slit diffraction pattern shown in Figure (25-34), repeated here as Figure (5a). For the case where y_{min} was much less than D we got the simple formula

$$y_{min} = \frac{\lambda D}{W}; \quad \frac{y_{min}}{D} = \frac{\lambda}{W} \qquad (25\text{-}14)$$

In Figure (5b) we see that the triangle with sides D and y_{min} is similar to the triangle with sides p_x and Δp_y in (5c). Thus we have from similar triangles

$$\frac{y_{min}}{D} = \frac{\Delta p_y}{p_x} \qquad (12)$$

Equating values of y_{min}/D we get

$$\frac{\Delta p_y}{p_x} = \frac{\lambda}{W}; \quad \Delta p_y = \frac{\lambda}{W}p_x$$

Now replace W by Δy, and use the de Broglie formula $p_x = h/\lambda$ for p_x, and we get

$$\Delta p_y = \frac{\lambda}{W}p_x = \frac{\lambda}{\Delta y}\frac{h}{\lambda} = \frac{h}{\Delta y}$$

The λ's cancel and we are left with

$$\boxed{\Delta p_y \Delta y = h} \qquad (13)$$

The uncertainty principle gives us

$$\Delta p_y \Delta y \geq h \qquad (9b)$$

We got an equal sign in Equation (13) because sending the particle through a slit causes the least possible uncertainty in the measurement of the y position of the particle. The $\geq$ sign in the uncertainty principle allows for experimental errors we might make.

Exercise 1

A microwave beam, consisting of 1.24×10^{-4} eV photons impinges on a slit of width (W).

(a) What is the wavelength λ of the microwave beam?

(b) What is the momentum p_x of the photons in the microwave beam before they get to the slit?

(c) When the photons pass through the slit, their y position is known to an uncertainty $\Delta y = W$, the slit width. Before the photons get to the slit, their y momentum has the definite value $p_y = 0$. Passing through the slit makes the photon's y momentum uncertain by an amount Δp_y. Using the uncertainty principle, calculate what the slit width (W) must be so that Δp_y is equal to the photon's original momentum p_x. How does W compare with the wavelength λ of the microwave beam?

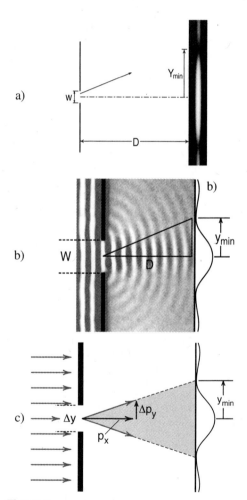

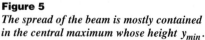

Figure 5
The spread of the beam is mostly contained in the central maximum whose height y_{min}.

DERIVATION OF THE TIME-ENERGY FORM OF THE UNCERTAINTY PRINCIPLE FOR NON RELATIVISTIC PARTICLES

In the next chapter we will use Fourier Analysis to do a fully relativistic discussion of the time-energy form of the uncertainty principle. Here we derive the time-energy form for a non relativistic particle whose kinetic energy is $1/2mv^2$. Our treatment in the next chapter is more general and has more profound implications. One can treat this section as an introduction to the time-energy form.

Suppose that a particle is moving by me and I want to measure its kinetic energy E in the shortest possible time with the greatest possible accuracy. I do not care what happens to the particle after I make the measurement.

First I use photons of wavelength λ to locate the particle. This tells me where the particle is within an uncertainty $\Delta x = \lambda$. But the uncertainty principle tells me that this position measurement makes the particle's momentum uncertain by at least the amount

$$\Delta p \Delta x = h; \quad \Delta x = \frac{h}{\Delta p} \tag{14}$$

Then I fire high frequency, short wavelength photons a distance λ from where I first saw the particle, as shown in Figure (6). I keep doing this until I hit the particle a time Δt later. This high energy photon kicks the particle out of the experiment, but tells me precisely where the particle was.

Figure 6
I make two measurements of the particle's position. First I use a long wavelength photon in order not to disturb the particle's momentum. Then I hit the particle with a short wavelength photon to accurately locate its position.

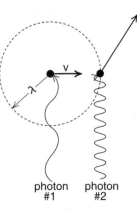

photon #1   photon #2

Since the second photon collision took place a time Δt after the first, a distance Δx away, my measurement of the particle's speed is

$$v = \frac{\Delta x}{\Delta t} = \frac{h}{\Delta p} \frac{1}{\Delta t}; \quad v \Delta p = \frac{h}{\Delta t} \tag{15}$$

where I used Equation (14) $\Delta x = h/\Delta p$.

Between the collisions, the particle's kinetic energy is

$$E = \frac{1}{2}mv^2 = \frac{1}{2m}m^2v^2 = \frac{p^2}{2m} \tag{16}$$

Because the momentum is uncertain by an amount Δp, this makes the kinetic energy uncertain by an amount ΔE given by

$$E + \Delta E = \frac{(p + \Delta p)^2}{2m}$$
$$= \frac{p^2}{2m} + \frac{2p\Delta p}{2m} + \frac{\Delta p^2}{2m} \tag{17}$$

If Δp is small compared to p, we can neglect the Δp^2 term compared to the $p\Delta p$ term. Since $p^2/2m$ is just E, the E's cancel and we are left with

$$\Delta E = \frac{p\Delta p}{m} = \frac{(mv)\Delta p}{m} = v\Delta p \tag{18}$$

Equating values of $v\Delta p$ from Equations (15) and (18) gives

$$\Delta E = \frac{h}{\Delta t} \tag{19}$$

or

$$\boxed{\Delta E \Delta t = h} \tag{20}$$

Of course a sloppy measurement of any quantity will make the uncertainties greater, thus the time-energy form of the uncertainty principle is usually written

$$\boxed{\Delta E \Delta t \geq h} \quad \begin{array}{l}\text{time–energy}\\ \text{form of the}\\ \text{uncertainty principle}\end{array} \tag{21}$$

Exercise 2

4a) Explain why in the first position measurement of Figure (6), the particle's position is uncertain by an amount $\Delta x = \lambda$.

(b) Explain physically why the first position measurement makes the particle's momentum uncertain by $\Delta p = h / \lambda$.

Exercise 3

 You want to make a moving picture of an electron falling from rest. You plan to have the frames 1/30 of a second apart, the standard movie and video frame rate. This means that the maximum time you have available to observe the electron for each frame is 1/30 of a second.

(a) What's the minimum uncertainty of your measurement of the energy of the electron?

(b) Theoretically, what is the kinetic energy of an electron 1/30 of a second after it is dropped from rest (in a lab at the surface of the earth)?

(c) If you want to measure the electron's energy in the first frame, what is the least possible percentage error in the measurement?

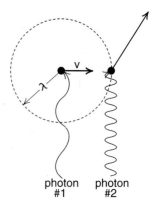

Figure 6 (repeated)
I make two measurements of the particle's position. First I use a long wavelength photon in order not to disturb the particle's momentum. Then I hit the particle with a short wavelength photon to accurately locate its position.

photon #1   photon #2

CHAPTER 32 REVIEW

While the probability interpretation of electron waves provides an explanation of the two slit interference experiment of the previous chapter, problems remain.

The dark bands in the interference pattern are supposedly created when the probability wave from one slit cancels a similar wave emerging from the other slit. Suppose we simply look and see which slit each electron went through. If we know that the electron went through the upper slit, then there would be no probability that it went through the bottom one. Thus there would be no probability of a wave emerging from the bottom slit, no cancellation, and we would have to end up with a single slit diffraction pattern, rather than the dark bands of the two slit pattern.

Can just knowing which slit the electron went through affect the results of the experiment? That may seem ridiculous.

The main feature of this chapter is a thought experiment in which we look at experiments we might perform to learn which slit the electron went through. To see an electron in a slit, we have to hit it with something. If we hit it with a photon, the photon wavelength has to be shorter than the separation d between the slits in order to see which slit the electron was in. But such a photon has momentum given by the de Broglie formula $p = h/\lambda$. If $\lambda = d$, the photon momentum is great enough to knock the electron into a dark band and destroy the two slit pattern. Thus we cannot use light or photons to see which slit the electron went through.

You might try to observe the electron more delicately with some other particle. But if all particles in nature have a particle-wave nature obeying the de Broglie relationship $p = h/\lambda$, there is nothing we can use that works better than a photon, there is no way we can get a two slit pattern and know which slit the electron went through, and the probability interpretation survives.

That there are some experiments we cannot do, some measurements we cannot make, is a consequence of the uncertainty principle. One form which we discussed says that if we simultaneously measure the position x and momentum p of a particle, and Δx is the uncertainty in the position measurement, and Δp the uncertainty in the momentum measurement, then the product $\Delta p \Delta x$ must be at least as large as Planck's constant h.

In an analysis of the single slit experiment, we saw that when a plane particle wave went through a slit of width W, its uncertainty Δy in position was precisely equal to the slit width W. In going through the slit, the emerging wave spreads out into a single slit pattern, showing that the particle has gained y directed momentum. Since the y momentum can point up or down, this y momentum represents the uncertainty Δp_y introduced by the slit. We calculated Δp_y by noting most of the emerging beam was between the upper and lower first minima Y_{min} of the pattern. Noting that $p_x = h/\lambda$, we ended up with the result $\Delta p_y \Delta y = h$. The equal sign tells us we have made essentially the smallest disturbance possible of the particle's y momentum p_y.

At the end of the chapter, we investigated how we could measure the energy of a non relativistic particle in the shortest possible time Δt. We found that the uncertainty ΔE of our energy measurement was related to Δt by $\Delta E \Delta t \geq h$. This is the time-energy form of the uncertainty principle. In the next chapter we have a better, fully relativistic derivation.

CHAPTER EXERCISES

Exercise 1 0n page 10

Analysis of a microwave beam passing through a slit of width W.

Exercise 2 0n page 12

Measuring the position and momentum of a particle.

Exercise 3 0n page 12

Try to take a moving picture or video of an electron dropped from rest.

Chapter 33 non calculus
Quantum Mechanics III
The Uncertainty Principle –
Time and Energy

In the last chapter we saw that if all particles had a particle-wave nature obeying the de Broglie relationship $p = h/\lambda$, then there would be a fundamental restriction to the accuracy with which one could make experimental measurements. This limit is known as the uncertainty principle which comes in two forms represented by the equations

$$\Delta p \Delta x \geq h$$

$$\Delta E \Delta t \geq h$$

The first form $\Delta p \Delta x \geq h$ tells us that if we make a position measurement to within an accuracy Δx, we have made the momentum uncertain by an amount at least as large as Δp. The second form $\Delta E \Delta t \geq h$ tells us that if we have only a limited time Δt in which to make an energy measurement, the energy will be uncertain at least as much as ΔE.

In the appendix to the last chapter, we derived the time energy form of the uncertainty principle from $\Delta p \Delta x \geq h$ for a non relativistic particle where E was the kinetic energy $1/2mv^2$. We asked you to apply this to an electron dropped from rest to see that it would be impossible to accurately track the motion of an electron in the first 1/30 of a second.

In this chapter we apply Fourier analysis to a short laser pulse and end up with a fully relativistic derivation of the uncertainty principle for the photons, or photon, in the pulse. In this derivation we more clearly see how the uncertainty principle is a direct consequence of the particle-wave nature of matter.

Perhaps the most interesting and important part of the chapter comes when we reconcile the time-energy form of the uncertainty principle with the law of conservation of energy. The result, which is totally outside the realm of classical physics, may have implications related to the origin of the universe.

A FEMTOSECOND LASER PULSE

In the last chapter, we used an analysis of the two slit electron diffraction experiment to introduce the position-momentum form of the uncertainty principle. In this chapter we will use an experiment involving the analysis of a pulsed laser beam to introduce the time-energy form.

Since the 1990s, it has been possible to build lasers that send out very short pulses, pulses only a few wavelengths long. Such pulses are useful for effectively taking "flash" pictures of the behavior of the electrons in chemical reactions.

The experiment we will discuss involves the pulse shown in Figure (1a). This is a graph of the intensity of the electric field in the pulse. The wave is called a *femtosecond laser pulse* because the main part of the pulse is about 20 femtoseconds (fs) long. (One femtosecond, fs, is 10^{-15} seconds, or one millionth of a nanosecond. In Figure (1a), the main part of the pulse starts at –10 fs and goes up to +10 fs.)

The second graph, Figure (1b), shows the spectrum of radiation in the pulse. The center frequency has a wavelength of 800 nanometers (nm) which is longer than the visible spectrum wavelengths that range from 300 nm for blue, up to 400 nm for red. Thus the pulse is in the longer wavelength *infrared* part of the spectrum.

A wave with an 800 nm wavelength λ has a period $T = \lambda/c$ of 2.67 femtoseconds. Thus in the range from –10 fs to + 10 fs, there should be about 7 cycles. In Figure (1a) you will count 14 maxima in this 20 fs range because you are looking at the intensity of the electric field. The intensity is proportional to the square of the field, and when you square a sine wave, you get two maxima per cycle.

What may be surprising about the spectrum in Figure (1b) is that the spectrum is not sharp. The range from 750 nm to 850 nm is a third as wide as the range from 400 nm to 700 nm for visible light. The lasers we used in Chapter 25 to study diffraction patterns had a distinct frequency. Send that laser light through a diffraction grating and you would get a sharp line rather than the spread out spectrum we see in Figure (1b).

One might be tempted to ask "What is wrong with the laser used in Figure (1a)?" "Why doesn't it give the pure single wavelength waves we expect from lasers?"

What is wrong is that the laser pulse is only a few wavelengths long. In the section after next, we will use Fourier analysis to demonstrate that such a short pulse must contain a spectrum of wavelengths. We will see that the spread in wavelengths is needed to cancel out the waves outside the pulse. In the meantime we will see that the spectrum in Figure (1b) is consistent with the time-energy form of the uncertainty principle.

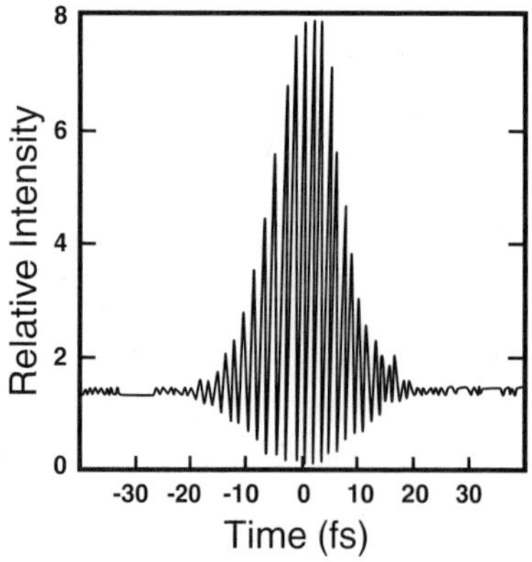

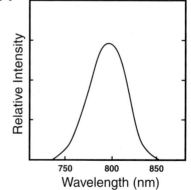

Figure 1a
Intensity of the electric field in a 20 femtosecond (fs) laser pulse. (From F. Hajiesmaeilbaigi and A. Azima Can. J. Phys. 76: p498 (1998).)

Figure 1b
Spectrum of the radiation in the laser pulse of Figure (1a). Visible light has a range from 400 nm to 700 nm, thus this spectrum, centered on 800 nm, is in the infrared.

USING THE UNCERTAINTY PRINCIPLE

As a laser pulse goes by us we have very little time, call it Δt, in which to measure the frequencies or energies of the photons in the pulse. The time-energy form of Heisenberg's uncertainty principle says that if only a short time Δt available for making an energy measurement, there will be an uncertainty ΔE in the result, where ΔE must be as large as $\Delta E = h/\Delta t$.

To apply the uncertainty principle to the laser pulse in Figure (1), we note that the pulse goes by in 20 fs. Thus we have only a time $\Delta t = 20$ fs in which to measure the spectrum of the laser light. But measuring the spectrum means measuring the frequencies or energies of the photons in the pulse. Thus measuring the spectrum is an energy measurement which must be uncertain by an amount $\Delta E = h/\Delta t$.

It is easier if we turn the argument around, first solving for the uncertainty ΔE in the energy of the photons in the pulse. Then we will use the uncertainty principle written as $\Delta t = h/\Delta E$ to see if we predict the correct length Δt of the pulse.

In Figure (1b) we see that the laser pulse consists of wavelengths ranging from as short as 750 nm up to 850 nm. The longer wavelength, lower frequency photons have a frequency f_- given by

$$f_- = \frac{c}{\lambda_-} = \frac{3 \times 10^8 \text{m/sec}}{850 \times 10^{-9}\text{m}} = .352 \times 10^{15}\text{sec}^{-1}$$

(1a)

(The dimensions of frequency, cycles/sec, is is actually 1/sec or sec^{-1} because cycles are dimensionless.) The shorter wavelength photons have the higher frequency f_+ given by

$$f_+ = \frac{c}{\lambda_+} = \frac{3 \times 10^8 \text{m/sec}}{750 \times 10^{-9}\text{m}} = .400 \times 10^{15}\text{sec}^{-1}$$

(1b)

From Einstein's photoelectric effect formula $E_{photon} = hf$ we see that photons in the pulse can have an energy as low as $E_- = hf_-$ up to an energy as high as $E_+ = hf_+$. We do not know what the energy of any given photon in the pulse is. All we know is that it is somewhere in the range between E_- and E_+.

We can say that the photon's energy is uncertain by an amount

$$\Delta E = E_+ - E_- \quad \begin{array}{l} \textit{uncertainty of the} \\ \textit{energy of any} \\ \textit{photon in the pulse} \end{array}$$

$$= hf_+ - hf_-$$

$$= h(.400 - .352) \times 10^{15}\text{sec}^{-1} \quad (2)$$

$$= h \times (.048) \times 10^{15}\text{sec}^{-1}$$

Using the uncertainty principle in the form $\Delta t = h/\Delta E$ we get

$$\Delta t = \frac{h}{\Delta E} = \frac{h}{h \times (.048) \times 10^{15}\text{sec}^{-1}}$$

The factors of h cancel and we are left with

$$\boxed{\Delta t = 20.8 \times 10^{-15}\text{sec} \approx 20 \text{ femtoseconds}} \quad (3)$$

which is the length of the pulse seen in Figure (1a). Thus the uncertainty principle, applied to the spectrum in Figure (1b) correctly predicts the length of the laser pulse.

The fact that Planck's constant cancelled in Equation (3) suggests that the uncertainty principle is something more than just some weird quantum effect. It suggests that it is a consequence of a more general behavior of waves. We will demonstrate that this is true by showing that the uncertainty principle is seen as a natural wave phenomena when we take the Fourier transform of a wave pulse.

PULSE FOURIER TRANSFORM

We have recently modified the MacScope II program so that we can easily study the Fourier transform of short wave pulses like the laser pulse in Figure (1a). We will use this section to explain how the *pulse Fourier transform* works. Then we will go on to see how the time-energy form of the uncertainty principle emerges as a consequence.

In Figure (2) we whistled into a microphone attached to MacScope, and recorded the wave shown. A whistle produces a fairly good sine wave. In that figure we have also selected one cycle of the sine wave. When we press the button labeled *Fourier*, we get the standard Fourier analysis window shown in Figure (3).

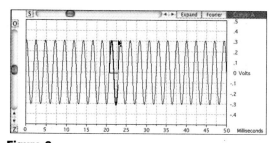

Figure 2
Selecting one cycle of a sine wave.

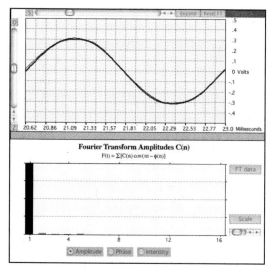

Figure 3
Fourier analysis of a sine wave. The assumption is that this cycle repeats indefinitely.

The way MacScope handles Fourier analysis is to assume that the selected section of the curve repeats indefinitely. In Figure (3) we selected one complete cycle of the sine wave. When that cycle is repeated indefinitely, we end up with a complete pure sine wave containing only the one frequency component which we see in the Fourier analysis window.

If, instead of pressing the *Fourier* button, we pressed the *Pulse* button of Figure (4a), we first get the window shown in Figure (4b) asking whether we want our pulse centered, left edge, or Gaussian. For this demonstration we chose *Zero at Center* and got the curve shown in Figure (5).

Now you can see what the *Pulse Fourier Transform* does. Instead of assuming that the selected section of the pulse repeats forever, the program zeros out all but the selected section of curve as shown in Figure (5). When we selected *Zero at Center*, the program drew the zero line at the center of our selected section of the curve.

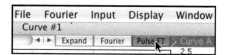

Figure 4a
Selecting the Pulse Fourier Transform.

Figure 4b
Choosing the Zero line.

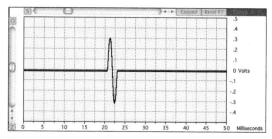

Figure 5
Selecting the Pulse Fourier Transform, which creates a pulse by zeroing all but the selected section of the curve.

Fourier Analysis of a Pulse

In Figure (6), we show the complete MacScope *Curve A* window. At the top we see our one cycle pulse with the rest of the curve zeroed out. Below in the Fourier analysis window we see a whole bunch of harmonics. Let us see where they came from.

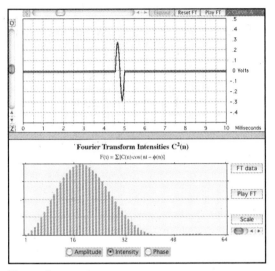

Figure 6
Harmonics in a short pulse.

In Figure (7a) we have selected the center harmonic, and in the upper window see that MacScope has drawn a pathetic little sine wave that has the same wavelength as our selected cycle. This is telling us that we are not going to reconstruct our pulse from a single harmonic.

In Figure (7b) we selected the five biggest harmonics. In the upper window we see the result of adding these five sine waves together. They are beginning to build a pulse centered on our selected pulse.

In Figures (7c) and (7d) we see that as we select more harmonics, the closer we come to reconstructing our pulse. The lesson here is that to build a sharp pulse out of harmonic sine waves, takes a lot of sine waves. All these waves must add up at the pulse, and completely cancel each other elsewhere.

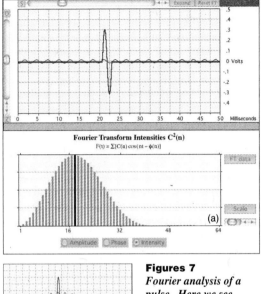

Fourier Transform Intensities C²(n)

$F(t) = \Sigma [C(n) \cos(nt - \phi(n)]$

(a)

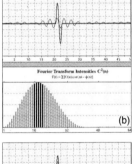

(b)

(c)

(d)

Figures 7
Fourier analysis of a pulse. Here we see how a short pulse is constructed from long sinusoidal waves.

In (a) we selected the largest harmonic and all it represents is a small sine wave.

When we add together the five biggest harmonics in (b), a pulse begins to form.

When we add up the 32 biggest harmonics, we get a close representation of the pulse in (d). We need a lot of harmonics to cancel the wave outside the pulse.

Intensity vs Amplitude

In our use of Fourier analysis so far, we have studied the *amplitudes* of the harmonics contained in a signal. But when we study the spectrum of light in a light wave, we measure the *intensity* of the electric field, which is the square of the field. If we want to compare the spectrum in the Fourier analysis of a short pulse, with the experimental spectrum of the laser pulse in Figure (1b), we should have MacScope plot the intensities rather than the amplitudes of the harmonics. This is easily done by looking at the buttons below the *Fourier Analysis Plot*, and selecting the one labeled *Intensity*, rather than the one labeled *Amplitude*.

Spectrum of a Pulse

Now we are ready to compare Figure (7d) where we have selected most of the harmonics, with Figure (1b) showing the spectrum of wavelengths in our six cycle laser pulse. In both cases we see a similar spectrum of harmonics. You should now see that the reason why the short laser pulse contained a spectrum of wavelengths ranging from 750 nm up to 850 nm. It takes all these different wavelengths to add up to a short pulse.

CHANGING Δt

At the beginning of the chapter, we used the uncertainty principle in the form $\Delta t = h/\Delta E$ to calculate the length Δt of the laser pulse. We found that with $\Delta E = h(f_+ - f_-)$ we got a time of Δt equal to 20 femtoseconds which accurately describes the length of the laser pulse.

What we want to do now is write the uncertainty principle equation in the form

$$\Delta E = \frac{h}{\Delta t} \tag{4}$$

and look at the consequences of changing the pulse length Δt.

The clear prediction of Equation (4) is that every time we double the length Δt of the pulse, we will cut the energy uncertainty ΔE in half. With MacScope, we can show that this is precisely what happens.

We can change the length of Δt by going back to our recording of a whistle, selecting more than one cycle of the sine wave, and doing a pulse Fourier transform. In Figure (8) we selected 2 cycles and see that we get a narrower spectrum.

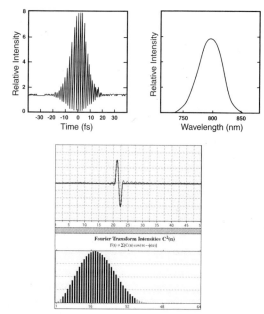

Figures 1 & 7d
Comparison of the spectra of short pulses.

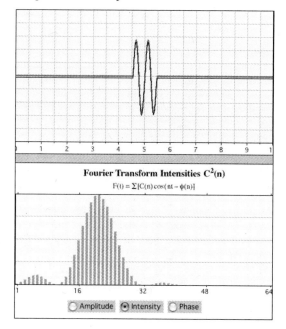

Figure 8
With 2 cycles the spectrum is narrower.

To get an overview of how the width of the spectrum of harmonics changes as we change Δt, in Figure (9) we kept doubling Δt from 1 cycle to 2 cycles to 4 cycles to 8 cycles. We see that the frequency spread in the main harmonics drops from 32 harmonics, to 16 harmonics, to 8 harmonics, to 4 harmonics. Clearly doubling the length of the pulse cuts the spread in harmonics in half.

The spread in harmonics tells us the range of frequencies $(f_+ - f_-)$ that are important in the pulse. Multiply this range of frequencies by Planck's constant h, and you get the formula for the range ΔE of photon energies in the pulse.

$$\Delta E = h(f_+ - f_-)$$

But this range of photon energies is the uncertainty in our knowledge of the energy of any one photon in the pulse. Thus we see that the uncertainty in the photon energy is cut in half every time we double the length of the pulse.

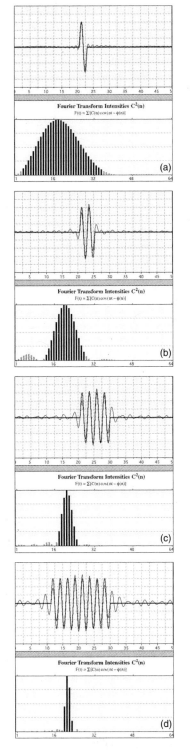

Figure 9
When we double the length Δt of the pulse, we cut the spread ΔE of the harmonics in half. The product $\Delta E \Delta t$ remains constant.

PROBABILITY INTERPRETATION

By now we should be quite comfortable with seeing the frequency or wavelength spectrum of the laser pulse in Figure (1b). The graph tells us that most of the photons have a wavelength around $\lambda = 800$ nm, while some photons have a wavelength as long as $\lambda_+ = 850$ nm, or as short as $\lambda_- = 750$ nm. If we change the horizontal scale from photon wavelengths to photon energies hc/λ, then we get a plot of the distribution of the energies of the photons in the pulse.

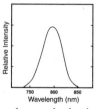

We can note that when we did a Fourier analysis of a pulse, we got a spectrum of the harmonic frequencies f_n. To get the spectrum of photon energies hf_n, you just multiply by Planck's constant h.

Now we are going to ask a question that, at first, may seem controversial. Suppose the laser pulse of Figure (1a) contained *only one photon*. Then how should we interpret the spectrum in Figure (1b)? What does it mean to have a spectrum of energies for a single photon?

The answer to this question lies in the probability interpretation of the photon wave. If there were only one photon in the Figure (1) laser pulse, then *the spectrum tells us the distribution of probabilities that the photon has the corresponding frequency or energy.* What was an energy spectrum when we had many photons, becomes a probability spectrum when we have one or a few photons.

Even if there are many photons in the pulse, we can still interpret the spectrum as a probability spectrum for each photon. Then, for example, if each photon in the laser pulse is most likely to have a wavelength of around 800 nm, then when we measure photon wavelengths, we should find the most photons in the 800 nm wavelength range.

With the probability interpretation, any given photon has some probability of being at the high energy part of the spectrum, and some probability of being at the low energy end. Thus the width ΔE of the spectrum is truly the uncertainty in the photon's energy.

Measuring Short Times

We have said that pulsed lasers can produce pulses as short as 2 femtoseconds. How do we know that? Suppose we gave you the job of measuring the length of the laser pulse, and the best oscilloscope you had could measure times no shorter than a nanosecond. This is a million times too slow to see a femtosecond pulse. What do you do?

We answered that question at the beginning of this chapter. We used the uncertainty principle $\Delta t = h/\Delta E$ to correctly calculate the 20 femtosecond length of the Figure (1) pulse. Essentially we are using a diffraction grating as a clock!

Exercise 1

An electron is in an excited state of the hydrogen atom, either the second energy level at –3.40 eV, or the third energy level at –1.51 eV. You want to do an experiment to decide which of these two states the electron is in. What is the least amount of time you must take to make this measurement?

Short Lived Elementary Particles

To drive home the fundamental nature of the relationship $\Delta E = h/\Delta t$, we will discuss an unstable elementary particle that lives for such a short time Δt that its rest mass energy $m_0 c^2$ is demonstrably uncertain. We will then use the equation $\Delta t = h/\Delta E$ to measure the very short lifetime of the particle.

We usually think of the rest energy of a particle as having a definite value. For example the rest energy of a proton is $938.2723 \times 10^6 eV$. The proton itself is a composite particle made of 3 quarks, and the number 938.2723 MeV represents the total energy of the quarks in the allowed wave pattern that represents a proton. This rest energy has a very definite value because the proton is a stable particle with plenty of time to settle into a precise wave pattern.

A rather different particle is the so-called "Lambda (1520)" or "$\Lambda(1520)$", which is another combination of 3 quarks, but very short lived. The name comes partly from the fact that the particle's rest mass energy is about 1520 million electron volts (MeV). As indicated in Figure (10), a $\Lambda(1520)$ can be created as a result of the collision between a K^- meson and a proton.

a) A K^- meson and a proton are about to collide. We are looking at the collision in a coordinate system where the total momentum is zero (the so-called "center of mass" system).

b) In the collision a $\Lambda(1520)$ particle is created. It is at rest in this center of mass system.

c) The $\Lambda(1520)$ then quickly decays into a lower energy Λ particle and two π mesons.

Figure 10
A $\Lambda(1520)$ particle can be created if the total energy (in the center of mass system) of the incoming particles equals the rest mass energy of the $\Lambda(1520)$.

We are viewing the collision in a special coordinate system, where the total momentum of the incoming particles is zero. In this coordinate system, the resulting $\Lambda(1520)$ will be at rest. By conservation of energy, the total energy of the incoming particles should equal the rest mass energy of the $\Lambda(1520)$. Thus if we collide K^- particles with protons, we expect to create a $\Lambda(1520)$ particle only if the incoming particles have the right total energy.

Figure (11) shows the results of some collision experiments, where a K^- meson and a proton collided to produce a Λ and two π mesons. The probability of such a result peaked when the energy of the incoming particles was 1,520 MeV. This peak occurred because the incoming K^- meson and proton created a $\Lambda(1520)$ particle, which then decayed into an ordinary Λ and two π mesons, as shown in Figure (10). The $\Lambda(1520)$ was not observed directly, because its lifetime is too short.

Figure (11) shows that the energy of the incoming particles does not have to be exactly 1520 MeV in order to create a $\Lambda(1520)$. The peak is in the range from about 1510 to 1530 Mev, which implies that the rest mass energy of the $\Lambda(1520)$ is 1520 MeV plus or minus about 10 MeV. From one experiment to another, the rest mass energy can vary by about 20 MeV. (The experimentalists quoted a variation of 16 MeV.)

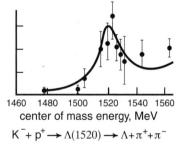

center of mass energy, MeV

$K^- + p^+ \longrightarrow \Lambda(1520) \longrightarrow \Lambda + \pi^+ + \pi^-$

Figure 11

The probability that a K^-meson and a proton collide to produce a Λ particle and two π mesons, peak at an energy of 1520 MeV. The peak results from the fact that a $\Lambda(1520)$ particle was created and quickly decayed into the Λ and two π mesons. The probability peaks at 1520 MeV, but can be seen to spread out over a range of about 16MeV. The small circles are experimental values, the vertical lines represent the possible error in the value. (Data from M.B. Watson et al., *Phys. Rev.* 131(1963).)

Why isn't the peak sharp? Why does the rest mass energy of the Λ (1520) particle vary by as much as 16 to 20 MeV from one experiment to another? The answer lies in the fact that *the lifetime of the Λ (1520) is so short, that the particle does not have enough time to establish a definite rest mass energy*. The 16 MeV variation is the uncertainty ΔE in the particle's rest mass energy that results from the fact that the particle's lifetime is limited.

The uncertainty principle relates the uncertainty in energy ΔE to the time Δt available to establish that energy. To establish the rest mass energy, the time Δt available is the particle's **lifetime**. Thus we can use the uncertainty principle to estimate the lifetime of the Λ (1520) particle. With $\Delta t = h/\Delta E$ we get

$$\Delta t = \frac{h}{\Delta E} = \frac{6.63 \times 10^{-34} \text{joule second}}{16 \times 10^{6} \text{eV} \times 1.6 \times 10^{-19} \dfrac{\text{joule}}{\text{eV}}}$$

$$\Delta t = 2.6 \times 10^{-22} \text{ seconds} \qquad (5)$$

The lifetime of the Λ (1520) particle is of the order of 10^{-22} seconds! This is only about 10 times longer than it takes light to cross a proton! Only by using the uncertainty principle could we possibly measure such short times.

THE UNCERTAINTY PRINCIPLE AND ENERGY CONSERVATION

The fact that for short times the energy of a particle is uncertain, raises an interesting question about basic physical laws like the law of conservation of energy. If a particle's energy is uncertain, how do we know that energy is conserved in some process involving that particle? The answer is — *we don't*.

One way to explain the situation is to say that nature will cheat if it can get away with it. Energy does not have to be conserved if we cannot do an experiment to demonstrate a lack of conservation of energy.

Consider the process shown in Figure (12). It shows a red, 2 eV photon traveling along in space. Suddenly the photon creates a positron-electron pair. The rest mass energy of both the positron and the electron are .51 MeV. Thus we have a 2 eV photon creating a pair of particles whose total energy is $1.02 \times 10^{6} \text{eV}$, a huge violation of the law of conservation of energy. A short time later the electron and positron come back together, annihilate, leaving behind a 2 eV photon. This is an equally huge violation of the conservation of energy.

But have we really violated the conservation of energy? During its lifetime, the positron-electron pair is a composite object whose total energy is uncertain. If the pair lived a long time, its total energy would be close to the expected energy of $1.02 \times 10^{6} \text{eV}$. But suppose the pair were in existence only for a very short time Δt, a time so short that the uncertainty in the energy could be as large as $1.02 \times 10^{6} \text{eV}$. Then there is some probability that the energy of the pair might be only 2 eV and the process shown in Figure (12) could happen.

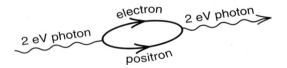

Figure 12
Consider a process where a 2 eV photon suddenly creates a positron-electron pair. A short time later the pair annihilates, leaving a 2 eV photon. In the long term, energy is conserved.

The length of time Δt that the pair could exist and have an energy uncertain by 1.02 MeV is

$$\Delta t = \frac{h}{\Delta E} = \frac{6.63 \times 10^{-34} \text{joule sec}}{1.02 \times 10^{6} \text{eV} \times 1.6 \times 10^{-19} \frac{\text{joule}}{\text{eV}}}$$

$$\Delta t = 4 \times 10^{-21} \text{sec} \qquad (6)$$

Another way to view the situation is as follows. Suppose the pair in Figure (12) lasted only 4×10^{-21} seconds or less. Even if the pair had an energy of $1.02 \times 10^{6} \text{eV}$, the lifetime is so short that any measurement of the energy of the pair would be uncertain by at least $1.02 \times 10^{6} \text{eV}$, and the experiment could not detect the violation of the law of conservation of energy. In this point of view, if we cannot perform an experiment to detect a violation of the conservation law, then the process should have some probability of occurring.

Does a process like that shown in Figure (12) actually occur? If so, is there any way that we can know that it does? The answer is yes, to both questions. It is possible to make extremely accurate studies of the energy levels of the electron in hydrogen, and to make equally accurate predictions of the energy using the theory of *quantum electrodynamics*.

We can view the binding of the electron to the proton in hydrogen as resulting from the continual exchange of photons between the electron and proton. During this continual exchange, there is some probability that the photon creates a positron-electron pair that quickly annihilates as shown in Figure (12). In order to predict the correct values of the hydrogen energy levels, the process shown in Figure (12) has to be included. Thus we have direct experimental evidence that for a short time the particle-antiparticle pair existed.

QUANTUM FLUCTUATIONS AND EMPTY SPACE

We began the text with a discussion of the principle of relativity—that you could not detect your own motion relative to empty space. The concept of empty space seemed rather obvious—space with nothing in it. But the idea of empty space is not so obvious after all.

With the discovery of the cosmic background radiation, we find that all the space in this universe is filled with a sea of photons left over from the big bang. We can accurately measure our motion relative to this sea of photons. The earth is moving relative to this sea at a velocity of 600 kilometers per second toward the Virgo cluster of galaxies. While this measurement does not violate the principle of relativity, it is in some sense a measurement of our motion relative to the universe as a whole.

Empty space itself may not be empty. Consider a process like that shown in Figure (13) where a photon, an electron, and a positron are all created at some point in space. A short while later the three particles come back together with the positron and electron annihilating and the photon being absorbed.

One's first reaction might be that such a process is ridiculous. How could these three particles just appear and then disappear? To do this we would have to violate both the laws of conservation of energy and momentum.

But, of course, the uncertainty principle allows us to do that. We can, in fact, use the uncertainty principle to estimate how long such an object could last. The arguments would be similar to the ones we used in the analysis of the process shown in Figure (12).

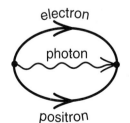

Figure 13
Quantum fluctuation. The uncertainty principle allows such an object to suddenly appear, and then disappear.

In the theory of quantum electrodynamics, a completely isolated process like that shown in Figure (13) does not affect the energy levels of the hydrogen atom and should be undetectable in electrical measurements. But such a process might affect gravity. A gravitational wave or a graviton might interact with the energy of such an object. Some calculations have suggested that such interactions could show up in Einstein's theory of gravity (as a contribution to his famous *cosmological constant*).

An object like that shown in Figure (13) is an example of what one calls a *quantum fluctuation*. Here we have something that appears and disappears in so-called empty space. If such objects can keep appearing and disappearing, then we have to revise our understanding of what we mean by empty.

The uncertainty principle allows us to tell the difference between a quantum fluctuation and a real particle. A quantum fluctuation like that in Figure (13) violates conservation of energy, and therefore cannot last very long. A real particle can last a long time because energy conservation is not violated.

However, there is not necessarily that much difference between a real object and a quantum fluctuation. To see why, let us take a closer look at the π meson. The π^+ is a particle with a rest mass energy of 140 MeV, that consists of a quark-antiquark pair. The quark in that pair is the so-called *up* quark that has a rest mass of roughly 400 MeV. The other is the *antidown* quark that has a rest mass of about 700 MeV. (Since we can't get at isolated quarks, the quark rest masses are estimates, but should not be too far off). Thus the two quarks making up the π meson have a total rest mass of about 1100 MeV. How could they combine to produce a particle whose rest mass is only 140 MeV?

The answer lies in the potential energy of the *gluon force* that holds the quarks together. As we have seen many times, the potential energy of an attractive force is negative. In this case the potential energy of the gluon force is almost as big in magnitude as the rest mass of the quarks, reducing the total energy from 1100 MeV to 140 MeV.

Suppose we had an object whose negative potential energy was as large as the positive rest mass energy. Imagine, for example, that the object consisted of a collection of point sized elementary particles so close together that their negative gravitational potential energy was the same magnitude as the positive rest mass and kinetic energy. Suppose such a collection of particles were created in a quantum fluctuation. How long could the fluctuation last?

Since such an object has no total energy, the violation ΔE of energy conservation is zero, and therefore the lifetime $\Delta t = h/\Delta E$ could be forever.

Suppose the laws of physics required that such a fluctuation rapidly expand, greatly increasing both the positive rest mass and kinetic energy, while maintaining the corresponding amount of negative gravitational potential energy. As long as ΔE remained zero, the expanding fluctuation could keep on going. Perhaps such a fluctuation occurred 13.7 billion years ago and we live in it now.

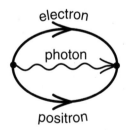

Figure 13 (repeated)
Quantum fluctuation. The uncertainty principle allows such an object to suddenly appear, and then disappear.

CHAPTER 33 REVIEW

This is one of the most important chapters in the text, because it gives an entirely new perspective on the basic nature of physics. In a sense, many of the previous chapters have been included in order to provide the background needed for this chapter.

We began the chapter with the experiment of Figure (1) which showed that a short laser pulse, about 12 cycles long, contained a broad spectrum of wavelengths. The pulse was in the infrared, and the spread of wavelengths, from 750 to 850 nanometers was a third as wide as the spread of visible wavelengths which range from 400 to 700 nanometers.

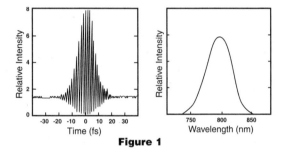

Figure 1

One usually thinks of a laser as having a pure color, like the red lasers that are so common. But the spread in wavelengths of the laser pulse was due not to poor equipment but to a fundamental property of waves. When we used MacScope to study the Fourier transform of a short pulse, we saw that any short pulse had to be made up from a spread of wavelengths or frequencies. The reason for this is that a sine wave is an infinitely long wave. If you are going to construct a short pulse out of sine waves, you need a distribution of wavelengths to get complete cancellation beyond the ends of the pulse.

Figure (9) shows the main feature of the spread in frequencies required to create a short pulse. As we go down from (9a) to (9d), we keep doubling the length of the pulse and see that the spread in frequencies is cut in half. In other words, if we call Δt the length of the pulse, and Δf the width of the spread in frequencies, the product $\Delta t \Delta f$ does not change as we keep doubling Δt.

Let us look at the product $\Delta t \Delta f$ for the laser pulse in Figure (1). Since the pulse is 20 femtoseconds long, we have for the length of the pulse

$$\Delta t = 20 \times 10^{-15} \text{ seconds}$$

The wavelengths range from $\lambda_- = 750 \times 10^{-9}$ meters to $\lambda_+ = 850 \times 10^{-9}$ meters. The related frequencies are

$$f_+ = \frac{c}{\lambda_-} = \frac{3 \times 10^8}{750 \times 10^{-9}} = 4.0 \times 10^{14} sec^{-1}$$

$$f_- = \frac{c}{\lambda_+} = \frac{3 \times 10^8}{850 \times 10^{-9}} = 3.5 \times 10^{14} sec^{-1}$$

and the spread in frequencies is

$$\Delta f = f_+ - f_- = 0.5 \times 10^{14} sec^{-1}$$

Thus the product $\Delta t \Delta f$ has the surprisingly simple result

$$\Delta t \Delta f = 20 \times 10^{-15} sec \times 0.5 \times 10^{14} \frac{1}{sec} = 1.0$$

As a final step, note that the laser pulse is made up of photons that obey Einstein's formula $E = hf$. Thus $h\Delta f$ is the energy spread ΔE of the photons in the laser pulse. With $\Delta E = h\Delta f$ or $\Delta f = \Delta E/h$, we get

$$\Delta f \Delta t = \frac{\Delta E}{h} \Delta t = 1 \qquad \boxed{\Delta E \Delta t = h}$$

for the photons in the pulse.

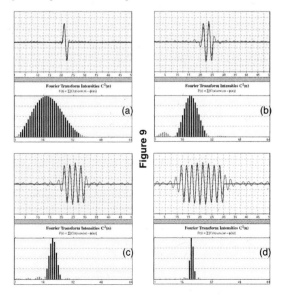

Figure 9

Probability Interpretation

*Let us take another look at the short pulse in Figure (9a), which is made up of a fairly wide distribution of frequencies. If this repre-sented a real laser pulse with many photons, the bottom graph would rep-resent the **distribution of frequencies or energies** of the photons in the pulse.*

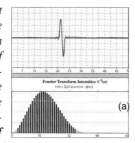

Fourier Transform Intensities $C^2(n)$

(a)

*Now comes the interesting question. Suppose there is **only one photon** in the pulse. What is the meaning of the distribution of frequencies or energies mean for a single photon? The answer is that it is the **distribution of probabilities** that the photon has the corresponding frequency or energy. There is some probability that the photon has a frequency or energy as low as the first few harmonics shown. And some probability that its energy is as high as that represented by the 32nd harmonic. The photon's energy can be anywhere in this range of frequency or energy. Thus our calculation of ΔE represents the uncertainty in the energy of the photon.*

If you read Figure (9) from (9d) to (9a), you see that as you make the laser pulse shorter, the uncertainty ΔE of the energy of the photon in the pulse becomes greater. The shorter the time Δt we have available to observe the photon, the more uncertain our mea-surement of the photon's energy becomes.

Energy Conservation

We introduced the concept of energy by saying that its main property was that it was conserved. Energy conservation became one of the most important laws in the text. Now we see that if you try to measure the energy of an object, be it the non relativistic particle discussed at the end of the last chapter, or a fully relativistic particle like a photon in a laser pulse, any measurement of the particle's energy will lead to uncertain results. How do we know that energy is conserved if we cannot measure it precisely?

*Nature's answer to this question appears to be— **energy only has to be conserved when you can measure it**.*

The most convincing evidence for this point of view comes from a detailed calculation of the energy of the electron in the hydrogen atom. In the theory of Quantum Electrodynamics, the electric force hold-ing the electron in the atom is caused by the ex-change of photons between the electron and the proton. Since the electron binding energy is only 13.6 eV, the photons on the average must have a small energy, not much larger than 13 eV.

But, the calculation shows that there is some finite probability for one of the photons to create an electron-positron pair during an exchange. Since the rest mass energy of a positron-electron pair is one million electron volts, we have a situation where a photon whose energy should be only a few electron volts creates a million electron volt pair.

How can this happen? The answer is that the pair lasts for such a short time Δt that the violation of energy conservation ΔE cannot be directly detected due to the uncertainty principle.

The uncertainty principle can also be used as a clock to measure very short times. We found that the rest mass of the so called $(\Lambda 1520)$ particle varied by as much as 16 million electron volts when the particle decayed. The reason for this variation is that the particle did not live long enough to accurately determine its own rest mass energy. Calling this variation the uncertainty ΔE of the particle's rest mass energy, and Δt its lifetime, we got

$$\Delta t = \frac{h}{\Delta E} = \frac{6.63 \times 10^{34} \, joule \, sec}{10^6 eV \times 1.6 \times 10^{-19} \, joule/eV}$$

$$= 4 \times 10^{-21} \, seconds$$

There is no other way to measure such short times.

Quantum Fluctuations

The uncertainty principle affects our view of what we used to call empty space. To say that I have a region of empty space, is to say that that region has zero energy exactly. But if I do an experiment to measure the energy in that region of space, my answer must be uncertain by an amount $\Delta E = h/\Delta t$. Thus for short times, something is probably there.

A candidate is the example of a quantum fluctuation shown in Figure (13). To have an electron, a positron, and a photon, suddenly appear in space, requires a violation ΔE of the conservation of energy of at least one million eV. But if these particles all annihilate each other in a time $\Delta t = h/\Delta E$, the violation of conservation of energy cannot be observed and there should be some probability of such a process occuring.

The Early Universe

Recent studies of the early universe suggest that quantum flucuations are responsible for the diversity of structure we now see in the universe.

In Chapter 26 on photons, we discussed the three degree radiation that was released when the universe became transparent at the young age of 1/3 of a million years. (The universe is now 13.7 billion years old.) The main feature of this radiation is that it is very uniform. It took specially designed satellites to detect any variation from point to point in the sky.

The latest satellite (NASA's Wilkinson Microwave Anisotropy Probe [WMAP]) detected a pattern of small variations that appear to have resulted from quantum fluctuations in the very, very early universe. The current theory is that once the universe became transparent, these small variations allowed the gravitational collapse of clouds of gas to form the stars, galaxies, and the clusters of galaxies we see today. If the universe had been perfectly uniform, with no lumps created by quantum fluctuations, the universe would not have the structure we observe.

CHAPTER EXERCISE

Exercise 1 On page 8

An electron is in an excited state of the hydrogen atom, either the second energy level at –3.40 eV, or the third energy level at –1.51 eV. You want to do an experiment to decide which of these two states the electron is in. What is the least amount of time you must take to make this measurement?

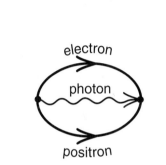

Figure 13 (repeated again)
Quantum fluctuation. The uncertainty principle allows such an object to suddenly appear, and then disappear.

Chapter on
Geometrical Optics

For over 100 years, from the time of Newton and Huygens in the late 1600s, until 1801 when Thomas Young demonstrated the wave nature of light with his two slit experiment, it was not clear whether light consisted of beams of particles as proposed by Newton, or was a wave phenomenon as put forward by Huygens. The reason for the confusion is that almost all common optical phenomena can be explained by tracing light rays. The wavelength of light is so short compared to the size of most objects we are familiar with, that light rays produce sharp shadows and interference and diffraction effects are negligible.

To see how wave phenomena can be explained by ray tracing, consider the reflection of a light wave by a metal surface. When a wave strikes a very small object, an object much smaller than a wavelength, a circular scattered wave emerges as shown in the ripple tank photograph of Figure (36-1) reproduced here. But when a light wave impinges on a metal surface consisting of many small atoms, represented by the line of dots in Figure (36-2), the circular scattered waves all add up to produce a reflected wave that emerges at an angle of reflection θ_r equal to the angle of incidence θ_i. Rather than sketching the individual crests and troughs of the incident wave, and adding up all the scattered waves, it is much easier to treat the light as a ray that reflected from the surface. This ray is governed by the law of reflection, namely $\theta_r = \theta_i$.

incident wave

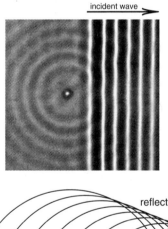

Figure 36-1
An incident wave passing over a small object produces a circular scattered wave.

Light ray reflected from a mirror.

angle of incidence — θ_i | θ_r — angle of reflection

mirror

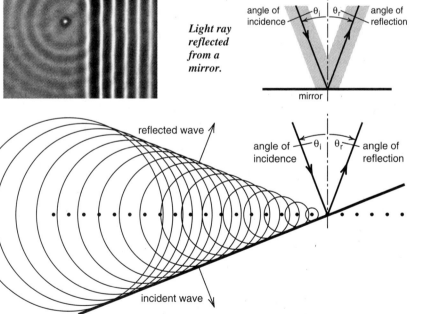

reflected wave

angle of incidence — θ_i | θ_r — angle of reflection

incident wave

Figure 36-2
Reflection of light. In the photograph, we see an incoming plane wave scattered by a small object. If the object is smaller than a wavelength, the scattered waves are circular. When an incoming light wave strikes an array of atoms in the surface of a metal, the scattered waves add up to produce a reflected wave that comes out at an angle of reflection θ_r equal to the angle of incidence θ_i.

*The subject of geometrical optics is the study of the behavior of light when the phenomena can be explained by ray tracing, where shadows are sharp and interference and diffraction effects can be neglected. The basic laws for ray tracing are extremely simple. At a reflecting surface $\theta_r = \theta_i$, as we have just seen. When a light ray passes between two media of different **indexes of refraction**, as in going from air into glass or air into water, the rule is $n_1 \sin \theta_1 = n_2 \sin \theta_2$, where n_1 and n_2 are constants called indices of refraction, and θ_1 and θ_2 are the angles that the rays made with the line perpendicular to the interface. This is known as **Snell's law**.*

This entire chapter is based on the two rules $\theta_r = \theta_i$ and $n_1 \sin \theta_1 = n_2 \sin \theta_2$. These rules are all that are needed to understand the function of telescopes, microscopes, cameras, fiber optics, and the optical components of the human eye. You can understand the operation of these instruments without knowing anything about Newton's laws, kinetic and potential energy, electric or magnetic fields, or the particle and wave nature of matter. In other words, there is no prerequisite background needed for studying geometrical optics as long as you accept the two rules which are easily verified by experiment.

In most introductory texts, geometrical optics appears after Maxwell's equations and theory of light. There is a certain logic to this, first introducing a basic theory for light and then treating geometrical optics as a practical application of the theory. But this is clearly not an historical approach since geometrical optics was developed centuries before Maxwell's theory. Nor is it the only logical approach, because studying lens systems teaches you nothing more about Maxwell's equations than you can learn by deriving Snell's law. Geometrical optics is an interesting subject full of wonderful applications, a subject that can appear anywhere in an introductory physics course.

We have a preference not to introduce geometrical optics after Maxwell's equations. With Maxwell's theory, the student is introduced to the wave nature of one component of matter, namely light. If the focus is kept on the basic nature of matter, the next step is to look at the photoelectric effect and the particle nature of light. You then see that light has both a particle and a wave nature, which opens the door to the particle-wave nature of all matter and the subject of quantum mechanics. We have a strong preference not to interrupt this focus on the basic nature of matter with a long and possibly distracting chapter on geometrical optics.

REFLECTION FROM CURVED SURFACES

The Mormon Tabernacle, shown in Figure (1), is constructed in the shape of an ellipse. If one stands at one of the focuses and drops a pin, the pin drop can be heard 120 feet away at the other focus. The reason why can be seen from Figure (2), which is similar to Figure (8-28) where we showed you how to draw an ellipse with a pencil, a piece of string, and two thumbtacks.

The thumbtacks are at the focuses, and the ellipse is drawn by holding the string taut as shown. As you move the pencil point along, the two sections of string always make equal angles θ_i and θ_r to a line perpen-dicular or normal to the part of the ellipse we are drawing. The best way to see that the angles θ_i and θ_r are always equal is to construct your own ellipse and measure these angles at various points along the curve.

If a sound wave were emitted from focus 1 in Figure (2), the part of the wave that traveled over to point A on the ellipse would be reflected at an angle θ_r equal to the angle of incidence θ_i, and travel over to focus 2. The part of the sound wave that struck point B on the ellipse, would be reflected at an angle θ_r equal to it's angle of incidence θ_i, and also travel over to focus 2. If you think of the sound wave as traveling out in rays, then all the rays radiated from focus 1 end up at focus 2, and that is why you hear the whisper there. We say that the rays are **focused** at focus 2, and that is why these points are called focuses of the ellipse. (Note also that the path lengths are the same, so that all the waves arriving at focus 2 are in phase.)

Mormon Tabernacle under construction, 1866.

Mormon Tabernacle finished, 1871.

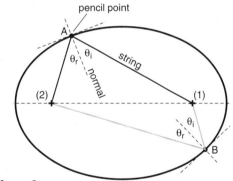

Figure 2
Drawing an ellipse using a string and two thumbtacks.

Mormon Tabernacle today.
Figure 1

Figure 2a
A superposition of the top half of Figure 2 on Figure 1.

The Parabolic Reflection

You make a parabola out of an ellipse by moving one of the focuses very far away. The progression from a parabola to an ellipse is shown in Figure (3). For a true parabola, the second focus has to be infinitely far away.

Suppose a light wave were emitted from a star and traveled to a parabolic reflecting surface. We can think of the star as being out at the second, infinitely distant, focus of the parabola. Thus all the light rays coming in from the star would reflect from the parabolic surface and come to a point at the near focus. The rays from the star approach the reflector as a parallel beam of rays, thus a parabolic reflector has the property of focusing parallel rays to a point, as shown in Figure (4a).

If parallel rays enter a deep dish parabolic mirror from an angle off axis as shown in Figure (4b), the rays do not focus to a point, with the result that an off axis star would appear as a blurry blob. (This figure corresponds to looking at a star 2.5° off axis, about 5 moon diameters from the center of the field of view.)

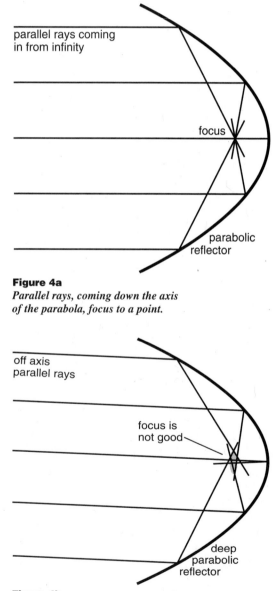

Figure 4a
Parallel rays, coming down the axis of the parabola, focus to a point.

Figure 4b
For such a deep dish parabola, rays coming in at an angle of 2.5° do not focus well.

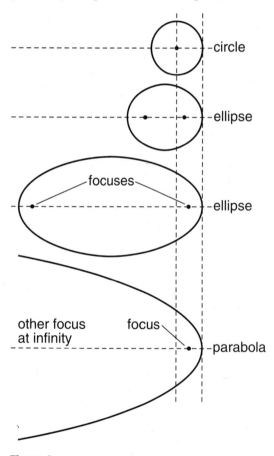

Figure 3
Evolution of an ellipse into a parabola. For a parabola, one of the focuses is out at infinity.

One way to get sharp images for parallel rays coming in at an angle is to use a shallower parabola as illustrated in Figure (4c). In that figure, the *focal length* (distance from the center of the mirror to the focus) is 2 times the mirror diameter, giving what is called an *f* 2 mirror. In Figure (4d), you can see that rays coming in at an angle of 2.5° (blue lines) almost focus to a point. Typical amateur telescopes are still shallower, around *f* 8, which gives a sharp focus for rays off angle by as much as 2° to 3°.

As we can see in Figure (4d), light coming from two different stars focus at two different points in what is called the *focal plane* of the mirror. If you placed a photographic film at the focal plane, light from each different star, entering as parallel beams from different angles, would focus at different points on the film, and you would end up with a photographic image of the stars. This is how distant objects like stars are photographed with what is called a *reflecting telescope*.

light from star on axis

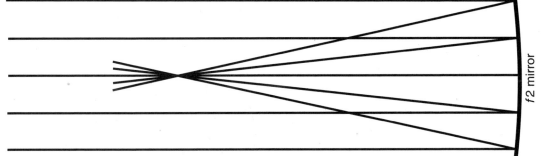

Figure 4c
A shallow dish is made by using only the shallow bottom of the parabola. Here the focal length is twice the diameter of the dish, giving us an f2 mirror. Typical amateur telescopes are still shallower, having a focal length around 8 times the mirror diameter (f8 mirrors). [The mirror in Figure 4b, that gave a bad focus, was f.125, having a focal length 1/8 the diameter of the mirror.]

light from star #2, 2.5° off axis

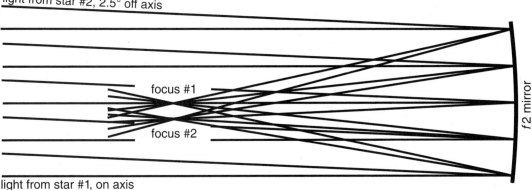

light from star #1, on axis

Figure 4d
We can think of this drawing as representing light coming in from a red star at the center of the field of view, and a blue star 2.5° (5 full moon diameters) away. Separate images are formed, which could be recorded on a photographic film. With this shallow dish, the off axis image is sharp (but not quite a point).

MIRROR IMAGES

The image you see in a mirror, although very familiar, is still quite remarkable in its reality. Why does it look so real? You do not need to know how your eye works to begin to see why.

Consider Figure (5a) where light from a point source reaches your eye. We have drawn two rays, one from the source to the top of the eye, and one to the bottom. In Figure (5b), we have placed a horizontal mirror as shown and moved the light source a distance h above the mirror equal to the distance it was below the mirror before the mirror was inserted. Using the rule that the angle of incidence equals the angle of reflection, we again drew two rays that went from the light source to

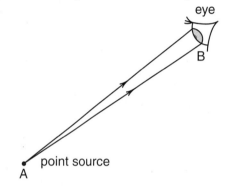

Figure 5a
Light from a point source reaching your eye.

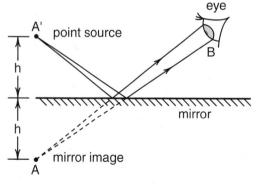

Figure 5b
There is no difference when the source is at point A, or at point A' and the light is reflected in a mirror.

the top and to the bottom of the eye. You can see that if you started at the eye and drew the rays back as straight lines, ignoring the mirror, the rays would intersect at the old source point A as shown by the dotted lines in Figure (5b).

To the eye (or a camera) at point B, there is no detectable difference between Figures (5a) and (5b). In both cases, the same rays of light, coming from the same directions enter the eye. Since the eye has no way of telling that the rays have been bent, we perceive that the light source is at the *image point* A rather than at the source point A'.

When we look at an extended object, its image in the mirror does not look identical to the object itself. In Figure (6), my granddaughter Julia is holding her right hand in front of a mirror and her left hand off to the side. The image of the right hand looks like the left hand. In particular, the fingers of the mirror image of the right hand curl in the opposite direction from those of the right hand itself. If she were using the right hand rule to find the direction of the angular momentum of a rotating object, the mirror image would look as if she were using a left hand rule.

It is fairly common knowledge that left and right are reversed in a mirror image. But if left and right are reversed, why aren't top and bottom reversed also? Think about that for a minute before you go on to the next paragraph.

Figure 6
The image of the right hand looks like a left hand.

To see what the image of an extended object should be, imagine that we place an arrow in front of a mirror as shown in Figure (7). We have constructed rays from the tip and the base of the arrow that reflect and enter the eye as shown. Extending these rays back to the image, we see that the image arrow has been reversed *front to back*. That is what a mirror does. The mirror image is reversed front to back, not left to right or top to bottom. It turns out that the right hand, when reversed front to back as in its image in Figure (6), has the symmetry properties of a left hand. If used to define angular momentum, you would get a left hand rule.

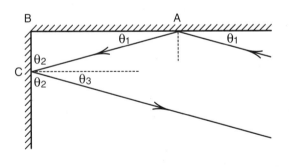

Figure 7
A mirror image changes front to back, not left to right.

The Corner Reflector

When two vertical mirrors are placed at right angles as shown in Figure (8a), a horizontal ray approaching the mirrors is reflected back in the direction from which it came. It is a little exercise in trigonometry to see that this is so. Since the angle of incidence equals the angle of reflection at each mirror surface, we see that the angles labeled θ_1 must be equal to each other and the same for the angles θ_2. From the right triangle ABC, we see that $\theta_1 + \theta_2 = 90°$. We also see that the angles $\theta_2 + \theta_3$ also add up to $90°$, thus $\theta_3 = \theta_1$, which implies the exiting ray is parallel to the entering one.

If you mount three mirrors perpendicular to each other to form the corner of a cube, then light entering this so called *corner reflector* from any angle goes back in the direction from which it came. The Apollo II astronauts placed the array of corner reflectors shown in Figure (8b) on the surface of the moon, so that a laser beam from the earth would be reflected back from a precisely known point on the surface of the moon. By measuring the time it took a laser pulse to be reflected back from the array, the distance to the moon could be measured to an accuracy of centimeters. With the distance to the moon known with such precision, other distances in the solar system could then be determined accurately.

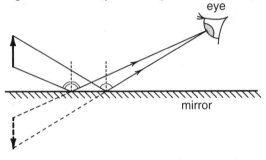

Figure 8a
With a corner reflector, the light is reflected back it the same direction from which it arrived.

Figure 8b
Array of corner reflectors left on the moon by the Apollo astronauts. A laser pulse from the earth, aimed at the reflectors, returns straight back to the laser. By measuring the time the pulse takes to go to the reflectors and back, the distance to that point on the moon and back can be accurately measured.

MOTION OF LIGHT THROUGH A MEDIUM

We are all familiar with the fact that light can travel through clear water or clear glass. With some of the new glasses developed for fiber optics communication, light signals can travel for miles without serious distortion. If you made a mile thick pane from this glass you could see objects through it.

From an atomic point of view, it is perhaps surprising that light can travel any distance at all through water or glass. A reasonable picture of what happens when a light wave passes over an atom is provided by the ripple tank photograph shown in Figure (36-1) reproduced here. The wave scatters from the atom, and since atoms are considerably smaller than a wavelength of visible light, the scattered waves are circular like those in the ripple tank photograph. The final wave is the sum of the incident and the scattered waves as shown in Figure (36-1a).

When light passes through a medium like glass or water, the wave is being scattered by a huge number of atoms. The final wave pattern is the sum of the incident wave and all of the many billions of scattered waves. You might suspect that this sum would be very complex, but that is not the case. At the surface some of the incident wave is reflected. Inside the medium, the *incident and scattered waves add up to a new wave* of the same frequency as the incident wave but which travels *at a reduced speed*. The speed of a light wave in water for example is 25% less than the speed of light in a vacuum.

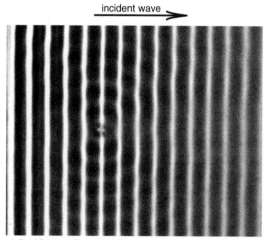

a) *Incident and scattered wave together.*

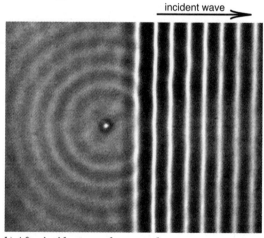

b) *After incident wave has passed.*

Figure 36-1

If the scattering object is smaller than a wavelength, we get circular scattered waves.

The optical properties of lenses are a consequence of this effective reduction in the speed of light in the lens. Figure (9) is a rather remarkable photograph of individual short pulses of laser light as they pass through and around a glass lens. You can see that the part of the wave front that passed through the lens is delayed by its motion through the glass. The thicker the glass, the greater the delay. You can also see that the delay changed the shape and direction of motion of the wave front, so that the light passing through the lens focuses to a point behind the lens. This is how a lens really works.

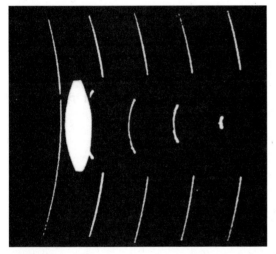

Figure 9
Motion of a wave front through a glass lens. The delay in the motion of the wave front as it passes through the glass changes the shape and direction of motion of the wave front, resulting in the focusing of light. (This photograph should not be confused with ripple tank photographs where wavelengths are comparable to the size of the objects. Here the wavelength of the light is about one hundred thousand times smaller than the diameter of the lens, with the result we get sharp shadows and do not see diffraction effects.)

In the 18/February/1999 issue of **Nature** *it was announced that a laser pulse travelled through a gas of supercooled sodium atoms at a speed of 17 meters per second! (You can ride a bicycle faster than that.) This means that the sodium atoms had an index of refraction of about 18 million, 7.3 million times greater than that of diamond!*

Index of Refraction

The amount by which the effective speed of light is reduced as the light passes through a medium depends both upon the medium and the wavelength of the light. There is very little slowing of the speed of light in air, about a 25% reduction in speed in water, and nearly a 59% reduction in speed in diamond. In general, blue light travels somewhat slower than red light in nearly all media.

It is traditional to describe the slowing of the speed of light in terms of what is called the ***index of refraction*** of the medium. The index of refraction n is defined by the equation

$$\left.\begin{array}{l}\text{speed of light}\\ \text{in a medium}\end{array}\right\} \quad v_{light} = \frac{c}{n} \qquad (1)$$

The index n has to equal 1 in a vacuum because light always travels at the speed 3×10^8 meters in a vacuum. The index n can never be less than 1, because nothing can travel faster than the speed c. For yellow sodium light of wavelength $\lambda = 5.89 \times 10^{-5}$ cm (589 nanometers), the index of refraction of water at 20° C is n = 1.333, which implies a 25% reduction in speed. For diamond, n = 2.417 for this yellow light. Table 1 gives the indices of refraction for various transparent substances for the sodium light.

Vacuum	1.00000	exactly
Air (STP)	1.00029	
Ice	1.309	
Water (20° C)	1.333	
Ethyl alcohol	1.36	
Fuzed quartz	1.46	
Sugar solution (80%)	1.49	
Typical crown glass	1.52	
Sodium Chloride	1.54	
Polystyrene	1.55	
Heavy flint glass	1.65	
Sapphire	1.77	
Zircon	1.923	
Diamond	2.417	
Rutile	2.907	
Gallium phosphide	3.50	
Very cold sodium atoms	18000000	for laser pulse

Table 1
Some indices of refraction for yellow sodium light at a wavelength of 589 nanometers.

CERENKOV RADIATION

In our discussion, in Chapter 1, of the motion of light through empty space, we saw that nothing, not even information, could travel faster than the speed of light. If it did, we could, for example, get answers to questions that had not yet been thought of.

When moving through a medium, the speed of a light wave is slowed by repeated scattering and it is no longer true that nothing can move faster than the speed of light in that medium. We saw for example that the speed of light in water is only 3/4 the speed c in vacuum. Many elementary particles, like the muons in the muon lifetime experiment, travel at speeds much closer to c. When a charged particle moves faster than the speed of light in a medium, we get an effect not unlike the sonic boom produced by a supersonic jet. We get a *shock wave of light* that is similar to a sound shock wave (sonic boom), or to the water shock wave shown in Figure (33-30) reproduced here. The light shock wave is called *Cerenkov radiation* after the Russian physicist Pavel Cerenkov who received the 1958 Nobel prize for discovering the effect.

In the muon lifetime picture, one observed how long muons lived when stopped in a block of plastic. The experiment was made possible by Cerenkov radiation. The muons that stopped in the plastic, entered moving faster than the speed of light in plastic, and as a result emitted a flash of light in the form of Cerenkov radiation. When the muon decayed, a charged positron and a neutral neutrino were emitted. In most cases the charged positron emerged faster than the speed of light in the plastic, and also emitted Cerenkov radiation. The two flashes of light were detected by the phototube which converted the light flashes to voltage pulses. The voltage pulses were then displayed on an oscilloscope screen where the time interval between the pulses could be measured. This interval represented the time that the muon lived, mostly at rest, in the plastic.

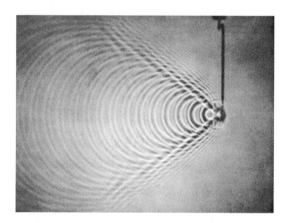

Figure 33-30
When the source of the waves moves faster than the speed of the waves, the wave fronts pile up to produce a shock wave as shown. This shock wave is the sonic boom you hear when a jet plane flies overhead faster than the speed of sound.

SNELL'S LAW

When a wave enters a medium of higher index of refraction and travels more slowly, the wavelength of the wave changes. The wavelength is the distance the wave travels in one period, and if the speed of the wave is reduced, the distance the wave travels in one period is reduced. (In most cases, the frequency or period of the wave is not changed. The exceptions are in fluorescence and nonlinear optics where the frequency or color of light can change.)

We can calculate how the wavelength changes with wave speed from the relationship

$$\lambda \frac{cm}{cycle} = \frac{v_{wave} \frac{cm}{sec}}{T \frac{sec}{cycle}}$$

Setting $v_{wave} = c/n$ for the speed of light in the medium, gives for the corresponding wavelength λ_n

$$\lambda_n = \frac{v_{wave}}{T} = \frac{c/n}{T} = \frac{1}{n}\frac{c}{T} = \frac{\lambda_0}{n} \qquad (2)$$

where $\lambda_0 = c/T$ is the wavelength in a vacuum. Thus, for example, the wavelength of light entering a diamond from air will be shortened by a factor of $1/2.42$.

What happens when a set of periodic plane waves goes from one medium to another is illustrated in the ripple tank photograph of Figure (10). In this photograph, the water has two depths, deeper on the upper part where the waves travel faster, and shallower in the lower part where the waves travel more slowly. You can see that the wavelengths are shorter in the lower part, but there are the same number of waves. (We do not gain or loose waves at the boundary.) The frequency, the number of waves that pass you per second, is the same on the top and bottom.

The only way that the wavelength can be shorter and still have the same number of waves is for the wave to bend at the boundary as shown. We have drawn arrows showing the direction of the wave in the deep water (the incident wave) and in the shallow water (what we will call the ***transmitted*** or ***refracted*** wave), and we see that the change in wavelength causes a sudden change in direction of motion of the wave. If you look carefully you will also see reflected waves which emerge at an angle of reflection equal to the angle of incidence.

Figure (11) shows a beam of yellow light entering a piece of glass. The index of refraction of the glass is 1.55, thus the wavelength of the light in the glass is only .65 times as long as that in air ($n \approx 1$ for air). You can see both the bending of the ray as it enters the glass and also the reflected ray. (You also see internal reflection and the ray emerging from the bottom surface.) You cannot see the individual wave crests, but otherwise Figures (10) and (11) show similar phenomena.

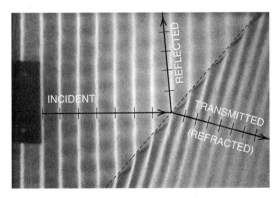

Figure 10
Refraction at surface of water. When the waves enter shallower water, they travel more slowly and have a shorter wavelength. The waves must travel in a different direction in order for the crests to match up.

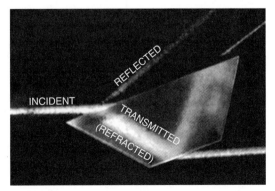

Figure 11
Refraction at surface of glass. When the light waves enter the glass, they travel more slowly and have a shorter wavelength. Like the water waves, the light waves must travel in a different direction in order for the crests to match up.

Derivation of Snell's Law

To calculate the angle by which a light ray is bent when it enters another medium, consider the diagram in Figure (12). The drawing represents a light wave, traveling in a medium of index n_1, incident on a boundary at an angle θ_1. We have sketched successive incident wave crests separated by the wavelength λ_1. Assuming that the index n_2 in the lower medium is greater than n_1, the wavelength λ_2 will be shorter than λ_1 and the beam will emerge at the smaller angle θ_2.

To calculate the angle θ_2 at which the transmitted or refracted wave emerges, consider the detailed section of Figure (12) redrawn in Figure (13a). Notice that we have labeled two apparently different angles by the same label θ_1. Why these angles are equal is seen in the construction of Figure (13b) where we see that the angles α and θ_1 are equal.

Exercise 2

Show that the two angles labeled θ_2 in Figure (13a) must also be equal.

Since the triangles ACB and ADB are right triangles in Figure (13a), we have

$$\lambda_1 = AB \sin\left(\theta_1\right) = \lambda_0/n_1 \qquad (3)$$

$$\lambda_2 = AB \sin\left(\theta_2\right) = \lambda_0/n_2 \qquad (4)$$

where AB is the hypotenuse of both triangles and λ_0 is the wavelength when $n_0 = 1$. When we divide Equation 4 by Equation (5), the distances AB and λ_0 cancel, and we are left with

$$\frac{\sin\left(\theta_1\right)}{\sin\left(\theta_2\right)} = \frac{n_2}{n_1}$$

or

$$\boxed{n_1 \sin\left(\theta_1\right) = n_2 \sin\left(\theta_2\right)} \qquad \textit{Snell's law} \qquad (5)$$

Equation (5), known as Snell's law, allows us to calculate the change in direction when a beam of light goes from one medium to another.

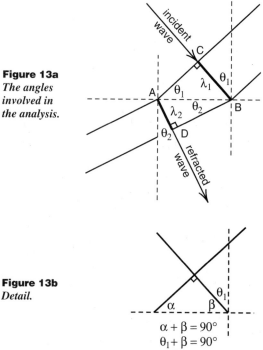

Figure 13a
The angles involved in the analysis.

Figure 13b
Detail.

$$\alpha + \beta = 90°$$
$$\theta_1 + \beta = 90°$$
$$\Rightarrow \alpha = \theta_1$$

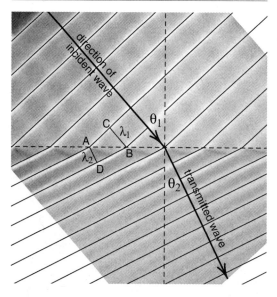

Figure 12
Analysis of refraction. The crests must match at the boundary between the different wavelength waves.

INTERNAL REFLECTION

Because of the way rays bend at the interface of two media, there is a rather interesting effect when light goes from a material of higher to a material of lower index of refraction, as in the case of light going from water into air. The effect is seen clearly in Figure (14). Here we have a multiple exposure showing a laser beam entering a tank of water, being reflected by a mirror, and coming out at different angles. The outgoing ray is bent farther away from the normal as it emerges from the water. We reach the point where the outgoing ray bends and runs parallel to the surface of the water. This is a critical angle, for if the mirror is turned farther, the ray can no longer get out and is completely reflected inside the surface.

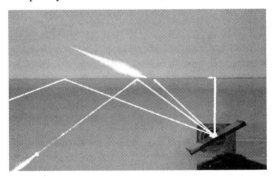

Figure 14
Internal reflection. We took three exposures of a laser beam reflecting off an underwater mirror set at different angles. In the first case the laser beam makes it back out of the water and strikes a white cardboard behind the water tank. In the other two cases, there is total internal reflection at the under side of the water surface. In the final exposure we used a flash to make the mirror visible.

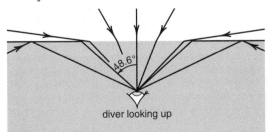

Figure 14a
When you are swimming under water and look up, you see the outside world through a round hole. Outside that hole, the surface is a silver mirror.

It is easy to calculate the critical angle θ_c at which this complete internal reflection begins. Set the angle of refraction, θ_2 in Figure (14), equal to 90° and we get from Snell's law

$$n_1 \sin\theta_c = n_2 \sin\theta_2 = n_2 \sin90° = n_2$$

$$\sin\theta_c = \frac{n_2}{n_1} \; ; \quad \boxed{\theta_c = \sin^{-1}\frac{n_2}{n_1}} \qquad (6)$$

For light emerging from water, we have $n_2 \approx 1$ for air and $n_1 = 1.33$ for water giving

$$\sin^{-1}\theta_2 = \frac{1}{1.33} = .75$$

$$\theta_c = 48.6° \qquad (7)$$

Anyone who swims underwater, scuba divers especially, are quite familiar with the phenomenon of internal reflection. When you look up at the surface of the water, you can see the entire outside world through a circular region directly overhead, as shown in Figure (14a). Beyond this circle the surface looks like a silver mirror.

Exercise 3

A glass prism can be used as shown in Figure (15) to reflect light at right angles. The index of refraction n_g of the glass must be high enough so that there is total internal reflection at the back surface. What is the least value n_g one can have to make such a prism work? (Assume the prism is in the air where $n \approx 1$.)

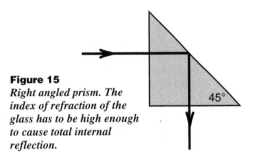

Figure 15
Right angled prism. The index of refraction of the glass has to be high enough to cause total internal reflection.

Fiber Optics

Internal reflection plays a critical role in modern communications and modern medicine through fiber optics. When light is sent down through a glass rod or fiber so that it strikes the surface at an angle greater than the critical angle, as shown in Figure (16a), the light will be completely reflected and continue to bounce down the rod with no loss out through the surface. By using modern very clear glass, a fiber can carry a light signal for miles without serious attenuation.

The reason it is more effective to use light in glass fibers than electrons in copper wire for transmitting signals, is that the glass fiber can carry information at a much higher rate than a copper wire, as indicated in Figure (16b). This is because laser pulses traveling through glass, can be turned on and off much more rapidly than electrical pulses in a wire. The practical limit for copper wire is on the order of a million pulses or bits of information per second (corresponding to a ***baud rate*** of one ***megabit***). Typically the information rate is

much slower over commercial telephone lines, not much in excess of 30 to 50 thousand bits of information per second (corresponding to 30 to 50 ***kilobaud***). These rates are fast enough to carry telephone conversations or transmit text to a printer, but painfully slow for sending pictures and much too slow for digital television signals. High definition digital television will require that information be sent at a rate of about 3 million bits or pulses every 1/30 of a second for a baud rate of 90 million baud. (Compare that with the baud rate on your computer modem.) In contrast, fiber optics cables are capable of carrying pulses or bits at a rate of about a billion (10^9) per second, and are thus well suited for transmitting pictures or many phone conversations at once.

By bundling many fine fibers together, as indicated in Figure (17), one can transmit a complete image along the bundle. One end of the bundle is placed up against the object to be observed, and if the fibers are not mixed up, the image appears at the other end.

To transmit a high resolution image, one needs a bundle of about a million fibers. The tiny fibers needed for this are constructed by making a rather large bundle of small glass strands, heating the bundle to soften the glass, and then stretching the bundle until the individual strands are very fine. (If you have heated a glass rod over a Bunsen burner and pulled out the ends, you have seen how fine a glass fiber can be made this way.)

Figure 16a
Because of internal reflections, light can travel down a glass fiber, even when the fiber is bent.

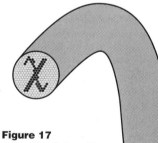

Figure 16b
A single glass fiber can carry the same amount of information as a fat cable of copper wires.

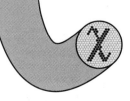

Figure 17
A bundle of glass fibers can be used to carry an image from one point to another. The order of a million fibers are needed to carry the medical images seen on the next page.

Medical Imaging

The use of fiber optics has revolutionized many aspects of medicine. It is an amazing experience to go down and look inside your own stomach and beyond, as the author did a few years ago. This is done with a flexible fiber optics instrument called a retroflexion, producing the results shown in Figure (18). An operation, such as the removal of a gallbladder, which used to require opening the abdomen and a long recovery period, can now be performed through a small hole near the navel, using fiber optics to view the procedure. You can see the viewing instrument and such an operation in progress in Figure (19).

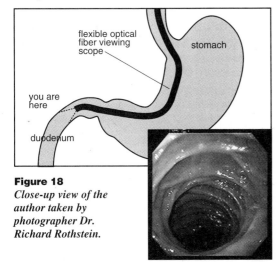

Figure 18
Close-up view of the author taken by photographer Dr. Richard Rothstein.

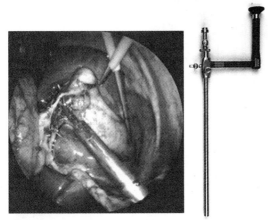

Figure 19
Gallbladder operation in progress, being viewed by the rigid laparoscope shown on the right. Such views are now recorded by high resolution television.

PRISMS

So far in our discussion of refraction, we have considered only beams of light of one color, one wavelength. Because the index of refraction generally changes with wavelength, rays of different wavelength will be bent at different angles when passing the interface of two media. Usually the index of refraction of visible light increases as the wavelength becomes shorter. Thus when white light, which is a mixture of all the visible colors, is sent through a prism as shown in Figure (20), the short wavelength blue light will be deflected by a greater angle than the red light, and the beam of light is separated into a rainbow of colors.

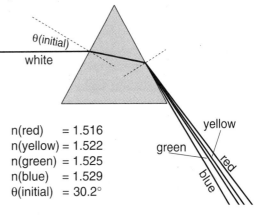

$$n(red) = 1.516$$
$$n(yellow) = 1.522$$
$$n(green) = 1.525$$
$$n(blue) = 1.529$$
$$\theta(initial) = 30.2°$$

Figure 20
When light is sent through a prism, it is separated into a rainbow of colors. In this scale drawing, we find that almost all the separation of colors occurs at the second surface where the light emerges from the glass.

Rainbows

Rainbows in the sky are formed by the reflection and refraction of sunlight by raindrops. It is not, however, particularly easy to see why a rainbow is formed. René Descartes figured this out by tracing rays that enter and leave a spherical raindrop.

In Figure (21a) we have used Snell's law to trace the path of a ray of yellow light that enters a spherical drop of water (of index n = 1.33), is reflected on the back side, and emerges again on the front side. (Only a fraction of the light is reflected at the back, thus the reflected beam is rather weak.) In this drawing, the angle θ_2 is determined by $\sin(\theta_1) = 1.33 \sin(\theta_2)$. At the back, the angles of incidence and reflection are equal, and at the front we have $1.33 \sin(\theta_2) = \sin(\theta_1)$ (taking the index of refraction of air = 1). Nothing is hard about this construction, it is fairly easy to do with a good drafting program like Adobe Illustrator and a hand calculator.

In Figure (21b) we see what happens when a number of parallel rays enter a spherical drop of water. (This is similar to the construction that was done by Descartes in 1633.) When you look at the outgoing rays, it is not immediately obvious that there is any special direction for the reflected rays. But if you look closely you will see that the ray we have labeled #11 is the one that comes back at the widest angle from the incident ray.

Ray #1, through the center, comes straight back out. Ray #2 comes out at a small angle. The angles increase up to Ray #11, and then start to decrease again for Rays #12 and #13. In our construction the maximum angle, that of Ray #11, was 41.6°, close to the theoretical value of 42° for yellow light.

What is more important than the fact that the maximum angle of deviation is 42° is the fact that the rays close to #11 emerge as more or less parallel to each other. The other rays, like those near #3 for example come out at diverging angles. That light is spread out. But the light emerging at 42° comes out as a parallel beam. When you have sunlight striking many raindrops, *more yellow light is reflected back at this angle of 42° than any other angle.*

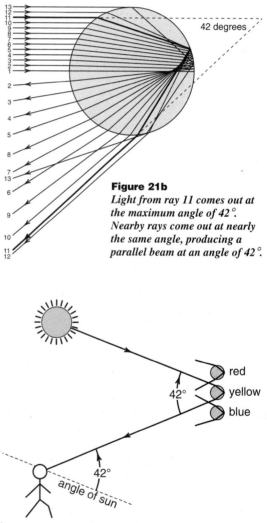

Figure 21b
Light from ray 11 comes out at the maximum angle of 42°. Nearby rays come out at nearly the same angle, producing a parallel beam at an angle of 42°.

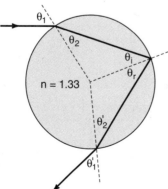

Figure 21a
Light ray reflecting from a raindrop.

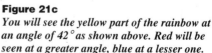

Figure 21c
You will see the yellow part of the rainbow at an angle of 42° as shown above. Red will be seen at a greater angle, blue at a lesser one.

Repeat the construction for red light where the index of refraction is slightly less than 1.33, and you find the maximum angle of deviation and the direction of the parallel beam is slightly greater than 42°. For blue light, with a higher index, the deviation is less.

If you look at falling raindrops with the sun at your back as shown in Figure (21c), you will see the yellow part of the rainbow along the arc that has an angle of 42° from the rays of sun passing you. The red light, having a greater angle of deviation will be above the yellow, and the blue will be below, as you can see in Figure (21d).

Sometimes you will see two or more rainbows if the rain is particularly heavy (we have seen up to 7). These are caused by multiple internal reflections. In the second rainbow there are two internal reflections and the parallel beam of yellow light comes out at an angle of 51°. Because of the extra reflection the red is on the inside of the arc and the blue on the outside.

Exercise 4

Next time you see a rainbow, try to measure the angle the yellow part of the arc makes with the rays of sun passing your head.

Figure 21d
Rainbow over Cook's Bay, Moorea.

The Green Flash

The so called green flash at sunset is a phenomenon that is supposed to be very rare, but which is easy to see if you can look at a distant sunset through binoculars. (Don't look until the very last couple of seconds so that you will not hurt your eyes.)

The earth's atmosphere acts as a prism, refracting the light as shown in Figure (22). The main effect is that when you look at a sunset, the sun has already set; only its image is above the horizon. But, as seen in Figure (20), the atmospheric prism also refracts the different colors in the white sunlight at different angles. Due to the fact that the blue light is refracted at a greater angle than the red light, the blue image of the sun is slightly higher above the horizon than the green image, and the green image is higher than the red image. We have over emphasized the displacement of the image in Figure (22). The blue image is only a few percent of the sun's diameter above the red image. Before the sun sets, the various colored images are more or less on top of each other and the sun looks more or less white.

If it is a very clear day, and you watch the sunset with binoculars, just as the sun disappears, for about 1/2 second, the sun turns a deep blue. The reason is that all the other images have set, and for this short time only this blue image is visible. We should call this the "blue flash".

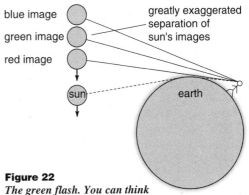

Figure 22
The green flash. You can think of the white sun as consisting of various colored disks that add up to white. The earth's atmosphere acts as a prism, diffracting the light from the setting sun, separating the colored disks. The blue disk is the last to set. Haze in the atmosphere can block the blue light, leaving the green disk as the last one seen.

If the atmosphere is not so clear, if there is a bit of haze or moisture as one often gets in the summer, the blue light is absorbed by the haze, and the last image we see setting is the green image. This is the origin of the green flash. With still more haze you get a red sunset, all the other colors having been absorbed by the haze.

Usually it requires binoculars to see the green or blue colors at the instant of sunset. But sometimes the atmospheric conditions are right so that this final light of the sun is reflected on clouds and can be seen without binoculars. If the clouds are there, there is probably enough moisture to absorb the blue image, and the resulting flash on the clouds is green.

Halos and Sun Dogs

Another phenomenon often seen is the reflection of light from hexagonal ice crystals in the atmosphere. The reflection is seen at an angle of 22° from the sun. If the ice crystals are randomly oriented then we get a complete halo as seen in Figure (23a). If the crystals are falling with their flat planes predominately horizontal, we only see the two pieces of the halo at each side of the sun, seen in Figure (24). These little pieces of rainbow are known as "sun dogs".

Figure 23
Halo caused by reflection by randomly oriented hexagonal ice crystals.

Figure 24
Sun dogs caused by ice crystals falling flat.

LENSES

The main impact geometrical optics has had on mankind is through the use of lenses in microscopes, telescopes, eyeglasses, and of course, the human eye. The basic idea behind the construction of a lens is Snell's law, but as our analysis of light reflected from a spherical raindrop indicated, we can get complex results from even simple geometries like a sphere.

Modern optical systems like the zoom lens shown in Figure (25) are designed by computer. Lens design is an ideal problem for the computer, for tracing light rays through a lens system requires many repeated applications of Snell's law. When we analyzed the spherical raindrop, we followed the paths of 12 rays for an index of refraction for only yellow light. A much better analysis would have resulted from tracing at least 100 rays for the yellow index of refraction, and then repeating the whole process for different indices of refraction, corresponding to different wavelengths or colors of light. This kind of analysis, while extremely tedious to do by hand, can be done in seconds on a modern desktop computer.

In this chapter we will restrict our discussion to the simplest of lens systems in order to see how basic instruments, like the microscope, telescope and eye, function. You will not learn here how to design a color corrected zoom lens like the Nikon lens shown below.

Figure 25
Nikon zoom lens.

Spherical Lens Surface

A very accurate spherical surface on a piece of glass is surprisingly easy to make. Take two pieces of glass, put a mixture of grinding powder and water between them, rub them together in a somewhat regular, somewhat irregular, pattern that one can learn in less than 5 minutes. The result is a spherical surface on the two pieces of glass, one being concave and the other being convex. The reason you get a spherical surface from this somewhat random rubbing is that only spherical surfaces fit together perfectly for all angles and rotations. Once the spheres have the desired radius of curvature, you use finer and finer grits to smooth out the scratches, and then jeweler's rouge to polish the surfaces. With any skill at all, one ends up with a polished surface that is perfectly spherical to within a fraction of a wavelength of light.

To see the optical properties of a spherical surface, we can start with the ray diagram we used for the spherical raindrop, and remove the reflections by extending the refracting medium back as shown in Figure (26a). The result is not encouraging. The parallel rays entering near the center of the surface come together—*focus*—quite a bit farther back than rays entering near the outer edge. This range of focal distances is not useful in optical instruments.

In Figure (26b) we have restricted the area where the rays are allowed to enter to a small region around the center of the surface. To a very good approximation all these parallel rays come together, focus, at one point. This is the characteristic we want in a simple lens, to bring parallel incoming rays together at one point as the parabolic reflector did.

Figure (26b) shows us that the way to make a good lens using spherical surfaces is to use only the central part of the surface. Rays entering near the axis as in Figure (26b) are deflected only by small angles, angles where we can approximate $\sin(\theta)$ by θ itself. When the angles of deflection are small enough to use small angle approximations, a spherical surface provides sharp focusing. As a result, in analyzing the small angle spherical lenses, we can replace the exact form of Snell's law

$$n_1 \sin(\theta_1) = n_2 \sin(\theta_2) \qquad \text{(5 repeated)}$$

by the approximate equation

$$n_1 \theta_1 = n_2 \theta_2 \qquad \begin{array}{l}\textit{Snell's law}\\\textit{for small}\\\textit{angles}\end{array} \qquad (8)$$

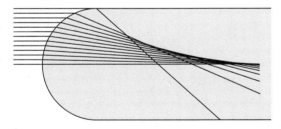

Figure 26a
Focusing properties of a spherical surface. (Not good!)

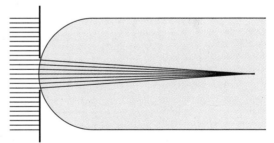

Figure 26b
We get a much better focus if we use only a small part of the spherical surface.

Focal Length of a Spherical Surface

Let us now use the simplified form of Snell's law to calculate the focal length f of a spherical surface, i.e., the distance behind the surface where entering parallel rays come to a point. Unless you plan to start making your own lenses, you do not really need this result, but the exercise provides an introduction to how focal lengths are related to the curvature of lenses.

Consider two parallel rays entering a spherical surface as shown in Figure (27). One enters along the axis of the surface, the other a distance h above it. The angle labeled θ_1 is the angle of incidence for the upper ray, while θ_2 is the refracted angle. These angles are related by Snell's law

$$n_1 \theta_1 = n_2 \theta_2$$

or

$$\theta_2 = \frac{n_1}{n_2} \theta_1 \tag{9}$$

If you recall your high school trigonometry you will remember that the outside angle of a triangle, θ_1 in Figure (27a), is equal to the sum of the opposite angles, θ_2 and α in this case. Thus

$$\theta_1 = \theta_2 + \alpha$$

or using Equation 9 for θ_2

$$\theta_1 = \frac{n_1}{n_2} \theta_1 + \alpha \tag{10}$$

Now consider the two triangles reproduced in Figures (27b) and (27c). Using the small angle approximation $\tan(\theta) \approx \sin(\theta) \approx \theta$, we have for Figure (27b)

$$\theta_1 \approx \frac{h}{r} \; ; \quad \alpha \approx \frac{h}{f} \tag{11}$$

Substituting these values for θ_1 and α into Equation (10) gives

$$\frac{h}{r} = \frac{n_1}{n_2} \frac{h}{r} + \frac{h}{f} \tag{12}$$

The height h cancels, and we are left with

$$\boxed{\frac{1}{f} = \frac{1}{r}\left(1 - \frac{n_1}{n_2}\right)} \tag{13}$$

The fact that the height h cancels means that parallel rays entering at any height h (as long as the small angle approximation holds) will focus at the same point a distance f behind the surface. This is what we saw in Figure (26b).

Figure (26b) was drawn for $n_1 = 1$ (air) and $n_2 = 1.33$ (water) so that $n_1/n_2 = 1/1.33 = .75$. Thus for that drawing we should have had

$$\frac{1}{f} = \frac{1}{r}(1 - .75) = \frac{1}{r}(.25) = \frac{1}{r}\left(\frac{1}{4}\right)$$

or

$$f = 4r \tag{14}$$

as the predicted focal length of that surface.

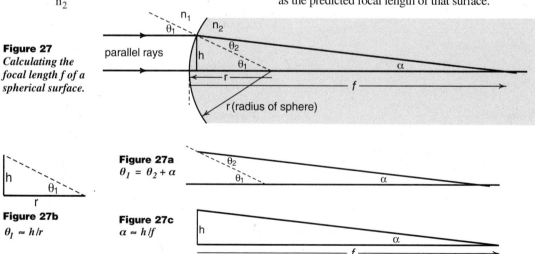

Figure 27
Calculating the focal length f of a spherical surface.

Figure 27a
$\boldsymbol{\theta_1 = \theta_2 + \alpha}$

Figure 27b
$\boldsymbol{\theta_1 \approx h/r}$

Figure 27c
$\boldsymbol{\alpha \approx h/f}$

Exercise 5

Compare the prediction of Equation (14) with the results we got in Figure (26b). That is, what do you measure for the relationship between *f* and r in that figure?

Exercise 6

The index of refraction for red light in water is slightly less than the index of refraction for blue light. Will the focal length of the surface in Figure (26b) be longer or shorter than the focal length for red light?

Exercise 7

The simplest model for a fixed focus eye is a sphere of index of refraction n_2. The index n_2 is chosen so that parallel light entering the front surface of the sphere focuses on the back surface as shown in Figure (27d). What value of n_2 is required for this model to work when $n_1 = 1$? Looking at the table of indexes of refraction, Table 1, explain why such a model would be hard to achieve.

Aberrations

When parallel rays entering a lens do not come to focus at a point, we say that the lens has an *aberration*. We saw in Figure (26a) that if light enters too large a region of a spherical surface, the focal points are spread out in back. This is called *spherical aberration*. One cure for spherical aberration is to make sure that the diameter of any spherical lens you use is small in comparison to the radius of curvature of the lens surface.

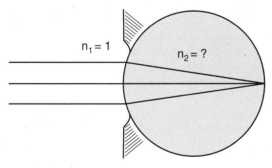

Figure 27d
A simple, but hard to achieve, model for an eye.

We get rainbows from raindrops and prisms because the index of refraction for most transparent substances changes with wavelength. As we saw in Exercise 6, this causes red light to focus at a different point than yellow or blue light, (resulting in colored bands around the edges of images). This problem is called *chromatic aberration*. The cure for chromatic aberration is to construct complex lenses out of materials of different indices of refraction. With careful design, you can bring the focal points of the various colors back together. Some of the complexity in the design of the zoom lens in Figure (25) is to correct for chromatic aberration.

Astigmatism is a common problem for the lens of the human eye. You get astigmatism when the lens is not perfectly spherical, but is a bit cylindrical. If, for example, the cylindrical axis is horizontal, then light from a horizontal line will focus farther back than light from a vertical line. Either the vertical lines in the image are in focus, or the horizontal lines, but not both at the same time. (In the eye, the cylindrical axis does not have to be horizontal or vertical, but can be at any angle.)

There can be many other aberrations depending upon what distortions are present in the lens surface. We once built a small telescope using a shaving mirror instead of a carefully ground parabolic mirror. The image of a single star stretched out in a line that covered an angle of about 30 degrees. This was an extreme example of an aberration called *coma*. That telescope provided a good example of why optical lenses and mirrors need to be ground very accurately.

What, surprisingly, does not usually cause a serious problem is a small scratch on a lens. You do not get an image of the scratch because the scratch is completely out of focus. Instead the main effect of a scratch is to scatter light and fog the image a bit.

Perhaps the most famous aberration in history is the spherical aberration in the primary mirror of the orbiting Hubble telescope. The aberration was caused by an undetected error in the complex apparatus used to test the surface of the mirror while the mirror was being ground and polished. The ironic part of the story is that the aberration could have easily been detected using the same simple apparatus all amateur telescope makers use to test their mirrors (the so called Foucault test), but such a simple minded test was not deemed necessary.

What saved the Hubble telescope is that the engineers found the problem with the testing apparatus, and could therefore precisely determine the error in the shape of the lens. A small mirror, only a few centimeters in diameter, was designed to correct for the aberration in the Hubble image. When this correcting mirror was inserted near the focus of the main mirror, the aberration was eliminated and we started getting the many fantastic pictures from that telescope.

Another case of historical importance is the fact that Issac Newton invented the reflecting telescope to avoid the chromatic aberration present in all lenses at that time. With a parabolic reflecting mirror, all parallel rays entering the mirror focus at a point. The location of the focal point does not depend on the wavelength of the light (as long as the mirror surface is reflecting at that wavelength). You also do not get spherical aberration either because a parabolic surface is the correct shape for focusing, no matter how big the diameter of the mirror is compared to the radius of curvature of the surface.

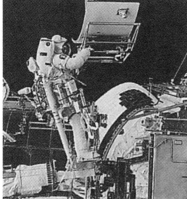

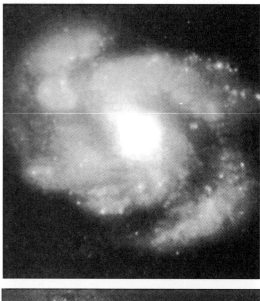

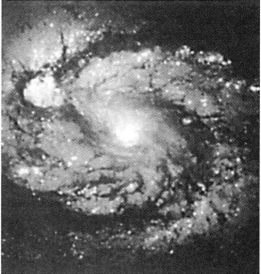

Figure 28
Correction of the Hubble telescope mirror. Top: before the correction. Bottom: same galaxy after correction. Left: astronauts installing correction mirror.

THIN LENSES

In Figure (29), we look at what happens when parallel rays pass through the two spherical surfaces of a lens. The top diagram (a) is a reproduction of Figure (26b) where a narrow bundle of parallel rays enters a new medium through a single spherical surface. By making the diameter of the bundle of rays much less than the radius of curvature of the surface, the parallel rays all focus to a single point. We were able to calculate where this point was located using small angle approximations.

In Figure (29b), we added a second spherical surface. The diagram is drawn to scale for indices of refraction n = 1 outside the gray region and n = 1.33 inside, and using Snell's law at each interface of each ray. (The drawing program Adobe Illustrator allows you to do this quite accurately.) The important point to note is that the parallel rays still focus to a point. The difference is that the focal point has moved inward.

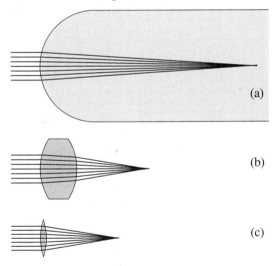

(a)

(b)

(c)

Figure 29
A two surface lens. Adding a second surface still leaves the light focused to a point, as long as the diameter of the light bundle is small compared to the radii of the lens surfaces.

In Figure (29c), we have moved the two spherical surfaces close together to form what is called a ***thin lens***. We have essentially eliminated the distance the light travels between surfaces. If the index of refraction outside the lens is 1 and has a value n inside, and surfaces have radii of curvature r_1 and r_2, then the focal length f of the lens given by the equation

$$\frac{1}{f} = (n-1)\left(\frac{1}{r_1} + \frac{1}{r_2}\right)$$
lens maker's equation (15)

Equation (15), which is known as the **lens maker's equation**, can be derived in a somewhat lengthy exercise involving similar triangles.

Unless you are planning to grind your own lenses, the lens maker's equation is not something you will need to use. When you buy a lens, you specify what focal length you want, what diameter the lens should be, and whether or not it needs to be corrected for color aberration. You are generally not concerned with how the particular focal length was achieved—what combination of radii of curvatures and index of refraction were used.

Exercise 8

(a) See how well the lens maker's equation applies to our scale drawing of Figure (29c). Our drawing was done to a scale where the spherical surfaces each had a radius of $r_1 = r_2 = 37\,mm$, and the distance f from the center of the lens to the focal point was 55 mm.

(b) What would be the focal length f of the lens if it had been made from diamond with an index of refraction n = 2.42?

The Lens Equation

What is important in the design of a simple lens system is where images are formed for objects that are different distances from the lens. Light from a very distant object enters a lens as parallel rays and focuses at a distance equal to the focal length f behind the lens. To locate the image when the object is not so far away, you can either use a simple graphical method which involves a tracing of two or three rays, or use what is called the *lens equation* which we will derive shortly from the graphical approach.

For our graphical work, we will use an arrow for the object, and trace out rays coming from the tip of the arrow. Where the rays come back together is where the image is formed. We will use the notation that the object is at a distance *(o)* from the lens, and that the image is at a distance *(i)* as shown in Figure (30).

In Figure (30) we have located the image by tracing three rays from the tip of the object. The top ray is parallel to the axis of the lens, and therefore must cross the axis at the focal point behind the lens. The middle ray, which goes through the center of the lens, is undeflected if the lens is thin. The bottom ray goes through the focal point in front of the lens, and therefore must come out parallel to the axis behind the lens. (Lenses are symmetric in that parallel light from either side focuses at the same distance f from the lens.) The image is formed where the three rays from the tip merge. To locate the image, you only need to draw two of these three special rays.

Exercise 9

(a) Graphically locate the image of the object in Figure (31).

(b) A ray starts out from the tip of the object in the direction of the dotted line shown. Trace out this ray through the lens and show where it goes on the back side of the lens.

In Exercise 9, you found that, once you have located the image, you can trace out any other ray from the tip of the object that passes through the lens, because these rays must all pass through the tip of the image.

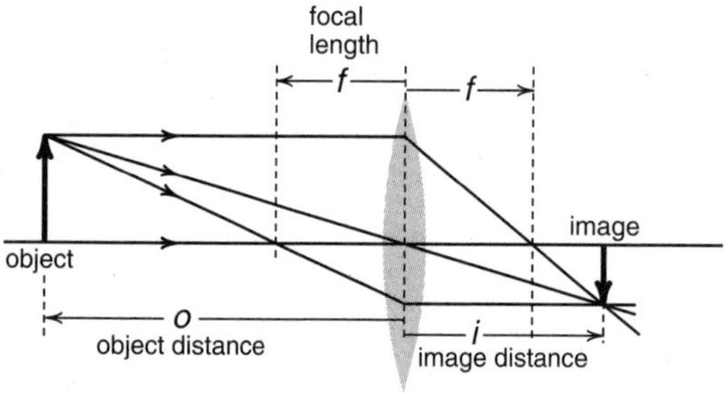

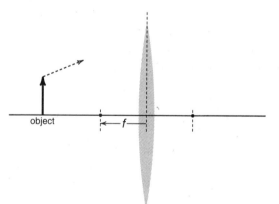

Figure 30
Locating the image using ray tracing. Three rays are easy to draw. One ray goes straight through the center of the lens. The top ray, parallel to the axis, intersects the axis where parallel rays would focus. A ray going through the left focus, comes out parallel to the axis. The image of the arrow tip is located where these rays intersect.

Figure 31
Locate the image of the arrow, and then trace the ray starting out in the direction of the dotted line.

There is a very, very simple relationship between the object distance o, the image distance i and the lens focal length f. It is

$$\boxed{\frac{1}{o} + \frac{1}{i} = \frac{1}{f}}$$ *the lens equation* (16)

Equation (16) is worth memorizing if you are going to do any work with lenses. It is the equation you will use all the time, it is easy to remember, and as you will see now, the derivation requires some trigonometry you are not likely to remember. We will take you through the derivation anyway, because of the importance of the result.

In Figure (32a), we have an object of height A that forms an inverted image of height B. We located the image by tracing the top ray parallel to the axis that passes through the focal point behind the lens, and by tracing the ray that goes through the center of the lens.

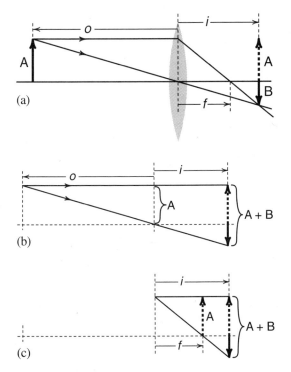

(a)

(b)

(c)

Figure 32
Derivation of the lens equation.

In Figure (32b) we have selected one of the triangles that appears in Figure (32a). The triangle starts at the tip of the object, goes parallel to the axis over to the image, and then down to the tip of the image. The length of the triangle is $(o + i)$ and the height of the base is (A+B). The lens cuts this triangle to form a smaller similar triangle whose length is o and base is (A). The ratio of the base to length of these similar triangles must be equal, giving

$$\frac{A}{o} = \frac{A+B}{(o+i)} \implies \frac{(A+B)}{A} = \frac{(o+i)}{o}$$ (17)

In Figure (32c) we have selected another triangle which starts where the top ray hits the lens, goes parallel to the axis over to the image, and down to the tip of the image. This triangle has a length i and a base of height (A+B) as shown. This triangle is cut by a vertical line at the focal plane, giving a smaller similar triangle of length f and base (A) as shown. The ratio of the length to base of these similar triangles must be equal, giving

$$\frac{A}{f} = \frac{A+B}{i} \implies \frac{(A+B)}{A} = \frac{i}{f}$$ (18)

Combining Equations (17) and (18) gives

$$\frac{i}{f} = \frac{o+i}{o} = 1 + \frac{i}{o}$$ (19)

Finally, divide both sides by i and we get

$$\frac{1}{f} = \frac{1}{i} + \frac{1}{o}$$ *lens equation* (16 repeated)

which is the lens equation, as advertised.

Note that the lens equation is an exact consequence of the geometrical construction shown back in Figure (30). There is no restriction about small angles. However if you are using spherical lenses, you have to stick to small angles or the light will not focus to a point.

Negative Image Distance

The lens equation is more general than you might expect, for it works equally well for positive and negative distances and focal lengths. Let us start by seeing what we mean by a negative image distance. Writing Equation (15) in the form

$$\frac{1}{i} = \frac{1}{f} - \frac{1}{o} \qquad (16a)$$

let us see what happens if $1/o$ is bigger than $1/f$ so that i turns out to be negative. If $1/o$ is bigger than $1/f$, that means that o is less than f and we have placed the object within the focal length as shown in Figure (33).

When we trace out two rays from the tip of the image, we find that the rays diverge after they pass through the lens. They diverge as if they were coming from a point behind the object, a point shown by the dotted lines. In this case we have what is called a *virtual image*, which is located at a *negative image distance* (i). This negative image distance is correctly given by the lens equation (16a).

(We will not drag you through another geometrical proof of the lens equation for negative image distances. It should be fairly convincing that just when the image distance becomes negative in the lens equation, the geometry shows that we switch from a real image on the right side of the lens to a virtual image on the left.)

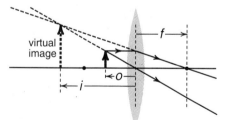

Figure 33
When the object is located within the focal length, we get a virtual image behind the object.

Negative Focal Length and Diverging Lenses

In Figure (33) we got a virtual image by moving the object inside the focal length. Another way to get a virtual image is to use a diverging lens as shown in Figure (34). Here we have drawn the three special rays, but the role of the focal point is reversed. The ray through the center of the lens goes through the center as before. The top ray parallel to the axis of the lens diverges outward as if it came from the focal point on the left side of the lens. The ray from the tip of the object headed for the right focal point, comes out parallel to the axis. Extending the diverging rays on the right, back to the left side, we find a virtual image on the left side.

You get diverging lenses by using concave surfaces as shown in Figure (34). In the lens maker's equation,

$$\frac{1}{f} = (n-1)\left(\frac{1}{r_1} + \frac{1}{r_2}\right) \quad \begin{array}{l}\textit{lensmaker's}\\ \textit{equation}\end{array} \quad \text{(15 repeated)}$$

you replace $1/r$ by $-1/r$ for any concave surface. If $1/f$ turns out negative, then you have a diverging lens. Using this negative value of f in the lens equation (with $f = -|f|$) we get

$$\frac{1}{i} = -\left(\frac{1}{|f|} + \frac{1}{o}\right) \qquad (16b)$$

This always gives a negative image distance i, which means that diverging lenses only give virtual images.

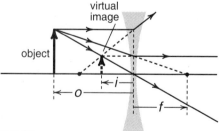

Figure 34
A diverging lens always gives a virtual image.

Exercise 10

You have a lens making machine that can grind surfaces, either convex or concave, with radius of curvatures of either 20 cm or 40 cm, or a flat surface. How many different kinds of lenses can you make? What is the focal length and the name of the lens type for each lens? Figure (35) shows the names given to the various lens types.

Negative Object Distance

With the lens equation, we can have negative image distances and negative focal lengths, and also negative object distances as well.

In all our drawings so far, we have drawn rays coming out of the tip of an object located at a positive object distance. A negative object distance means we have a virtual object where rays are converging toward the tip of the virtual object but don't get there. A comparison of the rays emerging from a real object and converging toward a virtual object is shown in Figure (36). The converging rays (which were usually created by some other lens) can be handled with the lens equation by assuming that the distance from the lens to the virtual object is negative.

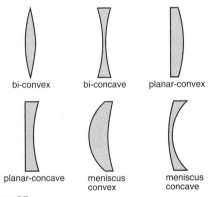

bi-convex   bi-concave   planar-convex

planar-concave   meniscus convex   meniscus concave

Figure 35
Various lens types. Note that eyeglasses are usually meniscus convex or meniscus concave.

As an example, suppose we have rays converging to a point, and we insert a diverging lens whose negative focal length $f = -|f|$ is equal to the negative object distance $o = -|o|$ as shown in Figure (37). The lens equation gives

$$\frac{1}{i} = \frac{1}{f} - \frac{1}{o} = \frac{1}{-|f|} - \frac{1}{-|o|} = \frac{1}{|o|} - \frac{1}{|f|} \quad (20)$$

If $|f| = |o|$, then $1/i = 0$ and the image is infinitely far away. This means that the light emerges as a parallel beam as we showed in Figure (37).

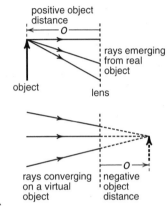

positive object distance

rays emerging from real object

object   lens

rays converging on a virtual object   negative object distance

Figure 36
Positive and negative object distances.

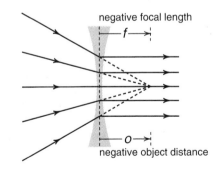

negative focal length

negative object distance

Figure 37
Negative focal length.

Multiple Lens Systems

Using the lens equation, and knowing how to handle both positive and negative distances and focal lengths, you can design almost any simple lens system you want. The idea is to work your way through the system, one lens at a time, where the image from one lens becomes the object for the next. We will illustrate this process with a few examples.

As our first example, consider Figure (38a) where we have two lenses of focal lengths $f_1 = 10$ cm and $f_2 = 12$ cm separated by a distance D = 40 cm. An object placed at a distance $o_1 = 17.5$ cm from the first lens creates an image a distance i_1 behind the first lens. Using the lens equation, we get

$$i_1 = \frac{1}{f_1} - \frac{1}{o_1} = \frac{1}{10} - \frac{1}{17.5} = \frac{1}{23.33} \qquad (21)$$

$$i_1 = 23.33 \text{ cm}$$

the same distance we got graphically in Figure (38a).

This image, which acts as the object for the second lens has an object distance

$$o_2 = D - i_1 = 40 \text{ cm} - 23.33 \text{ cm} = 16.67 \text{ cm}$$

This gives us a final upright image at a distance i_2 given by

$$\frac{1}{i_2} = \frac{1}{f_2} - \frac{1}{o_2} = \frac{1}{12} - \frac{1}{16.67} = \frac{1}{42.86} \qquad (22)$$

$$\boxed{i_2 = 42.86 \text{ cm}} \qquad (23)$$

which also accurately agrees with the geometrical construction.

In Figure (38b), we moved the second lens up to within 8 cm of the first lens, so that the first image now falls behind the second lens. We now have a negative object distance

$$o_2 = D - i_1 = 8 \text{ cm} - 23.33 \text{ cm} = -15.33 \text{ cm}$$

Using this negative object distance in the lens equation gives

$$\frac{1}{i_2} = \frac{1}{f_2} - \frac{1}{o_2} = \frac{1}{12} - \frac{1}{-15.33}$$

$$= \frac{1}{12} + \frac{1}{15.33} = \frac{1}{6.73}$$

$$\boxed{i_2 = 6.73 \text{ cm}} \qquad (24)$$

In the geometrical construction we find that the still inverted image is in fact located 6.73 cm behind the second image.

While it is much faster to use the lens equation than trace rays, it is instructive to apply both approaches for a few examples to see that they both give the same result. In drawing Figure (38b) an important ray was the one that went from the tip of the original object, down through the first focal point. This ray emerges from the first lens traveling parallel to the optical axis. The ray then enters the second lens, and since it was parallel to the axis, it goes up through the focal point of the second lens as shown. The second image is located by drawing the ray that passes straight through the second lens, heading for the tip of the first image. Where these two rays cross is where the tip of the final image is located.

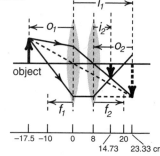

Figure 38b
We moved the second lens in so that the second object distance is negative. We now get an inverted image 6.73 cm from the second lens.

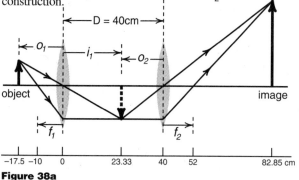

Figure 38a
Locating the image in a two lens system.

In Figure (38c) we sketched a number of rays passing through the first lens, heading for the first image. These rays are converging on the second lens, which we point out in Figure (36b) was the condition for a negative object distance.

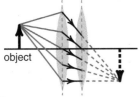

Figure 38c

Two Lenses Together

If you put two thin lenses together, as shown in Figure (39), you effectively create a new thin lens with a different focal length. To find out what the focal length of the combination is, you use the lens equation twice, setting the second object distance o_2 equal to minus the first image distance $-i_1$.

$$o_2 = -i_1 \quad \begin{array}{l}\textit{for two lenses} \\ \textit{together}\end{array} \qquad (25)$$

From the lens equations we have

$$\frac{1}{i_1} = \frac{1}{f_1} - \frac{1}{o_1} \qquad (26)$$

$$\frac{1}{i_2} = \frac{1}{f_2} - \frac{1}{o_2} \qquad (27)$$

Setting $o_2 = -i_1$ in Equation 27 gives

$$\frac{1}{i_2} = \frac{1}{f_2} - \frac{1}{\left(-i_1\right)} = \frac{1}{f_2} + \frac{1}{i_1}$$

Using Equation (26) for $1/i_1$ gives

$$\frac{1}{i_2} = \frac{1}{f_2} + \frac{1}{f_1} - \frac{1}{o_1}$$

$$\frac{1}{o_1} + \frac{1}{i_2} = \frac{1}{f_1} + \frac{1}{f_2} \qquad (28)$$

Now o_1 is the object distance and i_2 is the image distance for the pair of lenses. Treating the pair of lenses as a single lens, we should have

$$\frac{1}{o_1} + \frac{1}{i_2} = \frac{1}{f} \qquad (29)$$

where f is the focal length of the combined lens.

Comparing Equations (28) and (29) we get

$$\boxed{\frac{1}{f} = \frac{1}{f_1} + \frac{1}{f_2}} \quad \begin{array}{l}\textit{focal length of two} \\ \textit{thin lenses together}\end{array} \qquad (30)$$

as the simple formula for the combined focal length.

Exercise 11

(a) Find the image distances i_2 for the geometry of Figures (38), but with the two lenses reversed, i.e., with $f_1 = 12$ cm, $f_2 = 10$ cm. Do this for both length D = 40 cm and D = 8 cm.

(b) If the two lenses are put together (D = 0) what is the focal length of the combination?

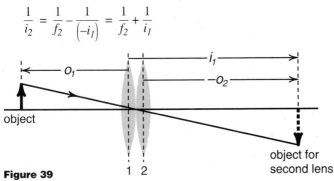

Figure 39
Two lenses together. Since the object for the second lens is on the wrong side of the lens, the object distance o_2 is negative in this diagram. If the lenses are close together, i_1 and $-o_2$ are essentially the same.

Magnification

It is natural to define the magnification created by a lens as the ratio of the height of the image to the height of the object. In Figure (40) we have reproduced Figure (38a) emphasizing the heights of the objects and images.

We see that the shaded triangles are similar, thus the ratio of the height B of the first image to the height A of the object is

$$\frac{B}{A} = \frac{i_1}{o_1} \tag{31}$$

We could define the magnification in the first lens as the ratio of B/A, but instead we will be a bit tricky and include a - (minus) sign to represent the fact that the image is inverted. With this convention we get

$$\boxed{m_1 = \frac{-B}{A} = \frac{-i_1}{o_1}} \quad \begin{array}{l} \textit{definition of} \\ \textit{magnification m} \end{array} \tag{32}$$

Treating B as the object for the second lens gives

$$m_2 = \frac{-C}{B} = \frac{-i_2}{o_2} \tag{33}$$

The total magnification m_{12} in going from the object A to the final image C is

$$m_{12} = \frac{C}{A} \tag{34}$$

which has a + sign because the final image C is upright. But

$$\frac{C}{A} = \left(\frac{-C}{B}\right)\left(\frac{-B}{A}\right) \tag{35}$$

Thus we find that the final magnification is the product of the magnifications of each lens.

$$\boxed{m_{12} = m_1 m_2} \tag{36}$$

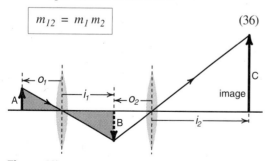

Figure 40
Magnification of two lenses.

Exercise 12

Figures (38) and (40) are scale drawings, so that the ratio of image to object sizes measured from these drawings should equal the calculated magnifications.

(a) Calculate the magnifications m_1, m_2 and m_{12} for Figure (38a) or (40) and compare your results with magnifications measured from the figure.

(b) Do the same for Figure (38b). In Figure (38b), the final image is inverted. Did your final magnification m_{12} come out negative?

Exercise 13

Figure (41a) shows a magnifying glass held 10 cm above the printed page. Since the object is inside the focal length we get a virtual image as seen in the geometrical construction of Figure (41b). Show that our formulas predict a positive magnification, and estimate the focal length of the lens. (Answer: about 17 cm.)

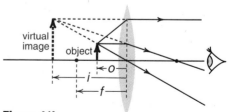

Figure 41a
Using a magnifying glass.

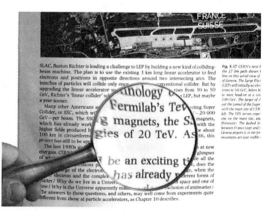

Figure 41b
When the magnifying glass is less than a focal length away from the object, we see an upright virtual image.

THE HUMAN EYE

A very good reason for studying geometrical optics is to understand how your own eye works, and how the situation is corrected when something goes wrong.

Back in Exercise 6 (p21), during our early discussion of spherical lens surfaces, we considered as a model of an eye a sphere of index of refraction n_2, where n_2 was chosen so that parallel

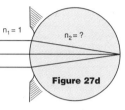

Figure 27d

rays which entered the front surface focused on the back surface as shown in Figure (27d). The value of n_2 turned out to be $n_2 = 2.0$. Since the only common substance with an index of refraction greater than zircon at $n = 1.923$ is diamond at $n = 2.417$, it would be difficult to construct such a model eye. Instead some extra focusing capability is required, both to bring the focus to the back surface of the eye, and to focus on objects located at various distances.

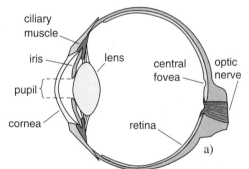

Figure 42
The human eye. The cornea and the lens together provide the extra focusing power required to focus light on the retina. (Photograph of the human eye by Lennart Nilsson.)

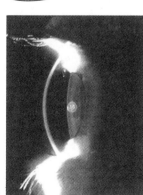

Figure (42a) is a sketch of the human eye and Figure (42b) a remarkable photograph of the eye. As seen in (42a), light enters the *cornea* at the front of the eye. The amount of light allowed to enter is controlled by the opening of the *iris*. Together the cornea and *crystalline lens* focuses light on the retina which is a film of *nerve fibers* on the back surface of the eye. Information from the new fibers is carried to the brain through the optic nerve at the back. In the retina there are two kinds of nerve fibers, called *rods* and *cones*. Some of the roughly 120 million rods and 7 million cones are seen magnified about 5000 times in Figure (43). The slender ones, the rods, are more sensitive to dim light, while the shorter, fatter, cones, provide our color sensitivity.

In our discussion of the human ear, we saw how there was a mechanical system involving the basilar membrane that distinguished between the various frequencies of incoming sound waves. Information from nerves attached to the basilar membrane was then enhanced through processing in the local nerve fibers before being sent to the brain via the auditory nerve. In the eye, the nerve fibers behind the retina, some of which can be seen on the right side of Figure (43), also do a considerable amount of information processing before the signal travels to the brain via the optic nerve. The way that information from the rods and cones is processed by the nerve fibers is a field of research.

Returning to the front of the eye we have the surface of the cornea and the crystalline lens focusing light on the retina. Most of the focusing is done by the cornea. The shape, and therefore the focal length of the crystalline lens can be altered slightly by the *ciliary muscle* in order to bring into focus objects located at different distances.

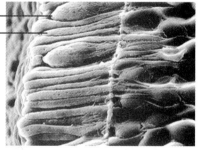

Figure 43
Rods and cones in the retina. The thin ones are the rods, the fat ones the cones.

In a normal eye, when the ciliary muscle is in its resting position, light from infinity is focused on the retina as shown in Figure (44a). To see a closer object, the ciliary muscles contract to shorten the focal length of the cornea-lens system in order to continue to focus light on the cornea (44b). If the object is too close as in Figure (44c), the light is no longer focused and the object looks blurry. The shortest distance at which the light remains in focus is called the **near point**. For children the near point is as short as 7 cm, but as one ages and the crystalline lens becomes less flexible, the near point recedes to something like 200 cm. This is why older people hold written material far away unless they have reading glasses.

Nearsightedness and Farsightedness

Not all of us have the so called *normal* eyes described by Figure (44). There is increasing evidence that those who do a lot of close work as children end up with a condition called *nearsightedness* or *myopia* where the eye is elongated and light from infinity focuses inside the eye as shown in Figure (45a). This can be corrected by placing a diverging lens in front of the eye to move the focus back to the retina as shown in Figure (45b).

The opposite problem, farsightedness, where light focuses behind the retina as shown in Figure (46a) is corrected by a converging lens as shown in Figure (46b).

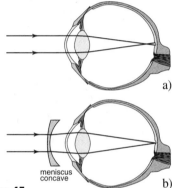

a)

meniscus
concave
b)

Figure 45
Nearsightedness can be corrected by a concave lens.

Figure 44a
Parallel light rays from a distant object are focuses on the retina when the ciliary muscles are in the resting position.

Figure 44b
The ciliary muscle contracts to shorten the focal length of the cornea-lens system in order to focus light from a more nearby object.

Figure 44c
When an object is too close, the light cannot be focused on the retina.

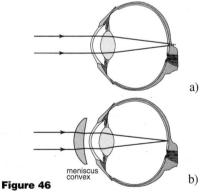

a)

meniscus
convex
b)

Figure 46
Farsightedness can be corrected by a convex lens.

THE CAMERA

There are a number of similarities between the human eye and a simple camera. Both have an iris to control the amount of light entering, and both record an image at the focal plane of the lens. In a camera, the focus is adjusted, not by changing the shape of the lens as in the eye, but by moving the lens back and forth. The eye is somewhat like a TV camera in that both record images at a rate of about 30 per second, and the information is transmitted electronically to either the brain or a TV screen.

Figure 47a
The Physics department's Minolta single lens reflex camera.

On many cameras you will find a series of numbers labeled by the letter f, called the f **number** or f **stop**. Just as for the parabolic reflectors in Figure (4) [p.4], the f number is the ***ratio of the lens focal length to the lens diameter***. As you close down the iris of the camera to reduce the amount of light entering, you reduce the effective diameter of the lens and therefore increase the f number.

Exercise 14

The iris on the human eye can change the diameter of the opening to the lens from about 2 to 8 millimeters. The total distance from the cornea to the retina is typically about 2.3 cm. What is the range of f values for the human eye? How does this range compare with the range of f value on your camera? (If you have one of the automatic point and shoot cameras, the f number and the exposure time are controlled electronically and you do not get to see or control these yourself.)

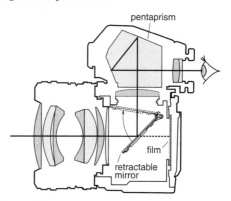

Figure 47b
The lens system for a Nikon single lens reflex camera. When you take the picture, the hinged mirror flips out of the way and the light reaches the film. Before that, the light is reflected through the prism to the eyepiece.

Depth of Field

There are three ways to control the exposure of the film in a camera. One is by the speed of the film, the second is the exposure time, and the third is the opening of the iris or *f* stop. In taking a picture you should first make sure the exposure is short enough so that motion of the camera and the subject do not cause blurring. If your film is fast enough, you can still choose between a shorter exposure time or a smaller *f* stop. This choice is determined by the ***depth of field*** that you want.

The concept of depth of field is illustrated in Figures (48a and b). In (48a), we have drawn the rays of light from an object to an image through an *f2* lens, a lens with a focal length equal to twice its diameter. (The effective diameter can be controlled by a flexible diaphram or iris like the one shown.) If you placed a film at the image distance, the point at the tip of the object arrow would focus to a point on the film. If you moved the film forward to position 1, or back to position 2, the image of the arrow tip would fill a circle about equal to the thickness of the three rays we drew in the diagram.

If the film were ideal, you could tell that the image at positions 1 or 2 was out of focus. But no film or recording medium is ideal. If you look closely enough there is always a graininess caused by the size of the basic medium like the silver halide crystals in black and white film, the width of the scan lines in an analog TV camera, or the size of the pixels in a digital camera. If the image of the arrow tip at position 1 is smaller than the grain or pixel size then you cannot tell that the picture is out of focus. You can place the recording medium anywhere between position 1 and 2 and the image will be as sharp as you can get.

In Figure (48b), we have drawn the rays from the same object passing through a smaller diameter *f8* lens. Again we show by dotted lines positions 1 and 2 where the image of the arrow point would fill the same size circle as it did at positions 1 and 2 for the *f2* lens above. Because the rays from the *f8* lens fill a much narrower cone than those from the *f2* lens, there is a much greater distance between positions 1 and 2 for the *f8* lens.

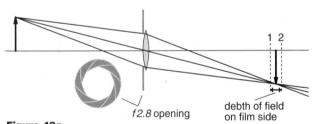

Figure 48a
A large diameter lens has a narrow depth of field.

Photograph taken at f 5.6.

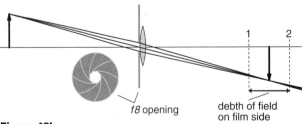

Figure 48b
Reducing the effective diameter of the lens increases the depth of field.

Photograph taken at f 22.

If Figures (48) represented a camera, you would not be concerned with moving the film back and forth. Instead you would be concerned with how far the image could be moved back and forth and still appear to be in focus. If the film were at the image position and you then moved the object in and out, you could not move it very far before it's image was noticeably out of focus with the $f2$ lens. You could move it much farther for the $f8$ lens.

This effect is illustrated by the photographs on the right side of Figures (48), showing a close-up tree and the distant tower on Baker Library at Dartmouth College. The upper picture taken at $f5.6$ has a narrow depth of field, and the tower is well out of focus. The bottom picture, taken at $f22$, has a much broader depth of field and the tower is more nearly in focus. (In both cases we focused on the nearby tree bark.)

Camera manufacturers decide how much blurring of the image is noticeable or tolerable, and then figure out the range of distances the object can be moved and still be acceptably in focus. This range of distance is called the ***depth of field***. It can be very short when the object is up close and you use a wide opening like $f2$. It can be quite long for a high f number like $f22$. The inexpensive fixed focus cameras use a small enough lens so that all objects are "in focus" from about 3 feet or 1 meter to infinity.

In the extreme limit when the lens is very small, the depth of field is so great that everything is in focus everywhere behind the lens. In this limit you do not even need a lens, a pinhole in a piece of cardboard will do. If enough light is available and the subject doesn't not move, you can get as good a picture with a pinhole camera as one with an expensive lens system. Our pinhole camera image in Figure (49) is a bit fuzzy because we used too big a pinhole.

(If you are nearsighted, you can see how a pinhole camera works by making a tiny hole with your fingers when looking at a distant light at night without your glasses. Just looking at the light, it will look blurry. But look at the light through the hole made by your fingers and the light will be sharp. You can also see the eye chart better at the optometrists, if you look through a small hole, but they don't let you do that.)

Figure 49a
We made a pinhole camera by replacing the camera lens with a plastic film case that had a small hole poked into the end.

Figure 48c
Camera lens. This lens is set to f11, and adjusted to a focus of 3 meters or 10 ft. At this setting, the depth of field ranges from 2 to 5 meters.

Figure 49b
Photograph of Baker library tower, taken with the pinhole camera above. If we had used a smaller hole we would have gotten a sharper focus.

Eye Glasses and a Home Lab Experiment

When you get a prescription for eyeglasses, the optometrist writes down number like -1.5, -1.8 to represent the *power* of the lenses you need. These cryptic numbers are the power of the lenses measured in *diopters*. What a diopter is, is simply the reciprocal of the focal length $1/f$, where f is measured in meters. A lens with a power of 1 diopter is a converging lens with a focal length of 1 meter. Those of us who have lenses closer to –4 in power have lenses with a focal length of –25 cm, the minus sign indicating a diverging lens to correct for nearsightedness as shown back in Figure (45).

If you are nearsighted and want to measure the power of your own eyeglass lenses, you have the problem that it is harder to measure the focal length of a diverging lens than a converging lens. You can quickly measure the focal length of a converging lens like a simple magnifying glass by focusing sunlight on a piece of paper and measuring the distance from the lens to where the paper is starting to smoke. But you do not get a real image for a diverging lens, and cannot use this simple technique for measuring the focal length and power of diverging lenses used by the nearsighted.

As part of a project, some students used the following method to measure the focal length and then determine the power in diopters, of their and their friend's eyeglasses. They started by measuring the focal length f_0

of a simple magnifying glass by focusing the sun. Then they placed the magnifying glass and the eyeglass lens together, measured the focal length of the combination, and used the formula

$$\frac{1}{f} = \frac{1}{f_1} + \frac{1}{f_2} \qquad \text{(30 repeated)}$$

to calculate the focal length of the lens.

(Note that if you measure distances in meters, then $1/f_1$ is the power of lens 1 in diopters and $1/f_2$ that of lens 2. Equation (30) tells you that the power of the combination $1/f$ is the sum of the powers of the two lenses.

Exercise 15

Assume that you find a magnifying lens that focuses the sun at a distance of 10 cm from the lens. You then combine that with one of your (or a friends) eyeglass lenses, and discover that the combination focus at a distance of 15 cm. What is the power, in diopters, of

(a) the magnifying glass.

(b) the combination.

(c) the eyeglass lens.

Exercise 16 – Home Lab

Use the above technique to measure the power of your or your friend's glasses. If you have your prescription compare your results with what is written on the prescription. (The prescription will also contain information about axis and amount of astigmatism. That you cannot check as easily.

THE EYEPIECE

When the author was a young student, he wondered why you do not put your eye at the focal point of a telescope mirror. That is where the image of a distance object is, and that is where you put the film in order to record the image. You do not put your eye at the image because it would be like viewing an object by putting your eyeball next to it. The object would be hopelessly out of focus. Instead you look through an eyepiece.

The eyepiece is a magnifying glass that allows your eye to comfortably view an image or small object up close. For a normal eye, the least eyestrain occurs when looking at a distant object where the light from the object enters the eye as parallel rays. It is then that the ciliary muscles in the eye are in a resting position. If the image or small object is placed at the focal plane of a lens, as shown in Figure (50), light emerges from the lens as parallel rays. You can put your eye right up to that lens, and view the object or image as comfortably as you would view a distant scene.

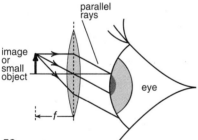

Figure 50
The eyepiece or magnifier. To look at small objects, or to study the image produced by another lens or mirror, place the image or object at the focal plane of a lens, so that the light emerges as parallel rays that your eye can comfortably focus upon.

Exercise 17 - The Magnifying Glass

There are three distinct ways of viewing an object through a magnifying glass, which you should try for yourself. Get a magnifying glass and use the letters on this page as the object to be viewed.

(a) First measure the focal length of the lens by focusing the image of a distant object onto a piece of paper. A light bulb across the room or scene out the window will do.

(b) Draw some object on the paper, and place the paper at least several focal lengths from your eye. Then hold the lens about 1/2 a focal length above the object as shown in Figure (51a). You should now see an enlarged image of the object as indicated in Figure (51a). You are now looking at the virtual image of the object. Check that the magnification is roughly a factor of 2×.

(c) Keeping your eye in the same position, several focal lengths and at least 20 cm from the paper, pull the lens back toward your eye. The image goes out of focus when the lens is one focal length above the paper, and then comes back into focus upside down when the lens is farther out. You are now looking at the real image as indicated in Figure (51b). Keep your head far enough back that your eye can focus on this real image.

Hold the lens two focal lengths above the page and check that the inverted real image of the object looks about the same size as the object itself. (As you can see from Figure (51b), the inverted image should be the same size as the object, but 4 focal lengths closer.)

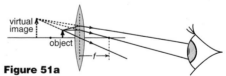

Figure 51a
Looking at the virtual image.

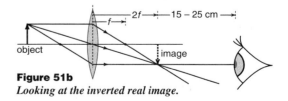

Figure 51b
Looking at the inverted real image.

(d) Now hold the lens one focal length above the page and put your eye right up to the lens. You are now using the lens as an eyepiece as shown in Figure (50). The letters will be large because your eye is close to them, and they will be comfortably in focus because the rays are entering your eye as parallel rays like the rays from a distant object. When you use the lens as an eyepiece you are not looking at an image as you did in parts (b) and (c) of this exercise, instead your eye is creating an image on your retina from the parallel rays.

(e) As a final exercise, hold the lens one focal length above a page of text, start with your eye next to the lens, and then move your head back. Since the light from the page is emerging from the lens as parallel rays, the size of the letters should not change as you move your head back. Instead what you should see is fewer and fewer letters in the magnifying glass as the magnifying glass itself looks smaller when farther away. This effect is seen in Figure (52).

The Magnifier

When jewelers work on small objects like the innards of a watch, they use what they call a ***magnifier*** which can be a lens mounted at one end of a tube as shown in Figure (53). The length of the tube is equal to the focal length of the lens, so that if you put the other end of the tube up against an object, the lens acts as an eyepiece and light from the object emerges from the lens as parallel rays. By placing your eye close to the lens, you get a close up, comfortably seen view of the object. You may have seen jewelers wear magnifiers like that shown in Figure (54).

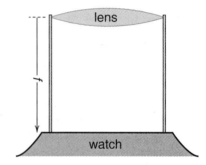

Figure 53
A magnifier.

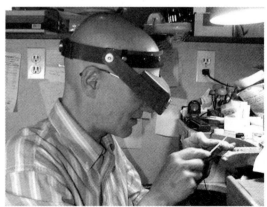

Figure 54
Jeweler Paul Gross with magnifier lenses mounted in visor.

Figure 52
When the lens is one focal length from the page, the emerging rays are parallel. Thus the image letters do not change size as we move away. Instead the lens looks smaller, and we see fewer letters in the lens.

Angular Magnification

Basically all the magnifier does is to allow you to move the object close to your eye while keeping the object comfortably in focus. It is traditional to define the *magnification* of the magnifier as the ratio of the size of the object as seen through the lens to the size of the object as you would see it without a magnifier. By size, we mean the angle the object subtends at your eye. This is often called the *angular magnification*.

The problem with this definition of magnification is that different people, would hold the object at different distances in order to look at it without a magnifier. For example, us nearsighted people would hold it a lot closer than a person with normal vision. To avoid this ambiguity, we can choose some standard distance like 25 cm, a standard near point, at which a person would normally hold an object when looking at it. Then the angular magnification of the magnifier is the ratio of the angle θ_m subtended by the object when using the magnifier, as shown in Figure (55a), to the angle θ_0 subtended by the object held at a distance of 25 cm, as shown in Figure (55b).

$$\frac{\text{angular}}{\text{magnification}} = \frac{\theta_m}{\theta_0} \qquad \begin{array}{l}\textit{angles defined}\\ \textit{in Figure 55}\end{array} \qquad (37)$$

To calculate the angular magnification we use the small angle approximation $\sin\theta \approx \theta$ to get

$$\theta_m = \frac{y}{f} \qquad \textit{from Figure 55a}$$

$$\theta_0 = \frac{y}{25\ \text{cm}} \qquad \textit{from Figure 55b}$$

which gives

$$\frac{\text{angular}}{\text{magnification}} = \frac{y/f}{y/25\ \text{cm}} = \frac{25\ \text{cm}}{f} \qquad (38)$$

Thus if our magnifier lens has a focal length of 5 cm, the angular magnification is $5\times$. Supposedly the object will look five times bigger using the magnifier than without it.

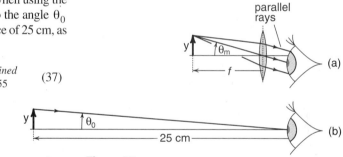

Figure 55
The angles used in defining angular magnification.

TELESCOPES

The basic design of a telescope is to have a large lens or parabolic mirror to create a bright real image, and then use an eyepiece to view the image. If we use a large lens, that lens is called an *objective lens*, and the telescope is called a *refracting telescope*. If we use a parabolic mirror, then we have a *reflecting telescope*.

The basic design of a refracting telescope is shown in Figure (56). Suppose, as shown in Figure (56a), we are looking at a constellation of stars that subtend an angle θ_0 as viewed by the unaided eye. The eye is directed just below the bottom star and light from the top star enters at an angle θ_0. In Figure (56b), the lens system from the telescope is placed in front of the eye, and we are following the path of the light from the top star in the constellation.

The parallel rays from the top star are focused at the focal length f_0 of the objective lens. We adjust the eyepiece so that the image produced by the objective lens is at the focal point of the eyepiece lens, so that light from the image will emerge from the eyepiece as parallel rays that the eye can easily focus.

As with the magnifier, we define the magnification of the telescope as the ratio of the size of (angle subtended by) the object as seen through the object to the size of (angle subtended by) the object seen by the unaided eye. In Figure (56) we see that the constellation subtends an angle θ_0 as viewed by the unaided eye, and an angle θ_i when seen through the telescope. Thus we define the magnification of the telescope as

$$m = \frac{\theta_i}{\theta_0} \qquad \begin{array}{l} \textit{magnification} \\ \textit{of telescope} \end{array} \qquad (39)$$

To calculate this ratio, we note from Figure (56c) that, using the small angle approximation $\sin\theta \approx \theta$, we have

$$\theta_0 = \frac{y_i}{f_0} \; ; \quad \theta_i = \frac{y_i}{f_e} \qquad (40)$$

where f_0 and f_e are the focal lengths of the objective and eyepiece lens respectively. In the ratio, the image height y_i cancels and we get

$$m = \frac{\theta_i}{\theta_0} = \frac{y_i/f_e}{y_i/f_0}$$

$$\boxed{m = \frac{f_0}{f_e}} \qquad (41)$$

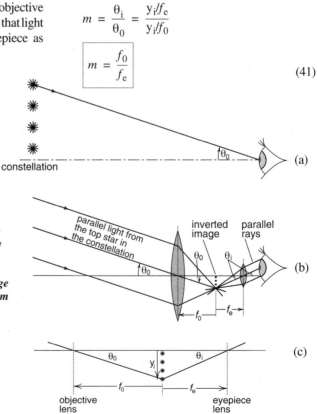

Figure 56a
The unaided eye looking at a constellation of stars that subtend an angle θ_o.

constellation

(a)

Figure 56b
Looking at the same constellation through a simple refracting telescope. The objective lens produces an inverted image which is viewed by the eyepiece acting as a magnifier. Note that the parallel light from the star focuses at the focal point of the objective lens. With the image at the focal point of the eyepiece lens, light from the image emerges as parallel rays that are easily focused by the eye.

parallel light from the top star in the constellation

inverted image

parallel rays

θ_0 θ_i

(b)

f_0 f_e

(c)

Figure 56c
Relationship between the angles θ_0, θ_i, and the focal lengths.

θ_0 θ_i

y_i

f_0 f_e

objective lens

eyepiece lens

The same formula also applies to a reflecting telescope with f_0 the focal length of the parabolic mirror. Note that there is no arbitrary number like 25 cm in the formula for the magnification of a telescope because telescopes are designed to look at distant objects where the angle θ_0 the object subtends to the unaided eye is the same for everyone.

The first and the last of the important refracting telescopes are shown in Figures (57). The telescope was invented in Holland in 1608 by Hans Lippershy. Shortly after that, Galileo constructed a more powerful instrument and was the first to use it effectively in astronomy. With a telescope like the one shown in Figure (57a), he discovered the moons of Jupiter, a result that provided an explicit demonstration that heavenly bodies could orbit around something other than the earth. This countered the long held idea that the earth was at the center of everything and provided support for the Copernican sun centered picture of the solar system.

When it comes to building large refracting telescopes, the huge amount of glass in the objective lens becomes a problem. The 1 meter diameter refracting telescope at the Yerkes Observatory, shown in Figure (57b), is the largest refracting telescope ever constructed. That was built back in 1897. The largest reflecting telescope is the new 10 meter telescope at the Keck Observatory at the summit of the inactive volcano Mauna Kea in Hawaii. Since the area and light gathering power of a telescope is proportional to the area or the square of the diameter of the mirror or objective lens, the 10 meter Keck telescope is 100 times more powerful than the 1 meter Yerkes telescope.

Figure 57a
Galileo's telescope. With such an instrument Galileo discovered the moons of Jupiter.

Exercise 18

To build your own refracting telescope, you purchase a 3 inch diameter objective lens with a focal length of 50 cm. You want the telescope to have a magnification $m = 25 \times$.

(a) What will be the *f* number of your telescope? (1 inch = 2.54 cm).

(b) What should the focal length of your eyepiece lens be?

(c) How far behind the objective lens should the eyepiece lens be located?

(d) Someone gives you an eyepiece with a focal length of 10 mm. Using this eyepiece, what magnification do you get with your telescope?

(e) You notice that your new eyepiece is not in focus at the same place as your old eyepiece. Did you have to move the new eyepiece toward or away from the objective lens, and by how much?

(f) Still later, you decide to take pictures with your telescope. To do this you replace the eyepiece with a film holder. Where do you place the film, and why did you remove the eyepiece?

Figure 57b
The Yerkes telescope is the world's largest refracting telescope, was finished in 1897. Since then all larger telescopes have been reflectors.

Reflecting telescopes

In several ways, the reflecting telescope is similar to the refracting telescope. As we saw back in our discussion of parabolic mirrors, the mirror produces an image in the focal plane when the light comes from a distant object. This is shown in Figure (58a) which is similar to our old Figure (4). If you want to look at the image with an eyepiece, you have the problem that the image is in front of the mirror where, for a small telescope, your head would block the light coming into the scope. Issac Newton, who invented the reflecting telescope, solved that problem by placing a small, flat, 45° reflecting surface inside the telescope tube to deflect the image outside the tube as shown in Figure (58b). There the image can easily be viewed using an eyepiece. Newton's own telescope is shown in Figure (58d). Another technique, used in larger telescopes, is to reflect the beam back through a hole in the mirror as shown in Figure (58c).

The reason Newton invented the reflecting telescope was to avoid an effect called ***chromatic aberration***. When white light passes through a simple lens, different wavelengths or colors focus at different distances behind the lens. For example if the yellow light is in focus the red and blue images will be out of focus. In contrast, all wavelengths focus at the same point using a parabolic mirror.

Figure 58d
Issac Newton's reflecting telescope.

However, problems with keeping the reflecting surface shinny, and the development of lens combinations that eliminated chromatic aberration, made refracting telescopes more popular until the late 1800s. The invention of the durable silver and aluminum coatings on glass brought reflecting telescopes into prominence in the twentieth century.

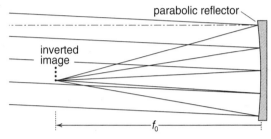

Figure 58a
A parabolic reflector focuses the parallel rays from a distant object, forming an image a distance f_0 in front of the mirror.

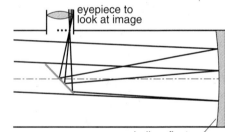

Figure 58b
Issac Newton's solution to viewing the image was to deflect the beam using a 45° reflecting surface so that the eyepiece could be outside the telescope tube.

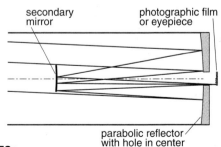

Figure 58c
*For large telescopes, it is common to reflect the beam back through a hole in the center of the primary mirror. This arrangement is known as the **Cassegrain** design.*

Large Reflecting Telescopes.

The first person to build a really large reflecting telescope was William Hershel, who started with a two inch reflector in 1774 and by 1789 had constructed the four foot diameter telescope shown in Figure (59a). Among Hershel's accomplishments was the discovery of the planet Uranus, and the first observation of a distant nebula. It would be another 130 years before Edwin Hubble, using the 100 inch telescope on Mt. Wilson would conclusively demonstrate that such nebula were in fact galaxies like our own Milky Way. This also led Hubble to discover the expansion of the universe.

During most of the second half of the twentieth century, the largest telescope has been the 200 inch (5 meter) telescope on Mt. Palomar, shown in Figure (59b). This was the first telescope large enough that a person could work at the prime focus, without using a secondary mirror. Hubbel himself is seen in the observing cage at the prime focus in Figure (59c).

Recently it has become possible to construct mirrors larger than 5 meters in diameter. One of the tricks is to cast the molten glass in a rotating container and keep the container rotating while the glass cools. A rotating liquid has a parabolic surface. The faster the rotation the deeper the parabola. Thus by choosing the right rotation speed, one can cast a mirror blank that has the correct parabola built in. The surface is still a bit rough, and has to be polished smooth, but the grinding out of large amounts of glass is avoided. The 6.5 meter mirror, shown in Figures (59d,e), being installed on top of Mt. Hopkins in Arizona, was built this way. Seventeen tons of glass would have to have been ground out if the parabola had not been cast into the mirror blank.

Figures 59b,c
The Mt. Palomar 200 inch telescope. Below is Edwin Hubble in the observing cage.

Figure 59a
William Hershel's 4 ft diameter, 40 ft long reflecting telescope which he completed in 1789.

Figures 59d,e
The 6.5 meter MMT telescope atop Mt. Hopkins. Above, the mirror has not been silvered yet. The blue is a temporary protective coating. Below, the mirror is being hoisted into the telescope frame.

Hubble Space Telescope

An important limit to telescopes on earth, in their ability to distinguish fine detail, is turbulence in the atmosphere. Blobs of air above the telescope move around causing the star image to move, blurring the picture. This motion, on a time scale of about 1/60 second, is what causes stars to appear to twinkle.

The effects of turbulence, and any distortion caused by the atmosphere, are eliminated by placing the telescope in orbit above the atmosphere. The largest telescope in orbit is the famous Hubble telescope with its 1.5 meter diameter mirror, seen in Figure (60). After initial problems with its optics were fixed, the Hubble telescope has produced fantastic images like that of the Eagle Nebula seen in Figure (7-17) reproduced here.

With a modern telescope like the Keck (see next page), the effects of atmospheric turbulance can mostly be eliminated by having a computer track the image of a bright star. The telescope's mirror is flexible enough that the shape of the mirror can then be be modified rapidly and by a tiny amount to keep the image steady.

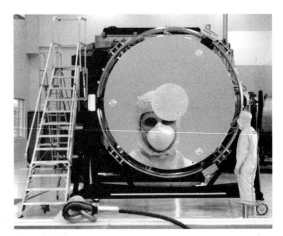

Figure 60a
The Hubble telescope mirror. How is that for a shaving mirror?

Figure 60b
Hubble telescope before launch.

Figure 7-17
The Eagle Nebula, birthplace of stars. This Hubble photograph, which apeared on the cover of Time magazine, is perhaps the most famous.

Figure 60c
Hubble telescope being deployed.

World's Largest Optical Telescope

As of 1999, the largest optical telescope in the world is the Keck telescope located atop the Mauna Kea volcano in Hawaii, seen in Figure (61a). Actually there are two identical Keck telescopes as seen in the close-up, Figure (61b). The primary mirror in each telescope consists of 36 hexagonal mirrors fitted together as seen in Figure (61c) to form a mirror 10 meters in diameter. This is twice the diameter of the Mt. Palomar mirror we discussed earlier.

The reason for building two Keck telescopes has to do with the wave nature of light. As we mentioned in the introduction to this chapter, geometrical optics works well when the objects we are studying are large compared to the wavelength of light. This is illustrated by the ripple tank photographs of Figures (33-3) and (33-8) reproduced here. In the left hand figure, we see we see a wave passing through a gap that is considerably wider than the wave's wavelength. On the other side of the gap there is a well defined beam with a distinct shadow. This is what we assume light waves do in geometrical optics.

In contrast, when the water waves encounter a gap whose width is comparable to a wavelength, as in the right hand figure, the waves spread out on the far side. This is a phenomenon called **diffraction**. We can even see some diffraction at the edges of the beam emerging from the wide gap.

Diffraction also affects the ability of telescopes to form sharp images. The bigger the diameter of the telescope, compared to the light wavelength, the less important diffraction is and the sharper the image that can be formed. By combining the output from the two Keck telescopes, one creates a telescope whose effective diameter, for handling diffraction effects, is equal to the 90 meter separation of the telescopes rather than just the 10 meter diameter of one telescope. The great improvement in the image sharpness that results is seen in Figure (61d). On the left is the best possible image of a star, taken using one telescope alone. When the two telescopes are combined, they get the much sharper image on the right.

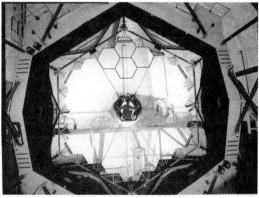

Figures 61 c
The 36 mirrors forming Keck's primary mirror. We have emphasized the outline of the upper 4 mirrors.

Figures 25-3,8
Unless the gap is wide in comparison to a wavelength, diffraction effects are important.

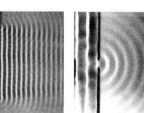

Figures 61 a,b
The Keck telescopes atop Mauna Kea volcano in Hawaii.

Figures 62
Same star, photographed on the left using one scope, on the right with the two Keck telescopes combined.

Infrared Telescopes

Among the spectacular images in astronomy are the large dust clouds like the ones that form the Eagle Nebula photographed by the Hubble telescope, and the famous Horsehead Nebula shown in Figure (63a). But a problem is that astronomers would like to see through the dust, to see what is going on inside the clouds and what lies beyond.

While visible light is blocked by the dust, other wavelength's of electromagnetic radiation can penetrate these clouds. Figure (63b) is a photograph of the same patch of sky as the Horsehead Nebula in (63a), but observed using infrared light whose wavelengths are about 3 times longer than the wavelengths of visible light. First notice that the brightest stars are at the same positions in both photographs. But then notice that the black cloud, thought to resemble a horses head, is missing in the infrared photograph. The stars in and behind the cloud shine through; their infrared light is not blocked by the dust.

a)
Visible light photograph

b)
Infrared light photograph

Figure 63
The Horsehead Nebula photographed in visible (a) and infrared light (b). The infrared light passes through the dust cloud.

Where does the infrared light come from? If you have studied Chapter 35 on the Bohr theory of hydrogen, you will recall that hydrogen atoms can radiate many different wavelengths of light. The only visible wavelengths are the three longest wavelengths in the Balmer series. The rest of the Balmer series and all of the Lyman series consist of short wavelength ultraviolet light. But all the other wavelengths radiated by hydrogen are infrared, like the Paschen series where the electron ends up in the third energy level. The infrared wavelengths are longer than those of visible light. Since hydrogen is the major constituent of almost all stars, it should not be surprising that stars radiate infrared as well as visible light.

A telescope designed for looking at infrared light is essentially the same as a visible light telescope, except for the camera. Figure (64) shows the infrared telescope on Mt. Hopkins used to take the infrared image of the Horsehead Nebula. We enlarged the interior photograph to show the infrared camera which is cooled by a jacket of liquid nitrogen (essentially a large thermos bottle surrounding the camera).

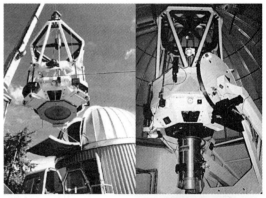

Figure 64
Infrared telescope on Mt. Hopkins. Note that the infrared camera, seen in the blowup, is in a container cooled by liquid nitrogen. You do not want the walls of the camera to be "infrared hot" which would fog the image.

You might wonder why you have to cool an infrared camera and not a visible light camera. The answer is that warm bodies emit infrared radiation. The hotter the object, the shorter the wavelength of the radiation. If an object is hot enough, it begins to glow in visible light, and we say that the object is red hot, or white hot. Since you do not want the infrared detector in the camera seeing camera walls glowing "infrared hot", the camera has to be cooled.

Not all infrared radiation can make it down through the earth's atmosphere. Water vapor, for example is very good at absorbing certain infrared wavelengths. To observe the wavelengths that do not make it through, infrared telescopes have been placed in orbit. Figure (65) is an artist's drawing of the Infrared Astronomical Satellite (IRAS) which was used to make the infrared map of the entire sky seen in Figure (66). The map is oriented so that the Milky Way, our own galaxy, lies along the center horizontal plane. In visible light photographs, most of the stars in our own galaxy are obscured by the immense amount of dust in the plane of the galaxy. But in an infrared photograph, the huge concentration of stars in the plane of the galaxy show up clearly.

At the center of our galaxy is a gigantic black hole, with a mass of millions of suns. For a visible light telescope, the galactic center is completely obscured by dust. But the center can be clearly seen in the infrared photograph of Figure (67), taken by the Mt. Hopkins telescope of Figure (64). This is not a single exposure, instead it is a composite of thousands of images in that region of the sky. Three different infrared wavelengths were recorded, and the color photograph was created by displaying the longest wavelength image as red, the middle wavelength as green, and the shortest wavelength as blue. In this photograph, you not only see the intense radiation from the region of the black hole at the center, but also the enormous density of stars at the center of our galaxy. (You do not see radiation from the black hole itself, but from nearby stars that may be in the process of being captured by the black hole.)

Figure 65
Artist's drawing of the infrared telescope IRAS in orbit.

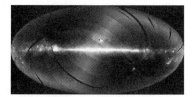

Figure 66
Map of the entire sky made by IRAS. The center of the Milky Way is in the center of the map. This is essentially a view of our galaxy seen from the inside.

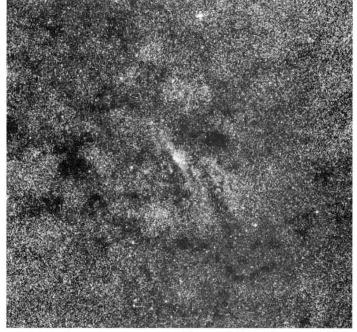

Figure 67
Center of our galaxy, where an enormous black hole resides. Not only is the galactic center rich in stars, but also in dust which prevents viewing this region in visible light.

Radio Telescopes

The earth's atmosphere allows not only visible and some infrared light from stars to pass through, but also radio waves in the wavelength range from a few millimeters to a good fraction of a meter. To study the radio waves emitted by stars and galaxies, a number of *radio telescopes* have been constructed.

For a telescope reflector to produce a sharp image, the surface of the reflector should be smooth and accurate to within about a fifth of a wavelength of the radiation being studied. For example, the surface of a mirror for a visible wavelength telescope should be accurate to within about 10^{-4} millimeters since the wavelength of visible light is centered around 5×10^{-4} millimeters. Radio telescopes that are to work with 5 millimeter wavelength radio waves, need surfaces accurate only to about a millimeter. Telescopes designed to study the important 21 cm wavelength radiation emitted by hydrogen, can have a rougher surface yet. As a result, radio telescopes can use sheet metal or even wire mesh rather than polished glass for the reflecting surface.

This is a good thing, because radio telescopes have to be much bigger than optical telescopes in order to achieve comparable images. The sharpness of an image, due to diffraction effects, is related to the ratio of the reflector diameter to the radiation wavelength. Since the radio wavelengths are at least 10^4 times larger than those for visible light, a radio telescope has to be 10^4 times larger than an optical telescope to achieve the same resolution.

The world's largest radio telescope dish, shown in Figure (68), is the 305 meter dish at the Arecibo Observatory in Puerto Rico. While this dish can see faint objects because of its enormous size, and has been used to make significant discoveries, it has the resolving ability of an optical telescope about 3 centimeters in diameter, or a good set of binoculars .

As we saw with the Keck telescope, there is a great improvement in resolving power if the images of two or more telescopes are combined. The effective resolving power is related to the separation of the telescopes rather than to the diameter of the individual telescopes. Figure (69) shows the *Very Large Array (VLA)* consisting of twenty seven 25 meter diameter radio telescopes located in southern New Mexico. The dishes are mounted on tracks, and can be spread out to cover an area 36 kilometers in diameter. At this spacing, the resolving power is nearly comparable to a 5 meter optical telescope at Mt. Palomar.

Figures 69
The "Very Large Array" (VLA) of radio telescopes. The twenty seven telescopes can be spread out to a diameter of 36 kilometers.

Figure 68
Arecibo radio telescope. While the world's largest telescope dish remains fixed in the earth, the focal point can be moved to track a star.

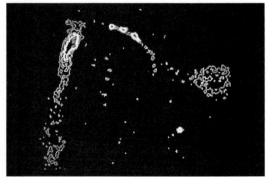

Figures 69b
Radio galaxy image from the VLA. Studying the radio waves emitted by a galaxy often gives a very different picture than visible light.

Figure 70
The Very Long Baseline Array of radio antennas. They are located at a) Hancock New Hampshire b) Ft. Davis Texas c) Kitt Peak Arizona d) North Liberty Iowa e) St. Croix Virgin Islands f) Brewster Washington g) Mauna Kea Hawaii h) Pie Town New Mexico i) Los Alamos New Mexico j) Owen's Valley California.

The Very Long Baseline Array (VLBA)

To obtain significantly greater resolving power, the *Very Long Baseline Array (VLBA)* was set up in the early 1990's. It consists of ten 25 meter diameter radio telescopes placed around the earth as shown in Figure (70). When the images of these telescopes are combined, the resolving power is comparable to an optical telescope 1000 meters in diameter (or an array of optical telescopes spread over an area one kilometer across).

The data from each telescope is recorded on a high speed digital tape with a time track created by a hydrogen maser atomic clock. The tapes are brought to a single location in Socorro, NM where a high speed computer uses the accurate time tracks to combine the data from all the telescopes into a single image. To do this, the computer has to correct, for example, for the time difference of the arrival of the radio waves at the different telescope locations.

Because of it's high resolution, the VLBA can be used to study the structure of individual stars. In Figure (72) we see two time snapshots of the radio emission from the stellar atmosphere of a star 1000 light years away. With any of the current optical telescopes, the image of this star is only a point.

"Snapshots" of the Envelope of the Star TX Cam

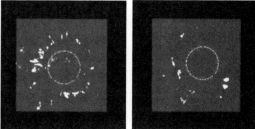

24 May 1997   29 October 1998

Figure 71
Very Long Baseline Array (VLBA) radio images of the variable star TX Cam which is located 1000 light years away. The approximate size of the star as it would be seen in visible light is indicated by the circle. The spots are silicon Monoxide (SiO) gas in the star's extended atmosphere. Motion of the these spots trace the periodic changes in the atmosphere of the star.
(Credit P.J. Diamond & A.J. Kembal, National Radio Astronomy, Associated Universities, Inc.)

MICROSCOPES

Optically, microscopes like the one seen in Figure (72), are telescopes designed to focus on nearby objects. Figure (73) shows the ray diagram for a simple microscope, where the objective lens forms an inverted image which is viewed by an eyepiece.

To calculate the magnification of a simple microscope, note that if an object of height y_0 were viewed unaided at a distance of 25 cm, it would subtend an angle θ_0 given by

$$\theta_0 = \frac{y_0}{25 \text{ cm}} \tag{42}$$

where throughout this discussion we will use the small angle approximation $\sin\theta \approx \tan\theta \approx \theta$.

A ray from the tip of the object (point A in Figure 73b), parallel to the axis, will cross the axis at point D, the focal point of the objective lens. Thus the height BC is equal to the height y_0 of the object, and the distance BD is the focal length f_0 of the objective, and the angle β is given by

$$\beta = \frac{y_0}{f_0} \quad \begin{array}{l}\textit{from triangle}\\ \textit{BCD}\end{array} \tag{43}$$

From triangle DEF, where the small angle at D is also β, we have

$$\beta = \frac{y_i}{L} \quad \begin{array}{l}\textit{from triangle}\\ \textit{DEF}\end{array} \tag{44}$$

where y_i is the height of the image and the distance L is called the **tube length** of the microscope.

Equating the values of β in Equations (29) and (30) and solving for y_i gives

$$\beta = \frac{y_0}{f_0} = \frac{y_i}{L} \; ; \quad y_i = y_0 \frac{L}{f_0} \tag{45}$$

The eyepiece is placed so that the image of the objective is in the focal plane of the eyepiece lens, producing parallel rays that the eye can focus. Thus the distance EG equals the focal length f_0 of the eyepiece. From triangle EFG we find that the angle θ_i that image subtends as seen by the eye is

$$\theta_i = \frac{y_i}{f_e} \quad \begin{array}{l}\textit{angle subtended}\\ \textit{by image}\end{array} \tag{46}$$

Substituting Equation (45) for y_i in Equation (46) gives

$$\theta_i = \frac{L}{f_0} \frac{y_0}{f_e} \tag{47}$$

Finally, the magnification m of the microscope is equal to the ratio of the angle θ_i subtended by the image in the microscope, to the angle θ_0 the object subtends at a distance of 25 cm from the unaided eye.

$$m = \frac{\theta_i}{\theta_0} = \frac{L}{f_0} \frac{y_0}{f_e} \times \frac{1}{y_0/25 \text{ cm}} \tag{48}$$

where we used Equation (47) for θ_i and Equation (42) for θ_0. The distance y_0 cancels in Equation (48) and we get

$$\boxed{m = \frac{L}{f_0} \times \frac{25 \text{ cm}}{f_e}} \quad \begin{array}{l}\textit{magnification of a}\\ \textit{simple microscope}\end{array} \tag{49}$$

(We could have inserted a minus sign in the formula for magnification to indicate that the image is inverted.)

Figure 72
Standard optical microscope, which my grandfather purchased as a medical student in the 1890s. Compare this with a microscope constructed 100 years later, seen in Figure (74) on the next page.

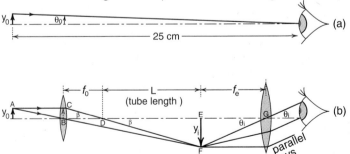

Figure 73
Optics of a simple microscope.

Scanning Tunneling Microscope

Modern research microscopes bear less resemblance to the simple microscope described above than the Hubble telescope does to Newton's first reflector telescope. In the research microscopes that can view and manipulate individual atoms, there are no lenses based on geometrical optics. Instead, the surface to be studied is scanned, line by line, by a tiny probe whose operation is based on the particle-wave nature of electrons. An image of the surface is then reconstructed by computer and displayed on a computer screen. These microscopes work at a scale of distance much smaller than the wavelength of light, a distance scale where the approximations inherent in geometrical optics do not apply.

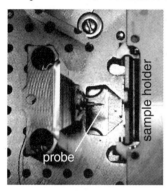

a) Probe and sample holder.

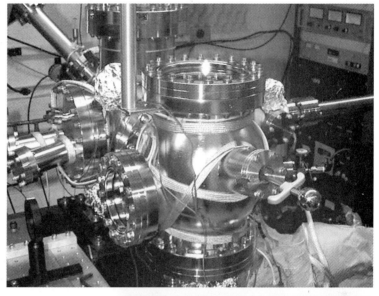

b) Vacuum chamber enclosing the probe and sample holder. Photograph taken in Geoff Nunes' lab at Dartmouth College.

Figure 74
Scanning Tunneling Microscope (STM). The tungsten probe seen in (a) has a very sharp point, about one atom across. With a couple of volts difference between the probe and the silicon crystal in the sample holder, an electric current begins to flow when the tip gets to within about fifteen angstroms (less than fifteen atomic diameters) of the surface. The current flows because the wave nature of the electrons allows them to "tunnel" through the few angstrom gap. The current increases rapidly as the probe is brought still closer. By moving the probe in a line sideways across the face of the silicon, while moving the probe in and out to keep the current constant, the tip of the probe travels at a constant height above the silicon atoms. By recording how much the probe was moved in and out, one gets a recording of the shape of the surface along that line. By scanning across many closely spaced lines, one gets a map of the entire surface. The fine motions of the tungsten probe are controlled by piezo crystals which expand or contract by tiny amounts when a voltage is applied to them. The final image you see was created by computer from the scanning data.

c) Surface (111 plane) of a silicon crystal imaged by this microscope. We see the individual silicon atoms in the surface.

PHOTOGRAPH CREDITS

CHAPTER EXERCISES

Exercise 1a On page 10
What is the speed of light in air, water, crown glass, and diamond.

Exercise 1b On page 10
In one of the experiments announced in *Nature,* a laser pulse took 7.05 microseconds to travel .229 millimeters through the gas of supercooled sodium atoms. What was the index of refraction of the gas for this particular experiment?

Exercise 2 On page 12
Show that the two angles labeled θ_2 in Figure (13a) must also be equal.

Exercise 3 On page 13
A glass prism can be used as shown in Figure (15) to reflect light at right angles. The index of refraction n_g of the glass must be high enough so that there is total internal reflection at the back surface. What is the least value n_g one can have to make such a prism work?

Exercise 4 On page 17
Next time you see a rainbow, try to measure the angle the yellow part of the arc makes with the rays of sun passing your head.

Exercise 5 On page 21
Compare the prediction of Equation (14) with the results we got in Figure (26b).

Exercise 6 On page 21
The index of refraction for red light in water is slightly less than the index of refraction for blue light. Will the focal length of the surface in Figure (26b) be longer or shorter than the focal length for red light?

Exercise 7 On page 21
The simplest model for a fixed focus eye is a sphere of index of refraction n_2. Looking at the table of indexes of refraction, Table 1, explain why such a model would be hard to achieve.

Exercise 8 On page 23
(a) See how well the lens maker's equation applies to our scale drawing of Figure (29c).

(b) What would be the focal length f of the lens if it had been made from diamond with an index of refraction $n = 2.42$?

Exercise 9 On page 24
(a) Graphically locate the image of the object in Figure (31).

(b) A ray starts out from the tip of the object in the direction of the dotted line shown. Trace out this ray through the lens and show where it goes on the back side of the lens.

Exercise 10 On page 27
You have a lens making machine that can grind surfaces, either convex or concave, with radius of curvatures of either 20 cm or 40 cm, or a flat surface. How many different kinds of lenses can you make? What is the focal length and the name of the lens type for each lens?

Exercise 11 On page 29
(a) Find the image distances i_2 for the geometry of Figures (38), but with the two lenses reversed.

(b) If the two lenses are put together (D = 0) what is the focal length of the combination?

Exercise 12 On page 30
Figures (38) and (40) are scale drawings, so that the ratio of image to object sizes measured from these drawings should equal the calculated magnifications.

(a) Calculate the magnifications m_1, m_2 and m_{12} for Figure (38a) or (40) and compare your results with magnifications measured from the figure.

(b) Do the same for Figure (38b).

Exercise 13 On page 30
Figure (41a) shows a magnifying glass held 10 cm above the printed page. Since the object is inside the focal length we get a virtual image as seen in the geometrical construction of Figure (41b). Show that our formulas predict a positive magnification, and estimate the focal length of the lens.

Exercise 14 On page 33
The iris on the human eye can change the diameter of the opening to the lens from about 2 to 8 millimeters. The total distance from the cornea to the retina is typically about 2.3 cm. What is the range of f values for the human eye? How does this range compare with the range of f value on your camera?

Continued next page.

Exercise 15 On page 36

Assume that you find a magnifying lens that focuses the sun at a distance of 10 cm from the lens. You then combine that with one of your (or a friends) eyeglass lenses, and discover that the combination focus at a distance of 15 cm. What is the power, in diopters, of (a) the magnifying glass, (b) the combination, and (c) the eyeglass lens.

Exercise 16 On page 36

Use the above technique to measure the power of your or your friend's glasses. If you have your prescription compare your results with what is written on the prescription.

Exercise 17 On page 37

There are three distinct ways of viewing an object through a magnifying glass, which you should try for yourself. Get a magnifying glass and use the letters on this page as the object to be viewed. Steps described on page (37).

Exercise 18 On page 41

To build your own refracting telescope, you purchase a 3 inch diameter objective lens with a focal length of 50 cm. You want the telescope to have a magnification $m = 25 \times$. See steps on page (41).

Index